LINEAR ALGEBRA:
THEORY, INTUITION, CODE

Dr. Mike X Cohen

0.1 Front matter

This page contains some important details about the book that basically no one reads but somehow is always in the first page.

ISBN: 9789083136608

This book was written and formatted in LaTeX by Mike X Cohen. (Mike X Cohen is the friendlier and more approachable persona of Professor Michael X Cohen; Michael deals with the legal and business aspects while Mike gets to have fun writing.)

Book edition 1.

0.2 Dedication

If you're reading this, then the book is dedicated to you. I wrote this book for *you*. Now turn the page and start learning math!

0.3 Forward

The past is immutable and the present is fleeting. Forward is the only direction.

Contents

CHAPTER 1
INTRODUCTION TO THIS BOOK

What is linear algebra and why learn it?

Linear algebra is the branch of mathematics concerned with vectors and matrices, their linear combinations, and operations acting upon them. Linear algebra has a long history in pure mathematics, in part because it provides a compact notation that is powerful and general enough to be used in geometry, calculus, differential equations, physics, economics, and many other areas.

But the importance and application of linear algebra is quickly increasing in modern applications. Many areas of science, technology, finance, and medicine are moving towards large-scale data collection and analysis. Data are often stored in matrices, and operations on those data—ranging from statistics to filtering to machine learning to computer graphics to compression—are typically implemented via linear algebra operations. Indeed, linear algebra has arguably exceeded statistics and time series analysis as the most important branch of mathematics in which to gain proficiency for data-focused areas of science and industry.

Human civilization is moving towards increasing digitization, quantitative methods, and data. Therefore, knowledge of foundational topics such as linear algebra are increasingly important. One may (indeed: *should*) question the appropriateness and utility of the trend towards "big data" and the over-reliance on algorithms to make decisions for us, but it is inarguable that familiarity with matrix analysis, statistics, and multivariate methods have become crucial skills for any data-related job in academia and in industry.

About this book

The purpose of this book is to teach you how to think about and work with matrices, with an eye towards applications in machine learning, multivariate statistics, time series, and image processing.

If you are interested in data science, quantitative biology, statistics, or machine learning and artificial intelligence, then this book is for you. If you don't have a strong background in mathematics, then don't be concerned: You need only high-school math and a bit of dedication to learn linear algebra from this book.

This book is written with the self-studying reader in mind. Many people do not realize how important linear algebra is until after university, or they do not meet the requirements of university-level linear algebra courses (typically, calculus). Linear algebra textbooks are often used as a compendium to a lecture-based course embedded in a traditional university math program, and therefore can be a challenge to use as an independent resource. I hope that this book is a self-contained resource that works well inside or outside of a formal course.

Many extant textbooks are theory-oriented, with a strong focus on abstract concepts as opposed to practical implementations. You might have encountered such books: They avoid showing numerical examples in the interest of generalizations; important proofs are left "as an exercise for the reader"; mathematical statements are simply plopped onto the page without discussion of relevance, importance, or application; and there is no mention of whether or how operations can be implemented in computers.

I do not write these as criticisms—abstract linear algebra is a beautiful topic, and infinite-dimensional vector spaces are great. But for those interested in using linear algebra (and mathematics more generally) as a tool for understanding data, statistics, deep learning, etc., then abstract treatments of linear algebra may seem like a frustrating waste of time. My goal here is to present applied linear algebra in an approachable and comprehensible way, with little focus on abstract concepts that lack a clear link to applications.

Ebook version The ebook version is identical to the physical version of this book, in terms of the text, formulas, visualizations, and code. However, the formatting is necesarily quite different. The book was designed to be a *physical* book; and thus, margins, fonts, text and figure placements, and code blocks are optimized for pages, not for ereaders.

Therefore, I recommend getting the physical copy of the book if you have the choice. If you get the ebook version, then please accept my apologies for any ugly or annoying formatting issues. If you have difficulties reading the code, please download it from github.com/mikexcohen/LinAlgBook.

Equations This is a math book, so you won't be surprised to see equations. But math is more than just equations: In my view, the purpose of math is to understand concepts; equations are one way to present those concepts, but words, pictures, and code are also important. Let me outline the balance:

1. Equations provide rigor and formalism, but they rarely provide intuition.
2. Descriptions, analogies, visualizations, and code provide intuition but often lack sufficient rigor.

This balance guides my writing: Equations are pointless if they lack descriptions and visualizations, but words and pictures without equations can be incomplete or misinterpreted.

So yes, there is a respectable number of equations here. There are three levels of *hierarchy* in the equations throughout this book. Some equations are simple or reminders of previously discussed equations; these are lowest on the totem pole are are presented in-line with text like this: $x(yz) = (xy)z$.

More important equations are given on their own lines. The number in parentheses to the right will allow me to refer back to that equation later in the text (the number left of the decimal point is the chapter, and the number to the right is the equation number).

$$\sigma = x(yz) = (xy)z \qquad (1.1)$$

And the most important equations—the ones you should really

make sure to understand and be comfortable using and reproducing—are presented in their own box with a title:

> **Something important!**
>
> $$\sigma = x(yz) = (xy)z \qquad (1.2)$$

Algebraic and geometric perspectives on matrices Many concepts in linear algebra can be formulated using both geometric and algebraic (analytic) methods. This "dualism" promotes comprehension and I try to utilize it often. The geometric perspective provides visual intuitions, although it is usually limited to 2D or 3D. The algebraic perspective facilitates rigorous proofs and computational methods, and is easily extended to N-D. When working on problems in $\mathbb{R}^2$ or $\mathbb{R}^3$, I recommend sketching the problem on paper or using a computer graphing program.

Just keep in mind that *not every* concept in linear algebra has both a geometric and an algebraic concept. The dualism is useful in many cases, but it's not a fundamental fact that necessarily applies to all linear algebra concepts.

1.3 Prerequisites

The obvious. Dare I write it? You need to be motivated to learn linear algebra. Linear algebra isn't so difficult, but it's also not so easy. An intention to learn applied linear algebra—and a willingness to expend mental energy towards that goal—is the single most important prerequisite. Everything below is minor in comparison.

High-school math. You need to be comfortable with arithmetic and basic algebra. Can you solve for x in $4x^2 = 9$? Then you have enough algebra knowledge to continue. Other concepts in geometry, trigonometry, and complex numbers (a $ib, e^{i\theta}$) will be introduced as the need arises.

Calculus. Simply put: none. I strongly object to calculus being taught before linear algebra. No offense to calculus, of course; it's a rich, beautiful, and incredibly important subject. But linear algebra can be learned without any calculus, whereas many topics in calculus involve some linear algebra. Furthermore, many modern applications of linear algebra invoke no calculus concepts. Hence, linear algebra should be taught assuming no calculus background.

Vectors, matrices and <insert fancy-sounding linear algebra term here>. If this book is any good, then you don't need to know anything about linear algebra before reading it. That said, some familiarity with matrices and matrix operations will be beneficial.

Programming. Before computers, advanced concepts in mathematics could be understood only by brilliant mathematicians with great artistic skills and a talent for being able to visualize equations. Computers changed that. Now, a reasonably good mathematics student with some perseverance and moderate computer skills can implement and visualize equations and other mathematical concepts. The computer deals with the arithmetic and low-level graphics, so you can worry about the concepts and intuition.

This doesn't mean you should forgo solving problems by hand; it is only through laboriously solving lots and lots of problems on paper that you will internalize a deep and flexible understanding of linear algebra. However, only simple (often, integer) matrices are feasible to work through by hand; computer simulations and plotting will allow you to understand an equation visually, when staring at a bunch of letters and Greek characters might give you nothing but a sense of dread. So, if you really want to learn modern, applied linear algebra, it's helpful to have some coding proficiency in a language that interacts with a visualization engine.

I provide code for all concepts and problems in this book in both MATLAB and Python. I find MATLAB to be more comfortable for implementing linear algebra concepts. If you don't have access to MATLAB, you can use Octave, which is a free cross-platform software that emulates nearly all MATLAB functionality. But the popularity of Python is undeniable, and you should use whichever program you (1) feel more comfortable using or (2) anticipate working with in the future. Feel free to use any other coding language you like, but it is your responsibility to translate the code into your preferred language.

I have tried to keep the code as simple as possible, so you need only minimal coding experience to understand it. On the other hand, this is not an intro-coding book, and I assume some basic coding familiarity. If you understand variables, for-loops, functions, and basic plotting, then you know enough to work with the book code.

To be clear: You do not *need* any coding to work through the book. The code provides additional material that I believe will help solidify the concepts as well as adapt to specific applications. But you can successfully and completely learn from this book without looking at a single line of code.

1.4 Practice, exercises and code challenges

Math is not a spectator sport. If you simply read this book without solving any problems, then sure, you'll learn something and I hope you enjoy it. But to really understand linear algebra, you need to solve problems.

Some math textbooks have a seemingly uncountable number of exercises. My strategy here is to have a manageable number of exercises, with the expectation that you can solve *all* of them.

There is a hierarchy of problems to solve in this book:

Practice problems are a few problems at the end of chapter subsections. They are designed to be easy, the answers are given immediately below the problems, and are simply a way for you to confirm that you get the basic idea of that section. If you can't solve the practice problems, go back and re-read that subsection.

Exercises are found at the end of each chapter and focus on drilling and practicing the important concepts. The answers (yes, *all* of them; not just the odd-numbered) follow the exercises, and in many cases you can also check your own answer by solving the problem on a computer (using MATLAB or Python). Keep in mind that these exercises are designed to be solved by hand, and you will learn more by solving them by hand than by computer.

Code challenges are more involved, require some effort and creativity, and can only be solved on a computer. These are opportunities for you to explore concepts, visualizations, and parameter spaces in ways that are difficult or impossible to do by hand. I provide my solutions to all code challenges, but keep in mind that there are many correct solutions; the point is for you to explore and understand linear algebra using code, not to reproduce my code.

If you are more interested in concepts than in computer implementation, feel free to skip the coding challenges.

Online and other resources

Although I have tried to write this book to be a self-contained one-stop-shop for all of your linear algebra needs, it is naive to think that everyone will find it to be the perfect resource that I intend it to be. Everyone learns differently and everyone has a different way of understanding and visualizing mathematical concepts.

If you struggle to understand something, don't jump to the conclusion that you aren't smart enough; a simpler possibility is that the explanation I find intuitive is not the explanation that you find intuitive. I try to give several explanations of the same concept, in hopes that you'll find traction with at least one of them.

Therefore, you shouldn't hesitate to search the Internet or other textbooks if you need different or alternative explanations, or if you want additional exercises to work through.

This book is based on an online course that I created. The book and the course are similar but not entirely redundant. You don't need to enroll in the online course to follow along with this book (or the other way around). I appreciate that some people prefer to learn from online video lectures while others prefer to learn from textbooks. I am trying to cater to both kinds of learners.

You can find a list of all my online courses at sincxpress.com.

. Introduction

CHAPTER 2

VECTORS

Welcome to the second step of conquering linear algebra! (The first step was investing in this book.) This and the next few chapters lay the foundation upon which all subsequent chapters (and, really, all of linear algebra) are built.

Scalars

We begin not with vectors but with scalars. You already know everything you need to know about scalars, even if you don't yet recognize the term.

A "scalar" is just a single number, like 4 or -17.3 or π. In other areas of mathematics, these could be called *constants*. Don't let their simplicity fool you—scalars play multiple important roles in linear algebra, and are central to concepts ranging from subspaces to linear combinations to eigendecomposition.

Why are single numbers called "scalars"? It's because single numbers "scale," or stretch, vectors and matrices without changing their direction. This will become clear and intuitive later in this chapter when you learn about the geometric interpretation of vectors.

Figure 2.1: Scalars as points on a line. The scalar 1.5 is demarcated.

Scalars can be represented as a point on a number line that has zero in the middle, negative numbers to the left, and positive numbers to the right (Figure 2.1). But don't confuse a point on this number line with an arrow from zero to that number—that's a vector, not a scalar.

Notation In this book (as in most linear algebra texts), scalars will be indicated using Greek lowercase letters such as λ, α, or γ. This helps disambiguate scalars from vectors and matrices.

Code   Variables representing scalars in Python and MATLAB are trivially easy to create. In fact, I'm only showing the code here to introduce you to the formatting of code blocks.

Code block 2.1: Python

```
1   aScalar = 4
```

Code block 2.2: MATLAB

```
1   aScalar = 4;
```

Computers have different numeric variable types, and distinguish between, for example, 4 and 4.0 (those are, respectively, an int and a float). However, variable typing is not relevant now, so you don't need to worry about it. I mention it here only for the experienced coders.

Practice problems   Solve for λ.

a) $2\lambda = 9$ b) $5/\lambda = 7$ c) $\pi^3 = e^\lambda$ d) $4(\lambda + 3) = -6$

e) $.5\lambda = .25$ f) $8\lambda = 0$ g) $\lambda^2 = 36$ h) $\lambda = 5\lambda^2$

Answers

a) $\lambda = 9/2$ b) $\lambda = 5/7$ c) $\lambda = 3\ln\pi$ d) $\lambda = -9/2$

e) $\lambda = .5$ f) $\lambda = 0$ g) $\lambda = \pm6$ h) $\lambda = \frac{1}{5}$ (for $\lambda \neq 0$)

2.2 Vectors: geometry and algebra

Geometry   A vector is a line, which is determined by a magnitude (length) and a direction. Lines can exist on a coordinate system with any number of dimensions greater than zero (we deal only with integer-dimensional spaces here; apologies to the fractal-enthusiasts). The dimensionality of the vector is the dimensionality of the coordinate system. Figure 2.2 illustrates vectors in two-dimensions (2D) and in 3D.

It is important to know that the definition of a vector does not include its starting or ending locations. That is, the vector [1 -2]

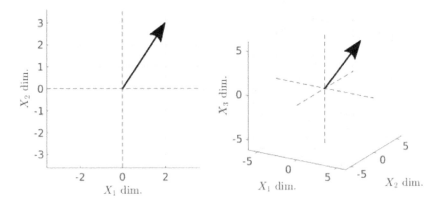

Figure 2.2: Vectors as lines with a direction and length. Left plot depicts vector [2 3] and right plot depicts vector [2 3 5]. The arrow is the head of the vector.

simply means a line that goes one unit in the positive direction in the first dimension, and two units in the negative direction in the second dimension. This is the key difference between a *vector* and a *coordinate*: For any coordinate system (think of the standard Cartesian coordinate system), a given coordinate is a unique point in space. A vector, however, is any line—anywhere—for which the end point (also called the *head* of the vector) is a certain number of units along each dimension away from the starting point (the *tail* of the vector).

On the other hand, coordinates and vectors are coincident when the vector starts at the origin (the [0,0] location on the graph). A vector with its tail at the origin is said to be in its *standard position*. This is illustrated in Figure 2.3: The *coordinate* [1 -2] and the *vector* [1 -2] are the same when the vector is in its standard position. But the three thick lines shown in the figure are all the same vector [1 -2].

For a variety of reasons, it's convenient to show vectors in their standard positions. Therefore, you may assume that vectors are always drawn in standard position unless otherwise stated.

Code Vectors are easy to create and visualize in MATLAB and in Python. The code draws the vector in its standard position.

Code block 2.3: Python

```
1  import numpy as np
2  import matplotlib.pyplot as plt
3  v = np.array([2,-1])
4  plt.plot([0,v[0]],[0,v[1]])
5  plt.axis([-3,3,-3,3]);
```

Code block 2.4: MATLAB

```
1  v = [2 -1];
2  plot([0,v(1)],[0,v(2)])
3  axis([-3,3,-3,3])
```

Note that Python requires you to load in libraries (here, numpy and matplotlib.pyplot) each time you run a new session. If you've already imported the library in your current session, you won't need to re-import it.

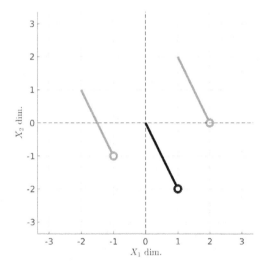

Figure 2.3: The three coordinates (circles) are distinct, but the three vectors (lines) are the same, because they have the same magnitude and direction ([1 -2]). When the vector is in its standard position (the black vector), the head of the vector [1 -2] overlaps with the coordinate [1 -2].

Algebra A vector is an ordered list of numbers. The number of numbers in the vector is called the *dimensionality* of the vector. Here are a few examples of 2D and 3D vectors.

$$\begin{bmatrix} 1 & -2 \end{bmatrix}, \begin{bmatrix} 4 & 1 \end{bmatrix}, \begin{bmatrix} 10000 & 0 \end{bmatrix}$$

$$\begin{bmatrix} \pi^3 & \sqrt{e^2} & 0 \end{bmatrix}, \begin{bmatrix} 3 & 1 & 4 \end{bmatrix}, \begin{bmatrix} 2 & -7 & 8 \end{bmatrix}$$

The ordering of the numbers is important. For example, the following two vectors are *not* the same, even though they have the same dimensionality and the same elements.

$$\begin{bmatrix} 3 \\ 1 \end{bmatrix}, \begin{bmatrix} 1 \\ 3 \end{bmatrix}$$

Brackets Vectors are indicated using either square brackets or parentheses. I think brackets are more elegant and less open to misinterpretation, so I use them consistently. But you will occasionally see parentheses used for vectors in other linear algebra sources. For example the following two objects are the same:

$$\begin{bmatrix} 2 & 5 & 5 \end{bmatrix}, \begin{pmatrix} 2 & 5 & 5 \end{pmatrix}$$

Be careful, however: Not all enclosing brackets simply signify vectors. The following two objects are different from the above. In fact, they are not even vectors—more on this in a few pages!

$$\begin{vmatrix} 2 & 5 & 5 \end{vmatrix}, \begin{Vmatrix} 2 & 5 & 5 \end{Vmatrix}$$

The geometric perspective on vectors is really useful in 2D and tolerable in 3D, but the algebraic perspective allows us to extend vectors into any dimensionality. Want to see a 6D vector algebraically? No problem: [3 4 6 1 -4 5]. Want to visualize that 6D vector as a line in a 6D coordinate space? Yeah, good luck with that.

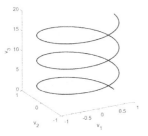

Figure 2.4: The geometric perspective of the vector in equation 2.1.

Vectors are not limited to numbers; the elements can also be functions. Consider the following vector function.

$$\mathbf{v} = \begin{bmatrix} \cos(t) & \sin(t) & t \end{bmatrix} \tag{2.1}$$

(t is itself a vector of time points.) Vector functions are used in multivariate calculus, physics, and differential geometry. However, in this book, vectors will comprise single numbers in each element. If you want to work with the above vector for N discrete time points, then you would use a $3{\times}N$ matrix instead of a vector-valued function.

Vector orientation   Vectors can be "standing up" or "lying down." An upright vector is called a *column vector* and a lying down vector is called a *row vector*. The dimensionality of a vector is simply the number of elements, regardless of its orientation. Column vs. row vectors are easy to distinguish visually:

$$\text{Column vectors: } \begin{bmatrix} 7 \\ 3 \\ 5 \\ 0 \end{bmatrix}, \begin{bmatrix} 1 \\ -9 \\ -9 \end{bmatrix}, \begin{bmatrix} 0 \\ 1 \end{bmatrix}$$

$$\text{Row vectors: } \begin{bmatrix} 1 & 4 & -4 & \sqrt{7} \end{bmatrix}, \begin{bmatrix} 0 & 1 \end{bmatrix}, \begin{bmatrix} 42 & 42 \end{bmatrix}$$

IMPORTANT: By convention, always assume that vectors are in column orientation, unless stated otherwise. Assuming that all vectors are column-oriented reduces ambiguity about other operations involving vectors. This is an arbitrary choice, but it's one that most people follows (not just in this book).

Sometimes, the orientation of a vector doesn't matter (this is more often the case in code), while other times it is hugely important and completely changes the outcome of an equation.

Code   The semicolon in MATLAB inside square brackets is used for vertical concatenation (that is, to create a column vector). In Python, lists and numpy arrays have no intrinsic orientation (meaning they are neither row nor column vectors). In some cases that doesn't matter, while in other cases (for example, in more advanced applications) it becomes as hassle. Additional square brackets can be used to impose orientations.

Code block 2.5: Python

```
1  v1 = [2,5,4,7]
2  v2 = np.array([2,5,4,7])
3  v3 = np.array([ [2],[5],[4],[7] ])
4  v4 = np.array([ [2,5,4,7] ])
```

Code block 2.6: MATLAB

```
1  v1 = [2  5  4  7];
2  v2 = [2;  5;  4;  7];
```

Notation In written texts, vectors are indicated using lower-case boldface letters, for example: vector **v**. When taking notes on paper (strongly encouraged to maximize learning!), you should draw a little arrow on top of the letter to indicate vectors, like this: $\vec{v}$

To indicate a particular element inside a vector, a subscript is used with a non-bold-faced letter of the vector. For example, the second element in the vector $\mathbf{v} = \begin{bmatrix} 4 & 0 & 2 \end{bmatrix}$ is indicated $v_2 = 0$. More generally, the ith element is indicated as v_i.

It's important to see that the letter is not bold-faced when referring to a particular element. This is because subscripts can also be used to indicate different vectors in a set of vectors. Thus, v_i is the ith element in vector **v**, but $\mathbf{v}_i$ is the ith vector is a series of related vectors ($\mathbf{v}_1$, $\mathbf{v}_2$, ..., $\mathbf{v}_i$). I know, it's a bit confusing, but unfortunately that's common notation and you'll have to get used to it. I try to make it clear from context whether I'm referring to vector element v_i or vector $\mathbf{v}_i$.

Zeros vector There is an infinite number of possible vectors, because there is an infinite number of ways of combining an infinity of numbers in a vector.

That said, there are some special vectors that you should know about. The vector that contains zeros in all of its elements is called the zeros vector. A vector that contains some zeros but other non-zero elements is not the zeros vector; it's just a regular vector with some zeros in it. To earn the distinction of being a "zeros vector," all elements must be equal to zero.

The zeros vector can also be indicated using a boldfaced zero: $\mathbf{0}$. That can be confusing, though, because $\mathbf{0}$ also indicates the zeros matrix. Hopefully, the correct interpretation will be clear from the context.

The zeros vector has some interesting and sometimes weird properties. One weird property is that it doesn't have a direction. I don't mean its direction is zero, I mean that its direction is undefined. That's because the zeros vector is simply a point at the origin of a graph. Without any magnitude, it doesn't make sense to ask which direction it points in.

Practice problems State the type and dimensionality of the following vectors (e.g., "four-dimensional column vector"). For 2D vectors, additionally draw the vector starting from the origin.

a) $\begin{bmatrix} 1 \\ 2 \\ 3 \\ 1 \end{bmatrix}$
   b) $\begin{bmatrix} 1 & 2 & 3 & 1 \end{bmatrix}$
   c) $\begin{bmatrix} -1 \\ \pi \end{bmatrix}$
   d) $\begin{bmatrix} 7 & 1/3 \end{bmatrix}$

Answers

a) 4D column   b) 4D row   c) 2D column   d) 2D row

Reflection $\begin{bmatrix} \text{This gentle introduction to scalars and vectors seems simple, but you may be surprised to learn that nearly all of linear algebra is built up from scalars and vectors. From humble beginnings, amazing things emerge. Just think of everything you can build with wood planks and nails. (But don't think of what } I \text{ could build — I'm a terrible carpenter.)} \end{bmatrix}$

2.3 Transpose operation

Now you know some of the basics of vectors. Let's start learning what you can do with them. The mathy term for doing stuff with vectors is *operations that act upon vectors.*

You can transform a column vector to a row vector by transposing it. The transpose operation simply means to convert columns to rows, and rows to columns. The values and ordering of the elements stay the same; only the orientation changes. The transpose operation is indicated by a super-scripted ^{T} (some authors use an italics ^{T} but I think it looks nicer in regular font). For example:

$$\begin{bmatrix} 4 & 3 & 0 \end{bmatrix}^{\mathrm{T}} = \begin{bmatrix} 4 \\ 3 \\ 0 \end{bmatrix}$$

$$\begin{bmatrix} 4 \\ 3 \\ 0 \end{bmatrix}^{\mathrm{T}} = \begin{bmatrix} 4 & 3 & 0 \end{bmatrix}$$

$$\begin{bmatrix} 4 & 3 & 0 \end{bmatrix}^{\mathrm{TT}} = \begin{bmatrix} 4 & 3 & 0 \end{bmatrix}$$

Double-transposing a vector leaves its orientation unchanged. It may seem a bit silly to double-transpose a vector, but it turns out to be a key property in several proofs that you will encounter in later chapters.

Reminder: Vectors are columns unless otherwise specified.

As mentioned in the previous section, we assume that vectors are columns. Row vectors are therefore indicated as a transposed column vector. Thus, $\mathbf{v}$ is a column vector while $\mathbf{v}^{\mathrm{T}}$ is a row vector. On the other hand, column vectors written inside text are often indicated as transposed row vectors, for example $\mathbf{w} = \begin{bmatrix} 1 & 2 & 3 \end{bmatrix}^{\mathrm{T}}$.

Code   Transposing is easy both in MATLAB and in Python.

Code block 2.7: Python

```
1  v1 = np.array([ [2,5,4,7] ]) # row vector
2  v2 = v1.T # column vector
```

Code block 2.8: MATLAB

```
1  v1 = [2 5 4 7]; % row vector
2  v2 = v1'; % column vector
```

2.4 Vector addition and subtraction

Geometry   To add two vectors **a** and **b**, put the start ("tail") of vector **b** at the end ("head") of vector **a**; the new vector that goes from the tail of **a** to the head of **b** is vector **a**+**b** (Figure 2.5).

Remember that a vector is defined by length and direction; the vector can start anywhere.

Vector addition is commutative, which means that $\mathbf{a} + \mathbf{b} = \mathbf{b} + \mathbf{a}$. This is easy to demonstrate: Get a pen and piece of paper, come up with two 2D vectors, and follow the procedure above. Of course, that's just a demonstration, not a proof. The proof will come with the algebraic interpretation.

There are two ways to think about subtracting two vectors. One way is to multiply one of the vectors by -1 and then add them as above (Figure 2.5, lower left). Multiplying a vector by -1 means to multiply each vector element by -1 (vector [1 1] becomes vector [-1 -1]). Geometrically, that flips the vector by 180°.

The second way to think about vector subtraction is to keep both vectors in their standard position, and draw the line that goes from the head of the subtracted vector (the one with the minus sign) to the head of the other vector (the one without the minus sign) (Figure 2.5, lower right). That resulting vector is the difference. It's not in standard position, but that doesn't matter.

You can see that the two subtraction methods give the same difference vector. In fact, they are not really *different* methods; just different ways of thinking about the same method. That will become clear in the algebraic perspective below.

The vectors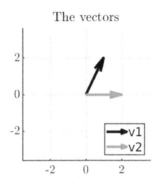

Addition: tail-to-head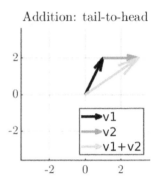

Subtraction: negative addition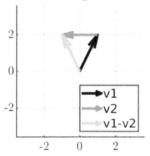

Subtraction: head-to-head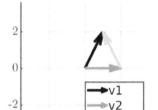

Figure 2.5: Two vectors (top left) can be added (top right) and subtracted (lower two plots).

Do you think that $a - b = b - a$? Let's think about this in terms of scalars. For example: $2 - 5 = -3$ but $5 - 2 = 3$. In fact, the magnitudes of the results are the same, but the signs are different. That's because $2 - 5 = -(5 - 2)$. Same story for vectors: $a - b = -(b - a)$. The resulting difference vectors are not the same, but they are related to each other by having the same magnitude but flipped directions. This should also be intuitive from inspecting Figure 2.5: $v_2 - v_1$ would be the same line as $v_1 - v_2$ but with the arrow on the other side; essentially, you just swap the tail with the head.

Algebra The algebraic interpretation of vector addition and subtraction is what you probably intuitively think it should be: element-wise addition or subtraction of the two vectors. Some examples:

$$\begin{bmatrix} 1 & 2 \end{bmatrix} + \begin{bmatrix} 3 & 4 \end{bmatrix} = \begin{bmatrix} 4 & 6 \end{bmatrix}$$

$$\begin{bmatrix} 0 \\ 12 \end{bmatrix} + \begin{bmatrix} -2 \\ -4 \end{bmatrix} = \begin{bmatrix} -2 \\ 8 \end{bmatrix}$$

$$\begin{bmatrix} 1 \\ 2 \\ 3 \end{bmatrix} - \begin{bmatrix} 9 \\ -8 \\ 7 \end{bmatrix} = \begin{bmatrix} -8 \\ 10 \\ -4 \end{bmatrix}$$

More formally:

Vector addition and subtraction

$$\mathbf{c} = \mathbf{a} + \mathbf{b} = \begin{bmatrix} a_1 + b_1 & a_2 + b_2 & \dots & a_n + b_n \end{bmatrix}^{\mathrm{T}} \qquad (2.2)$$

Important: Vector addition and subtraction are valid only when the vectors have the same dimensionality.

Practice problems Solve the following operations. For 2D vectors, draw both vectors starting from the origin, and the vector sum (also starting from the origin).

a) $\begin{bmatrix} 4 & 5 & 1 & 0 \end{bmatrix} + \begin{bmatrix} -4 & -3 & 3 & 10 \end{bmatrix}$

b) $\begin{bmatrix} 4 \\ 2 \\ 0 \end{bmatrix} - \begin{bmatrix} 6 \\ -4 \\ 60 \end{bmatrix} + \begin{bmatrix} 2 \\ -5 \\ 40 \end{bmatrix}$

c) $\begin{bmatrix} 1 \\ 0 \end{bmatrix} + \begin{bmatrix} 1 \\ 2 \end{bmatrix}$

d) $\begin{bmatrix} 2 \\ 2 \end{bmatrix} - \begin{bmatrix} 3 \\ 4 \end{bmatrix}$

e) $\begin{bmatrix} -3 \\ 1 \end{bmatrix} + \begin{bmatrix} 3 \\ -1 \end{bmatrix}$

f) $\begin{bmatrix} 1 \\ 4 \end{bmatrix} + \begin{bmatrix} 2 \\ 8 \end{bmatrix}$

Answers

a) $\begin{bmatrix} 0 & 2 & 4 & 10 \end{bmatrix}$

b) $\begin{bmatrix} 0 \\ 1 \\ 100 \end{bmatrix}$

c) $\begin{bmatrix} 2 \\ 2 \end{bmatrix}$

d) $\begin{bmatrix} -1 \\ -2 \end{bmatrix}$

e) $\begin{bmatrix} 0 \\ 0 \end{bmatrix}$

f) $\begin{bmatrix} 3 \\ 12 \end{bmatrix}$

Vector-scalar multiplication

Geometry *Scaling* a vector means making it shorter or longer without changing its angle (that is, without rotating it) (Figure 2.6).

The main source of confusion here is that scaling a vector by a negative number means having it point "backwards." You might think that this is a "different" direction, and arguably it is—the vector is rotated by 180°. For now, let's say that the result of vector-scalar multiplication (the scaled vector) must form either a 0° or a 180° angle with the original vector. There is a deeper and more important explanation for this, which has to do with an infinitely long line that the vector defines (a "1D subspace"); you'll learn about this in Chapter 4.

Still, the important thing is that the scalar does not rotate the vector off of its original orientation. In other words, vector direction is invariant to scalar multiplication.

Figure 2.6: Multiplying a scalar (λ) by a vector (v) means to stretch or shrink the vector without changing its angle. $\lambda > 1$ means the resulting vector will be longer than the original, and $0 < \lambda < 1$ means the resulting vector will be shorter. Note the effect of a negative scalar ($\lambda < 0$): The resulting scaled vector points "the other way" but it still lies on the same imaginary infinitely long line as the original vector.

Strange things can happen in mathematics when you multiply by 0. Vector-scalar multiplication is no different: Scaling a vector by 0 reduces it to a point at the origin. That point cannot be said to have any angle, so it's not really a sensible question whether scaling a vector by 0 preserves or changes the angle.

Algebra Scalar-vector multiplication is achieved by multiplying each element of the vector by the scalar. For scalar λ and vector **v**, a formal definition is:

Scalar-vector multiplication

$$\lambda\mathbf{v} = \begin{bmatrix} \lambda v_1 & \lambda v_2 & \dots & \lambda v_n \end{bmatrix}^{\mathrm{T}} \qquad (2.3)$$

This definition holds for any number of dimensions and for any scalar. Here is one example:

$$3\begin{bmatrix} -1 & 3 & 0 & 2 \end{bmatrix} = \begin{bmatrix} -3 & 9 & 0 & 6 \end{bmatrix}$$

Because the scalar-vector multiplication is implemented as element-wise multiplication, it obeys the commutative property. That is, a scalar times a vector is the same thing as that vector times that scalar: $\lambda\mathbf{v} = \mathbf{v}\lambda$. This fact becomes key to several proofs later in the book.

Code Basic vector arithmetic (adding, subtracting, and scalar-multiplying) is straightforward.

Code block 2.9: Python

```
1  import numpy as np
2  v1 = np.array([2,5,4,7])
3  v2 = np.array([4,1,0,2])
4  v3 = 4*v1 - 2*v2
```

Code block 2.10: MATLAB

```
1  v1 = [2 5 4 7];
2  v2 = [4 1 0 2];
3  v3 = 4*v1 - 2*v2
```

Practice problems Compute scalar-vector multiplication for the following pairs:

a) $-2 \begin{bmatrix} 4 & 3 & 0 \end{bmatrix}$ **b)** $(-9 + 2 \times 5) \begin{bmatrix} 0 \\ 4 \\ 3 \end{bmatrix}$ **c)** $0 \begin{bmatrix} 3 \\ 3.14 \times \pi^{3.14} \\ 9 \\ -234987234 \end{bmatrix}$ **d)** $\lambda \begin{bmatrix} 0 \\ 3 \\ 1 \\ 11 \end{bmatrix}$

Answers

a) $\begin{bmatrix} -8 & -6 & 0 \end{bmatrix}$ **b)** $\begin{bmatrix} 0 \\ 4 \\ 3 \end{bmatrix}$ **c)** $\begin{bmatrix} 0 \\ 0 \\ 0 \\ 0 \end{bmatrix}$ **d)** $\begin{bmatrix} 0 \\ \lambda 3 \\ \lambda \\ \lambda 11 \end{bmatrix}$

Reflection

Vector-scalar multiplication is conceptually and computationally simple, but do not underestimate its importance: Stretching a vector without rotating it is fundamental to many applications in linear algebra, including eigendecomposition. Sometimes, the simple things (in mathematics and in life) are the most powerful.

Exercises

1. Simplify the following vectors by factoring out common scalars. For example, [2 4] can be simplified to 2[1 2].

a) $\begin{bmatrix} 6 \\ 3 \\ 33 \\ 9 \end{bmatrix}$
b) $\begin{bmatrix} 48 \\ 12 \\ 24 \\ 60 \end{bmatrix}$
c) $\begin{bmatrix} 12 \\ 18 \\ 24 \end{bmatrix}$
d) $\begin{bmatrix} 45 \\ 36 \\ 99 \\ 72 \\ 27 \end{bmatrix}$

2. Draw the following vectors [ ] using the listed starting point ( ).

a) $\begin{bmatrix} 2 & 2 \end{bmatrix}$ (0,0)

b) $\begin{bmatrix} 6 & 12 \end{bmatrix}$ (1,-2)

c) $\begin{bmatrix} -1 & 0 \end{bmatrix}$ (4,1)

d) $\begin{bmatrix} \pi & e \end{bmatrix}$ (0,0)

e) $\begin{bmatrix} 1 & 2 \end{bmatrix}$ (0,0)

f) $\begin{bmatrix} 1 & 2 \end{bmatrix}$ (-3,0)

g) $\begin{bmatrix} 1 & 2 \end{bmatrix}$ (2,4)

h) $\begin{bmatrix} -1 & -2 \end{bmatrix}$ (0,0)

i) $\begin{bmatrix} -3 & 0 \end{bmatrix}$ (1,0)

j) $\begin{bmatrix} -4 & -2 \end{bmatrix}$ (0,3/2)

k) $\begin{bmatrix} 8 & 4 \end{bmatrix}$ (1,1)

l) $\begin{bmatrix} -8 & -4 \end{bmatrix}$ (8,4)

3. Label the following as column or row vectors, and state their dimensionality. Your answer should be in the form, e.g., "three-dimensional column vector."

a) $\begin{bmatrix} 1 & 2 & 3 & 4 & 5 \end{bmatrix}$
b) $\begin{bmatrix} 5 \\ 0 \\ 3 \end{bmatrix}$
c) $\begin{bmatrix} 0 & 0 \end{bmatrix}$

d) $\begin{bmatrix} \sin(2) \\ e^{\pi} \\ 1/3 \end{bmatrix}$
e) $\begin{bmatrix} 20 & 4000 & 80000 & .1 & 0 & 0 \end{bmatrix}$

4. Perform vector-scalar multiplication on the following. For 2D vectors, additionally draw the original and scalar-multiplied vectors.

a) $3 \begin{bmatrix} 1 \\ 2 \end{bmatrix}$

b) $\frac{1}{3} \begin{bmatrix} 12 & 6 \end{bmatrix}$

c) $0 \begin{bmatrix} e^{10000} \\ 1 \\ 0 \\ \sqrt{\pi} \end{bmatrix}$

d) $4 \begin{bmatrix} -3 \\ 3 \end{bmatrix}$

e) $\lambda \begin{bmatrix} a & b & c & d & e \end{bmatrix}$

f) $\gamma [0 \ 0 \ 0 \ 0 \ 0]$

5. Add or subtract the following pairs of vectors. Draw the individual vectors and their sum (all starting from the origin), and confirm that the algebraic and geometric interpretations match.

a) $\begin{bmatrix} 0 \\ 1 \end{bmatrix} + \begin{bmatrix} 1 \\ 0 \end{bmatrix}$

b) $\begin{bmatrix} 6 \\ -2 \end{bmatrix} - \begin{bmatrix} 2 \\ -6 \end{bmatrix}$

c) $\begin{bmatrix} 2 \\ 1 \end{bmatrix} + \begin{bmatrix} 1 \\ 2 \end{bmatrix}$

d) $\begin{bmatrix} 2 \\ 3 \end{bmatrix} + \begin{bmatrix} 2 \\ 3 \end{bmatrix}$

e) $\begin{bmatrix} 2 \\ 3 \end{bmatrix} - \begin{bmatrix} 2 \\ 3 \end{bmatrix}$

f) $\begin{bmatrix} 1 \\ 1 \end{bmatrix} + \begin{bmatrix} 1 \\ -1 \end{bmatrix}$

g) $\begin{bmatrix} 4 \\ 2 \end{bmatrix} + \begin{bmatrix} 1 \\ 0 \end{bmatrix}$

h) $\begin{bmatrix} -3 \\ -5 \end{bmatrix} + \begin{bmatrix} 7 \\ 3 \end{bmatrix}$

i) $\begin{bmatrix} -5 \\ -2 \end{bmatrix} + \begin{bmatrix} 7 \\ 7 \end{bmatrix}$

j) $\begin{bmatrix} 1 \\ 2 \end{bmatrix} + \begin{bmatrix} 1 \\ 3 \end{bmatrix} - \begin{bmatrix} 3 \\ -2 \end{bmatrix}$

k) $\begin{bmatrix} -2 \\ -5 \end{bmatrix} - \begin{bmatrix} -7 \\ -6 \end{bmatrix} - \begin{bmatrix} 0 \\ 4 \end{bmatrix}$

l) $\begin{bmatrix} 0 \\ 1 \end{bmatrix} - \begin{bmatrix} 3 \\ 3 \end{bmatrix} + \begin{bmatrix} 1 \\ 2 \end{bmatrix}$

Answers

1.

$$\text{a) } 3 \begin{bmatrix} 2 \\ 1 \\ 11 \\ 3 \end{bmatrix} \qquad \text{b) } 12 \begin{bmatrix} 4 \\ 1 \\ 2 \\ 5 \end{bmatrix} \qquad \text{c) } 6 \begin{bmatrix} 2 \\ 3 \\ 4 \end{bmatrix} \qquad \text{d) } 9 \begin{bmatrix} 5 \\ 4 \\ 11 \\ 8 \\ 3 \end{bmatrix}$$

2. This one you should be able to do on your own. You just need to plot the lines from their starting positions. The key here is to appreciate the distinction between vectors and coordinates (they overlap when vectors are in the standard position of starting at the origin).

3. **a)** 5D row vector **b)** 3D column vector **c)** 2D row vector

   d) 3D column vector **e)** 6D row vector

4. I'll let you handle the drawing; below are the algebraic solutions.

$$\text{a) } \begin{bmatrix} 3 \\ 6 \end{bmatrix} \qquad \text{b) } \begin{bmatrix} 4 & 2 \end{bmatrix} \qquad \text{c) } \begin{bmatrix} 0 \\ 0 \\ 0 \\ 0 \end{bmatrix}$$

$$\text{d) } \begin{bmatrix} -12 \\ 12 \end{bmatrix} \qquad \text{e) } \begin{bmatrix} \lambda a \\ \lambda b \\ \lambda c \\ \lambda d \\ \lambda e \end{bmatrix}^{\text{T}} \qquad \text{f) } \begin{bmatrix} 0 & 0 & 0 & 0 & 0 \end{bmatrix}$$

5. These should be easy to solve if you passed elementary school arithmetic. There is, however, a high probability of careless mistakes (indeed, the further along in math you go, the more likely you are to make arithmetic errors).

a) $\begin{bmatrix} 1 \\ 1 \end{bmatrix}$ b) $\begin{bmatrix} 4 \\ 4 \end{bmatrix}$

c) $\begin{bmatrix} 3 \\ 3 \end{bmatrix}$ d) $\begin{bmatrix} 4 \\ 6 \end{bmatrix}$

e) $\begin{bmatrix} 0 \\ 0 \end{bmatrix}$ f) $\begin{bmatrix} 2 \\ 0 \end{bmatrix}$

g) $\begin{bmatrix} 5 \\ 2 \end{bmatrix}$ h) $\begin{bmatrix} 4 \\ -2 \end{bmatrix}$

i) $\begin{bmatrix} 2 \\ 5 \end{bmatrix}$ j) $\begin{bmatrix} -1 \\ 7 \end{bmatrix}$

k) $\begin{bmatrix} 5 \\ -3 \end{bmatrix}$ l) $\begin{bmatrix} -2 \\ 0 \end{bmatrix}$

Code challenges

1. Create a 2D vector **v**, 10 scalars that are drawn at random from a normal (Gaussian) distribution, and plot all 10 scalar-vector multiplications on top of each other. What do you notice?

Code solutions

1. You'll notice that all scaled versions of the vector form a line. Note that the Python implementation requires specifying the vector as a numpy array, not as a list.

Code block 2.11: Python

```
1  import numpy as np
2  import matplotlib.pyplot as plt
3  v = np.array([1,2])
4  plt.plot([0,v[0]],[0,v[1]])
5  for i in range(10):
6      s = np.random.randn()
7      sv = s*v
8      plt..plot([0,sv[0]],[0,sv[1]])
9  plt.grid('on')
10 plt.axis([-4,4,-4,4]);
```

Code block 2.12: MATLAB

```
1  v = [ 1 2 ];
2  plot([0 v(1)],[0 v(2)])
3  hold on
4  for i=1:10
5      s = randn;
6      sv = s*v;
7      plot([0 sv(1)],[0 sv(2)])
8  end
9  grid on, axis([-1 1 -1 1]*4)
```

CHAPTER 3
VECTOR MULTIPLICATIONS

In this chapter, we continue our adventures through the land of vectors. Warning: There are a few sections here that might be challenging. Please don't get discouraged—once you make it through this chapter, you can be confident that you can make it through the rest of the book.

There are four ways to multiply a pair of vectors. They are: dot product, outer product, element-wise multiplication, and cross product. The dot product is the most important and owns most of the real estate in this chapter.

3.1 Vector dot product: Algebra

The dot product, also called the inner product or the scalar product (not to be confused with the scalar-vector product), is **one of the most important operations in all of linear algebra**. It is the basic computational building-block from which many operations and algorithms are built, including convolution, correlation, the Fourier transform, matrix multiplication, signal filtering, and so on.

The dot product is a single number that provides information about the relationship between two vectors. This fact (two vectors produce a scalar) is why it's sometimes called the "scalar product." The term "inner product" is used when the the two vectors are continuous functions. I will use only the term *dot product* for consistency.

Algebraically, to compute the dot product, you multiply the corresponding elements of the two vectors, and then sum over all the individual products. In the box on the next page, the middle three terms show the various notations to indicate the dot product, while the final term shows the algebraic definition.

The dot product

$$\alpha = \mathbf{a} \cdot \mathbf{b} = \langle \mathbf{a}, \mathbf{b} \rangle = \mathbf{a}^{\mathrm{T}} \mathbf{b} = \sum_{i=1}^{n} a_i b_i \qquad (3.1)$$

An example:

$$\begin{bmatrix} 1 & 2 & 3 & 4 \end{bmatrix} \cdot \begin{bmatrix} 5 & 6 & 7 & 8 \end{bmatrix} = 1 \times 5 + 2 \times 6 + 3 \times 7 + 4 \times 8$$

$$= 5 + 12 + 21 + 32$$

$$= \mathbf{70}$$

I will mostly use the notation $\mathbf{a}^{\mathrm{T}} \mathbf{b}$ for reasons that will become clear after learning about matrix multiplication.

Why does the dot product require two vectors of equal dimensionality? Try to compute the dot product between the following two vectors:

$$\begin{bmatrix} 3 \\ 4 \\ 5 \\ 0 \\ 2 \end{bmatrix} \cdot \begin{bmatrix} -2 \\ 0 \\ 1 \\ 8 \end{bmatrix} = 3 \times -2 + 4 \times 0 + 5 \times 1 + 0 \times 8 + 2 \times ???$$

You cannot complete the operation because there is nothing to multiply the final element in the left vector. Thus, the dot product is defined only between two vectors that have the same dimensionality.

You can compute the dot product between a vector and itself. Equation 3.2 shows that this works out to be the sum of squared elements, and is denoted $\|\mathbf{a}\|^2$. The term $\|\mathbf{a}\|$ is called the *magnitude*, the *length*, or the *norm* of vector $\mathbf{a}$. Thus, the dot product of a vector with itself is called the magnitude-squared, the length-squared, or the squared-norm, of the vector.

If the vector is mean-centered—the average of all vector elements is subtracted from each element—then the dot product of a vector with itself is call *variance* in statistics lingo.

$$\mathbf{a}^{\mathrm{T}} \mathbf{a} = \|\mathbf{a}\|^2 = \sum_{i=1}^{n} a_i a_i = \sum_{i=1}^{n} a_i^2 \qquad (3.2)$$

I guess there's a little voice in your head wondering whether it's called the length because it corresponds to the geometric length of the vector. Your intuition is correct, as you will soon learn. But first, we need to discuss some of the properties of the dot product that can be derived algebraically.

Code   There are several ways to compute the dot product in Python and in MATLAB; here I will show one method.

Code block 3.1: Python

```
1  v1 = np.array([2,5,4,7])
2  v2 = np.array([4,1,0,2])
3  dp = np.dot(v1,v2)
```

Code block 3.2: MATLAB

```
1  v1 = [2 5 4 7];
2  v2 = [4 1 0 2];
3  dp = dot(v1,v2)
```

3.2 Dot product properties

Associative property   The associative property of the dot product can be interpreted in two ways. First is the associative property of the vector dot product with a scalar. In fact, this is simply the associative property of scalar-vector multiplication embedded inside the dot product, so it's really nothing new. I mention it here because it is important for proofs later in the book

The *associative law* is that parentheses can be moved around, e.g., $(x+y)+z = x+(y+z)$ and $x(yz) = (xy)z$

$$\gamma(\mathbf{u}^T\mathbf{v}) = (\gamma\mathbf{u}^T)\mathbf{v} = \mathbf{u}^T(\gamma\mathbf{v}) = (\mathbf{u}^T\mathbf{v})\gamma \qquad (3.3)$$

But the second interpretation is what most people refer to when discussing dot products. Let us consider three vectors and investigate what happens when we move the parentheses around. In other words, is the following statement true?

$$\mathbf{u}^{\mathrm{T}}(\mathbf{v}^{\mathrm{T}}\mathbf{w}) = (\mathbf{u}^{\mathrm{T}}\mathbf{v})^{\mathrm{T}}\mathbf{w} \tag{3.4}$$

The answer is No. To understand why, let's start by assuming that all three vectors have the same dimensionality. In that case, each side of the equation is individually a valid mathematical operation, but the two sides of the equation will differ from each other. **In fact, neither side is a dot product.** The left-hand side of Equation 3.4 becomes the vector-scalar product between row vector $\mathbf{u}^{\mathrm{T}}$ and the scalar resulting from the dot product $\mathbf{v}^{\mathrm{T}}\mathbf{w}$. Thus, the left-hand side of the equation is a row vector. Similar story for the right-hand side: It is the scalar-vector multiplication between the scalar $\mathbf{u}^{\mathrm{T}}\mathbf{v}$ and the column vector $\mathbf{w}$ (don't be confused by transposing a scalar: $4^{\mathrm{T}} = 4$).

Therefore, the two sides of the equation are not equal; they wouldn't even satisfy a "soft equality" of having the same elements but in a different orientation.

Let's see a quick example to make sure this is clear.

$$\mathbf{u} = \begin{bmatrix} 1 \\ 2 \end{bmatrix}, \quad \mathbf{v} = \begin{bmatrix} 1 \\ 3 \end{bmatrix}, \quad \mathbf{w} = \begin{bmatrix} 2 \\ 3 \end{bmatrix}$$

$$\mathbf{u}^{\mathrm{T}}\left(\mathbf{v}^{\mathrm{T}}\mathbf{w}\right) = \begin{bmatrix} 1 & 2 \end{bmatrix}\left(\begin{bmatrix} 1 & 3 \end{bmatrix}\begin{bmatrix} 2 \\ 3 \end{bmatrix}\right) = \begin{bmatrix} 11 & 22 \end{bmatrix} \tag{3.5}$$

$$\left(\mathbf{u}^{\mathrm{T}}\mathbf{v}\right)^{\mathrm{T}}\mathbf{w} = \left(\begin{bmatrix} 1 & 2 \end{bmatrix}\begin{bmatrix} 1 \\ 3 \end{bmatrix}\right)^{\mathrm{T}}\begin{bmatrix} 2 \\ 3 \end{bmatrix} = \begin{bmatrix} 14 \\ 21 \end{bmatrix} \tag{3.6}$$

And it gets even worse, because if the three vectors have different dimensionalities, then one or both sides of Equation 3.4 might even be invalid. I'll let you do the work to figure this one out, but imagine what would happen if the dimensionalities of $\mathbf{u}$, $\mathbf{v}$, and $\mathbf{w}$, were, respectively, 3, 3, and 4.

The conclusion here is that the *vector dot product does not obey the associative property*. (Just to make life confusing, matrix multiplication does obey the associative property, but at least you don't need to worry about that for several more chapters.)

Commutative property The commutative property holds for the vector dot product. This means that you can swap the order of the vectors that are being "dot producted" together (I'm not sure if dot product can be used as a verb like that, but you know what I mean), and the result is the same.

The dot product is commutative

$$\mathbf{a}^{\mathrm{T}}\mathbf{b} = \mathbf{b}^{\mathrm{T}}\mathbf{a} \tag{3.7}$$

Commutivity holds because the dot product is implemented element-wise, and each element-wise multiplication is simply the product of two scalars. Scalar multiplication is commutative, and therefore the dot product is commutative.

$$\sum_{i=1}^{n} a_i b_i = \sum_{i=1}^{n} b_i a_i \tag{3.8}$$

The *distributive law* is that scalars distribute inside parentheses, e.g., $a(b+c) = ab+ac$

Distributive property This one also holds for the dot product, and it turns out to be really important for showing the link between the algebraic definition of the dot product with the geometric definition of the dot product, which you will learn below.

When looking at the equation below, keep in mind that the sum of two vectors is simply another vector. (Needless to say, Equation 3.9 is valid only when all three vectors have the same dimensionality.)

The dot product is distributive

$$\mathbf{w}^{\mathrm{T}}(\mathbf{u} + \mathbf{v}) = \mathbf{w}^{\mathrm{T}}\mathbf{u} + \mathbf{w}^{\mathrm{T}}\mathbf{v} \tag{3.9}$$

The distributive property says that we can break up a dot product into the sum of two dot products, by breaking up one of the vectors into the sum of two vectors. Conversely, you can turn this around: We can combine two dot products into one by summing two vectors into one vector, as long as the two dot products share a common vector (in this example, $\mathbf{w}$).

Why is Equation 3.9 true? This has to do with how the dot product is defined as the sum of element-wise multiplications. Common terms can be combined across sums, which brings us to the following:

$$\sum_{i=1}^{n} \mathrm{w}_i(\mathrm{u}_i + \mathrm{v}_i) = \sum_{i=1}^{n} \mathrm{w}_i \mathrm{u}_i + \sum_{i=1}^{n} \mathrm{w}_i \mathrm{v}_i \qquad (3.10)$$

Numerical examples always help build intuition. Let's have a look:

$$\mathbf{u} = \begin{bmatrix} 1 \\ 2 \end{bmatrix}, \quad \mathbf{v} = \begin{bmatrix} 1 \\ 3 \end{bmatrix}, \quad \mathbf{w} = \begin{bmatrix} 2 \\ 3 \end{bmatrix}$$

$$\mathbf{w}^{\mathrm{T}}(\mathbf{u} + \mathbf{v}) = \begin{bmatrix} 2 & 3 \end{bmatrix} \left(\begin{bmatrix} 1 \\ 2 \end{bmatrix} + \begin{bmatrix} 1 \\ 3 \end{bmatrix} \right) = \begin{bmatrix} 2 & 3 \end{bmatrix} \begin{bmatrix} 2 \\ 5 \end{bmatrix} = 19 \qquad (3.11)$$

$$\mathbf{w}^{\mathrm{T}}\mathbf{u} + \mathbf{w}^{\mathrm{T}}\mathbf{v} = \begin{bmatrix} 2 & 3 \end{bmatrix} \begin{bmatrix} 1 \\ 2 \end{bmatrix} + \begin{bmatrix} 2 & 3 \end{bmatrix} \begin{bmatrix} 1 \\ 3 \end{bmatrix} = 8 + 11 = 19 \qquad (3.12)$$

Equation 3.13 below shows an example of applying the distributive property to the dot product between a vector and itself, where the vector is expressed as the sum of two vectors. You've already learned that the dot product of a vector with itself is the magnitude squared; the equation below expands on this idea.

$$(\mathbf{u} + \mathbf{v})^{\mathrm{T}}(\mathbf{u} + \mathbf{v}) = \|\mathbf{u} + \mathbf{v}\|^2 = \mathbf{u}^{\mathrm{T}}\mathbf{u} + 2\mathbf{u}^{\mathrm{T}}\mathbf{v} + \mathbf{v}^{\mathrm{T}}\mathbf{v}$$

$$= \|\mathbf{u}\|^2 + \|\mathbf{v}\|^2 + 2\mathbf{u}^{\mathrm{T}}\mathbf{v} \qquad (3.13)$$

Notice that combining $\mathbf{u}^{\mathrm{T}}\mathbf{v}$ and $\mathbf{v}^{\mathrm{T}}\mathbf{u}$ into $2\mathbf{u}^{\mathrm{T}}\mathbf{v}$ is valid because of the commutivity property.

This result may seem like an uninteresting academic exercise, but it's not: Equation 3.13 will allow us to link the algebraic and geometric interpretations of the dot product.

Cauchy-Schwarz inequality The Cauchy-Schwarz inequality provides an upper bound for the dot product between two vectors. In particular, the inequality is:

$$|\mathbf{v}^T\mathbf{w}| \leq \|\mathbf{v}\|\|\mathbf{w}\| \qquad (3.14)$$

In English, this inequality says that the magnitude (absolute value) of the dot product between two vectors is no larger than the product of the norms of the individual vectors. The expressions will equal each other when one vector is a scaled version of the other vector, that is, when $\mathbf{v} = \lambda\mathbf{w}$.

The Cauchy-Schwarz inequality comes up often in linear algebra. In this book, it is relevant for normalizing the quadratic form of a matrix (Chapter 17), which in turn is part of the basis of the principal components analysis (Chapter 19).

There are many proofs of this inequality; I'm going to show one that relies on the geometric perspective of the dot product. So put a mental pin in this inequality and we'll come back to it in a few pages.

Practice problems Compute the dot product between the following pairs of vectors.

a) $\begin{bmatrix} -4 \\ -2 \end{bmatrix}^T \begin{bmatrix} 1 \\ 3 \end{bmatrix}$
b) $\begin{bmatrix} 2 \\ 3 \end{bmatrix}^T \begin{bmatrix} 2 \\ -3 \end{bmatrix}$
c) $\begin{bmatrix} 7 \\ -2 \end{bmatrix}^T \begin{bmatrix} -7 \\ -24 \end{bmatrix}$
d) $\begin{bmatrix} 3/2 \\ 4/5 \end{bmatrix}^T \begin{bmatrix} 2/3 \\ -5/4 \end{bmatrix}$

e) $\begin{bmatrix} 0 \\ 1 \\ 2 \end{bmatrix}^T \begin{bmatrix} -2 \\ -1 \\ 0 \end{bmatrix}$
f) $\begin{bmatrix} 4 \\ 1 \\ 3 \end{bmatrix}^T \begin{bmatrix} 4 \\ 1 \\ 3 \end{bmatrix}$
g) $\begin{bmatrix} 7/2 \\ -3 \\ 6 \end{bmatrix}^T \begin{bmatrix} 10 \\ 3.5 \\ -4 \end{bmatrix}$
h) $\begin{bmatrix} 81 \\ 3 \\ 9 \end{bmatrix}^T \frac{1}{3}\begin{bmatrix} 1 \\ 1 \\ 1 \end{bmatrix}$

Answers

a) -10   b) -5   c) -1   d) 0

e) -1   f) 26   g) 1/2   h) 31 = (81+3+9)/3

3.3 Vector dot product: Geometry

Geometrically, the dot product is the cosine of the angle between the two vectors, times the lengths of the two vectors. That seems very different from the algebraic definition, and it's also not intuitive that those are the same operation. In this section, we will discover some properties and implications of the geometric formula for the dot product; then, in the following section, you will see that the geometric and algebraic formulae are simply different ways of expressing the same concept.

Geometric definition of the dot product

$$\mathbf{a}^{\mathsf{T}}\mathbf{b} = \|\mathbf{a}\|\|\mathbf{b}\|\cos(\theta_{ab}) \qquad (3.15)$$

Note that if both vectors have unit length ($|\mathbf{a}| = |\mathbf{b}| = 1$), then Equation 3.15 reduces to the cosine of the angle between the two vectors.

Equation 3.15 can be rewritten to give an expression for the angle between two vectors.

$$\cos(\theta_{ab}) = \frac{\mathbf{a}^{\mathsf{T}}\mathbf{b}}{\|\mathbf{a}\|\|\mathbf{b}\|} \qquad (3.16)$$

$$\theta_{ab} = \cos^{-1}\left(\frac{\mathbf{a}^{\mathsf{T}}\mathbf{b}}{\|\mathbf{a}\|\|\mathbf{b}\|}\right) \qquad (3.17)$$

In statistics, Equation 3.16 with suitable normalization is called the *Pearson correlation coefficient*. More on this in Chapter 18!

One of the interesting features of Equation 3.17 is that it generalizes the concept of an angle between two lines in 2D, to an angle between two vectors in any higher-dimensional space.

The sign of the dot product between two vectors is determined entirely by the angle between the two vectors. This is a powerful relationship and it provides a geometric intuition for basically every application of the dot product (and there are many, as you will learn throughout this book and in your adventures in linear algebra).

First, let's understand *why* the sign of the dot product is determined exclusively by the angle between the two vectors. Equation 3.15 says that the dot product is the product of three quantities: two magnitudes and a cosine. Magnitudes are lengths, and therefore cannot be negative (magnitudes can be zero for the zeros vector, but let's assume for now that we are working with non-zero-magnitude vectors). The cosine of an angle can range between -1 and +1.

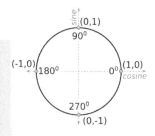

Figure 3.1: Unit circle. The x-axis coordinate corresponds to the cosine of the angle from the origin to each point.

Important: Vectors are *orthogonal* when they meet at a 90° angle, and orthogonal vectors have a dot product of 0.

Thus, the first two terms ($\|a\|\|b\|$) are necessarily non-negative, meaning the cosine of the angle between the two vectors alone determines whether the dot product is positive or negative. With that in mind, we can group dot products into five categories according to the angle between the vectors (Figure 3.2) (in the list below, θ is the angle between the two vectors and α is the dot product):

1. $\theta < 90° \rightarrow \alpha > 0$. The cosine of an acute angle is always positive, so the dot product will be positive.

2. $\theta > 90° \rightarrow \alpha < 0$. The cosine of an obtuse angle is always negative, so the dot product will be negative.

3. $\theta = 90° \rightarrow \alpha = 0$. The cosine of a right angle is zero, so the dot product will be zero, regardless of the magnitudes of the vectors. This is such an important case that it has its own name: **orthogonal**. Commit to memory that if two vectors meet at a right angle, their dot product is exactly zero, and they are said to be orthogonal to each other. This important concept is central to statistics, machine-learning, eigendecomposition, SVD, the Fourier transform, and so on. The symbol for perpendicularity is an upside-down "T." So you can write that two vectors are orthogonal as $\mathbf{w} \perp \mathbf{v}$.

4. $\theta = 0° \rightarrow \alpha = \|a\|\|b\|$. The cosine of 0 is 1, so the dot product reduces to the product of the magnitudes of the two vectors. The term for this situation is **collinear** (meaning on the same line). This also means that the dot product of a vector with itself is simply $\|\mathbf{a}\|^2$, which is the same result obtained algebraically in Equation 3.2.

5. $\theta = 180° \rightarrow \alpha = -\|a\|\|b\|$. Basically the same situation as above, but with a negative sign because $\cos(180°) = -1$. Still referred to as collinear.

Keep in mind that the *magnitude* of the dot product depends on all three terms (the magnitudes of the two vectors and the cosine of the angle); the discussion above pertains only to the *sign* of the dot product as negative, zero, or positive.

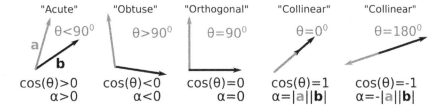

Figure 3.2: Inferences that can be made about the sign of the dot product (α), based on the angle (θ) between the two vectors. Visualization is in 2D, but the terms and conclusions extend to any number of dimensions.

3.4 Algebraic and geometric equivalence

Were you surprised that the algebraic and geometric equations for the dot product looked so different? It's hard to see that they're the same, but they really are, and that's what we're going to discover now. The two expressions are printed again below for convenience.

$$\mathbf{a}^{\mathrm{T}}\mathbf{b} = \sum_{i=1}^{n} a_i b_i = \|\mathbf{a}\|\|\mathbf{b}\|\cos(\theta_{ab}) \qquad (3.18)$$

Proving the equivalence between the algebraic and geometric formulations of the dot product requires knowing that the dot product is distributive and commutative (equations 3.7 and 3.9) and knowing a formula from geometry called the Law of Cosines. I'm going to start by proving the Law of Cosines, and then you'll see how that is used to prove Equation 3.18.

The Law of Cosines is an extension of the Pythagorean theorem ($a^2 + b^2 = c^2$) (you can also think of the Pythagorean theorem as a special case of the Law of Cosines). The Law of Cosines gives a formula for the length of side c, given the lengths of sides a and b and given the angle between a and b (Figure 3.3).

Now, if $\theta_{bc} = 90°$, then we have a right-triangle and the Pythagorean theorem applies. But how do we solve for c without any right an-

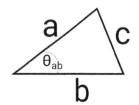

Figure 3.3: The Law of Cosines. The goal is to find the length of c given lengths a and b, and the angle between them.

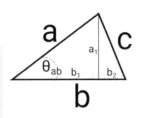

Figure 3.4: The Law of Cosines, part 2.

gles? The trick here is to create some right angles. In particular, we cut the triangle into two pieces, each of which is a right triangle (Figure 3.4).

Now c is the hypotenuse of right-triangle a_1-b_2-c. So now the goal is to find a_1 and b_2. We'll need to reach back to some high-school memories, in particular the Soh-Cah-Toa rule that relates the ratio of triangle sides to their angles. Let's start by defining a_1 in terms of a and the angle between a and b:

$$\sin(\theta_{ab}) = \frac{a_1}{a} \tag{3.19}$$

$$a_1 = a\sin(\theta_{ab}) \tag{3.20}$$

We can solve for b_1 in a similar way:

$$\cos(\theta_{ab}) = \frac{b_1}{a} \tag{3.21}$$

$$b_1 = a\cos(\theta_{ab}) \tag{3.22}$$

Next we need to find an expression for b_2. The trick here is to express b_2 in terms of quantities we already know.

$$b = b_1 + b_2 \tag{3.23}$$

$$b_2 = b - b_1 \tag{3.24}$$

$$b_2 = b - a\cos(\theta_{ab}) \tag{3.25}$$

At this point, we have created a right-triangle with side-lengths defined in terms of the original values a and b, and that means that we can apply the Pythagorean theorem on those quantities. From there, we simply work through some algebra to arrive at the Law of Cosines in Equation 3.30:

$$c^2 = a_1^2 + b_2^2 \tag{3.26}$$

$$= (a\sin(\theta_{ab}))^2 + (b - a\cos(\theta_{ab}))^2 \tag{3.27}$$

$$= a^2\sin^2(\theta_{ab}) + b^2 + a^2\cos^2(\theta_{ab}) - 2ab\cos(\theta_{ab}) \tag{3.28}$$

$$= a^2(\sin^2(\theta_{ab}) + \cos^2(\theta_{ab})) + b^2 - 2ab\cos(\theta_{ab}) \tag{3.29}$$

$$= a^2 + b^2 - 2ab\cos(\theta_{ab}) \tag{3.30}$$

Recall the trig identity that $\cos^2(\theta) + \sin^2(\theta) = 1$. Notice that when $\theta_{ab} = 90°$, the third term in Equation 3.30 drops out and we get the familiar Pythagorean theorem.

I realize this was a bit of a long tangent, but we need the Law of Cosines to prove the equivalence between the algebraic and geometric equations for the dot product.

Let's get back on track. Instead of thinking about the lengths of the triangles as a, b, and c, we can think about the edges of the triangles as *vectors* $\mathbf{a}$, $\mathbf{b}$, and $\mathbf{c}$, and thus their lengths are $\|\mathbf{a}\|$, $\|\mathbf{b}\|$, and $\|\mathbf{c}\|$.

Therefore, we can write Equation 3.30 as

$$a^2 + b^2 - 2ab\cos(\theta_{ab}) = \|\mathbf{a}\|^2 + \|\mathbf{b}\|^2 - 2\|\mathbf{a}\|\|\mathbf{b}\|\cos(\theta_{ab}) \tag{3.31}$$

Now that we're thinking of these triangle sides as vectors, we can re-write vector $\mathbf{c}$ as the subtraction of vectors $\mathbf{a}$ and $\mathbf{b}$ (see Figure 2.5): $\mathbf{c} = \mathbf{a} - \mathbf{b}$. And therefore,

$$\|\mathbf{c}\| = \|\mathbf{a} - \mathbf{b}\|$$

With that in mind, we can expand the definition of vector $\mathbf{c}$ using the distributive property:

$$\|\mathbf{a} - \mathbf{b}\|^2 = (\mathbf{a} - \mathbf{b})^{\mathrm{T}}(\mathbf{a} - \mathbf{b}) = \mathbf{a}^{\mathrm{T}}\mathbf{a} - 2\mathbf{a}^{\mathrm{T}}\mathbf{b} + \mathbf{b}^{\mathrm{T}}\mathbf{b}$$

$$= \|\mathbf{a}\|^2 + \|\mathbf{b}\|^2 - 2\mathbf{a}^{\mathrm{T}}\mathbf{b} \tag{3.32}$$

We're almost done with the proof; we just need to do some simplifications. Notice that we have discovered two different ways of writing out the magnitude-squared of $\mathbf{c}$. Let's set those equal to each other and do a bit of simplification.

$$\|\mathbf{a}\|^2 + \|\mathbf{b}\|^2 - 2\mathbf{a}^{\mathrm{T}}\mathbf{b} = \|\mathbf{a}\|^2 + \|\mathbf{b}\|^2 - 2\|\mathbf{a}\|\|\mathbf{b}\|\cos\theta$$

Notice that $\|\mathbf{a}\|^2$ and $\|\mathbf{b}\|^2$ appear on both sides of the equation, so these simply cancel. Same goes for the factor of -2. That leaves us with the remarkable conclusion of the equation we started with in this section, re-printed here for your viewing pleasure.

$$\mathbf{a}^{\mathrm{T}}\mathbf{b} = \|\mathbf{a}\|\|\mathbf{b}\|\cos\theta \tag{3.15}$$

Whew! That was a really long proof! I'm pretty sure it's the longest one in the entire book. But it was important, because we discovered that the algebraic and geometric definitions of the dot product are merely different interpretations of the same operation.

Proof of Cauchy-Schwarz inequality   I know you've been patiently waiting for this proof. As a brief reminder of what I wrote on page 50: The magnitude of the dot product between two vectors is less than or equal to the product of the norms of the two vectors. The proof comes from taking the absolute value of Equation 3.18:

$$|\mathbf{a}^{\mathrm{T}}\mathbf{b}| = \|\mathbf{a}\|\|\mathbf{b}\||\cos(\theta_{ab})| \tag{3.33}$$

$$|\mathbf{a}^{\mathrm{T}}\mathbf{b}| \leq \|\mathbf{a}\|\|\mathbf{b}\| \tag{3.34}$$

The absolute value of the cosine of an angle is between 0 and 1, and therefore, when dropping that term, it is trivial that the left-hand side cannot be larger than the right-hand side.

I also wrote that the equality holds when the two vectors form a linearly dependent set. Two co-linear vectors meet at an angle of $0°$ or $180°$, and the absolute value of the cosines of those angles is 1.

There is a lot to say about the dot product. That's no surprise—the dot product is one of the most fundamental computational building blocks in linear algebra, statistics, and signal processing, out of which myriad algorithms in math, signal processing, graphics, and other calculations are built. A few examples to whet your appetite for later chapters and real-world applications: In statistics, the cosine of the angle between a pair of normalized vectors is called the Pearson correlation coefficient; In the Fourier transform, the magnitude of the dot product between a signal and a sine wave is the power of the signal at the frequency of the sine wave; In pattern recognition and feature-identification, when the dot product is computed between multiple templates and an image, the template with the largest-magnitude dot product identifies the pattern or feature most present in the image.

3.5 Linear weighted combination

The term "linear weighted combination" comes up so often in linear algebra that it's worth honoring it with its own section. You might hear other related names for this same operation, such as "linear mixture" or "weighted combination" (the "linear" part is assumed). Sometimes, the term "coefficient" is used instead of "weight."

Linear weighted combination simply means scalar-vector multiplication and addition: Take some set of vectors, multiply each vector by any scalar, and add them to produce a single vector.

Linear weighted combination

$$\mathbf{w} = \lambda_1 \mathbf{v}_1 + \lambda_2 \mathbf{v}_2 + ... + \lambda_n \mathbf{v}_n \qquad (3.35)$$

It is assumed that all vectors $\mathbf{v}_i$ have the same dimensionality, otherwise the addition is invalid. The λ's can be any real number, including zero.

Technically, you could rewrite Equation 3.35 for subtracting vectors, but because subtraction can be handled by setting the λ_i to be negative, it's easier to discuss linear weighted combinations in terms of addition.

An example:

$$\lambda_1 = 1, \ \lambda_2 = 2, \ \lambda_3 = -3, \quad \mathbf{v_1} = \begin{bmatrix} 4 \\ 5 \\ 1 \end{bmatrix}, \ \mathbf{v_2} = \begin{bmatrix} -4 \\ 0 \\ -4 \end{bmatrix}, \ \mathbf{v_3} = \begin{bmatrix} 1 \\ 3 \\ 2 \end{bmatrix}$$

$$\mathbf{w} = \lambda_1 \mathbf{v_1} + \lambda_2 \mathbf{v_2} + \lambda_3 \mathbf{v_3} = \begin{bmatrix} -7 \\ -4 \\ -13 \end{bmatrix}$$

Code Linear weighted combinations are easy to implement, as the code below demonstrates. In Python, the data type is important; test what happens when the vectors are lists instead of numpy arrays. In Chapter 6, you will learn how to make these computations more compact using matrix-vector multiplication.

Code block 3.3: Python

```
1  import numpy as np
2  l1 = 1
3  l2 = 2
4  l3 = -3
5  v1 = np.array([4,5,1])
6  v2 = np.array([-4,0,-4])
7  v3 = np.array([1,3,2])
8  l1*v1 + l2*v2 + l3*v3
```

Code block 3.4: MATLAB

```
1  l1 = 1;
2  l2 = 2;
3  l3 = -3;
4  v1 = [4  5  1]';
5  v2 = [-4  0  -4]';
6  v3 = [1  3  2]';
7  l1*v1 + l2*v2 + l3*v3
```

3.6 The outer product

The outer product is a way of combining two vectors to produce a matrix. The outer product matrix has many applications in advanced linear algebra topics, including eigendecomposition and the singular value decomposition, image compression, and multivariate signal processing. In later chapters you will learn more about the properties of the outer product, for example that it is a rank-1 matrix. But for now, just focus on the mechanics of creating an outer product matrix from two vectors.

But let's start with a bit of notation. The outer product is indicated using a notation is that initially confusingly similar to that of the dot product. In the definitions below, $\mathbf{v}$ is an M-element column vector and $\mathbf{w}$ is an N-element column vector.

$$\text{Dot product}: \mathbf{v}^T\mathbf{w} = 1 \times 1$$

$$\text{Outer product}: \mathbf{v}\mathbf{w}^T = M \times N$$

This notation indicates that the dot product ($\mathbf{v}^T\mathbf{w}$) is a 1×1 array (just a single number; a scalar) whereas the outer product ($\mathbf{v}\mathbf{w}^T$) is a matrix whose sizes are defined by the number of elements in the vectors.

The vectors do not need to be the same size for the outer product, unlike with the dot product. Indeed, the dot product expression above is valid only when $M = N$, but the outer product is valid even if $M \neq N$.

I realize that this notation may seem strange. I promise it will make perfect sense when you learn about matrix multiplication. Essentially, the dot product and outer product are special cases of matrix multiplication.

Now let's talk about how to create an outer product. There are three perspectives for creating an outer product: The element perspective, the column perspective, and the row perspective. The result is the same; they are just different ways of thinking about the same operation.

Element perspective   Each element i, j in the outer product matrix is the scalar multiplication between the ith element in the first vector and the jth element in the second vector. This also leads to the formula for computing the outer product.

The outer product

$$(\mathbf{v}\mathbf{w}^{\mathrm{T}})_{i,j} = v_i w_j \tag{3.36}$$

Here is an example using letters instead of numbers, which helps make the formula clear.

$$\begin{bmatrix} a \\ b \\ c \end{bmatrix} \begin{bmatrix} d & e & f \end{bmatrix} = \begin{bmatrix} ad & ae & af \\ bd & be & bf \\ cd & ce & cf \end{bmatrix}$$

The element perspective lends itself well to a formula, but it's not always the best way to conceptualize the outer product.

Column perspective   Each column in the outer product matrix comes from repeating the left vector ($\mathbf{v}$ using the notation above) but scaled by each element in the row vector on the right ($\mathbf{w}^{\mathrm{T}}$). In other words, each column in the outer product matrix is the result of scalar-vector multiplication, where the vector is the column vector (repeated) and the scalar comes from each element of the row vector. Thus, the number of columns in the matrix equals the number of elements in the row vector. Notice that in the example below, each column of the outer product matrix is a scaled version of the left column vector.

$$\begin{bmatrix} 1 \\ 2 \\ 3 \\ 4 \end{bmatrix} \begin{bmatrix} 4 & 1 & -1 \end{bmatrix} = \begin{bmatrix} 4 & 1 & -1 \\ 8 & 2 & -2 \\ 12 & 3 & -3 \\ 16 & 4 & -4 \end{bmatrix}$$

Row perspective   I'm sure you can already guess how this is going to work: Form the outer product matrix one row at a time, by repeating the row vector M times (for M elements in vector $\mathbf{w}$), each time scaling the vector by each element in the column vector. In the example below, notice that each row in the outer product matrix is a scaled version of the row vector.

$$\begin{bmatrix} 4 \\ 1 \\ -1 \end{bmatrix} \begin{bmatrix} 1 & 2 & 3 & 4 \end{bmatrix} = \begin{bmatrix} 4 & 8 & 12 & 16 \\ 1 & 2 & 3 & 4 \\ -1 & -2 & -3 & -4 \end{bmatrix}$$

If you look closely at the two examples above, you'll notice that when we swapped the order of the two vectors, the two outer product matrices look the same but with the columns and rows swapped. In fact, that's not just a coincidence of this particular example; that's a general property of the outer product. It's fairly straightforward to prove that this is generally the case, but you need to learn more about matrix multiplications before getting to the proof. I'm trying to build excitement for you to stay motivated to continue with this book. I hope it's working!

Code   The outer product, like the dot product, can be implemented in several ways. Here are two of them. (Notice that MATLAB row vector elements can be separated using a space or a comma, but separating elements with a semicolon would produce a column vector, in which case you wouldn't need the transpose.)

Code block 3.5: Python

```python
1  v1 = np.array([2,5,4,7])
2  v2 = np.array([4,1,0,2])
3  op = np.outer(v1,v2)
```

Code block 3.6: MATLAB

```matlab
1  v1 = [2,5,4,7]';
2  v2 = [4 1 0 2]';
3  op = v1*v2';
```

Practice problems Compute the outer product of the following pairs of vectors.

a) $\begin{bmatrix} -1 \\ 1 \end{bmatrix} \begin{bmatrix} 2 \\ 3 \end{bmatrix}^{\mathrm{T}}$

b) $\begin{bmatrix} 4 \\ 6 \end{bmatrix} \begin{bmatrix} 2 \\ 3 \end{bmatrix}^{\mathrm{T}}$

c) $\begin{bmatrix} -1 \\ 0 \\ 1 \end{bmatrix} \begin{bmatrix} 1 \\ 2 \\ 3 \end{bmatrix}^{\mathrm{T}}$

d) $\begin{bmatrix} 1 \\ 3 \\ 5 \\ 7 \end{bmatrix} \begin{bmatrix} 0 \\ 1 \\ 1 \\ 0 \end{bmatrix}^{\mathrm{T}}$

Answers

a) $\begin{bmatrix} -2 & -3 \\ 2 & 3 \end{bmatrix}$

b) $\begin{bmatrix} 8 & 12 \\ 12 & 18 \end{bmatrix}$

c) $\begin{bmatrix} -1 & -2 & -3 \\ 0 & 0 & 0 \\ 1 & 2 & 3 \end{bmatrix}$

d) $\begin{bmatrix} 0 & 1 & 1 & 0 \\ 0 & 3 & 3 & 0 \\ 0 & 5 & 5 & 0 \\ 0 & 7 & 7 & 0 \end{bmatrix}$

3.7 Element-wise (Hadamard) vector product

This is actually the way of multiplying two vectors that you might have intuitively guessed before reading the past few sections.

Also called the Hadamard product, this operation involves multiplying each corresponding element in the two vectors. The resulting product vector therefore is the same size as the two multiplying vectors. And thus, Hadamard multiplication is defined only for two vectors that have the same number of elements.

There is no widely agreed-upon notation for Hadamard multiplication, but a circle with a dot is fairly common:

$$\mathbf{c} = \mathbf{a} \odot \mathbf{b} = \begin{bmatrix} a_1 b_1 & a_2 b_2 & ... & a_n b_n \end{bmatrix} \tag{3.37}$$

An example:

$$\begin{bmatrix} 3 \\ 6 \\ 9 \\ 0 \end{bmatrix} \odot \begin{bmatrix} 2 \\ -2 \\ 4 \\ -4 \end{bmatrix} = \begin{bmatrix} 6 \\ -12 \\ 36 \\ 0 \end{bmatrix}$$

Element-wise vector multiplication doesn't have too many applications in abstract linear algebra. In fact, it's arguably not really a *linear algebra operation*—it's more like a convenient and compact way to organize a set of regular scalar multiplications. In practical applications, that's how it's most often used: You might have two sets of variables that need to be individually multiplied, so you store them as vectors in MATLAB or Python, and then implement Hadamard multiplication.

Code There are many parts of Python and MATLAB syntax that are nearly identical. Matrix multiplication, however, is annoyingly—and confusingly—different between the languages. Notice that Python uses an asterisk (*) for element-wise multiplication whereas MATLAB uses a dot-asterisk (.*). It's a subtle but important distinction.

Code block 3.7: Python

```
1  v1 = np.array([2,5,4,7])
2  v2 = np.array([4,1,0,2])
3  v3 = v1 * v2
```

Code block 3.8: MATLAB

```
1  v1 = [2,5,4,7];
2  v2 = [4,1,0,2];
3  v3 = v1 .* v2;
```

Practice problems Compute the element-wise product between the following pairs of vectors.

a) $\begin{bmatrix} 1 \\ 3 \\ 2 \end{bmatrix} \odot \begin{bmatrix} -1 \\ 1 \\ -2 \end{bmatrix}$
b) $\begin{bmatrix} 0 \\ 0 \\ 0 \end{bmatrix} \odot \begin{bmatrix} \pi \\ e^5 \\ 2 \end{bmatrix}$
c) $\begin{bmatrix} 1.3 \\ 1.4 \\ 3.2 \end{bmatrix} \odot \begin{bmatrix} 3 \\ 5 \end{bmatrix}$

Answers

a) $\begin{bmatrix} -1 \\ 3 \\ -4 \end{bmatrix}$
b) $\begin{bmatrix} 0 \\ 0 \\ 0 \end{bmatrix}$
c) undefined!

3.8 Cross product

The cross product is defined only for two 3-element vectors, and the result is another 3-element vector. It is commonly indicated using a multiplication symbol ($\times$).

The formula for computing the cross-product seems a bit bizarre:

$$\mathbf{a} \times \mathbf{b} = \begin{bmatrix} a_2 b_3 - a_3 b_2 \\ a_3 b_1 - a_1 b_3 \\ a_1 b_2 - a_2 b_1 \end{bmatrix} \qquad (3.38)$$

The magnitude of the cross product has a geometry-based formula, which is interesting to compare to the geometric formula for the dot product (Equation 3.15).

$$\|\mathbf{a} \times \mathbf{b}\| = \|\mathbf{a}\| \|\mathbf{b}\| \sin(\theta_{ab}) \qquad (3.39)$$

The cross product is used often in geometry, for example to create a vector $\mathbf{c}$ that is orthogonal to the plane spanned by vectors $\mathbf{a}$ and $\mathbf{b}$. It is also used in vector and multivariate calculus to compute surface integrals. However, the cross product is not really used in data analysis, statistics, machine-learning, or signal-processing. I'm not going to discuss the cross-product again in this book; it is included here in the interest of completeness.

Practice problems Compute the cross-product between the following pairs of vectors.

a) $\begin{bmatrix} 5 \\ 3 \\ 4 \end{bmatrix}, \begin{bmatrix} -2 \\ 1 \\ -1 \end{bmatrix}$ b) $\begin{bmatrix} 1 \\ 1 \\ 1 \end{bmatrix}, \begin{bmatrix} 2 \\ 2 \\ 2 \end{bmatrix}$ c) $\begin{bmatrix} 1 \\ 0 \\ 0 \end{bmatrix}, \begin{bmatrix} 0 \\ 1 \\ 0 \end{bmatrix}$ d) $\begin{bmatrix} 1302 \\ 1403 \end{bmatrix}, \begin{bmatrix} 3 \\ 5 \end{bmatrix}$

Answers

a) $\begin{bmatrix} -7 \\ -3 \\ 11 \end{bmatrix}$ b) $\begin{bmatrix} 0 \\ 0 \\ 0 \end{bmatrix}$ c) $\begin{bmatrix} 0 \\ 0 \\ 1 \end{bmatrix}$ d) undefined.

Unit vectors

It is often useful to have a vector with a length of one: $\|\mathbf{v}\| = 1$ (Figure 3.5). Unit vectors are convenient in many linear algebra applications, particularly on computers (e.g., to avoid numerical precision inaccuracies for vectors with very small magnitudes). Unit vectors also allow for creating a special kind of matrix called an orthogonal matrix.

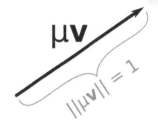

Figure 3.5: A unit vector.

Therefore, the goal of this section is to derive a formula for computing a unit vector in the same direction as some other vector $\mathbf{v}$ that is not necessarily a unit vector. The way to do this is to find some scalar μ that satisfies our criteria:

$$\mu\mathbf{v} \ \ s.t. \ \|\mu\mathbf{v}\| = 1 \tag{3.40}$$

How to choose μ? Let's start by thinking about how you would create a "unit-norm number" (that is, find μ such that μ times a number has an absolute value of 1). Let's figure this out using the number 3.

$$|\mu 3| = 1$$

$$\mu = 1/3$$

Deriving the solution is simple: Divide both sides by the magnitude (that is, the absolute value) of the number (the reason for the absolute value here is that we want $\mu = 1/3$ even if we start with -3 instead of +3).

s.t. means "such that" or "subject to"

Now extend this concept to vectors: set μ to be the reciprocal (the inverse) of the magnitude of the vector. In terms of notation, a unit vector is commonly given a hat to indicate that it has a magnitude of one ($\mathbf{v} \rightarrow \hat{\mathbf{v}}$).

Creating a unit-length vector

$$\hat{\mathbf{v}} = \frac{1}{\|\mathbf{v}\|}\mathbf{v} = \frac{1}{\sqrt{\sum_{i=1}^{n} v_i^2}}\mathbf{v} \qquad (3.41)$$

The norm of the vector, $\|\mathbf{v}\|$, is a scalar, which means (1) division is allowed (division by a full vector is not defined) and (2) importantly, *the direction of the vector does not change*. Here is a simple example:

$$\mathbf{v} = \begin{bmatrix} 0 \\ 2 \end{bmatrix}, \qquad \hat{\mathbf{v}} = \frac{1}{\sqrt{0^2 + 2^2}} \begin{bmatrix} 0 \\ 2 \end{bmatrix} = \begin{bmatrix} 0 \\ 1 \end{bmatrix}$$

This example also shows why the divisor is the magnitude (the square root of sum of squared vector elements), and not the squared magnitude $\mathbf{v}^\mathsf{T}\mathbf{v}$. It is also clear that the unit vector $\hat{\mathbf{v}}$ points in the same direction as $\mathbf{v}$.

It is worth mentioning explicitly what you might have already deduced: The unit vector is defined only for non-zero vectors. This makes sense both algebraically (Equation 3.41 would involve division by zero) and geometrically (a vector with no length has no direction, hence, another vector in the same direction is not a sensible construct).

Taking $\mu = 1/\|\mathbf{v}\|$ allows for a quick proof that the unit vector really does have unit length:

$$\|\mu\mathbf{v}\| = \frac{1}{\|\mathbf{v}\|}\|\mathbf{v}\| = 1 \qquad (3.42)$$

Code Fortunately, both Python and MATLAB have built-in functions for computing the norm of a vector.

Code block 3.9: Python

```python
1  v = np.array([2,5,4,7])
2  vMag = np.linalg.norm(v)
3  v_unit = v / vMag
```

Code block 3.10: MATLAB

```matlab
1  v = [2,5,4,7];
2  vMag = norm(v);
3  v_unit = v / vMag;
```

Practice problems Compute a unit vector in the same direction as the following vectors. Then confirm that the magnitude of the resulting vector is 1.

a) $\begin{bmatrix} 1 \\ 3 \end{bmatrix}$
b) $\begin{bmatrix} 3 \\ 4 \end{bmatrix}$
c) $\begin{bmatrix} 6 \\ -8 \end{bmatrix}$
d) $\begin{bmatrix} .1 \\ .2 \\ .4 \\ .2 \end{bmatrix}$

Answers

a) $\frac{1}{\sqrt{10}} \begin{bmatrix} 1 \\ 3 \end{bmatrix}$
b) $\begin{bmatrix} 3/5 \\ 4/5 \end{bmatrix}$
c) $\begin{bmatrix} 3/5 \\ -4/5 \end{bmatrix}$
d) $\frac{1}{\sqrt{.25}} \begin{bmatrix} .1 \\ .2 \\ .4 \\ .2 \end{bmatrix} = \begin{bmatrix} .2 \\ .4 \\ .8 \\ .4 \end{bmatrix}$

Exercises

1. Compute the dot product between the following pairs of vectors.

a) $\begin{bmatrix} 0 \\ a \end{bmatrix}, \begin{bmatrix} b \\ 0 \end{bmatrix}$
b) $\begin{bmatrix} a \\ b \end{bmatrix}, \begin{bmatrix} c \\ d \end{bmatrix}$
c) $\begin{bmatrix} a \\ c \end{bmatrix}, \begin{bmatrix} b \\ d \end{bmatrix}$

d) $\begin{bmatrix} 1 \\ 4 \end{bmatrix}, \begin{bmatrix} 3 \\ -3 \end{bmatrix}$
e) $\begin{bmatrix} 1 \\ 4 \\ 0 \end{bmatrix}, \begin{bmatrix} 3 \\ -3 \\ 9 \end{bmatrix}$
f) $\begin{bmatrix} 10 \\ 14 \\ -3 \end{bmatrix}, \begin{bmatrix} -1 \\ 1 \\ -6 \end{bmatrix}$

g) $\begin{bmatrix} 1 \\ a \end{bmatrix}, \begin{bmatrix} b \\ 1 \end{bmatrix}$
h) $\begin{bmatrix} 2i \\ 4-i \\ 3 \end{bmatrix}, \begin{bmatrix} 3 \\ 3 \\ 1 \end{bmatrix}$
i) $\begin{bmatrix} 1 \\ 2 \end{bmatrix}, \begin{bmatrix} 2 \\ -1 \end{bmatrix}$

j) $\begin{bmatrix} 1 \\ -2 \\ -3 \\ 4 \\ 5 \\ -6 \end{bmatrix}, \begin{bmatrix} -4 \\ 3 \\ 4 \\ -5 \\ 6 \\ -2 \end{bmatrix}$
k) $\begin{bmatrix} 2 \\ -5 \\ 0 \\ 0 \\ 2 \\ -8 \end{bmatrix}, \begin{bmatrix} -1 \\ 5 \\ 0 \\ -1 \\ 0 \\ -4 \end{bmatrix}$
l) $\begin{bmatrix} 2.47 \\ -2.47 \end{bmatrix}, \begin{bmatrix} \pi^3 \\ \pi^3 \end{bmatrix}$

m) $\begin{bmatrix} 2 \\ 3 \\ -3 \\ 2 \end{bmatrix}, \begin{bmatrix} 0 \\ 12 \\ -8 \\ 4 \end{bmatrix}$
n) $\begin{bmatrix} 2 \\ -1 \\ -2 \end{bmatrix}, \begin{bmatrix} -2 \\ 1 \\ -\frac{5}{2} \end{bmatrix}$
o) $\begin{bmatrix} 0 \\ 0 \end{bmatrix}, \begin{bmatrix} a \\ b \end{bmatrix}$

2. Assume that $\|\mathbf{x}\| = \|\mathbf{y}\| = 1$. Determine whether each of the following equations is necessarily true, necessarily false, or could be true depending on the elements in $\mathbf{x}$ and $\mathbf{y}$.

a) $(\mathbf{x} - \mathbf{y})^T(\mathbf{x} - \mathbf{y}) = 2(1 - \mathbf{x}^T\mathbf{y})$
b) $\|(\mathbf{x} - \frac{1}{2}\mathbf{y})\|^2 = \frac{5}{4} - \mathbf{x}^T\mathbf{y}$

c) $\frac{\mathbf{x}^T\mathbf{y}}{\mathbf{x}^T\mathbf{x}} - \frac{\mathbf{y}^T\mathbf{y}}{\mathbf{x}^T\mathbf{y}\mathbf{y}^T\mathbf{y}} = 0$
d) $\|\mathbf{y} + \frac{2}{3}\mathbf{x}\|^2 = \frac{4}{9}(1 + 4\mathbf{x}^T\mathbf{y})$

e) $\mathbf{x}^T\mathbf{x} + \mathbf{x}^T\mathbf{x} - 2\mathbf{y}^T\mathbf{y} = \mathbf{x}^T\mathbf{y}$
f) $\frac{\frac{1}{2}\mathbf{x}^T\mathbf{x}\frac{1}{2}\mathbf{y}^T\mathbf{y}}{\mathbf{y}^T(\frac{1}{4}\mathbf{y})} + \frac{\|\mathbf{x}\|^2}{\|\mathbf{x}\|^2\|\mathbf{y}\|^3} - \frac{\mathbf{y}^T\mathbf{y}\mathbf{y}^T\mathbf{y}}{\mathbf{x}^T\mathbf{x}} = 1$

3. Compute the angle θ between the following pairs of vectors. See if you can do with without a calculator!

a) $\begin{bmatrix} 1 \\ 2 \\ 3 \end{bmatrix}$, $\begin{bmatrix} -2 \\ 1 \\ 0 \end{bmatrix}$ b) $\begin{bmatrix} 10 \\ 12 \\ 4 \end{bmatrix}$, $\begin{bmatrix} 2.5 \\ 3 \\ 1 \end{bmatrix}$ c) $\begin{bmatrix} -1 \\ -2 \\ 3 \end{bmatrix}$, $\begin{bmatrix} 3 \\ 6 \\ -9 \end{bmatrix}$

4. Compute the outer product between the following pairs of vectors. Implement problems a-c element-wise (the i, j^{th} element in the product matrix is the product of the ith element in the left vector and the jth element in the right vector); problems d-f row-wise (each row in the product matrix is the right-vector scaled by each element in the left vector); and problems g-i column-wise (each column in the product matrix is the left-vector scaled by each element in the right-vector).

a) $\begin{bmatrix} 1 \\ 2 \end{bmatrix} \begin{bmatrix} 1 \\ 2 \end{bmatrix}^T$ b) $\begin{bmatrix} -1 \\ 3 \\ 0 \end{bmatrix} \begin{bmatrix} 0 \\ 1 \\ 3 \end{bmatrix}^T$ c) $\begin{bmatrix} 1 \\ 0 \\ 0 \end{bmatrix} \begin{bmatrix} 0 \\ 1 \\ 0 \end{bmatrix}^T$

d) $\begin{bmatrix} 1 \\ 2 \\ 3 \\ 4 \end{bmatrix} \begin{bmatrix} 5 \\ 6 \\ 7 \\ 8 \end{bmatrix}^T$ e) $\begin{bmatrix} 1 \\ 2 \\ 3 \\ 4 \end{bmatrix} \begin{bmatrix} 10 \\ 20 \\ 30 \\ 40 \end{bmatrix}^T$ f) $\begin{bmatrix} 1 \\ 1 \\ 2 \\ 2 \end{bmatrix} \begin{bmatrix} a \\ b \\ c \\ d \end{bmatrix}^T$

g) $\begin{bmatrix} 4 \\ 2 \\ 3 \\ 1 \end{bmatrix} \begin{bmatrix} 6 \\ 7 \\ 5 \end{bmatrix}^T$ h) $\begin{bmatrix} 3 \\ 40 \end{bmatrix} \begin{bmatrix} 10 \\ 2 \\ 30 \\ 4 \end{bmatrix}^T$ i) $\begin{bmatrix} a \\ b \\ c \\ d \end{bmatrix}^T \begin{bmatrix} 1 \\ 1 \\ 2 \\ 2 \end{bmatrix}$

5. Determine whether the following vectors are unit vectors.

a) $\frac{1}{\sqrt{3}} \begin{bmatrix} 1 \\ 1 \\ 1 \end{bmatrix}$ b) $\begin{bmatrix} .2 \\ .64 \\ .1 \\ .4 \end{bmatrix}$ c) $\begin{bmatrix} 3/5 \\ 0 \\ 0 \\ .8 \end{bmatrix}$ d) $\frac{1}{\sqrt{90}} \begin{bmatrix} 1 \\ 3 \\ 5 \\ 2 \\ 4 \\ 6 \end{bmatrix}$

6. What is the magnitude of vector $\mu\mathbf{v}$ for the following μ?

a) $\mu = 0$ b) $\mu = \|\mathbf{v}\|$ c) $\mu = 1/\|\mathbf{v}\|$ d) $\mu = 1/\|\mathbf{v}\|^2$

 **Answers**

1.

a) 0   **b)** $ac + bd$ **c)** $ab + cd$

d) -9 **e)** -9 **f)** 22

g) $a + b$ **h)** $15 + 3i$ **i)** 0

j) 0   **k)** 5   **l)** 0

m) 68   **n)** 0   **o)** 0

2.

a) True   **b)** True   **c)** Depends

d) False   **e)** Depends   **f)** True

3. These you can solve by inspecting the elements of the vectors, without applying the dot product formula.

a) $\theta = \pi/2 \; (90°)$ **b)** $\theta = 0$ **c)** $\theta = \pi \; (180°)$

4. Of course, the answers are the same regardless of the perspective you use; the goal is to become comfortable with different ways of thinking about the outer product.

a) $\begin{bmatrix} 1 & 2 \\ 2 & 4 \end{bmatrix}$

b) $\begin{bmatrix} 0 & -1 & -3 \\ 0 & 3 & 9 \\ 0 & 0 & 0 \end{bmatrix}$

c) $\begin{bmatrix} 0 & 1 & 0 \\ 0 & 0 & 0 \\ 0 & 0 & 0 \end{bmatrix}$

d) $\begin{bmatrix} 5 & 6 & 7 & 8 \\ 10 & 12 & 14 & 16 \\ 15 & 18 & 21 & 24 \\ 20 & 24 & 28 & 32 \end{bmatrix}$

e) $\begin{bmatrix} 10 & 20 & 30 & 40 \\ 20 & 40 & 60 & 80 \\ 30 & 60 & 90 & 120 \\ 40 & 80 & 120 & 160 \end{bmatrix}$

f) $\begin{bmatrix} a & b & c & d \\ a & b & c & d \\ 2a & 2b & 2c & 2d \\ 2a & 2b & 2c & 2d \end{bmatrix}$

g) $\begin{bmatrix} 24 & 28 & 20 \\ 12 & 14 & 10 \\ 18 & 21 & 15 \\ 6 & 7 & 5 \end{bmatrix}$

h) $\begin{bmatrix} 30 & 400 \\ 6 & 80 \\ 90 & 1200 \\ 12 & 160 \end{bmatrix}^{\mathrm{T}}$

i) $\begin{bmatrix} a & a & 2a & 2a \\ b & b & 2b & 2b \\ c & c & 2c & 2c \\ d & d & 2d & 2d \end{bmatrix}$

5. **a)** Yes   **b)** No   **c)** Yes   **d)** No

6. **a)** 0   **b)** $\|\mathbf{v}\|^2$ **c)** 1   **d)** $1/\|\mathbf{v}\|$

3.12 Code challenges

1. Create a linear weighted combination of three vectors. You'll learn in later chapters that linear combinations are most efficiently represented as matrix-vector multiplication, but we'll keep things simple for now. Create three 5-D vectors and a fourth vector that contains the weights for each vector. Then create the weighted sum of those vectors. Next, modify the code to compute the weighted mixture of four 5-D vectors. What is the relationship between the dimensionality of the to-be-summed vectors, the number of vectors to sum, and the dimensionality of the coefficients vector?

2. Develop a method to use the dot product to compute the average of a set of numbers in a vector. (Hint: consider the vector of all ones, sometimes written $\mathbf{1}$.)

3. What if some numbers were more important than other numbers? Modify your answer to the previous question to devise a method to use the dot product to compute a weighted mean of a set of numbers.

3.13 Code solutions

1. Only the basic code solutions are presented here. Keep in mind that these challenges are also about critical thinking, not just writing a few lines of code.

Code block 3.11: Python

```
1    v1 = np.array([1,2,3,4,5])
2    v2 = np.array([2,3,4,5,6])
3    v3 = np.array([3,4,5,6,7])
4    w = [-1,3,-2]
5    result = v1*w[0] + v2*w[1] + v3*w[2]
```

Code block 3.12: MATLAB

```
1    v1 = [1,2,3,4,5];
2    v2 = [2,3,4,5,6];
3    v3 = [3,4,5,6,7];
4    w = [-1 3 -2];
5    result = v1*w(1) + v2*w(2) + v3*w(3)
```

2. The trick is to compute the average of N numbers by summing them together after multiplying by 1/N. Mathematically, you would write this as $\mathbf{v}^\mathrm{T}\mathbf{1}\frac{1}{N}$.

Code block 3.13: Python

```
1    v = [ 7, 4, -5, 8, 3 ]
2    o = np.ones(len(v))
3    ave = np.dot(v,o) / len(v)
```

Code block 3.14: MATLAB

```
1    v = [ 7 4 -5 8 3 ]';
2    o = ones(size(v));
3    ave = dot(v,o) / length(v)
```

3. We don't know which numbers are more important than others, so I will use randomized weights. In fact, the solution here is simply the the dot product between the data vector and any other vector that sums to one.

Code block 3.15: Python

```
1    v = [ 7, 4, −5, 8, 3 ]
2    w = np.random.rand(len(v))
3    wAve = np.dot(v, w/sum(w))
```

Code block 3.16: MATLAB

```
1    v = [ 7, 4, −5, 8, 3 ];
2    w = rand(size(v));
3    wAve = dot(v, w/sum(w))
```

CHAPTER 4
VECTOR SPACES

Dimensions and fields in linear algebra

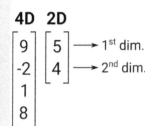

4D 2D

Figure 4.1: Each position in a vector is a dimension, and the element in that position is that value along that dimension.

Dimension I provided a brief definition of the term "dimension" in the previous chapter—the number of elements in a vector—but given the importance of this concept for understanding vector/matrix subspaces, systems, and decompositions, it's worth expanding on the concept of dimension in more detail.

Algebraically, the dimensionality of a vector is simply the number of elements in the vector. The order is meaningful: In the vector [3 1 5], the element in the second dimension is 1, and the number 5 is in the third dimension (Figure 4.1). On the other hand, there is no hierarchical relationship amongst the dimensions — the first dimension isn't intrinsically more important than the second dimension.

Geometrically, the dimensionality of a vector is the number of coordinate axes in which that vector exists. A 2D vector is a line in a 2D space (think of the typical Cartesian XY plane); a 3D vector is a line in a 3D space. Note that both a 2D vector and a 3D vector are both *lines*, but they exist in a different number of *dimensions*. Higher dimensional spaces are often indicated in the style of Figure 4.2.

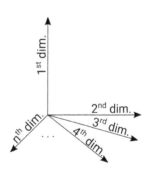

Figure 4.2: Depicting a high-dimensional space on 2D paper.

As you learned in the previous chapter, the value of each vector element tells you how far along that coordinate axis to travel. This is easiest to conceptualize for vectors in their standard position, because the endpoint of the vector is the same as the coordinate. For example, the vector [1 3] in standard position is a line that goes from the origin to the coordinate point (1,3). Hence: two elements, two coordinate axes.

A major departure from the typical Cartesian axis you're familiar with—and a beautiful feature of linear algebra—is that the coordinate axes need not be orthogonal; that is, they need not meet at right angles (Figure 4.3). Orthogonal axes have several useful properties, but non-orthogonal axes also have many useful properties, and are key to many applications, including data compression.

More on this in the section on Bases.

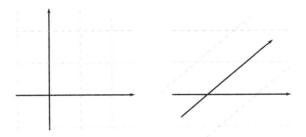

Figure 4.3: The familiar Cartesian plane (left) has orthogonal coordinate axes. However, axes in linear algebra are not constrained to be orthogonal (right), and non-orthogonal axes can be advantageous.

Fields The term "field" in mathematics might be new to you. Perhaps you've seen these fancy capital letters like $\mathbb{R}$, $\mathbb{C}$, $\mathbb{Q}$, or $\mathbb{Z}$. These letters (typeface *blackboard bold* and sometimes called "hollow letters") refer to fields. A field in mathematics is a set of numbers for which the basic arithmetic operations (addition, subtraction, multiplication, division) are defined.

The $\mathbb{R}$ stands for real, as in, real numbers. In Chapter 9, we'll use the field $\mathbb{C}$ for complex numbers. There's also the field $\mathbb{Q}$ for rational numbers (a rational number is not a number that makes good decisions; it's one that is defined by a ratio $\frac{p}{q}$).

In this book, we'll use fields mainly to indicate dimensionality. For example, $\mathbb{R}^2$ is the set of all real two-dimensional vectors, and $\mathbb{R}^4$ means a 4-element vector of the form $\begin{bmatrix} a & b & c & d \end{bmatrix}$, where a, b, c, and d are any real numbers.

Sometimes, the exact dimensionality doesn't matter but the relative dimensionalities do. For example, if I told you that vector $\mathbf{w}$ is in $\mathbb{R}^M$ and $\mathbf{v}$ is in $\mathbb{R}^N$, then you would know that the dot product $\mathbf{w}^T\mathbf{v}$ is defined only if $M = N$.

When taking notes by hand, fields are often written as R^2, and when typing on a computer, fields are often indicated as R2 or R^6.

Practice problems Identify the N in $\mathbb{R}^N$ for the following vectors.

a) $\begin{bmatrix} 1 & -3 & 4 & 2 \end{bmatrix}$

b) $\begin{bmatrix} 0 \\ 0 \\ 3 \end{bmatrix}$

c) $\begin{bmatrix} \pi & e^e \end{bmatrix}$

d) 17

Answers

a) $\mathbb{R}^4$

b) $\mathbb{R}^3$

c) $\mathbb{R}^2$

d) $\mathbb{R}^1$

4.2 Vector spaces

An *axiom* is a state-ment that is taken to be true without re-quiring a formal proof.

A *vector space* refers to any set of objects for which addition and scalar multiplication are defined. Addition and scalar multiplica-tion obey the following axioms; these should all be sensible require-ments based on your knowledge of arithmetic:

$$Additive\ inverse : \mathbf{v} + (-\mathbf{v}) = \mathbf{0}$$

$$Associativity : (\mathbf{v} + \mathbf{w}) + \mathbf{u} = \mathbf{v} + (\mathbf{w} + \mathbf{u})$$

$$Commutativity : \mathbf{v} + \mathbf{w} = \mathbf{w} + \mathbf{v}$$

$$Additive\ identity : \mathbf{v} + \mathbf{0} = \mathbf{v}$$

$$Multiplicative\ identity : \mathbf{v}1 = \mathbf{v}$$

$$Distributivity : (\alpha + \beta)(\mathbf{v} + \mathbf{w}) = \alpha\mathbf{v} + \alpha\mathbf{w} + \beta\mathbf{v} + \beta\mathbf{w}$$

Vector spaces make little appearance in this book outside this sec-tion. Instead, vector *sub*spaces are much more prominent. In fact, I bring up vector spaces here only so they are not confused with vector *sub*spaces. Three letters can make a big difference, as people struggling to finish their PhD can confirm.

Subspaces and ambient spaces

Vector subspaces are central to nearly all advanced concepts in, and applications of, linear algebra. Fortunately, the concept of a subspace is not so complicated, and it has geometric and algebraic explanations that I hope will become intuitive after some exposure and a few examples.

Geometry A subspace is the set of all points that you can reach by stretching and combining a collection of vectors (that is, addition and scalar multiplication).

Let's start with a simple example of the vector $\mathbf{v}=[\text{-}1\ 2]$. In its standard position, this is a line from the origin to the coordinate (-1,2). This vector on its own is not a subspace. However, consider the set of all possible vectors that can be obtained by $\lambda\mathbf{v}$ for the infinity of possible real-valued λ's, ranging from $-\infty$ to $+\infty$: That set describes an infinitely long line *in the same direction* as $\mathbf{v}$, and is depicted in Figure 4.4 (showing the entire subspace would require an infinitely long page).

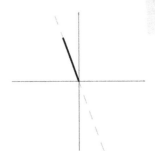

Figure 4.4: A 1D subspace (gray dashed line) created from a vector (solid black line).

That gray dashed line is the set of all points that you can reach by scaling and combining all vectors in our collection (in this case, it's a collection of one vector). That gray line extends infinitely far in both directions, although the vector $\mathbf{v}$ is finite.

This is the important sense in which $\lambda\mathbf{v}$ does not change the "direction" of $\mathbf{v}$, which was mentioned in a previous chapter.

So the subspace obtained from one vector is an infinitely long line. What happens when you have two vectors? They each individually have an associated infinitely long 1D subspace. But the definition of a vector subspace allows us to combine these vectors. And you learned in the previous chapter that adding two vectors geometrically gives a third vector that can point in a different direction compared to the two adding vectors.

So by scaling and adding two vectors, we can reach many points that are not within the 1D subspaces defined by either vector alone. Figure 4.5 shows an example of combining two vectors to reach a point that could not be reached by either vector's subspace alone.

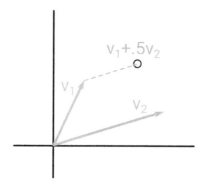

Figure 4.5: The linear combination of two vectors can reach a point that is not within the 1D subspaces defined by either vector alone.

In fact, the set of *all* points reachable by scaling and adding two vectors (that is, the linear weighted combination of those two vectors) creates a new 2D subspace, which is a *plane* that extends infinitely far in all directions of that plane. Figure 4.6 shows how this looks in 3D: The subspace created from two vectors is a plane. Any point in the plane can be reached by some linear combination of the two grey vectors.

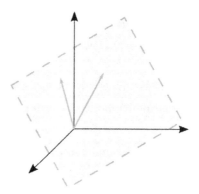

Figure 4.6: A 2D subspace in a 3D ambient space, created by all possible weighted linear combinations of two vectors (gray lines). The dashed border indicates that the plane extends to ∞ in all directions.

Ambient dimensionality Figure 4.6 also shows the distinction between a *subspace* and the *ambient space* in which that subspace is embedded. In this case, the subspace is 2-dimensional, and it is embedded in an ambient 3-dimensional space. The ambient dimensionality is the dimensionality of the vectors—the N in $\mathbb{R}^N$.

Note that in *linear* algebra we deal only with *linear* dimensions.

So, how many subspaces are possible within an ambient space? The answer is infinity, for any ambient dimensionality more than 1.

But let me unpack that answer by working through the answer to a slightly different question: How many *subspace dimensionalities* are possible with an N-dimensional ambient space? That answer is a finite number, and it turns out to be N+1. Let us count the dimensionalities, using $\mathbb{R}^3$ as a visualizable example.

The smallest possible subspace is the one defined by the zeros vector [0 0 0]. This vector is at the origin of the ambient 3D space, and any scalar λ times this vector is still at the origin. This is the only subspace that is a single point, and it is thus a zero-dimensional subspace.

Next, we have 1-dimensional subspaces, which are defined as the scalar multiples of any non-zeros vector. Basically, any line in 3D can give rise to a 1D subspace that is embedded in the ambient 3 dimensions, as long as that line goes through the origin (any subspace must contain the origin for the case $\lambda = 0$). How many such 1D subspaces are there? The answer is the number of unique lines in 3D that pass through the origin, which is infinity: there is an infinite number of lines in 3D that pass through the origin.

Now for the 2-dimensional subspaces. These are formed by taking all linear combinations of two vectors—two lines—in 3D. These vectors themselves don't need to pass through the origin, but the plane that is formed by combining all scaled versions of these vectors must include the origin (Figure 4.7). It is also intuitive that there is an infinite number of 2D planes in 3D ambient space that pass through the origin.

But wait a minute—will *any* two vectors form a plane? No, the vectors must be distinct from each other. This should make sense intuitively: two vectors that lie on the same line cannot define a unique plane. In a later section, I'll define this concept as *linear independence* and provide a formal explanation; for now, try to use your visual intuition and high-school geometry knowledge to understand that a unique plane can be defined only from two vectors that are different from each other.

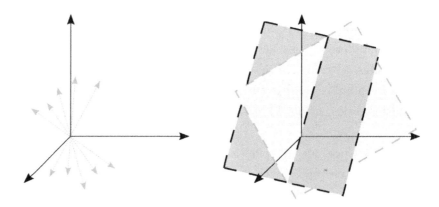

Figure 4.7: Left: five (grey lines) of the infinity of possible 1D subspaces embedded in an ambient 3D space. Right: two of the infinity of possible 2D subspaces in the same ambient space. Remember that all subspaces must pass through the origin.

Finally, we have the 3D subspace defined by all linear combinations of three vectors. As with the plane case, the three vectors that span this 3D subspace must point in different directions from each other, otherwise you could form only a plane or a line. How many distinct 3D subspaces are possible in a 3D ambient space? Exactly one: the entire ambient space. The subspace already is the entire ambient space, so there is no way to get an extra, unique, subspace. (Of course, there are different sets of vectors that you could use to create this subspace; more on this in the section on Bases!)

So there you have it: For an N-dimensional ambient space, there are N+1 possible dimensions for subspaces (0 through N), and an infinite number of possible subspaces, except for the one 0-dimensional subspace and the one N-dimensional subspace.

The visualization gets a bit hairy after three dimensions. In a 4D ambient space, there is an infinite number of unique 3D subspaces. Each of those 3D subspaces is like a cube that extends infinitely in all directions and yet is somehow still only an infinitely thin slice of the 4D space. I can make this work in my mind by thinking about time as the 4th dimension: There is a single instant in time in which an infinitely expansive space exists, but for all of time before and after, that space doesn't exist (and yes, I am aware that time had a beginning and might have an end; it's just a visualization trick, not a perfect analogy). Now take a moment to try to visualize what an 18D subspace embedded in an ambient $\mathbb{R}^{96}$ "looks like." You can understand why we need the algebraic perspective to prevent overcrowding at psychiatric institutions...

Algebra Except for a bit of additional notation (possibly funny-looking, if you are not used to proofs-based math texts), you'll see that the algebraic definition is the same as the geometric definition, but it might feel more rigorous because there are equations.

A subspace is the set of all points that can be created by all possible linear combinations of vector-scalar multiplication for a given set of vectors in $\mathbb{R}^N$ and all scalars in $\mathbb{R}$. Subspaces are often indicated using italicized upper-case letters, for example: the subspace V. That same notation is also used to indicate a set of vectors. You'll need to infer the correct reference from context.

In words, a subspace is the set of all points that satisfies the following conditions:

- Closed under addition and scalar multiplication.
- Contains the zeros vector $\mathbf{0}$.

"Closed" means that what happens in the subspace, stays in the subspace.

The first condition means that for some vector $\mathbf{v} \in V$ (a vector $\mathbf{v}$ contained in vector subspace V), multiplying $\mathbf{v}$ by any scalar λ and/or adding any other scaled vector $\alpha\mathbf{w}$ that is also contained inside the vector subspace V produces a new vector that remains in that same subspace.

In math terms, that first definition for a subspace translates to:

Algebraic definition of a subspace

$$\forall \mathbf{v}, \mathbf{w} \in V, \quad \forall \lambda, \alpha \in \mathbb{R}; \quad \lambda \mathbf{v} + \alpha \mathbf{w} \in V \qquad (4.1)$$

Read outloud: "The subspace V is defined as the set of all real-valued scalar multiples of the row vector [1 3 4]."

Read outloud, this statement would be "for any vectors $\mathbf{v}$ and $\mathbf{w}$ contained in the vector subspace V, and for any real-valued scalars λ and α, any linearly weighted combination of $\mathbf{v}$ and $\mathbf{w}$ is still inside vector subspace V." Below is an example of a 1D subspace V defined by all linear combinations of a row vector in $\mathbb{R}^3$.

$$V = \{\lambda \begin{bmatrix} 1 & 3 & 4 \end{bmatrix}, \lambda \in \mathbb{R}\} \qquad (4.2)$$

Note that this example is not a line in $\mathbb{R}^1$; it is a 1D subspace embedded in a 3D ambient space $\mathbb{R}^3$. Now consider the following specific vectors.

$$\begin{bmatrix} 3 & 9 & 12 \end{bmatrix} \in V$$
$$\begin{bmatrix} -2 & -6 & -8 \end{bmatrix} \in V$$
$$\begin{bmatrix} 1 & 3 & 5 \end{bmatrix} \notin V$$

The first two vectors are contained in the subspace V. Algebraically that's the case because you can find some λ such that $\lambda[\,1\,3\,4\,] = [\,3\,9\,12\,]$; same for the second vector. Geometrically, the first two vectors are collinear with the original vector $[\,1\,3\,4\,]$; they're on the same infinitely long time, just scaled by some factor.

That third vector, however, is *not* contained in the subspace V because there is no possible λ that can multiply the vector to produce $[\,1\,3\,5\,]$. Geometrically, that vector points in some direction that is different from the subspace V.

Let's consider another example: The set of all points in $\mathbb{R}^2$ with non-negative y-values. Is this a vector subspace? It contains the point $[0,0]$, which is a requirement. However, you can find some point in the set (e.g., **v**=[2,3]) and some scalar λ (e.g., -1) such that λ**v** is *outside the set*. Thus, this set is *not* closed under scalar multiplication, and it is therefore not a subspace. In fact, this an example of a *subset*.

Subsets

In linear algebra, *subspace* and *subset* are two entirely different concepts, but they are easily confused because of the similarity of the names. Subsets are actually not important for the linear algebra topics covered in this book. But it is important to be able to distinguish subsets from subspaces.

A *subset*, in contrast to a subspace, is a region in space that can have boundaries instead of extending to infinity, and it need not include the origin. Examples include a quadrant of the 2D Cartesian plane, a collection of equally spaced points around some center coordinate, and sphere in 3D. A few additional examples:

- The set of all points on the XY plane such that $x > 0$ and $y > 0$.
- The set of all points such that $4 > x > 2$ and $y > x^2$.
- The set of all points such that $y = 4x$, for x ranging from $-\infty$ to $+\infty$.

These are all valid sub*sets*. The third example is also a sub*space*, because the definition of that set is consistent with the definition of a subspace: an infinitely long line that passes through the origin.

Practice problems   Identify whether the following subsets are also subspaces.
If they are not subspaces, find a vector in the set and a scalar such that $\lambda\mathbf{v}$ is outside the set.

  a) All points in $\mathbb{R}^2$
  b) All points on the line $y = 2x + .1$
  c) Points satisfying $x^2 + y^2 + z^2 = 1$
  d) All points on the line $y = 2x + 0$

Answers

  a) subspace and subset
  b) subset
  c) subset (doesn't contain the origin!)
  d) subspace and subset

Span

Geometry   Span is a really similar concept as subspace, and they are easy to confuse. A subspace is the region of ambient space that can be reached by any linear combination of a set of vectors. And then those vectors *span* that subspace. You can think about the difference using grammar: a subspace is a noun and span is a verb. A set of vectors spans, and the result of their spanning is a subspace.

For example, the subspace defined as all of $\mathbb{R}^2$ can be created by the span of the vectors [0 1] and [1 0]. That is to say, all of $\mathbb{R}^2$ can be reached by some linear weighted combination of those two vectors.

Another example: The vector [0 1] spans a 1D subspace that is embedded inside $\mathbb{R}^2$ (not $\mathbb{R}^1$! It's in $\mathbb{R}^2$ because the vector has two elements). The vector [1 2] also spans a 1D subspace, but it's a different 1D subspace from that spanned by [0 1].

Algebra   The span of a set of vectors is the set of all points that can be obtained by any linear weighted combination of those vectors (Equation 4.3).

Algebraic definition of span

$$span(\{\mathbf{v}_1, \ldots, \mathbf{v}_n\}) = \{\alpha_1 \mathbf{v}_1 + \ldots + \alpha_n \mathbf{v}_n, \; \alpha \in \mathbb{R}\} \quad (4.3)$$

You will recognize the right-hand-side of this equation as the definition of linear weighted combination, introduced in Equation 3.35.

Span comes up often in discussions of matrix spaces, least-squares fitting, and eigendecomposition. In Chapter 8, for example, you will learn that something called the "column space" of a matrix is essentially the subspace spanned by the columns of that matrix.

In the span? A frequent question in linear algebra is whether one vector is "in the span" of another vector or set of vectors. This is just some fancy math-speak for asking whether you can create some vector $\mathbf{w}$ by scalar-multiplying and adding vectors from set S.

Thus, a vector $\mathbf{w}$ is in the span of the vector set S if $\mathbf{w}$ can be exactly created by some linear combination of vectors in set S. For example, consider the following two vectors $\mathbf{w}$ and $\mathbf{v}$ and set S. The question at hand is whether either of these vectors is in the span of S. The answers are given and justified below, but see if you can work through the problem on your own before reading further.

$$\mathbf{v} = \begin{bmatrix} 1 \\ 2 \\ 0 \end{bmatrix}, \; \mathbf{w} = \begin{bmatrix} 3 \\ 2 \\ 1 \end{bmatrix}. \quad S = \left\{ \begin{bmatrix} 1 \\ 1 \\ 0 \end{bmatrix}, \begin{bmatrix} 1 \\ 7 \\ 0 \end{bmatrix} \right\}$$

Let's start with vector $\mathbf{v}$. We have a positive answer here: $\mathbf{v}$ is in the span of S. Written formally:

$$\mathbf{v} \in span(S) \text{ because } \begin{bmatrix} 1 \\ 2 \\ 0 \end{bmatrix} = \frac{5}{6} \begin{bmatrix} 1 \\ 1 \\ 0 \end{bmatrix} + \frac{1}{6} \begin{bmatrix} 1 \\ 7 \\ 0 \end{bmatrix}$$

Thus, $\mathbf{v}$ can be obtained by a weighted combination of vectors in set S. The weightings (in this case, 5/6 and 1/6) might not be immediately obvious just from looking at the vectors. In fact, it is generally not trivial to find the correct weights just by visual inspection, unless you have a really nice linear algebra teacher who gives you easy problems. There are algorithms for determining whether a vector is in the span of some vector set, and, if so, for finding the correct weights. Those algorithms are not too complicated, but they rely on concepts that you haven't yet learned about (primarily: determinant and Gaussian elimination). So we'll come back to those algorithms later.

For now, it's important to understand the concept that the span of a set of vectors is the entire subspace that can be reached by any linear combination of those vectors (often verbalized as "this vector set spans that subspace"), and that we often want to determine whether a given vector is contained in the span of that set.

In contrast to the difficulty of finding whether **v** was in the span of S, it should be obvious why **w** is *not* in the span of S: The third element in **w** is nonzero, whereas all vectors in set S have a third element of zero. There is no linear combination of zeros that will produce a nonzero value, therefore **w** cannot possibly be in the span of S.

There is a geometric interpretation of this example (Figure 4.8): The span of S is a 2D plane embedded in a 3D ambient space; vector **v** is a line in the plane, whereas vector **w** pops out of that plane. We could also describe **v** as being coplanar to set S.

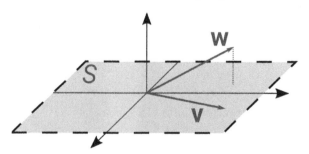

Figure 4.8: The span of set S is a 2D plane at z=0. Vector v is in the span of that set, and thus lies in that plane. Vector w is outside the span, which means it points out of the plane.

One thing to keep in mind about span: It doesn't matter if the vectors in the set are linear combinations of other vectors in that same set. For example, the following set spans a 2D subspace (a plane) embedded in ambient $\mathbb{R}^4$. There are five vectors, but notice that the first three and the last two are collinear. Hence, five vectors in total, but together they span a 2D subspace.

$$\left\{ \begin{bmatrix} 1 \\ 2 \\ 0 \\ 1 \end{bmatrix}, \begin{bmatrix} -3 \\ -6 \\ 0 \\ -3 \end{bmatrix}, \begin{bmatrix} 10 \\ 20 \\ 0 \\ 10 \end{bmatrix}, \begin{bmatrix} 0 \\ 4 \\ 1 \\ 0 \end{bmatrix}, \begin{bmatrix} 0 \\ 2 \\ .5 \\ 0 \end{bmatrix} \right\}$$

How do I know that this set spans only a 2D subspace? Well, I know because I've already read the chapter on matrix rank and so I know the algorithm for determining the subspace dimensionality. As I wrote in the section on determining whether a vector is in the span of a set, it is, in most cases, impossible to look at a set of vectors and "see" the subspace dimensionality. You will learn several algorithms for computing this, but for now, focus on the concept that it is possible for a set to contain five 4D vectors that together span a 2D subspace.

Reflection

Span makes me think of a robot holding a laser pointer in a dark room, and each new vector in the set is a degree of freedom of movement, like an extra joint in the robot's arm. With one vector the robot can shine the light only in one fixed direction. With two vectors the robot can swivel its arm and illuminate a plane. Three vectors means the robot can move its arm in all directions and can follow a mosquito around the room so I can finally kill it. The analogy kindof breaks down in higher dimensions. Maybe there are quantum curled-up mosquitos and we need better robots to hunt them down.

Practice problems Determine whether each vector is in the span of the associated set.

a) $\mathbf{v} = \begin{bmatrix} \pi^3 \\ \ln(e^3) \end{bmatrix}$, $\mathbf{w} = \begin{bmatrix} -\sqrt{2} \\ 1 \end{bmatrix}$. $S = \left\{ \begin{bmatrix} 1 \\ 0 \end{bmatrix}, \begin{bmatrix} 0 \\ 1 \end{bmatrix} \right\}$

b) $\mathbf{p} = \begin{bmatrix} -5 \\ 5 \\ 25 \end{bmatrix}$, $\mathbf{q} = \begin{bmatrix} 5 \\ 5 \\ 25 \end{bmatrix}$. $T = \left\{ \begin{bmatrix} -1 \\ 0 \\ 4 \end{bmatrix}, \begin{bmatrix} 0 \\ 1 \\ 1 \end{bmatrix} \right\}$

c) $\mathbf{m} = \begin{bmatrix} 0 \\ 1 \\ 2 \\ 3 \end{bmatrix}$, $\mathbf{x} = \begin{bmatrix} 3 \\ 2 \\ 4 \\ 0 \end{bmatrix}$. $U = \left\{ \begin{bmatrix} 1 \\ 1 \\ 0 \end{bmatrix}, \begin{bmatrix} 0 \\ 1 \\ 1 \end{bmatrix} \right\}$

Answers

a) both   b) **p** yes, **q** no   c) Invalid dimensions

4.6 Linear independence

Some authors abbreviate linear independence as L.I.; I will refrain from this indulgence to avoid overburdening you with abbreviations to memorize.

Linear independence (sometimes simplified to "independence"; formally, linear algebra is concerned only with *linear* independence), like many concepts introduced in these first three chapters, is central to many theoretical and applied topics in linear algebra, ranging from matrix rank to statistics to the singular value decomposition.

One important thing to know about linear independence before reading the rest of this section is that independence is a property of a *set* of vectors. That is, a set of vectors can be linearly independent or linearly dependent; it doesn't make sense to ask whether a single vector, or a vector within a set, is independent. You will learn why this is the case over the next few pages.

A set of vectors is independent if the subspace dimensionality equals the number of vectors.

Geometry A set of vectors is independent if the dimensionality of the subspace spanned by that set of vectors is equal to the number of vectors in that set. For example, a set with one vector spans a line (assuming it is not the zeros vector) and is always an independent set (1 vector, 1 dimension); a linearly independent set of two vectors spans a plane (2 vectors, 2 dimensions); an independent set with three vectors spans a 3D space (3 vectors, 3 dimensions).

But having two vectors in a set doesn't necessarily endow that set with linear independence. Consider the sets of vectors in Figure 4.9; assume these are all 2D vectors. The left-hand set (panel A) contains two vectors that are collinear; this set is linearly *dependent* because you can create one vector as a scaled version of another vector. Now consider the middle set (panel B): Again, two vectors, but they point in different directions; it is not possible to create one vector as a scaled version of the other vector.

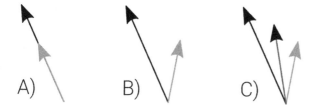

Figure 4.9: Geometric sets of vectors in $\mathbb{R}^2$ illustrating (in)dependence. The set in panel A is dependent because there are two vectors but they span a 1D subspace. The set in panel B is independent because the two vectors span a 2D subspace. The set in panel C is dependent because three vectors cannot span more than a 2D subspace in $\mathbb{R}^2$.

Finally, consider the right-hand set (panel C): This set of three vectors in $\mathbb{R}^2$ is linearly dependent, because any one of the vectors can be obtained by a linear combination of the other two vectors. In this example, the middle vector can be obtained by averaging the other two vectors (that is, summing them and scalar-multiplying by $\lambda = .5$). But that's not just a quirk of this example. In fact, there is a theorem about independence that is illustrated in Figure 4.9:

Any set of $M > N$ vectors in $\mathbb{R}^N$ is necessarily linearly dependent.
Any set of $M \leq N$ vectors in $\mathbb{R}^N$ *could be* linearly independent.

The proof of this theorem involves creating a matrix out of the set of vectors and then computing the rank of that matrix. That's beyond the scope of this chapter, but I wanted to present this theorem now anyway, because I think it is intuitive: For example, three vectors that lie on the same plane (a 2D subspace) cannot possibly create a cube (a 3D subspace).

Also notice the clause *could be*: $M \leq N$ merely creates the opportunity for independence; it is up to the vectors themselves to be independent or not. For example, imagine a set of 20 vectors in $\mathbb{R}^{25}$ that all lie on the same line (that is, the same 1D subspace embedded in ambient $\mathbb{R}^{25}$). That set contains 20 vectors, but geometrically, they're occupying a 1D subspace, hence, that set is linearly dependent.

With these examples in mind, we can return to our geometric definition of independence: A set of vectors is independent if the number of vectors in the set equals the dimensionality of the subspace spanned by that set. Another way to think about this is that no vector in the set is in the span of the other vectors in that set.

Algebra   A set of vectors is dependent if at least one vector in the set can be expressed as a linear weighted combination of the other vectors in that set. Consider the following examples.

$$\{\mathbf{w}_1, \mathbf{w}_2\} = \left\{ \begin{bmatrix} 1 \\ 2 \\ 3 \end{bmatrix}, \begin{bmatrix} 2 \\ 4 \\ 6 \end{bmatrix} \right\}. \quad \mathbf{w}_2 = 2\mathbf{w}_1 \qquad (4.4)$$

$$\{\mathbf{v}_1, \mathbf{v}_2, \mathbf{v}_3\} = \left\{ \begin{bmatrix} 0 \\ 2 \\ 5 \end{bmatrix}, \begin{bmatrix} -27 \\ 5 \\ -37 \end{bmatrix}, \begin{bmatrix} 3 \\ 1 \\ 8 \end{bmatrix} \right\}. \quad \mathbf{v}_2 = 7\mathbf{v}_1 - 9\mathbf{v}_3 \qquad (4.5)$$

Both examples show *dependent* sets. The way I've written the equations on the right, it seems like $\mathbf{w}_2$ and $\mathbf{v}_2$ are the dependent vectors while the other vectors are independent. But remember from the beginning of this section that linear (in)dependence is a property of a set of vectors, not of individual vectors. You could just as easily isolate $\mathbf{v}_1$ or $\mathbf{v}_3$ on the left-hand side of Equation 4.5.

The important point is that it is possible to create any one vector in the set as some linear weighted combination of the other vectors in the same set.

On the other hand, it is possible to create subsets of those sets that are linearly independent. For example, the sets $\{\mathbf{v}_2, \mathbf{v}_3\}$, $\{\mathbf{v}_1, \mathbf{v}_3\}$, and $\{\mathbf{v}_1, \mathbf{v}_2\}$ are all independent sets.

The next two examples show *independent* sets.

$$\{\mathbf{w}_1, \mathbf{w}_2\} = \left\{ \begin{bmatrix} 1 \\ 2 \\ 3 \end{bmatrix}, \begin{bmatrix} 2 \\ 4 \\ 7 \end{bmatrix} \right\}$$

$$\{\mathbf{v}_1, \mathbf{v}_2, \mathbf{v}_3\} = \left\{ \begin{bmatrix} 0 \\ 2 \\ 5 \end{bmatrix}, \begin{bmatrix} -27 \\ 0 \\ -37 \end{bmatrix}, \begin{bmatrix} 3 \\ 1 \\ 9 \end{bmatrix} \right\}$$

Try as hard as you can and for as long as you like; you will never be able to define any one vector in each set using a linear weighted combination of the other vectors in the same set. That's easy to see in the first set: When considering only the first two rows, then $\mathbf{w}_1 = 2\mathbf{w}_2$. However, this weighted combination fails for the third row. Mapping this back onto the geometric perspective, these two vectors are two separate lines in $\mathbb{R}^3$; they point in similar directions but are definitely not collinear.

The second set is more difficult to figure out by trial-and-error guessing. This shows that even simple examples get out of hand rather quickly. Determining whether a set of vectors is linearly independent is really important in linear algebra, and we're going to need more rigorous methods that will scale to any size matrix. For example, you can put those vectors into a matrix and compute the rank of the matrix; if the rank is the same as the number of vectors, then the set is independent, and if the rank is less than the number of vectors, the set is dependent. This is called the "augment-rank" algorithm, and you will learn more about it in chapters 7 and 8.

The formal definition of linear dependence is related to determining whether a weighted combination of the vectors equals the zeros vector, where not all weights (λ's in the equation below) are equal to zero.

> **Linear dependence**
>
> $$\mathbf{0} = \lambda_1 \mathbf{v}_1 + \lambda_2 \mathbf{v}_2 + ... + \lambda_n \mathbf{v}_n, \quad \lambda \in \mathbb{R} \qquad (4.6)$$

$\mathbf{0}$ (sometimes written $\vec{0}$) indicates the zeros vector. Of course, if all λ's are zero, then equation 4.6 is trivially true, so we require that at least one $\lambda \neq 0$. If equation 4.6 is *not* true for at least one $\lambda \neq 0$, then the set is linearly *in*dependent.

This may seem like a strange definition: Where does it come from and why is the zeros vector so important? Some rearranging, starting with subtracting $\lambda_1 \mathbf{v}_1$ from both sides of the equation, will reveal why this equation indicates dependence:

$$\lambda_1 \mathbf{v}_1 = \lambda_2 \mathbf{v}_2 + ... + \lambda_n \mathbf{v}_n$$

$$\mathbf{v}_1 = \frac{\lambda_2}{\lambda_1} \mathbf{v}_2 + ... + \frac{\lambda_n}{\lambda_1} \mathbf{v}_n, \quad \lambda \in \mathbb{R}, \lambda_1 \neq 0 \qquad (4.7)$$

Because the λ's are scalars, then λ_n / λ_1 is also just some scalar. If you like, you could replace all the fractional constants with some other constant, e.g., $\beta_n = \lambda_n / \lambda_1$.

The point is that with a bit of re-arranging, equation 4.6 states that one vector can be expressed as some linear weighted combination of the other vectors in the set. Now you can see the correspondence between the math equation and the English definition of linear dependence. You can also see another justification for the claim that at least one $\lambda \neq 0$.

Equation 4.6 also reveals an interesting property of linear dependence: Any set of vectors that contains the zeros vector is guaranteed to be linearly dependent. Why is that the case?

Imagine that $\mathbf{v_1} = \mathbf{0}$, $\lambda_1 = 1000$, and all other $\lambda_n = 0$. Then the right-hand side of the equation equals the left-hand side of the equation for at least one $\lambda \neq 0$. Thus, any set of vectors that contains the zeros vector is a dependent set.

Determining whether a set is linearly dependent or independent Before learning about matrix-based algorithms for computing whether a set is linear independent, you can apply a 4-step procedure to determine the linear dependency of a set of vectors. Note that this is a strategy for solving exercise problems or exam problems by hand; this method does not scale up to larger matrices, and it's way too time-consuming to use in any real-world applications. Nonetheless, this procedure is useful to understand to help you internalize the concept of linear independence.

Step 1:   Count the number of vectors (call that number M) in the set and compare to N in $\mathbb{R}^N$. As mentioned earlier, if $M > N$, then the set is necessarily dependent. If $M \leq N$ then you have to move on to step 2.

Step 2:   Check for a vector of all zeros. Any set that contains the zeros vector is a dependent set.

Step 3:   If you've gotten this far, it means you need to start doing some trial-and-error educated guesswork. Start by looking for zeros in the entries of some vectors, with the knowledge that zeros in some vectors in combination with non-zero entries in corresponding dimensions in other vectors is a tip towards independence (you cannot create something from nothing, with the possible exception of the big bang).

Step 4:   This is where the real educated guesswork comes in. Start by creating one element as a weighted combination of other vectors, and see whether that same weighted combination will work for the other dimensions. Consider the following set of vectors:

$$\left\{ \begin{bmatrix} 1 \\ 2 \\ 3 \end{bmatrix}, \begin{bmatrix} 2 \\ 1 \\ 3 \end{bmatrix}, \begin{bmatrix} 4 \\ 5 \\ 8 \end{bmatrix} \right\}$$

Look across the first dimension (top row of vector elements) and notice that 2 times the first vector plus 1 times the second vector produces the first element in the third vector. That same set of weights is also true for the second dimension. However, it doesn't work for the third dimension. That proves that the third vector cannot be expressed as this linear combination of the first two. You have to repeat this process (try to find weights of M-1 vector entries that equal the Mth vector entry) for each of M vectors. Eventually, you will determine that the set is linearly independent or dependent.

Here is another, slightly different, way to think about step 4, which brings back the formal definition of linear dependence, and also will help prepare you for matrix concepts like null space, inverse, and eigendecomposition: The goal is to come up with a set of coefficients for each vector such that the weighted sum of all vectors gives the zeros vector. For the first dimension, the coefficients (-2, -1, 1) will produce a zero ($-2 \times 1 + -1 \times 2 + 1 \times 4 = 0$). Those same coefficients will also work for the second dimension, but they don't work for the third dimension. This means either (1) a different set of coefficients could work for all three dimensions, or (2) the set is linearly independent.

Step 4 is really the limiting factor here. Again, by this point in the book, your main concern should be with the concept and definition of linear independence; scalable and rigorous methods will be introduced in later chapters.

Consistent terminology is important in any branch of knowledge, and confusing or redundant terminology can hinder progress and create confusion. Unfortunately, the term *independence* has different meanings in different areas of mathematics. In statistics, two variables are "independent" if the correlation coefficient between them is zero. In linear algebra, that case would be called "orthogonal." What is called "independent" in linear algebra would be called "correlated" in statistics. There is no easy solution to terminological confusions; you just have to be flexible and make sure to clarify your terms when talking to an audience from a different background.

Reflection

Practice problems Determine whether each set is linearly dependent or independent. If the set is dependent, come up with a set of coefficients that illustrates their dependence.

a) $\left\{ \begin{bmatrix} 0 \\ 0 \\ 0 \end{bmatrix}, \begin{bmatrix} 1 \\ 1 \\ 1 \end{bmatrix}, \begin{bmatrix} 2 \\ 2 \\ 2 \end{bmatrix} \right\}$

b) $\left\{ \begin{bmatrix} 1 \\ 1 \\ 2 \end{bmatrix}, \begin{bmatrix} 1 \\ 1 \\ 1 \end{bmatrix}, \begin{bmatrix} 2 \\ 2 \\ 1 \end{bmatrix} \right\}$

c) $\left\{ \begin{bmatrix} 0 \\ 7 \\ 2 \end{bmatrix}, \begin{bmatrix} 1 \\ 2 \\ 6 \end{bmatrix}, \begin{bmatrix} -2 \\ 17 \\ -6 \end{bmatrix} \right\}$

d) $\left\{ \begin{bmatrix} 1 \\ 1 \end{bmatrix}, \begin{bmatrix} 2 \\ 2.000001 \end{bmatrix} \right\}$

Answers

a) Dependent (1,0,0)

c) Dependent (-3, 2, 1)

b) Dependent (1,-3,1)

d) Independent

4.7

Basis

A basis is the combination of span and independence: A set of vectors $\{\mathbf{v}_1, \mathbf{v}_2, ..., \mathbf{v}_n\}$ forms a *basis* for some subspace of $\mathbb{R}^N$ if it (1) spans that subspace and (2) is an independent set of vectors.

Geometrically, a basis is like a ruler for a space. The basis vectors tell you the fundamental units (length and direction) to measure the space they describe. For example, the most common basis set is the familiar Cartesian axis basis vectors, which contains only 0s and 1s:

$$\mathbb{R}^2 : \left\{ \begin{bmatrix} 1 \\ 0 \end{bmatrix}, \begin{bmatrix} 0 \\ 1 \end{bmatrix} \right\}, \qquad \mathbb{R}^3 : \left\{ \begin{bmatrix} 1 \\ 0 \\ 0 \end{bmatrix}, \begin{bmatrix} 0 \\ 1 \\ 0 \end{bmatrix}, \begin{bmatrix} 0 \\ 0 \\ 1 \end{bmatrix} \right\}$$

These are called the "standard" basis vector sets.

This basis set is so widely used because of its simplicity: Each basis vector has unit length and all vectors in the set are mutually orthogonal (that is, the dot product of any vector with any other vector is zero). These sets fulfill the definition of basis because they (1) are linearly independent sets that (2) span $\mathbb{R}^2$ or $\mathbb{R}^3$.

However, it is not necessary to span all of $\mathbb{R}^N$ to be a basis. The two examples below are basis sets for subspaces embedded in $\mathbb{R}^2$ and $\mathbb{R}^3$.

$$S_1 = \left\{ \begin{bmatrix} 1 \\ 0 \end{bmatrix} \right\}, \qquad S_2 = \left\{ \begin{bmatrix} 1 \\ 0 \\ 0 \end{bmatrix}, \begin{bmatrix} 0 \\ 1 \\ 0 \end{bmatrix} \right\}$$

Set S_1 is an independent set but does not cover all of $\mathbb{R}^2$—instead, it spans a 1D subspace of $\mathbb{R}^2$, which is the line at Y=0. Set S_2 is a basis for a plane on the XY axes where Z=0.

Now consider the following sets of vectors; which of these forms a basis for $\mathbb{R}^3$ How about $\mathbb{R}^2$?

$$M_1 = \left\{ \begin{bmatrix} -3 \\ 0 \\ 0 \end{bmatrix}, \begin{bmatrix} -1 \\ 0 \\ 0 \end{bmatrix}, \begin{bmatrix} 13 \\ 0 \\ 0 \end{bmatrix} \right\}$$

$$M_2 = \left\{ \begin{bmatrix} -4 \\ 1 \\ 0 \end{bmatrix}, \begin{bmatrix} \pi \\ 3 \\ 0 \end{bmatrix}, \begin{bmatrix} 3 \\ 2\pi \\ 3 \end{bmatrix} \right\}$$

$$M_3 = \left\{ \begin{bmatrix} -3 \\ 0 \\ 0 \end{bmatrix}, \begin{bmatrix} -1 \\ 0 \\ 0 \end{bmatrix}, \begin{bmatrix} 13 \\ 0 \\ 1 \end{bmatrix} \right\}$$

The answers are that set M_2 is a basis for $\mathbb{R}^3$ because there are three vectors in $\mathbb{R}^3$ that form a linearly independent set.

None of the sets is a basis of $\mathbb{R}^2$ because all of these vectors live in $\mathbb{R}^3$.

Set M_1 is not a basis set, because the set is linearly dependent. However, a set comprising any one of those vectors would be a basis for a 1D subspace (a line) embedded in ambient 3D space, which, for a Cartesian space, would be the line on the X-axis at Y=Z=0.

Set M_3 is also not a basis set because one can define the first or second vectors as a linear combination of the other vectors. However, the third vector and either the first or second vector would form a basis for a 2D subspace, which is a plane in $\mathbb{R}^3$.

Let's consider the geometric consequence of different bases for the same subspace. The graph in Figure 4.10 shows a point p; how would you identify this point using the three basis sets below?

$$S = \left\{ \begin{bmatrix} 1 \\ 0 \end{bmatrix}, \begin{bmatrix} 0 \\ 1 \end{bmatrix} \right\}, \qquad T = \left\{ \begin{bmatrix} 1 \\ 1 \end{bmatrix}, \begin{bmatrix} 0 \\ 2 \end{bmatrix} \right\}, \qquad U = \left\{ \begin{bmatrix} 0 \\ 0 \end{bmatrix}, \begin{bmatrix} 0 \\ 1 \end{bmatrix} \right\}$$

Identifying point p using different bases means to determine the set of coefficients that multiply each basis vector to get from the origin to p. Let's start with basis set S. Actually, this is the standard Cartesian basis set. Thus, $p_{[S]}$ (this is the notation to indicate point p using basis set S) is simply [2,1].

For basis set T, we have $p_{[T]} = [2,-.5]$. Why is this the correct answer? Starting from the origin, draw a vector that is two times the first vector in set T, and then add -.5 times the second vector in set T. That will get you from the origin to point p.

Now for set U. Ah, this is a trick. In fact, set U is not a basis set, because it is not a linearly independent set. No set with the zeros vector can be independent. For our exercise here, it is impossible to reach point p using the vectors in set U, because $span(U)$ is a 1D subspace that does not touch point p.

Why is it important that the set be linearly independent? You

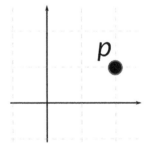

Figure 4.10: A point on a graph has different coordinates depending on the basis vectors.

might think that it should be sufficient for the set to span the subspace, and any additional vectors are just there, you know, for fun. But any given vector in the subspace spanned by a basis should have a *unique* coordinate using that basis. For example, consider the following set:

$$\left\{ \begin{bmatrix} 1 \\ 1 \end{bmatrix}, \begin{bmatrix} 1 \\ 3 \end{bmatrix}, \begin{bmatrix} 0 \\ 2 \end{bmatrix} \right\}$$

This set is **not** a basis for $\mathbb{R}^2$, but let's pretend for a moment that it is. The vector that, in standard coordinates, is given by [-2 6] can be obtained by scaling these "basis vectors" by (-6,4,0) or (0,-2,6) or (-2,0,4), or an infinite number of other possibilities. That's confusing. Therefore, mathematicians decided that a vector must have *unique* coordinates within some basis set, which happens only when the set is linearly independent.

Independent bases ensure uniqueness.

Infinite bases Although any given vector has unique coordinates within a basis (assuming that basis spans the subspace the vector lives in), the reverse is not the case: There is an infinite number of bases that describe any subspace. You might have already guessed that this is the case from the discussion around Figure 4.10. Here is an example of a small and finite number of distinct bases for $\mathbb{R}^2$. (In fact, *any* linearly independent set of two 2D vectors is a basis for all of $\mathbb{R}^2$.)

$$\left\{ \begin{bmatrix} 1 \\ 0 \end{bmatrix}, \begin{bmatrix} 0 \\ \frac{1}{2} \end{bmatrix} \right\}, \quad \left\{ \begin{bmatrix} -1 \\ 0 \end{bmatrix}, \begin{bmatrix} 0 \\ 1 \end{bmatrix} \right\}, \quad \left\{ \begin{bmatrix} e \\ 2 \end{bmatrix}, \begin{bmatrix} .5 \\ 4^{74} \end{bmatrix} \right\}$$

For example, using the first two sets, the Cartesian-basis coordinate (3,4) would be obtained by scaling the basis vectors by [3,8] and [-3,4], respectively.

Why have so many possible bases? Shouldn't we be happy with a small number of bases, for example the familiar Cartesian basis sets?

The truth is that not all basis sets are created equal. Some bases are better than others, and some problems are easier to solve in certain bases and harder to solve in other bases. For example, that third basis set above is valid, but would be a huge pain to work with. In fact, finding optimal basis sets is *one of the most important problems* in multivariate data science, in particular data compression and components analyses.

Consider Figure 4.11: The dots correspond to data points, and the black lines correspond to basis vectors. The basis set in the left graph was obtained via principal components analysis (PCA) whereas the basis set in the right graph was obtained via independent components analysis (ICA). (You'll learn the math and implementation of PCA in Chapter 19.) Thus, these two analyses identified two different basis sets for $\mathbb{R}^2$; both bases are valid, but which one describes the patterns in the data better?

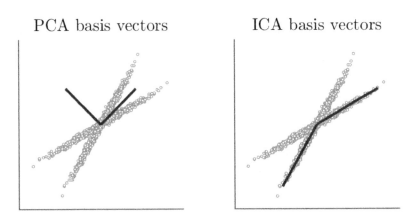

PCA basis vectors   ICA basis vectors

Figure 4.11: This example of 2D datasets (both graphs show the same data) with different basis vectors (black lines) is an example of the importance of choosing basis sets for characterizing and understanding patterns in datasets.

Reflection In this section we are discussing only basis *vectors*. You may have also heard about basis *functions* or basis *images*. The concept is the same—a basis is the set of the minimum number of metrics needed to describe something. In the Fourier transform, for example, sine waves are basis functions, because all signals can be represented using sine waves of different frequencies, phases, and amplitudes.

Exercises

1. Determine whether each vector is in the span of sets S and T, and if so, what coefficients could produce the given vectors from the sets.

$$S = \left\{ \begin{bmatrix} 0 \\ 1 \\ 3 \end{bmatrix}, \begin{bmatrix} 1 \\ 0 \\ 3 \end{bmatrix} \right\} \qquad T = \left\{ \begin{bmatrix} 1 \\ .5 \\ 0 \end{bmatrix}, \begin{bmatrix} 4 \\ 1 \\ 1 \end{bmatrix} \right\}$$

a) $\begin{bmatrix} 2 \\ 2 \\ 6 \end{bmatrix}$ b) $\begin{bmatrix} 0 \\ 4 \\ 12 \end{bmatrix}$ c) $\begin{bmatrix} 0 \\ 0 \\ 0 \end{bmatrix}$ d) $\begin{bmatrix} -10 \\ -2 \\ -3 \end{bmatrix}$ e) $\begin{bmatrix} -3 \\ 2 \\ -3 \end{bmatrix}$

2. Determine whether the following vector is in the set spanned by the bracketed vectors, in other words, whether $\mathbf{u} \in S = \{\mathbf{v_1}, ..., \mathbf{v_n}\}$

a) $\begin{bmatrix} 5 \\ 0 \\ 1 \end{bmatrix}, \left\{ \begin{bmatrix} 1 \\ 0 \\ 3 \end{bmatrix}, \begin{bmatrix} 1 \\ 1 \\ 3 \end{bmatrix} \right\}$ b) $\begin{bmatrix} 4 \\ 1 \\ 12 \end{bmatrix}, \left\{ \begin{bmatrix} 1 \\ 0 \\ 3 \end{bmatrix}, \begin{bmatrix} 1 \\ 1 \\ 3 \end{bmatrix} \right\}$

c) $\begin{bmatrix} 0 \\ 1 \\ 3 \end{bmatrix}, \left\{ \begin{bmatrix} 1 \\ 0 \\ 3 \end{bmatrix}, \begin{bmatrix} -1 \\ 1 \\ 2 \end{bmatrix} \right\}$

3. Label the following sets as independent or dependent. For dependent sets, determine whether it is possible to modify only one element of one vector to change it to an independent set.

a) $\left\{ \begin{bmatrix} 1 \\ 2 \end{bmatrix}, \begin{bmatrix} 2 \\ 1 \end{bmatrix} \right\}$ b) $\left\{ \begin{bmatrix} 1 \\ 2 \end{bmatrix}, \begin{bmatrix} 1 \\ -2 \end{bmatrix} \right\}$

c) $\left\{ \begin{bmatrix} 1 \\ 2 \end{bmatrix}, \begin{bmatrix} -1 \\ -2 \end{bmatrix} \right\}$ d) $\left\{ \begin{bmatrix} 1 \\ 2 \end{bmatrix}, \begin{bmatrix} 1 \\ -2 \end{bmatrix}, \begin{bmatrix} -1 \\ -2 \end{bmatrix} \right\}$

e) $\left\{ \begin{bmatrix} 1 \\ 0 \end{bmatrix}, \begin{bmatrix} 3 \\ 0 \end{bmatrix} \right\}$ f) $\left\{ \begin{bmatrix} 5 \\ 12 \end{bmatrix}, \begin{bmatrix} -3 \\ 4 \end{bmatrix}, \begin{bmatrix} 10 \\ 23 \end{bmatrix} \right\}$

g) $\left\{ \begin{bmatrix} 1 \\ 2 \\ 3 \end{bmatrix}, \begin{bmatrix} 1 \\ 2 \\ 4 \end{bmatrix} \right\}$

h) $\left\{ \begin{bmatrix} 1 \\ 2 \\ 3 \end{bmatrix}, \begin{bmatrix} 8 \\ 16 \\ 24 \end{bmatrix} \right\}$

i) $\left\{ \begin{bmatrix} 1 \\ 0 \\ 1 \end{bmatrix}, \begin{bmatrix} 2 \\ 1 \\ 2 \end{bmatrix}, \begin{bmatrix} 3 \\ 1 \\ 3 \end{bmatrix} \right\}$

4. Determine the value of λ that would make the following sets of vectors dependent.

a) $\left\{ \begin{bmatrix} 1 \\ 2 \\ 3 \end{bmatrix}, \begin{bmatrix} 4.5 \\ \lambda \\ 13.5 \end{bmatrix} \right\}$

b) $\left\{ \begin{bmatrix} 0 \\ 0 \\ \lambda \\ 0 \\ 0 \end{bmatrix}, \begin{bmatrix} a \\ b \\ 5 \\ c \\ d \end{bmatrix} \right\}$

c) $\left\{ \begin{bmatrix} 1 \\ 2 \\ 3 \end{bmatrix}, \begin{bmatrix} 4 \\ \lambda \\ 5 \end{bmatrix}, \begin{bmatrix} 5 \\ 0 \\ 8 \end{bmatrix}, \begin{bmatrix} 1 \\ 1 \\ 1 \end{bmatrix} \right\}$

5. The following sets of vectors are dependent sets. For each set, determine the number of vectors to remove to create an independent set with the most number of vectors.

a) $\left\{ \begin{bmatrix} 1 \\ 1 \\ 0 \\ 0 \\ 0 \end{bmatrix}, \begin{bmatrix} 0 \\ 3 \\ 4 \\ 5 \\ 0 \end{bmatrix}, \begin{bmatrix} 2 \\ 5 \\ 4 \\ 5 \\ 0 \end{bmatrix}, \begin{bmatrix} 0 \\ 6 \\ 8 \\ 10 \\ 0 \end{bmatrix}, \begin{bmatrix} 1 \\ 4 \\ 4 \\ 5 \\ 1 \end{bmatrix} \right\}$

b) $\left\{ \begin{bmatrix} 4 \\ 3 \\ 2 \end{bmatrix}, \begin{bmatrix} 4 \\ 4 \\ 3 \end{bmatrix}, \begin{bmatrix} 7 \\ 1 \\ 2 \end{bmatrix}, \begin{bmatrix} 1 \\ 3 \\ 1 \end{bmatrix}, \begin{bmatrix} 1 \\ 2 \\ 4 \end{bmatrix} \right\}$

6. Determine whether the following are descriptions of subspaces and subsets, or only subsets.

a) The set of points y such that $y = 2x$.

b) The set of points y such that $y = 2x + .01$.

c) The point at the origin in $\mathbb{R}^5$.

d) The set of all points in $\mathbb{R}^3$ with positive magnitude.

7. What is the dimensionality of the subspace spanned by the following vector subspaces?

a) $\left\{ \begin{bmatrix} 1 \\ 0 \\ 0 \\ 0 \end{bmatrix}, \begin{bmatrix} 7 \\ 0 \\ 0 \\ 0 \end{bmatrix} \right\}$
b) $\left\{ \begin{bmatrix} 1 \\ 2 \\ 6 \\ 0 \end{bmatrix}, \begin{bmatrix} 2 \\ 4 \\ 12 \\ 6 \end{bmatrix} \right\}$

c) $\left\{ \begin{bmatrix} 1 \\ 1 \\ 1 \end{bmatrix}, \begin{bmatrix} 2 \\ 0 \\ 1 \end{bmatrix}, \begin{bmatrix} 1 \\ 2 \\ 3 \end{bmatrix} \right\}$
d) $\left\{ \begin{bmatrix} 6 \\ 9 \\ 3 \end{bmatrix}, \begin{bmatrix} 2 \\ 3 \\ 1 \end{bmatrix}, \begin{bmatrix} 4 \\ 6 \\ 2 \end{bmatrix} \right\}$

8. Remove one vector in the following sets to create a basis set for a 2D subspace.

a) $\left\{ \begin{bmatrix} 1 \\ 2 \\ 3 \end{bmatrix}, \begin{bmatrix} 1 \\ 2 \\ 3 \end{bmatrix}, \begin{bmatrix} 1 \\ 2 \\ 2 \end{bmatrix} \right\}$
b) $\left\{ \begin{bmatrix} 1 \\ 4 \\ 3 \end{bmatrix}, \begin{bmatrix} 0 \\ -4 \\ 5 \end{bmatrix}, \begin{bmatrix} 3 \\ 12 \\ 9 \end{bmatrix} \right\}$

c) $\left\{ \begin{bmatrix} -3 \\ 2 \\ 13 \end{bmatrix}, \begin{bmatrix} 4.5 \\ -3 \\ -19.5 \end{bmatrix}, \begin{bmatrix} -1.5 \\ 1 \\ 6 \end{bmatrix} \right\}$

Answers

1.   **a)** Neither   **b)** S: [4,0]   **c)** Both [0,0]

     d) T: [2,-3]   **e)** S: [2,-3]

2.   **a)** no   **b)** yes   **c)** no

3. Most dependent sets can be made independent with one value-change if there are $N \leq M$ vectors in $\mathbb{R}^M$.

     a) Independent   **b)** Independent   **c)** Dependent, yes

     d) Dependent, no   **e)** Dependent, yes   **f)** Dependent, no

     g) Independent   **h)** Dependent, yes   **i)** Dependent, yes

4.   **a)** $\lambda = 9$ **b)** $\lambda = 0$ or any-   **c)** Any λ
                                    thing if
                                    $a=b=c=d=0$

5. The answers below indicate the number of vectors that can be removed. In these examples, there are different collections of vectors that could produce linearly independent sets.

     a) 2   **b)** 2

6. The strategy is to think about whether any point or vector $\mathbf{p}$ in the subset would still be in the subset for any scalar-multiple $\mu\mathbf{p}$, including $\mu = 0$.

     a) Both.   **b)** Subset only.

     c) Both.   **d)** Subset only.

7.   **a)** 1D   **b)** 2D   **c)** 3D   **d)** 1D

8.   **a)** First or second   **b)** First or third   **c)** First or second

CHAPTER 5
MATRICES

Interpretations and uses of matrices

The goal of this chapter is to introduce you to matrices: what they look like, how to refer to them, several important special matrices, and basic matrix arithmetic.

In this book, we will work only with matrices that are rows × columns, or matrices that you could print out and lay flat on a table. The terminology can get a bit confusing here, because you might think that these are 2D matrices. However, although they would be in two physical dimensions when printed on a piece of paper, the number of dimensions in which a matrix lives is more open to interpretation compared to vector dimensionality (more on this later). Matrices that would require a 3D printer (or, for higher dimensions, a hyper-printer) occupy cubes or hypercubes in physical space, and are called *tensors*. Tensors are useful for storing data and for representing, for example, various physical forces acting on an object. But they will not be further discussed in this book.

Below are two example matrices. It's sometimes useful to think of a matrix as a set of column vectors standing next to each other, or as a set of row vectors stacked on top of each other.

$$\begin{bmatrix} 1 & 4 & 0 & 2 \\ -4 & 5 & 0 & 0 \end{bmatrix}, \quad \begin{bmatrix} a & b & c \\ b & d & e \\ c & e & f \end{bmatrix}$$

Matrices are ubiquitous in pure and applied mathematics because they have many different purposes. To give you an idea of their versatility, below is a non-exhaustive list of some uses of matrices.

- Representing a linear transformation or mapping
- Storing partial derivatives of a multivariable system
- Representing a system of equations
- Storing data (e.g., features × observations)
- Representing regressors for statistical modeling
- Storing geometric transformations for computer graphics
- Storing kernels used in filtering or convolution

- Representing finance information from different sectors of an economy or business
- Housing parameters for a model that predicts changes in the spread of an infectious disease

5.2 Matrix terminology and notation

The first step of learning anything new is to become acquainted with the terminology. When referring to an entire matrix, a boldface capital letter is used (matrix $\mathbf{A}$), and when referring to individual elements of a matrix, a lower-case letter with subscripts is used (matrix $\mathbf{A}$ contains elements $a_{i,j}$). The matrix-related terms that you need to know include row, column, element, block, diagonal, skew-diagonal, and off-diagonal. Several of these are illustrated in Figure 5.1.

A matrix can comprise smaller matrices, which leads to a useful block-matrix notation (Figure 5.2). Block matrices are not featured in this book, but it's good to know about the notation.

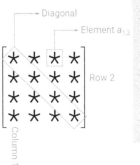

Figure 5.1: Terminology for several key matrix components.

$$\mathbf{A} = \begin{bmatrix} \mathbf{D} & \mathbf{0} \\ \mathbf{1} & \mathbf{D} \end{bmatrix} = \begin{bmatrix} 3 & 0 & 0 & 0 \\ 0 & 4 & 0 & 0 \\ 1 & 1 & 3 & 0 \\ 1 & 1 & 0 & 4 \end{bmatrix}$$

$$\mathbf{D} = \begin{bmatrix} 3 & 0 \\ 0 & 4 \end{bmatrix} \quad \mathbf{0} = \begin{bmatrix} 0 & 0 \\ 0 & 0 \end{bmatrix} \quad \mathbf{1} = \begin{bmatrix} 1 & 1 \\ 1 & 1 \end{bmatrix}$$

Figure 5.2: A "block matrix" is a matrix that comprises smaller matrices. This can facilitate visual inspection and computations.

When referring to matrix sizes, and when referring to indices in a matrix, it is assumed that you refer first to *rows* then to *columns*. The number of rows is typically indicated as M while the number of

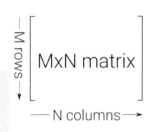

columns is typically indicated as N. This is, of course, an arbitrary choice, but common convention curtails confusion.

Figure 5.3: Notation for referring to matrix sizes: "Mr. Nice guy": M rows, N columns. I know, it's cheesey, but that makes it memorable.

A mnemonic for remembering this convention is **M**R **Ni**Ce guy, for **M** Rows and **N** Columns (Figure 5.3). When multiple matrices are shown, the sizes might be indicated by other letters like K and L, or by subscripts like M_1, M_2 and N_1, N_2.

5.3 Matrix dimensionalities

The dimensionality of matrices is more flexible and more versatile—and therefore more confusing—compared to the dimensionality of vectors. The dimensionality of a vector is simply the number of elements in that vector. Matrices can have different interpretations of dimensionality, depending on the application and the information stored in the matrix. The possible dimensionalities of an $M \times N$ matrix containing real-valued numbers include:

- $\mathbb{R}^{M \times N}$
- $\mathbb{R}^{MN}$, if each matrix element is its own dimension (this is the closest interpretation to the vector dimensionality definition).
- $\mathbb{R}^M$, if the matrix is conceptualized as a series of column vectors (each column contains M elements and is thus in $\mathbb{R}^M$).
- $\mathbb{R}^N$, if the matrix is conceptualized as a stack of row vectors.

In practice, the dimensionality of a given matrix is made on a case-by-case basis, and is either explicitly stated or is inferred from context.

The transpose operation

You learned about the *transpose* operation on vectors. Transposing matrices is the same concept: swap rows for columns and vice-versa.

The notation is also the same as for vectors: the transpose of $\mathbf{A}$ is $\mathbf{A}^T$ (also as mentioned previously, the T is sometimes italicized, so $\mathbf{A}^T = \mathbf{A}^T$). Setting $\mathbf{B}$ to be the transpose of $\mathbf{A}$ (that is, $\mathbf{B} = \mathbf{A}^T$ leads to the formal definition:

Transposing a vector or matrix

$$\mathbf{B}_{i,j} = \mathbf{A}_{j,i} \tag{5.1}$$

Notice that element (*row, column*) in matrix $\mathbf{B}$ corresponds to element (*column, row*) in matrix $\mathbf{A}$.

An important property of the transpose is that the transpose of a transposed matrix is the original matrix. This property will have a central role in many linear algebra proofs.

$$\mathbf{A}^{\mathrm{TT}} = \mathbf{A} \tag{5.2}$$

Here is an example of a matrix transposed.

$$\begin{bmatrix} 1 & 2 & 3 \\ 4 & 5 & 6 \end{bmatrix}^{\mathrm{T}} = \begin{bmatrix} 1 & 4 \\ 2 & 5 \\ 3 & 6 \end{bmatrix}$$

One easy-to-make mistake when taking the transpose is to change the order of the rows and columns accidentally. Compare the following result (**not** the transpose!) to above:

$$\begin{bmatrix} 1 & 2 & 3 \\ 4 & 5 & 6 \end{bmatrix}^{\mathrm{T}} \neq \begin{bmatrix} 4 & 1 \\ 5 & 2 \\ 6 & 3 \end{bmatrix}$$

Code Transposing matrices is the same as transposing vectors. The code below shows additional ways to transpose a matrix.

Code block 5.1: Python

```
1  A = np.random.randn(2,5)
2  At1 = A.T
3  At2 = np.transpose(A)
```

Code block 5.2: MATLAB

```
1  A = randn(2,5);
2  At1 = A';
3  At2 = transpose(A);
```

Practice problems Apply the transpose operator as indicated.

a) $\begin{bmatrix} 0 & 1 & 0 \\ 2 & 0 & 3 \end{bmatrix}^T$

b) $\begin{bmatrix} 16 & 6 & 0 \\ 6 & 10 & -3 \\ 0 & -3 & 22 \end{bmatrix}^T$

c) $\begin{bmatrix} -1 & -3 & 1 \\ -4 & 5 & 1 \\ -5 & -4 & 6 \\ 0 & 5 & 5 \end{bmatrix}^{TT}$

Answers

a) $\begin{bmatrix} 0 & 2 \\ 1 & 0 \\ 0 & 3 \end{bmatrix}^T$

b) $\begin{bmatrix} 16 & 6 & 0 \\ 6 & 10 & -3 \\ 0 & -3 & 22 \end{bmatrix}$

c) $\begin{bmatrix} -1 & -3 & 1 \\ -4 & 5 & 1 \\ -5 & -4 & 6 \\ 0 & 5 & 5 \end{bmatrix}$

Matrix zoology

There are many categories of special matrices that are given names according to their properties, or sometimes according to the person who discovered or characterized them.

Following is a non-exhaustive list and description of several special matrices. It's useful to have some familiarity with these kinds of matrices now; throughout the book (and your adventures through the wonderland of linear algebra and its applications) you'll see these matrices many times. For now, try to familiarize yourself with these classes of matrices without worrying too much about their applications or myriad special properties.

Square or rectangular   Very simply: A square matrix is a matrix that has the same number of rows as columns, thus an $N \times N$ matrix or $M \times N$ if $M = N$.

A non-square matrix is called a rectangular matrix. You can see a square and a rectangular matrix below.

$$\begin{bmatrix} 0 & 1 \\ -1 & 0 \end{bmatrix}, \begin{bmatrix} 0 & 1 & 2 & 3 & -5 \\ -1 & 0 & 3 & 23 & 0 \\ -2 & -3 & 0 & 0 & 0 \end{bmatrix}$$

Let me guess what you are thinking: "But Mike, a square is also a rectangle!" Yes, dear reader, that's technically true. However, for ease of comprehension, it is assumed that a "rectangular matrix" is one in which the number of rows does not equal the number of columns, thus $M \neq N$. "Non-square" is also acceptable.

Rectangular matrices are also sometimes referred to as "fat" or "wide" if they have more columns than rows, or as "skinny" or "tall" if they have more rows than columns. Below you can see a wide matrix (left) and a tall matrix (right).

$$\begin{bmatrix} 1 & 2 & 3 & 4 & 5 \\ 6 & 7 & 8 & 9 & 10 \end{bmatrix}, \begin{bmatrix} 1 & 2 \\ 3 & 4 \\ 5 & 6 \\ 7 & 8 \\ 9 & 10 \end{bmatrix}$$

Symmetric   A matrix is symmetric if it is "mirrored" across the diagonal, meaning the upper-right of the matrix is a flipped version of the lower-left of the matrix. Formally, matrix $\mathbf{A}$ is symmetric if it equals its transpose:

Definitions of a symmetric matrix

$$\mathbf{A} = \mathbf{A}^{\mathrm{T}} \tag{5.3}$$

$$a_{i,j} = a_{j,i} \tag{5.4}$$

Only square matrices can be symmetric, because if a matrix is size $M \times N$, its transpose is size $N \times M$, and Equation 5.3 says that the matrix must equal its transpose. Thus, $M = N$ is a necessary (though not sufficient) condition for symmetry. For this reason, vectors cannot be symmetric.

Here are a few examples of symmetric matrices.

$$\begin{bmatrix} 1 & 4 & \pi \\ 4 & 7 & 2 \\ \pi & 2 & 0 \end{bmatrix}, \begin{bmatrix} a & b \\ b & c \end{bmatrix}, \begin{bmatrix} a & e & f & g \\ e & b & h & i \\ f & h & c & j \\ g & i & j & d \end{bmatrix}$$

Figure 5.4: Symmetric matrices can have a nice visual representation. The grayscale of each box corresponds to the numerical value of the matrix.

A matrix that is not symmetric is called non-symmetric or asymmetric. All rectangular matrices, for example, are non-symmetric.

Symmetric matrices have lots of special properties, as you will learn throughout this book. If matrices lived in a capitalist society, symmetric matrices would be the beautiful, cultured, educated, generous, happy, successful, and wealthy upper-class that get all the attention and special privileges.

Fortunately, hope is not lost for non-symmetric matrices. It is possible to create a symmetric matrix from a non-symmetric (even rectangular!) matrix. Indeed, creating symmetric from non-symmetric matrices is central to many statistics and machine learning applications, such as least-squares and eigendecomposition. For example, you might have heard of a "covariance matrix"; this is simply a symmetric matrix created from a rectangular data matrix. There are two ways to create a symmetric matrix from a non-symmetric matrix, both of which will be discussed in the next chapter.

Skew-symmetric   A skew-symmetric matrix is a matrix where the lower-triangle is the sign-flipped version of the upper-triangle. Here are two examples of 3×3 skew-symmetric matrices.

$$\begin{bmatrix} 0 & 1 & 2 \\ -1 & 0 & 3 \\ -2 & -3 & 0 \end{bmatrix}, \begin{bmatrix} 0 & -4 & 8 \\ 4 & 0 & -5 \\ -8 & 5 & 0 \end{bmatrix}$$

It is no accident that the diagonal elements are all zeros. The diagonal must equal its negative, and the only number for which that is true is 0 $(0 = -0)$. Thus, all skew-symmetric matrices have diagonals of all zeros.

More formally, a skew-symmetric matrix has the following matrix and element definitions.

$$\mathbf{A} = -\mathbf{A}^{\mathrm{T}} \tag{5.5}$$

$$a_{i,j} = -a_{j,i} \tag{5.6}$$

Identity   The identity matrix is the matrix equivalent of the number 1, in that any number x times 1 is x. In the case of matrices, any vector $\mathbf{v}$ times the identity matrix (indicated by $\mathbf{I}$) is that same vector $\mathbf{v}$, and any matrix $\mathbf{A}$ times $\mathbf{I}$ is still $\mathbf{A}$. In other words:

$$\mathbf{vI} = \mathbf{v}$$

$$\mathbf{AI} = \mathbf{A}$$

You might initially think that the identity matrix would be a matrix of all 1's, however, it actually has 1's only on the diagonal and all 0's on the off-diagonals. $\mathbf{I}$ is always a square matrix.

The matrix indicated by $\mathbf{1}$ has all elements equal to 1; this is called a "ones matrix."

$$\mathbf{I} = \begin{bmatrix} 1 & 0 & \cdots & 0 \\ 0 & 1 & \cdots & 0 \\ \vdots & \vdots & \ddots & \vdots \\ 0 & 0 & \cdots & 1 \end{bmatrix}$$

Subscripts are sometimes provided to indicate the size of the matrix, as in the following examples. If there is no subscript, you can assume that $\mathbf{I}$ is the appropriate size to make the equation valid.

$$\mathbf{I}_2 = \begin{bmatrix} 1 & 0 \\ 0 & 1 \end{bmatrix}, \quad \mathbf{I}_3 = \begin{bmatrix} 1 & 0 & 0 \\ 0 & 1 & 0 \\ 0 & 0 & 1 \end{bmatrix}$$

The identity matrix has many important functions. It features in many proofs, in the matrix inverse, and in eigendecomposition and regularization.

Although it is simply called "the identity matrix," a more accurate term would be "the multiplicative identity matrix." That can be contrasted with the *additive* identity matrix, which is the zeros matrix.

Zeros The zeros matrix is a matrix of all zeros. That might sound like a pretty boring matrix, but... well, it is. As you might guess, any matrix times the zeros matrix is still the zeros matrix, just like any number times 0 is 0 (let's stick to finite numbers to avoid headaches from thinking about what happens when you multiply 0 by infinity).

The zeros matrix is indicated by $\mathbf{0}$. As with the matrix $\mathbf{I}$, a subscript is sometimes used when it's necessary to indicate the size of the matrix $\mathbf{0}$. This can be confusing, because the zeros *vector* can also be indicated using $\mathbf{0}$. Hopefully the context will clarify the correct interpretation.

$$\mathbf{0}_N = \begin{bmatrix} 0 & 0 & \dots & 0 \\ 0 & 0 & \dots & 0 \\ \vdots & \vdots & \ddots & \vdots \\ 0 & 0 & \dots & 0 \end{bmatrix}$$

Zeros matrices can be square or rectangular, but in most cases you can assume that the zeros matrix is square; rectangular matrices are often used in code, for example when initializing data matrices.

Analogous to how $\mathbf{I}$ is actually the *multiplicative identity matrix*, $\mathbf{0}$ is more accurately called the *additive identity matrix*. This is because $\mathbf{AI} = \mathbf{A}$ but $\mathbf{A} + \mathbf{I} \neq \mathbf{A}$, and $\mathbf{A} + \mathbf{0} = \mathbf{A}$ but $\mathbf{A0} \neq \mathbf{A}$

Code   Many special matrices can be created easily using dedicated functions. Notice that zeros matrices in Python require two numbers to specify the size (the number of rows and the number of columns).

Code block 5.3: Python

```
1  I = np.eye(4)
2  O = np.ones(4)
3  Z = np.zeros((4,4))
```

Code block 5.4: MATLAB

```
1  I = eye(4);
2  O = ones(4);
3  Z = zeros(4);
```

$\mathbf{A}^\mathsf{T}\mathbf{A}$ Pronounced "A transpose A" and sometimes written "AtA," this is one of the most important matrix forms in all of applied linear algebra. Creating $\mathbf{A}^\mathsf{T}\mathbf{A}$ involves matrix multiplication, which is the topic of the next chapter. However, there are several key properties of $\mathbf{A}^\mathsf{T}\mathbf{A}$ that are worth listing here. Their true value will become apparent as you progress through this book. Each of the following claims will be discussed and proven in later chapters; for now, simply marvel at the glorious existential goodness of $\mathbf{A}^\mathsf{T}\mathbf{A}$:

- It is a square matrix, even if $\mathbf{A}$ is rectangular.
- It is symmetric, even if $\mathbf{A}$ isn't.
- It is full-rank if $\mathbf{A}$ is full column-rank.
- It is invertible if $\mathbf{A}$ is full column-rank.
- It has the same row space as $\mathbf{A}$.
- It has orthogonal eigenvectors.
- It is positive (semi)definite.
- It has non-negative, real-valued eigenvalues.
- It is called a "covariance matrix" if $\mathbf{A}$ is a data matrix.
- It often looks pretty (e.g., Figure 5.4).

All of these properties arise simply from multiplying a matrix by its transpose. These same properties hold for $\mathbf{A}\mathbf{A}^\mathsf{T}$ as well, but $\mathbf{A}^\mathsf{T}\mathbf{A}$ looks nicer in print.

Diagonal A diagonal matrix has all zeros on the off-diagonals, and only the diagonal elements (going from top-left to bottom-right) may contain non-zero elements. $\mathbf{I}$ is an example of a diagonal matrix, as are the following two matrices.

It's OK if some or all diagonal elements are zero, as long as all off-diagonal elements are zero.

$$\begin{bmatrix} 1 & 0 & 0 \\ 0 & 2 & 0 \\ 0 & 0 & 3 \end{bmatrix}, \begin{bmatrix} \pi & 0 & 0 & 0 \\ 0 & e^{x^2} & 0 & 0 \\ 0 & 0 & 0 & 0 \\ 0 & 0 & 0 & 1 \end{bmatrix}$$

More formally, a diagonal matrix is defined as follows.

$$a_{i,j} = \begin{cases} \alpha_n, & \text{if } i = j \\ 0, & \text{if } i \neq j \end{cases} \tag{5.7}$$

If all diagonal elements are the same, then the matrix can be written as a constant times the identity matrix, or $\lambda\mathbf{I}$. For example,

$$\begin{bmatrix} 7 & 0 \\ 0 & 7 \end{bmatrix} = 7 \begin{bmatrix} 1 & 0 \\ 0 & 1 \end{bmatrix} = 7\mathbf{I}_2$$

Diagonal matrices can be rectangular, as in the following examples.

$$\begin{bmatrix} 2 & 0 & 0 & 0 \\ 0 & 6 & 0 & 0 \end{bmatrix}, \begin{bmatrix} 7 & 0 \\ 0 & 1 \\ 0 & 0 \\ 0 & 0 \end{bmatrix}$$

Diagonal matrices are useful because they simplify operations including matrix multiplication and matrix powers $(\mathbf{A}^n)$. Transforming a matrix into a diagonal matrix is called *diagonalization* and can be achieved via eigendecomposition or singular value decomposition, as you will learn in later chapters.

The bold-faced $\mathbf{D}$ is often used to indicate a diagonal matrix. However, there are also plenty of diagonal matrices that are not labeled $\mathbf{D}$. For example, $\mathbf{\Lambda}$ and $\mathbf{\Sigma}$ are diagonal matrices used in eigendecomposition and singular value decomposition, respectively.

The opposite of a diagonal matrix is called a hollow matrix. A hollow matrix has all zeros on the diagonal, while the off-diagonal elements may be non-zero (they can also be zero, as long as the diagonal elements are zero). Skew-symmetric matrices are hollow. Hollow matrices appear in applications as distance matrices (every node is zero distance away from itself), but I won't discuss them further in this book.

As shown in Figure 5.1, the diagonal of a matrix goes from the top-left to the lower-right. The *anti-diagonal* goes from the top-right to the lower left.

Code In both Python and MATLAB, the same function extracts the diagonal elements of a matrix, and produces a diagonal matrix given an input vector.

Code block 5.5: Python

```
1  D = np.diag([1,2,3,5]) # diagonal matrix
2  R = np.random.randn(3,4)
3  d = np.diag(R) # diagonal elements
```

Code block 5.6: MATLAB

```
1  D = diag([1,2,3,5]); % diagonal matrix
2  R = randn(3,4);
3  d = diag(R); % diagonal elements
```

Augmented An augmented matrix is the result of concatenating two or more matrices column-wise, as in this example:

$$\begin{bmatrix} 1 & 4 & 2 \\ 3 & 1 & 9 \\ 4 & 2 & 0 \end{bmatrix} \sqcup \begin{bmatrix} 7 & 2 \\ 7 & 2 \\ 7 & 1 \end{bmatrix} = \left[\begin{array}{ccc|cc} 1 & 4 & 2 & 7 & 2 \\ 3 & 1 & 9 & 7 & 2 \\ 4 & 2 & 0 & 7 & 1 \end{array} \right]$$

The symbol || is sometimes used to indicate concatenation, but it's also used for vector magnitude and parallel lines.

Two matrices can be augmented only if they have the same number of rows; the number of columns need not match.

The vertical bar in the concatenated matrix indicates the break between the two original matrices, and is sometimes omitted. Augmented matrices are used in various applications including solving systems of linear equations and computing the matrix inverse.

Code "Augmenting" is called concatenation in Python and MAT-LAB. In Python, make sure to state the correct axis along which to concatenate.

Code block 5.7: Python

```python
1  A = np.random.randn(3,5)
2  B = np.random.randn(3,4)
3  AB = np.concatenate((A,B),axis=1)
```

Code block 5.8: MATLAB

```matlab
1  A = randn(3,5);
2  B = randn(3,4);
3  AB = [A B];
```

Triangular Triangular matrices are half-way between a diagonal matrix and a full matrix. Triangular matrices come in two forms: upper-triangular (meaning only the diagonal and elements above it may contain non-zero elements) and lower-triangular (meaning only the diagonal and elements below it may contain non-zero elements). Here are two examples of triangular matrices.

$$\begin{bmatrix} 1 & 8 & 4 \\ 0 & 2 & 1 \\ 0 & 0 & 9 \end{bmatrix}, \begin{bmatrix} 1 & 0 & 0 & 0 \\ 3 & 2 & 0 & 0 \\ 6 & 5 & 9 & 0 \\ 2 & 0 & 4 & 1 \end{bmatrix}$$

Triangular matrices can be rectangular. Sometimes, the zeros are omitted (either to save ink, because the author was too lazy to type in the 0's, or for visual aesthetics). Here are two more examples of triangular matrices.

$$\begin{bmatrix} 1 & 0 & 0 & 0 & 0 \\ 3 & 2 & 0 & 0 & 0 \\ 6 & 0 & 9 & 0 & 0 \end{bmatrix}, \begin{bmatrix} 1 & 3 & 2 & 1 \\ & 2 & 7 & 9 \\ & & 0 & 5 \\ & & & 2 \end{bmatrix}$$

Triangular matrices appear in matrix decompositions including QR decomposition, LU decomposition, and Cholesky decomposition.

Code MATLAB and Python have dedicated functions to extract upper and lower triangular matrices. Tip: You can provide an optional second input k to isolate the elements above or below the kth diagonal.

Dense and sparse A matrix in which most or all matrix elements are non-zero is called a dense matrix (sometimes also called a "full matrix"). This term is used only when it is necessary in context, for example, when comparing a diagonal matrix with a dense matrix. You wouldn't normally call every matrix a "dense matrix."

A sparse matrix is one that contains mostly zeros and a relatively small number of non-zero elements. Sparse matrices are extremely computationally efficient, and therefore, a lot of modern algorithms in numerical linear algebra emphasize sparse matrices. Notice that the 10×10 sparse matrix below can be efficiently represented by listing the row and column indices that contain non-zero elements.

$$
\begin{bmatrix}
0 & 0 & 4 & 0 & 0 & 0 & 0 & 0 & 0 & 0 \\
0 & 0 & 0 & 0 & 0 & 0 & 0 & 0 & 0 & 0 \\
0 & 0 & 0 & 0 & 0 & 0 & 0 & 0 & 0 & 0 \\
0 & 0 & 0 & 0 & 0 & 8 & 0 & 0 & 0 & 0 \\
0 & 0 & 0 & 0 & 0 & 0 & 0 & 0 & 0 & 0 \\
0 & 0 & 0 & 0 & 0 & 0 & 0 & 0 & 0 & 0 \\
0 & 0 & 0 & 0 & 0 & 0 & 0 & 0 & 0 & 0 \\
0 & 0 & 0 & 0 & 0 & 0 & 0 & 0 & 0 & 0 \\
0 & 0 & 0 & 0 & 0 & 0 & 0 & 0 & 0 & 0 \\
0 & 0 & 0 & 0 & 0 & 0 & 0 & 0 & 0 & 0
\end{bmatrix}
\Rightarrow
\begin{matrix}
(1,3) & 4 \\
(4,6) & 8
\end{matrix}
$$

Orthogonal   A matrix is called orthogonal if it satisfies the following two criteria.

1. All of its columns are pairwise orthogonal. That means that the dot product between any two columns is exactly 0.
2. Each column i has $\|\mathbf{Q}_i\| = 1$, in other words, each column is unit magnitude. Remember that the magnitude of a vector (in this case, the column of a matrix) is computed as the dot product of that vector with itself.

The letter $\mathbf{Q}$ is often used to indicate an orthogonal matrix (though not exclusively). The formal definition of an orthogonal matrix is:

Definitions of an orthogonal matrix

$$
\langle \mathbf{Q}_i, \mathbf{Q}_j \rangle =
\begin{cases}
1, & \text{if } i = j \\
0, & \text{if } i \neq j
\end{cases}
\tag{5.8}
$$

Recall that $\langle\rangle$ is one of the dot-product notations. A more compact way of writing Equation 5.8 using matrix multiplication is

$$
\mathbf{Q}^{\mathrm{T}}\mathbf{Q} = \mathbf{I}
\tag{5.9}
$$

You'll learn in the next chapter why this notation is equivalent, but it's worth already being exposed to it here, because it will set you up to understand the relationship between the transpose and the inverse of an orthogonal matrix.

Toeplitz Toeplitz and Hankel matrices (below) are closely related to each other. Both involve creating new rows of a matrix as systematic rearrangements of elements in previous rows. One of the remarkable properties of Toeplitz and Hankel matrices is that they can have rank $r > 1$ even if they are created from a rank $r = 1$ vector.

In a Toeplitz matrix, all diagonals contain the same element. The matrix below shows a Toeplitz matrix created from a vector. This Toeplitz matrix is also symmetric.

$$\begin{bmatrix} a & b & c & d \end{bmatrix} \Rightarrow \begin{bmatrix} a & b & c & d \\ b & a & b & c \\ c & b & a & b \\ d & c & b & a \end{bmatrix}$$

Notice that the main diagonal is the same as the first element of the vector (a), the next off-diagonal is the second element of the vector (b), and so on.

Hankel A Hankel matrix is kindof like a rotated Toeplitz matrix. Compare the following matrix to the Toeplitz matrix above, created from the same vector.

$$\begin{bmatrix} a & b & c & d \end{bmatrix} \Rightarrow \begin{bmatrix} a & b & c & d \\ b & c & d & 0 \\ c & d & 0 & 0 \\ d & 0 & 0 & 0 \end{bmatrix}$$

A Hankel matrix can also "wrap around" to produce a full matrix, like this:

$$\begin{bmatrix} a & b & c & d \\ b & c & d & a \\ c & d & a & b \\ d & a & b & c \end{bmatrix}$$

Notice that the ith column (and the ith row) of the Hankel matrix comes from starting the vector at the ith element and wrapping around. You can also see how the anti-diagonals relate to the vector.

Toeplitz

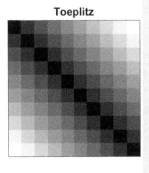

Hankel

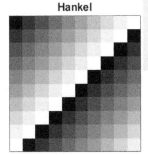

Figure 5.5: Visualization of Toeplitz and Hankel matrices created from a vector with integers from 1 to 10.

The algorithm to compute a Hankel matrix involves populating a matrix $\mathbf{Y}$ from elements of a vector $\mathbf{x}$:

Creating a Hankel matrix from a vector

$$\mathbf{Y}_{i,j} = \mathbf{x}_{i+j-1} \qquad (5.10)$$

Hankel matrices are used in time series convolution and in advanced signal-processing methods such as time-delay embedding. Hankel matrices also look pretty (Figure 5.5) and have aesthetically pleasing properties in eigendecomposition.

Code Creating Toeplitz matrices is intuitive; creating dense Hankel matrices looks a bit strange at first, but you need to specify the final row of the matrix, or else it will have zeros like in the first example above.

Code block 5.11: Python

```
1  from scipy.linalg import hankel,toeplitz
2  t = [1,2,3,4]
3  T = toeplitz(t)
4  H = hankel(t,r=[2,3,4,1])
```

Code block 5.12: MATLAB

```
1  t = 1:4;
2  T = toeplitz(t);
3  H = hankel(t,t([end 1:end-1]));
```

5.6 Matrix addition and subtraction

Now that you know some matrix terminology and some special matrices, it is time to begin learning how to work with matrices. The rest of this chapter focuses on the "easy" arithmetic operations on matrices, and the next few chapters will deal with more advanced topics. We begin with basic matrix arithmetic.

Matrix addition is simple, and it works how you would think it should work: Add or subtract each corresponding element in the two matrices. For addition to be a valid operation, both matrices must be the same size—$M \times N$—and the resulting matrix will also be $M \times N$.

Writing out matrix addition looks like this: $\mathbf{C} = \mathbf{A} + \mathbf{B}$. Each element in $\mathbf{C}$ is defined as

$$c_{i,j} = a_{i,j} + b_{i,j} \tag{5.11}$$

Below is one example.

$$\begin{bmatrix} 1 & 2 & 5 \\ 9 & 8 & 7 \end{bmatrix} + \begin{bmatrix} -1 & 0 & -5 \\ 3 & a & \pi \end{bmatrix} = \begin{bmatrix} 0 & 2 & 0 \\ 12 & 8+a & 7+\pi \end{bmatrix}$$

Needless to say, matrix subtraction works exactly the same way, except with a minus sign instead of a plus sign.

Like vector addition, matrix addition is commutative, meaning that

$$\mathbf{C} = \mathbf{A} + \mathbf{B} = \mathbf{B} + \mathbf{A}$$

This may seem trivial based on your elementary-school arithmetic knowledge, but it is important to mention these properties explicitly, because, for example, matrix multiplication is not commutative. The commutivity of matrix addition is also a key step in a proof about creating symmetric matrices, which you will see in a few pages!

5.7 Scalar-matrix multiplication

Matrix multiplication is sufficiently varied and involved that it requires its own chapter. However, *scalar-matrix multiplication* is simple and intuitive.

Scalar-matrix multiplication means to multiply a matrix by a single number. It works by multiplying each matrix element by that scalar—exactly the same as scalar-vector multiplication:

$$\delta \begin{bmatrix} a & b \\ c & d \end{bmatrix} = \begin{bmatrix} \delta a & \delta b \\ \delta c & \delta d \end{bmatrix} = \begin{bmatrix} a\delta & b\delta \\ c\delta & d\delta \end{bmatrix} = \begin{bmatrix} a & b \\ c & d \end{bmatrix} \delta \qquad (5.12)$$

Notice that because scalar-matrix multiplication is implemented element-wise, it is commutative. Each individual matrix element is simply a number, and scalar multiplication obeys the commutative law.

This means that you can move the scalar around, and the result is unchanged. That feature turns out to be crucial for several proofs and derivations. The following illustrates the idea.

$$\lambda \mathbf{AB} = \mathbf{A}\lambda\mathbf{B} = \mathbf{AB}\lambda$$

"Shifting" a matrix

We can combine matrix addition with scalar-matrix multiplication to apply a procedure called "shifting" a matrix. To "shift" a matrix means to add to the matrix a multiple of the identity matrix. Shifting is applied only to square matrices. The new, shifted, matrix is often denoted as $\tilde{\mathbf{A}}$; the tilde character on top indicates that the matrix is similar to, but not the same as, the original matrix $\mathbf{A}$.

> **"Shifting" a matrix**
>
> $$\tilde{\mathbf{A}} = \mathbf{A} + \lambda\mathbf{I}, \qquad \mathbf{A} \in \mathbb{R}^{M \times M}, \lambda \in \mathbb{R} \qquad (5.13)$$

Here is an example with real numbers.

$$\begin{bmatrix} 1 & 3 & 0 \\ 1 & 3 & 0 \\ 2 & 2 & 7 \end{bmatrix} + .1 \begin{bmatrix} 1 & 0 & 0 \\ 0 & 1 & 0 \\ 0 & 0 & 1 \end{bmatrix} = \begin{bmatrix} 1.1 & 3 & 0 \\ 1 & 3.1 & 0 \\ 2 & 2 & 7.1 \end{bmatrix}$$

There are three properties of matrix shifting that can be seen from this example:

1. Only the diagonal elements are affected; shifting does not change the off-diagonal elements. This is obvious from Equation 5.13 because the identity matrix has all zeros on the off-diagonal elements.
2. The first two rows of the example matrix are identical before shifting, and different after shifting. Thus, shifting a matrix can make matrices with redundant rows (or columns) distinct.
3. When λ is close to zero, then $\tilde{\mathbf{A}}$ is really similar to $\mathbf{A}$. Indeed, when $\lambda = 0$, then $\tilde{\mathbf{A}} = \mathbf{A}$. In practical applications, λ is often selected to be as small as possible while large enough to satisfy other constraints.

Shifting a matrix has important applications in statistics, machine learning, deep learning, and other related fields. For example, a procedure called "regularization" involves shifting matrices. Regularization is a crucial operation for solving systems of equations or fitting statistical models to low-rank data. When you learn about matrix rank (chapter 7), you'll see that shifting will transform any rank-deficient matrix into a full-rank matrix.

Code Shifting in code illustrates both scalar multiplication and addition. Also note the potential for confusion that the variable 1 (lower-case letter "L") can look like the number 1 and the upper-case letter "I."

Code block 5.13: Python

```
1  import numpy as np
2  l = .01
3  I = np.eye(4)
4  A = np.random.randn(4,4)
5  As = A + l*I
```

Code block 5.14: MATLAB

```
1  l = .01;
2  I = eye(4);
3  A = randn(4);
4  As = A + l*I;
```

Practice problems Shift the following matrices according to the specified λ.

a) $\begin{bmatrix} .4 & 3 & 0 \\ 2 & 1 & 0 \\ .1 & .4 & 0 \end{bmatrix}$, $\lambda = .1$

b) $\begin{bmatrix} 43 & 42 & 42 \\ 234 & 746 & 12 \\ 0 & 33 & 1001 \end{bmatrix}$, $\lambda = -1$

Answers

a) $\begin{bmatrix} .5 & 3 & 0 \\ 2 & 1.1 & 0 \\ .1 & .4 & .1 \end{bmatrix}$

b) $\begin{bmatrix} 42 & 42 & 42 \\ 234 & 745 & 12 \\ 0 & 33 & 1000 \end{bmatrix}$

5.9 Diagonal and trace

The diagonal elements of a matrix can be extracted and placed into a vector. This is used, for example, in statistics: the diagonal elements of a covariance matrix contain the variance of each variable. The following defines the procedure.

Extracting the diagonal elements into a vector

$$\mathbf{v} = diag(\mathbf{A})$$

$$v_i = a_{i,i}, \quad i = \{1, 2, ..., \min(M, N)\} \qquad (5.14)$$

Note that this formula does not require the matrix to be square. Observe the following examples (diagonal elements highlighted).

$$diag\left(\begin{bmatrix} \boxed{5} & 3 & 8 \\ 1 & \boxed{0} & 4 \\ 8 & 6 & \boxed{2} \end{bmatrix}\right) = \begin{bmatrix} 5 \\ 0 \\ 2 \end{bmatrix}, \quad diag\left(\begin{bmatrix} \boxed{5} & 3 & 8 & 3 & 9 \\ 1 & \boxed{0} & 4 & 3 & 1 \\ 8 & 6 & \boxed{2} & 9 & 9 \end{bmatrix}\right) = \begin{bmatrix} 5 \\ 0 \\ 2 \end{bmatrix}, \quad diag\left(\begin{bmatrix} \boxed{5} & 3 \\ 1 & \boxed{0} \\ 8 & 6 \\ 3 & 5 \\ 9 & 7 \\ 8 & 2 \end{bmatrix}\right) = \begin{bmatrix} 5 \\ 0 \end{bmatrix}$$

Trace The trace is an operation that produces a single number from a squre matrix. It is indicated as $tr(\mathbf{A})$ and is defined as the sum of all diagonal elements of a matrix:

Trace is the sum of diagonal elements

$$tr(A) = \sum_{i=1}^{M} a_{i,i} \qquad (5.15)$$

Notice that the off-diagonal elements do not contribute to the trace; thus, two very different matrices (different sizes, different off-diagonal elements) can have the same trace.

The trace operation has two applications in machine learning: It is used to compute the Frobenius norm of a matrix (a measure of the magnitude of a matrix) and it is used to measure the "distance" between two matrices.

IMPORTANT The trace is defined only for square matrices. This may seem strange, considering that the trace is the sum of the diagonal elements and the diagonal exists for rectangular matrices. The reason for this rule has to do with a property of eigendecomposition: The trace of a matrix equals the sum of its eigenvalues. Eigendecomposition is valid only on square matrices, and so ancient and wise linear algebraticians decreed that only square matrices can have a trace.

Code Extracting the diagonal from a matrix was shown on page 119.

Code block 5.15: Python

```
1  import numpy as np
2  A = np.random.randn(4,4)
3  tr = np.trace(A)
```

Code block 5.16: MATLAB

```
1  A = randn(4);
2  tr = trace(A);
```

Practice problems Compute the trace of the following matrices.

a) $\begin{bmatrix} -3 & 8 & 0 \\ 0 & -3 & -6 \\ -2 & 3 & -3 \end{bmatrix}$
b) $\begin{bmatrix} -3 & -5 & 4 \\ 1 & -3 & 1 \\ 6 & -1 & 10 \end{bmatrix}$
c) $\begin{bmatrix} 8 & -8 & 9 \\ 7 & -3 & 5 \\ 0 & 5 & -5 \end{bmatrix}$

Answers

a) -9
b) 4
c) 0

Exercises

1. For the following matrix and vectors, solve the given arithmetic problems, or state why they are not solvable.

$$\mathbf{u} = \begin{bmatrix} 2 \\ 4 \\ 1 \end{bmatrix}, \quad \mathbf{v} = \begin{bmatrix} 3 \\ 5 \\ 0 \\ 2 \end{bmatrix}, \quad \mathbf{w} = \begin{bmatrix} 1 \\ 0 \\ 1 \\ 5 \end{bmatrix}, \quad \mathbf{A} = \begin{bmatrix} -1 & -2 & -6 & -6 \\ 1 & -1 & 0 & -2 \\ -1 & 0 & -1 & -4 \end{bmatrix}$$

a) $\mathbf{wu}^T + \mathbf{A}$ **b)** $\mathbf{wu}^T + \mathbf{A}^T$ **c)** $\mathbf{uv}^T - \mathbf{A}$

d) $\mathbf{vw}^T - \mathbf{A}$ **e)** $\mathbf{vw}^T + \mathbf{A}^T$

2. Perform the following matrix operations, when the operation is valid.

$$\mathbf{A} = \begin{bmatrix} 2 & 4 & 3 \\ 0 & 1 & 3 \end{bmatrix}, \quad \mathbf{B} = \begin{bmatrix} -2 & -1 & 3 \\ 6 & -7 & 7 \end{bmatrix},$$

$$\mathbf{C} = \begin{bmatrix} 0 & -6 \\ -3 & -2 \\ -2 & 7 \end{bmatrix} \quad \mathbf{D} = \begin{bmatrix} 1 & 2 \\ 3 & 4 \\ 2 & 4 \end{bmatrix}$$

a) $\mathbf{A} + 3\mathbf{B}$ **b)** $\mathbf{A} + \mathbf{C}$ **c)** $\mathbf{C} - \mathbf{D}$

d) $\mathbf{D} + \mathbf{C}$ **e)** $\mathbf{A}^T + \mathbf{D}$ **f)** $(\mathbf{A} + \mathbf{B})^T + 2\mathbf{C}$

g) $3\mathbf{A} + (\mathbf{B}^T + \mathbf{C})^T$ **h)** $-4(\mathbf{A}^T + \mathbf{C})^T + \mathbf{D}$

3. An N×N matrix has N^2 elements. For a symmetric matrix, however, not all elements are unique. Create 2×2 and 3×3 symmetric matrices and count the number of total elements and the number of possible unique elements. Then work out a formula for the number of possible unique elements in such a matrix.

4. Identify the following types of matrices from the list provided in the section "A zoo of matrices." Note that some matrices can be given multiple labels.

a) $\begin{bmatrix} 1 & 0 & 0 \\ 0 & 1 & 0 \\ 0 & 0 & 2 \end{bmatrix}$
b) $\begin{bmatrix} 1 & 2 & 3 \\ 0 & 4 & 5 \\ 0 & 0 & 6 \end{bmatrix}$
c) $\begin{bmatrix} 1 & 2 & 3 \\ 2 & 4 & 5 \\ 3 & 5 & 6 \end{bmatrix}$

d) $\begin{bmatrix} a & b & c \\ -b & d & e \\ -c & -e & f \end{bmatrix}$
e) $\begin{bmatrix} 0 & b & c \\ -b & 0 & f \\ -c & -e & 0 \end{bmatrix}$
f) $\begin{bmatrix} 1 & 0 & 0 & 0 \\ 0 & 32 & 0 & 0 \\ 0 & 0 & 42 & 0 \end{bmatrix}$

5. To "decompose" a matrix means to represent a matrix using the sum or product of other matrices. Let's consider an additive decomposition, thus starting from some matrix **A** and setting $\mathbf{A} = \mathbf{B} + \mathbf{C}$. You can also use more matrices: $\mathbf{A} = \mathbf{B} + ... + \mathbf{N}$. Decompose the following matrices **A**. Are your decompositions unique? (A decomposition is "unique" if it has exactly one solution.)

$$\begin{bmatrix} 1 & 3 \\ 2 & 5 \end{bmatrix}, \quad \begin{bmatrix} 1 & 3 & 3 \\ 2 & 5 & 7 \end{bmatrix}$$

6. Create a Hankel matrix from the vector

$$\begin{bmatrix} 1 & 2 & 3 & 1 & 2 & 3 \end{bmatrix}$$

7. Determine whether the following matrices are orthogonal.

a) $\begin{bmatrix} 1 & 0 & 0 \\ 0 & 1 & 0 \\ 0 & 0 & 2 \end{bmatrix}$
b) $\frac{1}{\sqrt{9}} \begin{bmatrix} 1 & 2 \\ -2 & 2 \\ -2 & 1 \end{bmatrix}$
c) $\mathbf{I}_{17}$

8. Consider two $M \times N$ matrices **A** and **B**. Is the sum of their traces equal to the trace of their sum? That is, $tr(\mathbf{A}) + tr(\mathbf{B}) = tr(\mathbf{A} + \mathbf{B})$? Try for a few examples, then see if you can work out a proof for this property.

a) $\begin{bmatrix} 3 & -4 \\ 3 & -9 \end{bmatrix}, \begin{bmatrix} 4 & 4 \\ 6 & 0 \end{bmatrix}$
b) $\begin{bmatrix} 1 & 2 & 5 \\ -5 & 0 & 5 \\ -9 & 4 & 3 \end{bmatrix}, \begin{bmatrix} 5 & 5 & 5 \\ 4 & 3 & 4 \\ 1 & 1 & 9 \end{bmatrix}$

c) $\begin{bmatrix} a & d & e \\ f & b & g \\ h & i & c \end{bmatrix}$, $\begin{bmatrix} j & m & n \\ o & k & p \\ q & r & l \end{bmatrix}$

9. Here's another neat property of the trace: The trace of the outer product is equal to the dot product: $tr(\mathbf{v}\mathbf{w}^T) = \mathbf{v}^T\mathbf{w}$. Demonstrate this property using the following sets of vectors.

a) $\begin{bmatrix} 3 \\ -5 \\ 1 \end{bmatrix} \begin{bmatrix} -2 \\ 1 \\ 5 \end{bmatrix}$ **b)** $\begin{bmatrix} 1 \\ -3 \\ 5 \\ 2 \end{bmatrix} \begin{bmatrix} 5 \\ 6 \\ 1 \\ 4 \end{bmatrix}$ **c)** $\begin{bmatrix} a \\ b \\ c \\ d \end{bmatrix} \begin{bmatrix} e \\ f \\ g \\ h \end{bmatrix}$

10. Perform the indicated matrix operations using the following matrices and scalars. Determine the underlying principle regarding trace, matrix addition, and scalar multiplication.

$$\mathbf{A} = \begin{bmatrix} 5 & -3 \\ 2 & -3 \end{bmatrix}, \quad \mathbf{B} = \begin{bmatrix} -4 & -1 \\ 1 & 3 \end{bmatrix}, \quad \mathbf{C} = \begin{bmatrix} a & c \\ b & d \end{bmatrix}, \quad \lambda = 5, \quad \alpha = -3$$

a) $tr(\mathbf{A})$ b) $tr(\mathbf{B})$ c) $tr(\mathbf{A} + \mathbf{B})$

d) $tr(\lambda\mathbf{C})$ e) $\lambda\, tr(\mathbf{C})$ f) $\lambda\, tr(\alpha\mathbf{C})$

g) $\alpha\, tr(\lambda\mathbf{C})$ h) $tr(\alpha\mathbf{A} + \lambda\mathbf{B})$ i) $(\lambda\alpha)\, tr(\mathbf{A} + \mathbf{B})$

j) $tr(\lambda\mathbf{A} + \lambda\mathbf{B})$ k) $\lambda\, tr(\mathbf{A} + \mathbf{B})$ l) $tr(\mathbf{A} + \mathbf{B}^T)$

Answers

1.

   a) Size mismatch.   **b)** $\begin{bmatrix} 1 & 5 & 0 \\ -2 & -1 & 0 \\ -4 & 4 & 0 \\ 4 & 18 & 1 \end{bmatrix}$ **c)**

   d) Size mismatch.   **e)** Size mismatch.

2.

   a) $\begin{bmatrix} -4 & 1 & 12 \\ 18 & -20 & 24 \end{bmatrix}$ **b)** Invalid.   **c)** $\begin{bmatrix} -1 & -8 \\ -6 & -6 \\ -4 & 3 \end{bmatrix}$

   d) $\begin{bmatrix} 1 & -4 \\ 0 & 2 \\ 0 & 11 \end{bmatrix}$ **e)** $\begin{bmatrix} 3 & 2 \\ 7 & 5 \\ 5 & 7 \end{bmatrix}$ **f)** $\begin{bmatrix} 0 & -6 \\ -3 & -10 \\ 2 & 24 \end{bmatrix}$

   g) $\begin{bmatrix} 4 & 8 & 10 \\ 0 & -6 & 23 \end{bmatrix}$ **h)** Invalid.

3. n(n+1)/2

4.   **a)** square, diagonal, symmetric   **b)** square, upper-triangular

   c) symmetric   **d)** square, skew-symmetric
                                   if $a = d = f = 0$

   e) square, skew-symmetric   **f)** rectangular, diagonal
     if $e = f$

5. The additive decomposition is definitely not unique; there is an infinity of possible matrices that can sum to produce a given **A**. One interesting solution is to create matrices of all zeros and one non-zero element. For example:

$$\begin{bmatrix} 1 & 3 \\ 2 & 5 \end{bmatrix} = \begin{bmatrix} 1 & 0 \\ 0 & 0 \end{bmatrix} + \begin{bmatrix} 0 & 3 \\ 0 & 0 \end{bmatrix} + \begin{bmatrix} 0 & 0 \\ 2 & 0 \end{bmatrix} + \begin{bmatrix} 0 & 0 \\ 0 & 5 \end{bmatrix}$$

The reason why this is an interesting decomposition is that the four matrices are convenient *basis matrices* for the vector space $\mathbb{R}^{2\times2}$

6.

$$\begin{bmatrix} 1 & 2 & 3 & 1 & 2 & 3 \\ 2 & 3 & 1 & 2 & 3 & 1 \\ 3 & 1 & 2 & 3 & 1 & 2 \\ 1 & 2 & 3 & 1 & 2 & 3 \\ 2 & 3 & 1 & 2 & 3 & 1 \\ 3 & 1 & 2 & 3 & 1 & 2 \end{bmatrix}$$

7. **a)** No, the third column does not have magnitude $= 1$.

b) No, because columns are not orthogonal.

c) Yes, all identities matrices are orthogonal.

8. This property (sum of traces equals trace of sums) holds because of the element-wise definition of both trace and matrix addition:

$$\sum_{i=1}^{M} a_{i,i} + \sum_{i=1}^{M} b_{i,i} = \sum_{i=1}^{M} (a_{i,i} + b_{i,i})$$

a) -2 in both cases   **b)** 21 in both cases   **c)** $a+b+c+j+k+l$ in both cases

9. **a)** -6   **b)** 0   **c)** $ae + bf + cg + dh$

10. The underlying principle here is the same as in question 8: The trace is a linear operator, so you can scalar-multiply and sum, and trace remains the same.

a) 2   **b)** -1   **c)** 1

d) $5a + 5d$ **e)** $5(a + d)$ **f)** $5(-3a - 3d)$

g) $-3(5a + 5d)$ **h)** -11   **i)** -15

j) 5   **k)** 5   **l)** 1

5.12 Code challenges

1. The goal of this exercise is to create a matrix that contains the dot products between all pairs of columns in two other matrices. First, create two 4x2 matrices (that is, 4 rows, 2 columns) of random numbers. Then write a double-for loop in which you compute the dot products between each column of both matrices. The i, j element of the resulting matrix will be the dot product between column i of the first matrix and column j of the second matrix.

2. Create a symmetric matrix by starting with a dense random numbers matrix and applying three matrix operations: convert to triangular, transpose, matrix addition.

3. Create a diagonal matrix of size 4x8 without using the `diag()` function. The diagonal elements should be 1,2,3,4. How much of your code would you need to change to create an 8x4 diagonal matrix?

5.13 Code solutions

1. The purpose of this challenge is to get you thinking about the mechanics of matrix multiplication.

Code block 5.17: Python

```python
1  A = np.random.randn(4,2)
2  B = np.random.randn(4,2)
3  C = np.zeros((2,2))
4  for coli in range(2):
5    for colj in range(2):
6      C[coli,colj]=np.dot(A[:,coli],B[:,colj])
```

Code block 5.18: MATLAB

```matlab
1  A = randn(4,2);
2  B = randn(4,2);
3  C = zeros(2);
4  for coli=1:2
5    for colj=1:2
6      C(coli,colj) = dot(A(:,coli),B(:,colj));
7    end
8  end
```

2. You just discovered one way to make a symmetric matrix!

Code block 5.19: Python

```python
1  A = np.random.randn(4,4)
2  Al = np.tril(A)
3  S = Al + Al.T
```

Code block 5.20: MATLAB

```matlab
1  A = randn(4);
2  Al = tril(A);
3  S = Al + Al';
```

3. The point here is to appreciate that indexing the diagonal of a matrix involves the i, i indices.

Code block 5.21: Python

```python
1  D = np.zeros((4,8))
2  for d in range(min(D.shape)):
3      D[d,d] = d+1
```

Code block 5.22: MATLAB

```matlab
1  D = zeros(4,8);
2  for d=1:min(size(D))
3      D(d,d) = d;
4  end
```

CHAPTER 6
MATRIX MULTIPLICATION

Multiplying matrices is considerably more complicated than multiplying regular numbers. The normal rules you know about multiplication (e.g., $a \times b = b \times a$) often don't apply to matrices, and there are extra rules you will need to learn. Furthermore, there are several ways of multiplying matrices. And to make matters more complicated, not all pairs of matrices can be multiplied. So, take a deep breath, because this chapter is your first deep-dive into linear algebra!

6.1 "Standard" matrix multiplication

For lack of a better term, this method will be called the "standard" method. Unless otherwise explicitly stated, you can assume (in this book and elsewhere) that two matrices next to each other (like this: $\mathbf{AB}$) indicates "standard" matrix multiplication.

Terminology The first thing to know about matrix multiplication is that it is not commutative, so $\mathbf{AB} \neq \mathbf{BA}$. There are exceptions where this is the case (for example, $\mathbf{AI} = \mathbf{IA}$), but those exceptions are rare. For this reason, even the terminology of matrix multiplication is complicated.

The following five statements are ways to say the operation $\mathbf{AB}$ out loud (e.g., when trying to show off to your math-inclined friends and family):

"$\mathbf{A}$ times $\mathbf{B}$"
"$\mathbf{A}$ left-multiplies $\mathbf{B}$"
"$\mathbf{A}$ pre-multiplies $\mathbf{B}$"
"$\mathbf{B}$ right-multiplies $\mathbf{A}$"
"$\mathbf{B}$ post-multiplies $\mathbf{A}$"

Validity   Before learning how standard matrix multiplication works, you need to learn when matrix multiplication *is valid*. The rule for multiplication validity is simple and visual, and you need to memorize this rule before learning the mechanics of multiplication.

If you write the matrix sizes underneath the matrices, then matrix multiplication is valid only when the two "inner dimensions" match, and the size of the resulting product matrix is given by the "outer dimensions." By "inner" and "outer" I'm referring to the spatial organization of the matrix sizes, as in Figure 6.1.

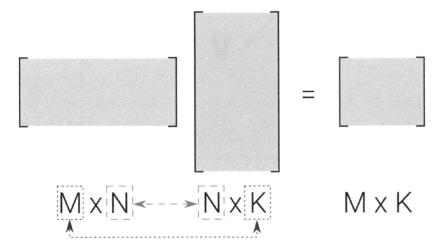

Figure 6.1: Visualization of the rule for matrix multiplication validity. Note the reference to "inner dimensions" (**N**) and "outer dimensions" (**M** and **K**).

Consider the following matrices; are these multiplications valid?

The first pair (**AB**) is valid because the "inner" dimensions match (both 2). The resulting product matrix will be of size 5×7. The second pair shows the lack of commutativity in matrix multiplication: The "inner" dimensions (7 and 5) do not match, and thus the multiplication is not valid. The third pair is an interesting case. You might be tempted to call this an invalid operation; however, when transposing **C**, the rows and columns swap, and so the "inner" dimensions become consistent (both 5). So this multiplication is valid.

Here's something exciting: you are now armed with the knowledge to understand the notation for the dot product and outer product. In particular, you can now appreciate why the order of transposition ($\mathbf{v}^T\mathbf{w}$ or $\mathbf{vw}^T$) determines whether the multiplication is the dot product or the outer product (Figure 6.2).

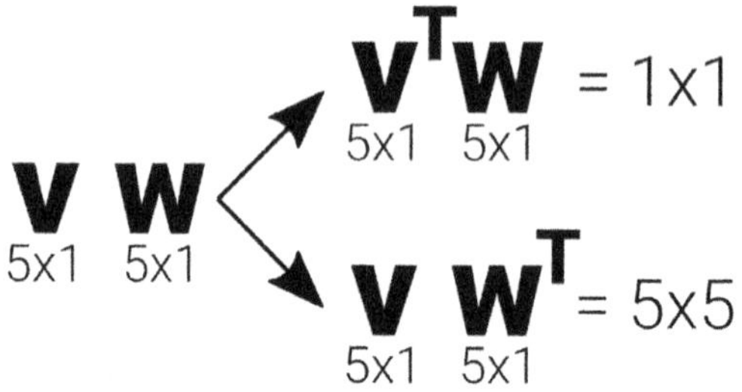

Figure 6.2: For two adjacent column vectors, transposing the first vs. the second vector is the difference between the dot product vs. the outer product.

Practice problems For the following matrices, determine whether matrix multiplication is valid, and, if so, the size of the product matrix.

$$\mathbf{A} \in \mathbb{R}^{2\times4}, \quad \mathbf{B} \in \mathbb{R}^{3\times4}, \quad \mathbf{C} \in \mathbb{R}^{4\times4}$$

a) $\mathbf{AB}$ b) $\mathbf{AC}$ c) $\mathbf{AB}^T$ d) $\mathbf{BCA}^T$ e) $\mathbf{BB}^T\mathbf{A}$

Answers

a) no   b) 2×4 c) 2×3 d) 3×2 e) no

Code Unfortunately, matrix multiplication is confusingly different between MATLAB and Python. Pay close attention to the subtle but important differences (@ vs. *).

Code block 6.1: Python

```
1  M1 = np.random.randn(4,3)
2  M2 = np.random.randn(3,5)
3  C = M1 @ M2
```

```
1  M1 = randn(4,3);
2  M2 = randn(3,5);
3  C = M1 * M2
```

It is now time to learn how to multiply matrices. There are four ways to think about and implement matrix multiplication. All four methods give the same result, but provide different perspectives on what matrix multiplication means. It's useful to understand all of these perspectives, because they provide insights into matrix computations in different contexts and for different problems. It is unfortunate that many linear algebra textbooks teach only the dot-product method (what I call the "element perspective").

(1) The "element perspective"   Each element $c_{i,j}$ in $\mathbf{AB} = \mathbf{C}$ is the dot product between the ith row in $\mathbf{A}$ and the jth column in $\mathbf{B}$. The equation below shows how you would create the top-left element in the product matrix.

$$\begin{bmatrix} 1 & 2 \\ 3 & 4 \end{bmatrix} \begin{bmatrix} a & b \\ c & d \end{bmatrix} = \begin{bmatrix} 1a + 2c & \end{bmatrix} \qquad (6.1)$$

For convenience, I will label all matrices in the following examples as $\mathbf{AB} = \mathbf{C}$.

This makes it clear that element $c_{i,j}$ comes from the dot product between row $\mathbf{a}_i$ and column $\mathbf{b}_j$.

Here is another example; make sure you see how each element in the product matrix is the dot product between the corresponding row or the left matrix and column in the right matrix.

$$\begin{bmatrix} 3 & 4 \\ -1 & 2 \\ 0 & 4 \end{bmatrix} \begin{bmatrix} 5 & 1 \\ 3 & 1 \end{bmatrix} = \begin{bmatrix} 3 \cdot 5 + 4 \cdot 3 & 3 \cdot 1 + 4 \cdot 1 \\ -1 \cdot 5 + 2 \cdot 3 & -1 \cdot 1 + 2 \cdot 1 \\ 0 \cdot 5 + 4 \cdot 3 & 0 \cdot 1 + 4 \cdot 1 \end{bmatrix} = \begin{bmatrix} 27 & 7 \\ 1 & 1 \\ 12 & 4 \end{bmatrix}$$

There is a hand gesture that you can apply to remember this rule: extend your pointer fingers of both hands; simultaneously move your left hand from left to right (across the row of the left matrix) while moving your right hand down towards you (down the column of the right matrix) (Figure 6.3).

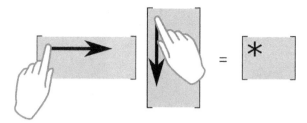

Figure 6.3: Visual representation of the mechanism of computing each element of the matrix multiplication product as the vector dot product between each row of the left matrix (from left-to-right and each column of the right matrix (from top-to-bottom).

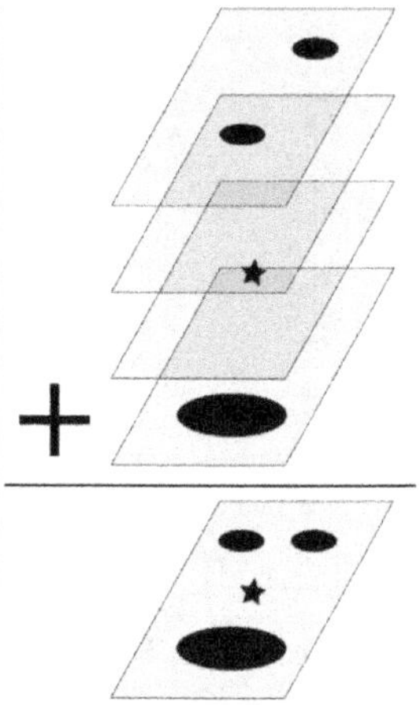

Below you can see another visualization of matrix multiplication from the element perspective. This visualization facilitates three important features of matrix multiplication.

$$\begin{bmatrix} - & a_1 & - \\ - & a_2 & - \\ & \vdots & \\ - & a_n & - \end{bmatrix} \begin{bmatrix} | & | & & | \\ b_1 & b_2 & \cdots & b_n \\ | & | & & | \end{bmatrix} = \begin{bmatrix} a_1{\cdot}b_1 & a_1{\cdot}b_2 & \cdots & a_1{\cdot}b_n \\ a_2{\cdot}b_1 & a_2{\cdot}b_2 & & a_2{\cdot}b_n \\ \vdots & & \ddots & \vdots \\ a_n{\cdot}b_1 & a_n{\cdot}b_2 & \cdots & a_n{\cdot}b_n \end{bmatrix}$$

Figure 6.4: A simulacrum of building up a matrix one layer at a time. Each layer is the same size as the product yet provides only partial information.

- The diagonal of the product matrix $\mathbf{C}$ contains dot products between rows and columns of the same ordinal position (row i in $\mathbf{A}$ and column i in $\mathbf{B}$).
- The lower-triangle of $\mathbf{C}$ contains dot products between *later* rows in $\mathbf{A}$ and *earlier* columns in $\mathbf{B}$ (row i in $\mathbf{A}$ and column j in $\mathbf{B}$, where $i > j$).
- The upper-triangle of $\mathbf{C}$ contains dot products between *earlier* rows in $\mathbf{A}$ and *later* columns in $\mathbf{B}$ (row i in $\mathbf{A}$ and column j in $\mathbf{B}$, where $i < j$).

The first point above is relevant for understanding data covariance matrices. The second and third points are important for understanding several matrix decompositions, most importantly QR decomposition and generalized eigendecomposition.

(2) The "layer perspective" In contrast to the element perspective, in which each element is computed independently of each other element, the layer perspective involves conceptualizing the product matrix as a series of layers, or "sheets," that are summed together. This is implemented by creating outer products from the columns of **A** and the rows of **B**, and then summing those outer products together.

Remember that the outer product is a matrix. Each outer product is the same size as **C**, and can be thought of as a layer. By analogy, imagine constructing an image by laying transparent sheets of paper on top of each other, with each sheet containing a different part of the image (Figure 6.4).

Below is an example using the same matrix as in the previous section. Make sure you understand how the two outer product matrices are formed from column $\mathbf{a}_i$ and row $\mathbf{b}_j$. You can also use nearly the same hand gesture as with the element perspective (Figure 6.3), but swap the motions of the left and right hands.

$$\begin{bmatrix} 3 & 4 \\ -1 & 2 \\ 0 & 4 \end{bmatrix} \begin{bmatrix} 5 & 1 \\ 3 & 1 \end{bmatrix} = \begin{bmatrix} 15 & 3 \\ -5 & -1 \\ 0 & 0 \end{bmatrix} + \begin{bmatrix} 12 & 4 \\ 6 & 2 \\ 12 & 4 \end{bmatrix} = \begin{bmatrix} 27 & 7 \\ 1 & 1 \\ 12 & 4 \end{bmatrix}$$

Each of these layers is a rank-1 matrix. Rank will be discussed in more detail in a separate chapter, but for now, you can think of a rank-1 matrix as containing only a single column's worth of information; all the other columns are scaled versions.

Notice that in each of the "layer matrices," the columns form a dependent set (the same can be said of the rows). However, the sum of these singular matrices—the product matrix—has columns that form a linearly *in*dependent set.

The layer perspective of matrix multiplication is closely related to the spectral theorem of matrices, which says that any matrix can be represented as a sum of rank-1 matrices. It's like each rank-1 matrix is a single color and the matrix is the rainbow. This important and elegant idea is the basis for the singular value decomposition, which you will learn about in Chapter 16.

(3) The "column perspective" From the column perspective, all matrices (the multiplying matrices and the product matrix) are thought of as sets of column vectors. Then the product matrix is created one column at a time.

The first column in the product matrix is a linear weighted combination of all columns in the left matrix, where the weights are defined by the elements in the first column of the right matrix. The second column in the product matrix is again a weighted combination of all columns in the left matrix, except that the weights now come from the second column in the right matrix. And so on for all N columns in the right matrix. Let's start with a simple example:

$$\begin{bmatrix} 1 & 2 \\ 3 & 4 \end{bmatrix} \begin{bmatrix} a & b \\ c & d \end{bmatrix} = \begin{bmatrix} a\begin{bmatrix} 1 \\ 3 \end{bmatrix} + c\begin{bmatrix} 2 \\ 4 \end{bmatrix} & b\begin{bmatrix} 1 \\ 3 \end{bmatrix} + d\begin{bmatrix} 2 \\ 4 \end{bmatrix} \end{bmatrix} \quad (6.2)$$

Let's go through Equation 6.2 slowly. The first column of the product matrix is the sum of all columns in matrix **A**. But it's not just the columns added together—each column in **A** is weighted according to the corresponding element from the first column of matrix **B**. Then, the second column of matrix **C** is created by again summing all of the columns in matrix **A**, except now each column is weighted by a different element of column 2 from matrix **B**. Equation 6.2 shows only two columns, but this procedure would be repeated for however many columns are in matrix **B**.

Now for the same numerical example you've seen in the previous two perspectives:

$$\begin{bmatrix} 3 & 4 \\ -1 & 2 \\ 0 & 4 \end{bmatrix} \begin{bmatrix} 5 & 1 \\ 3 & 1 \end{bmatrix} = \begin{bmatrix} 5\begin{bmatrix} 3 \\ -1 \\ 0 \end{bmatrix} + 3\begin{bmatrix} 4 \\ 2 \\ 4 \end{bmatrix} & 1\begin{bmatrix} 3 \\ -1 \\ 0 \end{bmatrix} + 1\begin{bmatrix} 4 \\ 2 \\ 4 \end{bmatrix} \end{bmatrix} = \begin{bmatrix} 27 & 7 \\ 1 & 1 \\ 12 & 4 \end{bmatrix}$$

The column perspective of matrix multiplication is useful in statistics, when the columns of the left matrix contain a set of *regressors* (a simplified model of the data), and the right matrix contains *coefficients*. The coefficients encode the importance of each regressor, and the goal of statistical model-fitting is to find the best coefficients such that the weighted combination of regressors matches the data. More on this in Chapter 14!

(4) The "row perspective" You guessed it—it's the same concept as the column perspective but you build up the product matrix one row at a time, and everything is done by taking weighted combinations of rows. Thus: each *row* in the product matrix is the weighted sum of all *rows* in the right matrix, where the weights are given by the elements in each *row* of the left matrix. Let's begin with the simple example:

$$\begin{bmatrix} 1 & 2 \\ 3 & 4 \end{bmatrix} \begin{bmatrix} a & b \\ c & d \end{bmatrix} = \begin{bmatrix} 1 \begin{bmatrix} a & b \end{bmatrix} + 2 \begin{bmatrix} c & d \end{bmatrix} \\ 3 \begin{bmatrix} a & b \end{bmatrix} + 4 \begin{bmatrix} c & d \end{bmatrix} \end{bmatrix} \qquad (6.3)$$

The top row of the product matrix is created by summing together the two rows of the right matrix, but each row is weighted according to the corresponding element of the top row of the left matrix. Same story for the second row. And of course, this would continue for however many rows are in the left matrix.

I won't repeat the other example multiplication I've been showing in previous pages; that's for you to do on your own with pencil and paper. (Hint: The result will be identical.)

The row perspective is useful, for example in principal components analysis, where the rows of the right matrix contain data (observations in rows and features in columns) and the rows of the left matrix contain weights for combining the features. Then the weighted sum of data creates the principal component scores.

Figure 6.5 (next page) visually summarizes the different perspectives.

Practice problems Multiply the following pairs of matrices four times, using each of four perspectives. Make sure you get the same result each time.

a) $\begin{bmatrix} 3 & 0 & 3 \\ 1 & 1 & 0 \end{bmatrix} \begin{bmatrix} 4 & 4 \\ 0 & 1 \\ 4 & 1 \end{bmatrix}$
b) $\begin{bmatrix} 1 & 2 & 3 \\ 4 & 5 & 6 \\ 7 & 8 & 9 \end{bmatrix} \begin{bmatrix} a & b & c \\ d & e & f \\ g & h & i \end{bmatrix}$

Answers

a) $\begin{bmatrix} 24 & 15 \\ 4 & 5 \end{bmatrix}$
b) $\begin{bmatrix} 1a + 2d + 3g & 1b + 2e + 3h & 1c + 2f + 3i \\ 4a + 5d + 6g & 4b + 5e + 6h & 4c + 5f + 6i \\ 7a + 8d + 9g & 7b + 8e + 9h & 7c + 8f + 9i \end{bmatrix}$

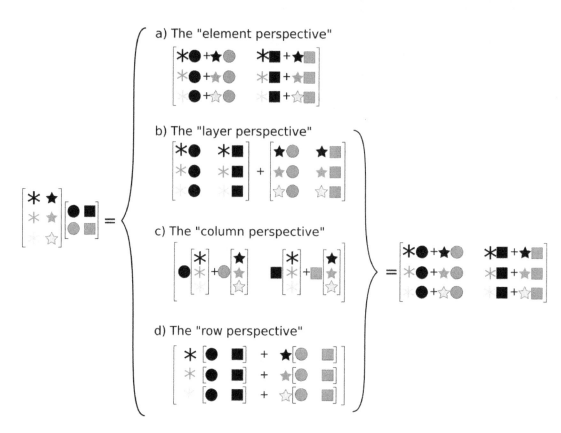

Figure 6.5: Visual representation of the four perspectives on matrix multiplication.

Practice problems Perform the following matrix multiplications. Use whichever perspective you find most confusing (that's the perspective you need to practice!).

a) $\begin{bmatrix} 3 & 4 & 0 \\ 0 & 4 & 1 \end{bmatrix} \begin{bmatrix} 2 & -1 & 2 \\ 4 & 0 & 0 \\ 0 & 1 & 1 \end{bmatrix}$

b) $\begin{bmatrix} 1 & 1 \\ 1 & 2 \end{bmatrix} \begin{bmatrix} 3 & 2 \\ 0 & 1 \end{bmatrix}$

Answers

a) $\begin{bmatrix} 22 & -3 & 6 \\ 16 & 1 & 1 \end{bmatrix}$

b) $\begin{bmatrix} 3 & 3 \\ 3 & 4 \end{bmatrix}$

Multiplication and equations

You know from your high-school algebra course that you are allowed to add and multiply terms to an equation, as long as you apply that operation to both sides. For example, I can multiply both sides of this equation by 7:

$$4 + x = 5(y + 3)$$

$$7(4 + x) = 7(5(y + 3))$$

$$7(4 + x) = (5(y + 3))7$$

Notice that the bottom two equations are the same: Because scalars obey the commutative law, the 7 can go on the left or the right of the parenthetic term.

However, because matrix multiplication is not commutative, you need to be mindful to put the matrices on the same side of the equation. For example, the following is OK:

$$\mathbf{B} = \lambda(\mathbf{C} + \mathbf{D})$$

$$\mathbf{AB} = \lambda\mathbf{A}(\mathbf{C} + \mathbf{D})$$

$$\mathbf{AB} = \mathbf{A}(\mathbf{C} + \mathbf{D})\lambda$$

Matrix sizes are not stated, so assume that the sizes make the operations valid.

The λ can be moved around because it is a scalar, but $\mathbf{A}$ must pre-multiply both sides (or post-multiply both sides, but it must be consistent on the left- and right-hand sides of the equation). In contrast to the above, the following progression of equations is **WRONG**.

$$\mathbf{B} = \lambda(\mathbf{C} + \mathbf{D})$$

$$\mathbf{AB} = \lambda(\mathbf{C} + \mathbf{D})\mathbf{A}$$

In other words, if you pre-multiply on one side of an equation, you must pre-multiply on the other side of the equation. Same goes for post-multiplication. If there are rectangular matrices in the equation, it is possible that pre- or post-multiplying isn't even valid.

Code The non-commutivity of matrix multiplication is easy to confirm in code. Compare matrices C1 and C2.

Code block 6.3: Python

```
1  A = np.random.randn(2,2)
2  B = np.random.randn(2,2)
3  C1 = A@B
4  C2 = B@A
```

Code block 6.4: MATLAB

```
1  A = randn(2,2);
2  B = randn(2,2);
3  C1 = A*B;
4  C2 = B*A;
```

6.3 Matrix multiplication with a diagonal matrix

There is a special property of multiplication when one matrix is a diagonal matrix and the other is a dense matrix:

- Pre-multiplication by a diagonal matrix scales the *rows* of the right matrix by the diagonal elements.
- Post-multiplication by a diagonal matrix scales the *columns* of the left matrix by the diagonal elements.

Let's see two examples of 3×3 matrices; notice how the diagonal elements appear in the rows (pre-multiply) or the columns (post-multiply). Also notice how the product matrix is the same as the dense matrix, but either the columns or the rows are scaled by each corresponding diagonal element of the diagonal matrix.

$$\begin{bmatrix} a & 0 & 0 \\ 0 & b & 0 \\ 0 & 0 & c \end{bmatrix} \begin{bmatrix} 1 & 2 & 3 \\ 4 & 5 & 6 \\ 7 & 8 & 9 \end{bmatrix} = \begin{bmatrix} 1a & 2a & 3a \\ 4b & 5b & 6b \\ 7c & 8c & 9c \end{bmatrix} \qquad (6.4)$$

$$\begin{bmatrix} 1 & 2 & 3 \\ 4 & 5 & 6 \\ 7 & 8 & 9 \end{bmatrix} \begin{bmatrix} a & 0 & 0 \\ 0 & b & 0 \\ 0 & 0 & c \end{bmatrix} = \begin{bmatrix} 1a & 2b & 3c \\ 4a & 5b & 6c \\ 7a & 8b & 9c \end{bmatrix} \qquad (6.5)$$

Of course, the mechanism of matrix multiplication is exactly the same as what you learned in the previous section. But all the zeros in the diagonal matrices allow us to simply things a bit.

It is worth remembering this property of diagonal matrix multiplication, because you will see applications of this in several subsequent chapters, including systems of equations (Chapter 10), diagonalization (Chapter 15), and singular-value decomposition (Chapter 16). I tried to come up with an easy mnemonic for remembering this rule. It is, admittedly, not such a great mnemonic, but you should take this as a challenge to come up with a better one.

Order of matrices for modulating rows vs. columns

PRe-multiply to affect Rows

POst-multiply to affect cOlumns.

Practice problems Perform the following matrix multiplications. Note the differences between **a** and **c**, and between **b** and **d**.

a) $\begin{bmatrix} 2 & 0 \\ 0 & 3 \end{bmatrix} \begin{bmatrix} 1 & 1 \\ 1 & 1 \end{bmatrix}$
b) $\begin{bmatrix} 5 & 0 \\ 0 & 6 \end{bmatrix} \begin{bmatrix} 4 & 3 \\ 3 & 4 \end{bmatrix}$
c) $\begin{bmatrix} 1 & 1 \\ 1 & 1 \end{bmatrix} \begin{bmatrix} 2 & 0 \\ 0 & 3 \end{bmatrix}$
d) $\begin{bmatrix} 4 & 3 \\ 3 & 4 \end{bmatrix} \begin{bmatrix} 5 & 0 \\ 0 & 6 \end{bmatrix}$

Answers

a) $\begin{bmatrix} 2 & 2 \\ 3 & 3 \end{bmatrix}$
b) $\begin{bmatrix} 20 & 15 \\ 18 & 24 \end{bmatrix}$
c) $\begin{bmatrix} 2 & 3 \\ 2 & 3 \end{bmatrix}$
d) $\begin{bmatrix} 20 & 18 \\ 15 & 24 \end{bmatrix}$

Multiplying two diagonal matrices The product of two diagonal matrices is another diagonal matrix whose diagonal elements are the products of the corresponding diagonal elements. That's a long sentence, but it's a simple concept. Here's an example:

$$
\begin{bmatrix} a & 0 & 0 \\ 0 & b & 0 \\ 0 & 0 & c \end{bmatrix} \begin{bmatrix} d & 0 & 0 \\ 0 & e & 0 \\ 0 & 0 & f \end{bmatrix} = \begin{bmatrix} ad & 0 & 0 \\ 0 & be & 0 \\ 0 & 0 & cf \end{bmatrix} \tag{6.6}
$$

Take a minute to work through the mechanics of matrix multiplication to convince yourself that this is the correct answer. And then you can just remember that multiplying two diagonal matrices is easy—in fact, for two diagonal matrices, standard matrix multiplication is the same as element-wise multiplication. That becomes relevant when learning about eigendecomposition!

6.4 LIVE EVIL! (a.k.a. order of operations)

Let's start with an example to highlight the problem that we need a solution for. Implement the following matrix multiplication and then transpose the result:

$$
\left(\begin{bmatrix} 2 & 4 \\ 1 & 2 \end{bmatrix} \begin{bmatrix} 0 & 1 \\ 1 & 1 \end{bmatrix} \right)^{\mathrm{T}} = \quad ?
$$

I assume you got the matrix $\begin{bmatrix} 4 & 2 \\ 6 & 3 \end{bmatrix}$. Now let's try it again, but this time transpose each matrix individually before multiplying them:

$$
\begin{bmatrix} 2 & 4 \\ 1 & 2 \end{bmatrix}^{\mathrm{T}} \begin{bmatrix} 0 & 1 \\ 1 & 1 \end{bmatrix}^{\mathrm{T}} = \quad ?
$$

Did you get the same matrix as above? Well, if you did the math correctly, then you will have gotten $\begin{bmatrix} 1 & 3 \\ 2 & 6 \end{bmatrix}$, which is the not the same as the previous result. It's not even the same result but transposed. In fact, it is an entirely different matrix.

OK, now let's try it one more time. But now, instead of applying the transpose operation to each individual matrix, *swap the order of the matrices.* Thus:

$$\begin{bmatrix} 0 & 1 \\ 1 & 1 \end{bmatrix}^{\mathrm{T}} \begin{bmatrix} 2 & 4 \\ 1 & 2 \end{bmatrix}^{\mathrm{T}} = \quad ?$$

And now you get the same result as the first multiplication: $\begin{bmatrix} 4 & 2 \\ 6 & 3 \end{bmatrix}$.

And this brings us to the main topic of this section: An operation applied to multiplied matrices gets applied to each matrix individually *but in reverse order.*

It's a weird rule, but that's just how it works. **"LIVE EVIL"** is a mnemonic that will help you remember this important rule. Notice that LIVE spelled backwards is EVIL. It's a palindrome.

n.b.: LIVE EVIL is *not* a recommendation for how to interact with society. Please be nice, considerate, and generous.

> **The LIVE EVIL rule: Reverse matrix order**
>
> $$(\mathbf{A} \dots \mathbf{B})^{\mathrm{T}} = \mathbf{B}^{\mathrm{T}} \dots \mathbf{A}^{\mathrm{T}} \tag{6.7}$$

Basically, an operation on multiplied matrices gets applied to each matrix in reverse order. Here's how it would look for four matrices:

$$(\mathbf{ABCD})^{\mathrm{T}} = \mathbf{D}^{\mathrm{T}}\mathbf{C}^{\mathrm{T}}\mathbf{B}^{\mathrm{T}}\mathbf{A}^{\mathrm{T}}$$

The LIVE EVIL rule applies to other operations as well, such as the matrix inverse. For example:

$$(\mathbf{ABC})^{-1} = \mathbf{C}^{-1}\mathbf{B}^{-1}\mathbf{A}^{-1}$$

LIVE EVIL is, admittedly, a strange and counter-intuitive rule. But it is important, so let's look at another example, which will also highlight why this rule needs to be the case. In the equations below, the top row implements matrix multiplication first, then transposes the result; while the second row first transposes each matrix in reverse order and then performs the matrix multiplication.

$$\left(\begin{bmatrix} a & b \\ c & d \end{bmatrix} \begin{bmatrix} e & f \\ g & h \end{bmatrix} \right)^{\mathrm{T}} = \begin{bmatrix} ae+bg & af+bh \\ ce+dg & cf+dh \end{bmatrix}^{\mathrm{T}} = \begin{bmatrix} ae+bg & ce+dg \\ af+bh & cf+dh \end{bmatrix}$$

$$= \begin{bmatrix} e & g \\ f & h \end{bmatrix} \begin{bmatrix} a & c \\ b & d \end{bmatrix} = \begin{bmatrix} ae+bg & ce+dg \\ af+bh & cf+dh \end{bmatrix}$$

For square matrices, ignoring the LIVE EVIL rule still gives a result (though incorrect). However, for rectangular matrices, multiplication would be impossible when ignoring the LIVE EVIL rule. This is illustrated in Figure 6.6.

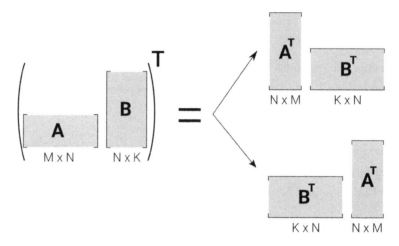

Figure 6.6: Example of the LIVE EVIL law for transposing matrix multiplication. Pay attention to the matrix sizes: Ignoring the LIVE EVIL rule and transposing without reversing leads to an invalid expression (top), whereas the multiplication remains valid when swapping matrix order (bottom).

Be careful with Equation 6.7—an operation may be valid on the product of matrices but invalid on the individual matrices. This comes up frequently in statistics and the singular value decomposition. For example, the expression $(\mathbf{X}^{\mathrm{T}}\mathbf{X})^{-1}$ may be valid whereas $\mathbf{X}^{-1}\mathbf{X}^{\mathrm{-T}}$ may be undefined. You'll see examples of this situation in later chapters. Fortunately, all matrices can be transposed, so for now you can always apply the LIVE EVIL rule without concern.

Practice problems Perform the following matrix multiplications. Compare with the problems and answers on page 148.

a) $\begin{bmatrix} 2 & -1 & 2 \\ 4 & 0 & 0 \\ 0 & 1 & 1 \end{bmatrix}^{\mathrm{T}} \begin{bmatrix} 3 & 4 & 0 \\ 0 & 4 & 1 \end{bmatrix}^{\mathrm{T}}$

b) $\begin{bmatrix} 3 & 2 \\ 0 & 1 \end{bmatrix}^{\mathrm{T}} \begin{bmatrix} 1 & 1 \\ 1 & 2 \end{bmatrix}^{\mathrm{T}}$

Answers

a) $\begin{bmatrix} 22 & 16 \\ -3 & 1 \\ 6 & 1 \end{bmatrix}$

b) $\begin{bmatrix} 3 & 3 \\ 3 & 4 \end{bmatrix}$

6.5 Matrix-vector multiplication

Matrix-vector multiplication is the same thing as normal matrix-matrix multiplication, where you think of the vector as an $M \times 1$ or as a $1 \times N$ matrix. The important feature of matrix-vector multiplication—which is obvious when you think about it but is worth mentioning explicitly—is that the result is always a vector. This is important because it provides the connection between linear transformations and matrices: To apply a transform to a vector, you convert that transform into a matrix, and then you multiply the vector by that matrix. Here are two examples of matrix-vector multiplication.

$$\mathbf{Ab} = \begin{bmatrix} 4 & 2 \\ 1 & 3 \end{bmatrix} \begin{bmatrix} 5 \\ 2 \end{bmatrix} = \begin{bmatrix} 4 \cdot 5 + 2 \cdot 2 \\ 1 \cdot 5 + 3 \cdot 2 \end{bmatrix} = \begin{bmatrix} 24 \\ 11 \end{bmatrix}$$

$$\mathbf{b}^{\mathrm{T}}\mathbf{A} = \begin{bmatrix} 5 & 2 \end{bmatrix} \begin{bmatrix} 4 & 2 \\ 1 & 3 \end{bmatrix} = \begin{bmatrix} 4 \cdot 5 + 1 \cdot 2 & 5 \cdot 2 + 2 \cdot 3 \end{bmatrix} = \begin{bmatrix} 24 & 16 \end{bmatrix}$$

Three observations here:

1. $\mathbf{bA}$ is not defined (assuming $\mathbf{b}$ is a column vector)
2. If $\mathbf{A}$ is rectangular, then either $\mathbf{b}^{\mathrm{T}}\mathbf{A}$ or $\mathbf{Ab}$ is undefined (depending on the sizes, but they can't both be valid)
3. $\mathbf{Ab} \neq \mathbf{b}^{\mathrm{T}}\mathbf{A}$ even when both are valid operations

There is an interesting exception to this third observation, which is that if the matrix is symmetric, then pre-multiplying the vector is the same as post-multiplying the transpose of the vector. (Technically, the results are not *literally the same*, because one result is a column vector while the other is a row vector, but the elements of those vectors are identical.)

> **Symmetric matrix times a vector**
>
> $$if \ \mathbf{A} = \mathbf{A}^{\mathrm{T}} \ then \ \mathbf{Ab} = (\mathbf{b}^{\mathrm{T}}\mathbf{A})^{\mathrm{T}} \qquad (6.8)$$

Let's work through a proof of this claim. The proof works by transposing $\mathbf{Ab}$ and doing a bit of algebra (including applying the LIVE

EVIL rule!) to simplify and re-arrange.

$$(\mathbf{Ab})^{\mathrm{T}} = \mathbf{b}^{\mathrm{T}}\mathbf{A}^{\mathrm{T}} = \mathbf{b}^{\mathrm{T}}\mathbf{A}$$

Notice that our proof here involved transposing, expanding, and simplifying. This strategy underlies many linear algebra proofs.

The proof works because $\mathbf{A} = \mathbf{A}^{\mathrm{T}}$. If the matrix weren't symmetric, then $\mathbf{A} \neq \mathbf{A}^{\mathrm{T}}$, in other words, $\mathbf{A}$ and $\mathbf{A}^{\mathrm{T}}$ would be different matrices. And of course, $\mathbf{b}$ and $\mathbf{b}^{\mathrm{T}}$ are the same except for orientation.

Let's look at an example.

$$\mathbf{Ab} = \begin{bmatrix} a & b \\ b & c \end{bmatrix} \begin{bmatrix} d \\ e \end{bmatrix} = \begin{bmatrix} ad + be \\ bd + ce \end{bmatrix}$$

$$\mathbf{b}^{\mathrm{T}}\mathbf{A} = \begin{bmatrix} d & e \end{bmatrix} \begin{bmatrix} a & b \\ b & c \end{bmatrix} = \begin{bmatrix} ad + be & bd + ce \end{bmatrix}$$

Notice, as mentioned above, that the two results are not *identical vectors* because one is a column and the other is a row. However, they have *identical elements* in a different orientation.

Now watch what happens when matrix $\mathbf{A}$ is non-symmetric. In the matrices below, assume $b \neq f$.

$$\mathbf{Ab} = \begin{bmatrix} a & b \\ f & c \end{bmatrix} \begin{bmatrix} d \\ e \end{bmatrix} = \begin{bmatrix} ad + be \\ fd + ce \end{bmatrix}$$

$$\mathbf{b}^{\mathrm{T}}\mathbf{A} = \begin{bmatrix} d & e \end{bmatrix} \begin{bmatrix} a & b \\ f & c \end{bmatrix} = \begin{bmatrix} ad + fe & bd + ce \end{bmatrix}$$

Practice problems Perform the following matrix multiplications.

a) $\begin{bmatrix} 4 & 3 & 0 \\ 1 & 1 & 9 \\ 0 & 3 & 0 \\ 1 & 1 & 1 \end{bmatrix} \begin{bmatrix} 0 \\ 7 \\ 1 \end{bmatrix}$

b) $\begin{bmatrix} 4 & 0 & 2 & 0 & 8 & 0 \\ 0 & 3 & 0 & 5 & 0 & 1 \end{bmatrix} \begin{bmatrix} 4 \\ 6 \\ 1 \\ 2 \\ 1 \\ 6 \end{bmatrix}$

Answers

a) $\begin{bmatrix} 21 \\ 16 \\ 21 \\ 8 \end{bmatrix}$

b) $\begin{bmatrix} 26 \\ 34 \end{bmatrix}$

6.6 Creating symmetric matrices

In the previous chapter, I claimed that all hope is not lost for non-symmetric matrices who aspire to the glorious status of their symmetric conspecifics, upon whom so many luxuries of linear algebra are bestowed. How can a non-symmetric matrix become a symmetric matrix?

There are two methods: Additive and multiplicative. The additive method is not widely used in practical applications (to my knowledge), but it is worth learning. The additive method to create a symmetric matrix from a non-symmetric matrix is to add the matrix to its transpose. This method is valid only for square matrices.

$$\mathbf{C} = \frac{1}{2}(\mathbf{A}^{\mathrm{T}} + \mathbf{A}) \tag{6.9}$$

An example will illustrate why Equation 6.9 works. Notice that the diagonal elements are doubled, which is why dividing by 2 is an appropriate normalization factor. (In the matrices below, assume that $b \neq d$, $c \neq h$, and $f \neq i$.)

$$\begin{bmatrix} a & b & c \\ d & e & f \\ h & i & j \end{bmatrix} + \begin{bmatrix} a & d & h \\ b & e & i \\ c & f & j \end{bmatrix} = \begin{bmatrix} a+a & b+d & c+h \\ b+d & e+e & f+i \\ c+h & f+i & j+j \end{bmatrix} \tag{6.10}$$

This is just one example of a 3×3 matrix. What if this is some quirk of this particular matrix? How do we know that this method will always work? This is an important question, because there are several special properties of 2×2 or 3×3 matrices that do not generalize to larger matrices.

The proof that Equation 6.9 will always produce a symmetric matrix from a non-symmetric square matrix comes from the definition of symmetric matrices ($\mathbf{C} = \mathbf{C}^{\mathrm{T}}$). Therefore, the proof works by transposing both sides of Equation 6.9, doing a bit of algebra to simplify, and seeing what happens (I'm omitting the scalar division by 2 because that doesn't affect symmetry).

The matrices are summed, not multiplied, so the LIVE EVIL rule does not apply.

$$\mathbf{C} = \mathbf{A}^{\mathrm{T}} + \mathbf{A} \qquad (6.11)$$

$$\mathbf{C}^{\mathrm{T}} = (\mathbf{A}^{\mathrm{T}} + \mathbf{A})^{\mathrm{T}} \qquad (6.12)$$

$$\mathbf{C}^{\mathrm{T}} = \mathbf{A}^{\mathrm{TT}} + \mathbf{A}^{\mathrm{T}} \qquad (6.13)$$

$$\mathbf{C}^{\mathrm{T}} = \mathbf{A} + \mathbf{A}^{\mathrm{T}} \qquad (6.14)$$

Because matrix addition is commutative, $\mathbf{A} + \mathbf{A}^{\mathrm{T}} = \mathbf{A}^{\mathrm{T}} + \mathbf{A}$. The right-hand side of Equation 6.14 is the same as the right-hand side of Equation 6.11. And if the right-hand sides of the equations are equal, then the left-hand sides must also be equal. This proves that $\mathbf{C} = \mathbf{C}^{\mathrm{T}}$, which is the definition of a symmetric matrix. This proof does not depend on the size of the matrix, which shows that our example above was not a fluke.

Practice problems Create symmetric matrices from the following matrices using the additive method.

a) $\begin{bmatrix} 1 & 11 & 1 \\ -5 & -2 & 1 \\ -1 & -5 & 2 \end{bmatrix}$

b) $\begin{bmatrix} -3 & 0 & -2 & -2 \\ -1 & -3 & -2 & -6 \\ -4 & -8 & -7 & 4 \\ 6 & -2 & 5 & 4 \end{bmatrix}$

Answers

a) $\begin{bmatrix} 1 & 3 & 0 \\ 3 & -2 & -2 \\ 0 & -2 & 2 \end{bmatrix}$

b) $\begin{bmatrix} -3 & -\frac{1}{2} & -3 & 2 \\ -\frac{1}{2} & -3 & -5 & -4 \\ -3 & -5 & -7 & \frac{9}{2} \\ 2 & -4 & \frac{9}{2} & 4 \end{bmatrix}$

The multiplicative method This involves multiplying a matrix by its transpose. In fact, this is the $\mathbf{A}^{\mathrm{T}}\mathbf{A}$ matrix that you learned about in the previous chapter.

I claimed in the previous chapter that $\mathbf{A}^{\mathrm{T}}\mathbf{A}$ is guaranteed to be symmetric (and therefore also square), even if $\mathbf{A}$ is non-symmetric— and even if $\mathbf{A}$ is non-square. Now that you know about matrix multiplication and about the LIVE EVIL rule, you are able to prove these two important claims.

First we prove that $\mathbf{A}^\mathrm{T}\mathbf{A}$ is a square matrix. Let's say that $\mathbf{A}$ is size $M \times N$ (assume $M \neq N$). First note that $\mathbf{A}\mathbf{A}$ is not a valid multiplication. Now consider that $\mathbf{A}^\mathrm{T}\mathbf{A}$ means $(M \times N) \times (N \times M)$. The "inner" dimensions (N) match, and the result will be $M \times M$. So there you go: we just proved that $\mathbf{A}^\mathrm{T}\mathbf{A}$ is a square matrix.

Now let's prove that $\mathbf{A}^\mathrm{T}\mathbf{A}$ is symmetric. The proof follows the same strategy that we applied for the additive method: transpose $\mathbf{A}^\mathrm{T}\mathbf{A}$, do a bit of algebra, and see what happens.

$$(\mathbf{A}^\mathrm{T}\mathbf{A})^\mathrm{T} = \mathbf{A}^\mathrm{T}\mathbf{A}^\mathrm{TT} = \mathbf{A}^\mathrm{T}\mathbf{A} \tag{6.15}$$

We transposed the matrix, applied the LIVE EVIL rule (and the property that a double-transpose leaves the matrix unchanged), and got back to the original matrix. A matrix that equals its transpose is the definition of a symmetric matrix.

Are these two features unique to $\mathbf{A}^\mathrm{T}\mathbf{A}$? What about $\mathbf{A}\mathbf{A}^\mathrm{T}$—is that also square and symmetric? The answer is Yes, but I want you to get a piece of paper and prove it to yourself.

Reflection

$$\left[\begin{array}{l} \text{In practical applications, particularly in data analysis,} \\ \mathbf{A}^\mathrm{T}\mathbf{A} \text{ appears as often as } \mathbf{A}\mathbf{A}^\mathrm{T}. \text{ The correct form de-} \\ \text{pends on how the data are stored (e.g., observations} \times \\ \text{features vs. features} \times \text{observations), which usually de-} \\ \text{pends on coding preferences or software format. In the} \\ \text{written medium, I prefer } \mathbf{A}^\mathrm{T}\mathbf{A} \text{ because of the aesthetic} \\ \text{symmetry of having the } ^\mathrm{T} \text{ in the middle.} \end{array} \right]$$

Practice problems Create two symmetric matrices from each of the following matrices, using the multiplicative method ($\mathbf{A}^\mathrm{T}\mathbf{A}$ and $\mathbf{A}\mathbf{A}^\mathrm{T}$).

a) $\begin{bmatrix} 3 & 0 & 3 \\ 0 & 7 & 0 \end{bmatrix}$

b) $\begin{bmatrix} 1 & 6 \\ 6 & 1 \end{bmatrix}$

Answers

a) $\mathbf{A}^\mathrm{T}\mathbf{A} = \begin{bmatrix} 9 & 0 & 9 \\ 0 & 49 & 0 \\ 9 & 0 & 9 \end{bmatrix}$, $\mathbf{A}\mathbf{A}^\mathrm{T} = \begin{bmatrix} 18 & 0 \\ 0 & 49 \end{bmatrix}$

b) $\mathbf{A}^\mathrm{T}\mathbf{A} = \begin{bmatrix} 37 & 12 \\ 12 & 37 \end{bmatrix}$, $\mathbf{A}\mathbf{A}^\mathrm{T} = \begin{bmatrix} 37 & 12 \\ 12 & 37 \end{bmatrix}$

6.7 Multiplication of two symmetric matrices

If you multiply two symmetric matrices, will the product matrix also be symmetric? Let's try an example to find out:

$$\begin{bmatrix} a & b \\ b & c \end{bmatrix} \begin{bmatrix} d & e \\ e & f \end{bmatrix} = \begin{bmatrix} ad + be & ae + bf \\ bd + ce & be + cf \end{bmatrix} \qquad (6.16)$$

Is the result symmetric? On its face, it seems like it isn't. However, this equation reveals an interesting condition on the symmetry of the result of multiplying two 2×2 symmetric matrices: If $a = c$ and $d = f$ (in other words, the matrix has a constant diagonal), then the product of two symmetric matrices is itself symmetric. Observe and be amazed!

$$\begin{bmatrix} a & b \\ b & a \end{bmatrix} \begin{bmatrix} d & e \\ e & d \end{bmatrix} = \begin{bmatrix} ad + be & ae + bd \\ bd + ae & be + ad \end{bmatrix} \qquad (6.17)$$

Is this a general rule that applies to symmetric matrices of any size? Let's repeat with 3×3 matrices, using the constant-diagonal idea.

$$\begin{bmatrix} a & b & c \\ b & a & d \\ c & d & a \end{bmatrix} \begin{bmatrix} e & f & g \\ f & e & h \\ g & h & e \end{bmatrix} = \begin{bmatrix} ae + bf + cg & af + be + ch & ag + bh + ce \\ be + af + dg & bf + ae + dh & bg + ah + de \\ ce + df + ag & cf + de + ah & cg + dh + ae \end{bmatrix}$$

A quick glance reveals the lack of symmetry. For example, compare the element in position $2,1$ with that in position $1,2$. I won't write out the product of two 4×4 symmetric matrices (if you want to try it, go for it), but you can take my word for it: the resulting product matrix will not be symmetric.

The lesson here is that, in general, *the product of two symmetric matrices is not a symmetric matrix*. There are exceptions to this rule, like the 2×2 case with constant diagonals, or if one of the matrices is the identity or zeros matrix.

Is this a surprising result? Refer back to the discussion at the end of the "element perspective" of matrix multiplication (page 144) concerning how the upper-triangle vs. the lower-triangle of the product matrix is formed from earlier vs. later rows of the left matrix. Different parts of the two multiplying matrices meet in the lower triangle vs. the upper triangle of the product matrix.

You can also see that the product matrix is not symmetric by trying to prove that it *is* symmetric (the proof fails, which is called proof-by-contradition). Assume that **A** and **B** below are both symmetric matrices.

$$(\mathbf{AB})^{\mathrm{T}} = \mathbf{B}^{\mathrm{T}}\mathbf{A}^{\mathrm{T}} = \mathbf{BA} \neq \mathbf{AB} \qquad (6.18)$$

To be sure, Equation 6.18 is a perfectly valid equation, and all of the individual multiplications are valid. However, matrix multiplication is not commutative, which is why we had to put a $\neq$ sign at the end of the equation. Thus, we cannot assume that $\mathbf{AB} = (\mathbf{AB})^{\mathrm{T}}$, therefore, the multiplication of two symmetric matrices is, in general, not a symmetric matrix.

$$\begin{bmatrix} \text{This may seem like a uselessly academic factoid, but it} \\ \text{leads to one of the biggest limitations of principal compo-} \\ \text{nents analysis, and one of the most important advantages} \\ \text{of generalized eigendecomposition, which is the computa-} \\ \text{tional backbone of many machine-learning methods, most} \\ \text{prominently linear classifiers and discriminant analyses.} \end{bmatrix}$$

Reflection

6.8 Element-wise (Hadamard) multiplication

Before having had any exposure to matrix multiplication (in this chapter or elsewhere), Hadamard multiplication is probably what you would have answered if someone asked you to guess what it means to multiply two matrices.

Hadamard multiplication involves multiplying each element of one matrix by the corresponding element in the other matrix. You have already learned about Hadamard multiplication in Chapter 3;

the concept and notation is the same for matrices as for vectors. Thus:

$$\mathbf{C} = \mathbf{A} \odot \mathbf{B} \tag{6.19}$$

The formal definition of Hadamard multiplication is

> **Hadamard (element-wise) multiplication**
>
> $$c_{i,j} = a_{i,j} \times b_{i,j} \tag{6.20}$$

You might have already guessed that Hadamard multiplication is valid only for two matrices that are both $M \times N$, and the product matrix is also size $M \times N$.

One example will suffice for understanding.

$$\begin{bmatrix} 0 & 1 & 2 \\ -1 & 6 & 3 \end{bmatrix} \odot \begin{bmatrix} 3 & 8 & 5 \\ 4 & 1 & -5 \end{bmatrix} = \begin{bmatrix} 0 & 8 & 10 \\ -4 & 6 & -15 \end{bmatrix} \tag{6.21}$$

Because Hadamard multiplication is implemented element-wise, it obeys the commutative law just like individual numbers (scalars). That is,

$$\mathbf{A} \odot \mathbf{B} = \mathbf{B} \odot \mathbf{A}$$

There is also element-wise division, which is the same principle but for division. This operation is valid only when the divisor matrix contains all non-zero elements.

$\oslash$ indicates element-wise division.

$$\begin{bmatrix} 0 & 1 & 2 \\ -1 & 6 & 3 \end{bmatrix} \oslash \begin{bmatrix} 3 & 8 & 5 \\ 4 & 1 & -5 \end{bmatrix} = \begin{bmatrix} 0/3 & 1/8 & 2/5 \\ -1/4 & 6/1 & -3/5 \end{bmatrix}$$

One can debate whether Hadamard multiplication and division are really *matrix* operations; arguably, they are simply scalar multiplication or division, implemented *en masse* using compact notation. Indeed, element-wise matrix multiplication in computer applications facilitates convenient and efficient coding (e.g., to avoid using for-loops), as opposed to utilizing some special mathematical properties of Hadamard multiplication. That said, Hadamard multiplication does have applications in linear algebra. For example, it is key to one of the algorithms for computing the matrix inverse.

Code Here is another case where matrix multiplication is confusingly different between MATLAB and Python. In MATLAB, `A*B` indicates standard matrix multiplication and `A.*B` indicates Hadamard multiplication (note the *dot-star*). In Python, `A@B` gives standard matrix multiplication and `A*B` gives Hadamard multiplication.

Code block 6.5: Python

```
1  M1 = np.random.randn(4,3)
2  M2 = np.random.randn(4,3)
3  C = M1 * M2
```

Code block 6.6: MATLAB

```
1  M1 = randn(4,3);
2  M2 = randn(4,3);
3  C = M1 .* M2
```

Practice problems Hadamard-multiply the following pairs of matrices.

a) $\begin{bmatrix} -4 & -3 & -9 \\ -5 & -2 & 3 \\ 0 & -7 & 7 \end{bmatrix}, \begin{bmatrix} -1 & 4 & -3 \\ -3 & -4 & 2 \\ 3 & 2 & 5 \end{bmatrix}$ b) $\begin{bmatrix} -4 & -5 & -16 \\ -4 & -1 & 2 \\ 7 & 1 & 5 \end{bmatrix}, \begin{bmatrix} -3 & 6 & -10 & 0 \\ -4 & 9 & -6 & 4 \\ 1 & 2 & -6 & 0 \end{bmatrix}$

Answers

a) $\begin{bmatrix} 4 & -12 & 27 \\ 15 & 8 & 6 \\ 0 & -14 & 35 \end{bmatrix}$ b) Undefined!

6.9 Frobenius dot product

The Frobenius dot product, also called the Frobenius inner product, is an operation that produces a scalar (a single number) given two matrices of the same size ($M \times N$).

To compute the Frobenius dot product, you first *vectorize* the two matrices and then compute their dot product as you would for regular vectors.

Vectorizing a matrix means concatenating all of the columns in a matrix to produce a single column vector. It is a function that maps a matrix in $\mathbb{R}^{M \times N}$ to a vector in $\mathbb{R}^{MN}$.

Vectorizing a matrix

$$\mathbf{v}_n = a_{i,j}\,,\text{such that}$$

$$\mathbf{v} = [a_{1,1}, \ldots, a_{m,1}, a_{1,2}, \ldots, a_{m,2}, \ldots, a_{m,n}] \qquad (6.22)$$

Here is an example of a matrix and the result of vectorizing it.

$$vec\left(\begin{bmatrix} a & c & e \\ b & d & f \end{bmatrix}\right) = \begin{bmatrix} a \\ b \\ c \\ d \\ e \\ f \end{bmatrix}$$

As with many other operations you've learned about so far, there is some arbitrariness in vectorization: Why not concatenate across the rows instead of down the columns? It could go either way, but following a common convention facilitates comprehension.

Code Note that Python defaults to row-based vectorization, which can be changed by specifying to use Fortran convention.

Code block 6.7: Python

```
1  A = np.array([ [1,2,3],[4,5,6] ])
2  A.flatten(order='F')
```

Code block 6.8: MATLAB

```
1  A = [ 1,2,3; 4,5,6 ];
2  A(:)
```

Anyway, with that tangent out of the way, we can now compute the Frobenius dot product. Here is an example:

$$\langle \mathbf{A}, \mathbf{B} \rangle_F = \left\langle \begin{bmatrix} 1 & 5 & 0 \\ -4 & 0 & 2 \end{bmatrix}, \begin{bmatrix} 4 & -1 & 3 \\ 2 & 6 & 7 \end{bmatrix} \right\rangle_F = 5$$

Note the notation for the Frobenius dot product: $\langle \mathbf{A}, \mathbf{B} \rangle_F$

A curious yet useful way to compute the Frobenius dot product between matrices $\mathbf{A}$ and $\mathbf{B}$ is by taking the trace of $\mathbf{A}^T\mathbf{B}$. Therefore, the Frobenius dot product can also be written as follows.

Frobenius dot product as the trace of $\mathbf{A}^T\mathbf{B}$

$$\langle \mathbf{A}, \mathbf{B} \rangle_F = tr(\mathbf{A}^T\mathbf{B}) \tag{6.23}$$

I've omitted the matrix sizes in this equation, but you can tell from inspection that the operation is valid if both matrices are size $M \times N$, because the trace is defined only on square matrices.

The reason why Equation 6.23 is valid can be seen by working through a few examples, which you will have the opportunity to do in the exercises.

The Frobenius dot product has several uses in signal processing and machine learning, for example as a measure of "distance," or similarity, between two matrices.

The Frobenius inner product of a matrix with itself is the sum of all squared elements, and is called the *squared Frobenius norm* or *squared Euclidean norm* of the matrix. More on this in the next section.

Code The code below shows the trace-transpose trick for computing the Frobenius dot product.

Code block 6.9: Python

```
1  A = np.random.randn(4,3)
2  B = np.random.randn(4,3)
3  f = np.trace(A.T@B)
```

```
1  A = randn(4,3);
2  B = randn(4,3);
3  f = trace(A'*B);
```

Practice problems Compute the Frobenius dot product between the following pairs of matrices.

a) $\begin{bmatrix} 4 & 2 \\ 3 & 2 \\ -5 & -1 \end{bmatrix}, \begin{bmatrix} 7 & -2 \\ -7 & -8 \\ -1 & 8 \end{bmatrix}$

b) $\begin{bmatrix} 6 & 1 & 2 \\ 3 & 3 & -2 \end{bmatrix}, \begin{bmatrix} 4 & -11 & 1 \\ 6 & 1 & -2 \end{bmatrix}$

Answers

a) -16

b) 40

6.10 Matrix norms

In section 3.9 you learned that the square root of the dot product of a vector with itself is the magnitude or length of the vector, which is also called the norm of the vector.

Annoyingly, the norm of a matrix is more complicated, just like everything gets more complicated when you move from vectors to matrices. Part of the complication with matrix norms is that there are many of them! They all have some things in common, for example, all matrix norms are a single number that somehow corresponds to the "magnitude" of the matrix, but different norms correspond to different interpretations of "magnitude." In this section, you will learn a few of the common matrix norms, and we'll continue the discussion of matrix norms in Chapter 16 in the context of the singular value decomposition.

Let's start with the Frobenius norm, because it's fresh in your mind from the previous section. The equation below is an alternative way to express the Frobenius norm.

Frobenius matrix norm

$$\|\mathbf{A}\|_F = \sqrt{\sum_{i=1}^{m}\sum_{j=1}^{n}(a_{i,j})^2} \qquad (6.24)$$

Now you know three ways to compute the Frobenius norm: (1) directly implementing Equation 6.24, (2) vectorizing the matrix and computing the dot product with itself, (3) computing $tr(\mathbf{A}^T\mathbf{A})$.

If we think of a matrix space as Euclidean, then the Frobenius norm of the subtraction of two matrices provides a measure of Euclidean distance between those matrices. The right-hand side of the formula below should look familiar from computing Euclidean distance between two points.

Euclidean distance between two matrices

$$\|\mathbf{A} - \mathbf{B}\|_F = \sqrt{\sum_{i,j}(a_{i,j} - b_{i,j})^2} \qquad (6.25)$$

Of course, this formula is valid only for two matrices that have the same size.

The Frobenius norm is also called the $\ell2$ norm (the ℓ character is just a fancy-looking l, or a lower-case cursive L). There is also an $\ell1$ matrix norm. To compute the $\ell1$ norm, you sum the absolute values of all individual elements in each column, then take the largest maximum column sum.

There are many other matrix norms with varied formulas. Different applications use different norms to satisfy different criteria or to minimize different features of the matrix. Rather than overwhelm you with an exhaustive list, I will provide one general formula for the *matrix p-norm*; you can see that for $p = 2$, the following formula is equal to the Frobenius norm.

$$\|\mathbf{A}\|_p = \left(\sum_{i=1}^{M}\sum_{j=1}^{N}|a_{ij}|^p\right)^{1/p} \qquad (6.26)$$

Cauchy-Schwarz inequality In Chapter 3 you learned about the Cauchy-Schwarz inequality (the magnitude of the dot product between two vectors is no larger than the product of the norms of the two vectors). There is a comparable inequality for the Frobenius norm of a matrix-vector multiplication:

$$\|\mathbf{A}\mathbf{v}\| \leq \|\mathbf{A}\|_F \|\mathbf{v}\| \tag{6.27}$$

The proof for this inequality comes from integrating (1) the row perspective of multiplication, (2) the Cauchy-Schwarz inequality for the vector dot product introduced in Chapter 3, and (3) linearity of the Frobenius norm across the rows (that is, the Frobenius norm of a matrix equals the sum of the Frobenius norms of the rows; this comes from the summation in Equation 6.24).

Let's start by re-writing the norm of the matrix-vector multiplication as the sum of vector norms coming from the dot products of each row of $\mathbf{A}$ with $\mathbf{v}$ (m is the number of rows and $\mathbf{a}_i$ is the ith row of $\mathbf{A}$).

$$\|\mathbf{A}\mathbf{v}\| = |\mathbf{a}_1^T\mathbf{v}| + ... + |\mathbf{a}_n^T\mathbf{v}| = \sum_{i=1}^{m} |\mathbf{a}_i^T\mathbf{v}| \tag{6.28}$$

The dot-product Cauchy-Schwarz inequality allows us to write the following.

$$\sum_{i=1}^{m} |\mathbf{a}_i^T\mathbf{v}| \leq \sum_{i=1}^{m} \|\mathbf{a}_i\|\|\mathbf{v}\| \tag{6.29}$$

Finally, we re-sum the norms of the rows back to the norm of the matrix. And that brings us back to our original conclusion in Equation 6.27: The norm of a matrix-vector product is less than or equal to the product of the Frobenius norms of the matrix and the vector.

Code Different matrix norms can be obtained by specifying different inputs into the **norm** functions. The code below shows Frobenius norm.

Code block 6.11: Python

```python
1  A = np.random.randn(4,3)
2  np.linalg.norm(A, 'fro')
```

$$\text{Code block 6.12: MATLAB}$$

```
1  A = randn(4,3);
2  norm(A,'fro')
```

Practice problems Compute Euclidean distance between the following pairs of matrices (note: compare with the exercises on page 166).

a)
$$\begin{bmatrix} 4 & 2 \\ 3 & 2 \\ -5 & -1 \end{bmatrix}, \begin{bmatrix} 7 & -2 \\ -7 & -8 \\ -1 & 8 \end{bmatrix}$$

b)
$$\begin{bmatrix} 6 & 1 & 2 \\ 3 & 3 & -2 \end{bmatrix}, \begin{bmatrix} 4 & -11 & 1 \\ 6 & 1 & -2 \end{bmatrix}$$

Answers

a) $\sqrt{322} \approx 17.94$

b) $\sqrt{162} \approx 12.73$

6.11 WHAT ABOUT MATRIX DIVISION?

6.11 What about matrix division?

All this fuss about matrix multiplications... what about division? You did learn about element-wise matrix division in section 6.8, but that's not really *matrix* division; that's a compact notation for describing lots of scalar divisions. When you hear "matrix division" you're probably thinking about something like this:

$$\frac{\mathbf{A}}{\mathbf{B}}$$

This would be the equivalent of a scalar division like $\frac{2}{3}$. Well, that doesn't exist for matrices; it is not possible to *divide* one matrix by another. However, there is a conceptually comparable operation, and it is based on the idea of re-writing scalar division like this:

$$\frac{2}{3} = 2 \times 3^{-1}$$

The matrix version of this is $\mathbf{AB}^{-1}$. The matrix $\mathbf{B}^{-1}$ is called the *matrix inverse*. It is such an important topic that it merits its own chapter (Chapter 12). For now, I'll leave you with two important facts about the matrix inverse.

1. The matrix inverse is the matrix such that $\mathbf{AA}^{-1} = \mathbf{I}$
2. Not all matrices have an inverse. A matrix has a full inverse only if it is square and full-rank.

169

Exercises

1. Determine whether each of the following operations is valid, and, if so, the size of the resulting matrix.

$$\mathbf{A} \in \mathbb{R}^{2\times 3}, \quad \mathbf{B} \in \mathbb{R}^{3\times 3}, \quad \mathbf{C} \in \mathbb{R}^{3\times 4}$$

a) $\mathbf{CB}$

b) $\mathbf{C}^{\mathsf{T}}\mathbf{B}$

c) $(\mathbf{CB})^{\mathsf{T}}$

d) $\mathbf{C}^{\mathsf{T}}\mathbf{BC}$

e) $\mathbf{ABCB}$

f) $\mathbf{ABC}$

g) $\mathbf{C}^{\mathsf{T}}\mathbf{BA}^{\mathsf{T}}\mathbf{AC}$

h) $\mathbf{B}^{\mathsf{T}}\mathbf{BCC}^{\mathsf{T}}\mathbf{A}$

i) $\mathbf{AA}^{\mathsf{T}}$

j) $\mathbf{A}^{\mathsf{T}}\mathbf{A}$

k) $\mathbf{BBA}^{\mathsf{T}}\mathbf{ABBCC}$

l) $(\mathbf{CBB}^{\mathsf{T}}\mathbf{CC}^{\mathsf{T}})^{\mathsf{T}}$

m) $(\mathbf{A} + \mathbf{ACC}^{\mathsf{T}}\mathbf{B})^{\mathsf{T}}\mathbf{A}$

n) $\mathbf{C} + \mathbf{CA}^{\mathsf{T}}\mathbf{ABC}$

o) $\mathbf{C} + \mathbf{BA}^{\mathsf{T}}\mathbf{ABC}$

p) $\mathbf{B} + 3\mathbf{B} + \mathbf{A}^{\mathsf{T}}\mathbf{A} - \mathbf{CC}^{\mathsf{T}}$

q) $\mathbf{A} \odot (\mathbf{ABC})$

r) $\mathbf{A} \odot \mathbf{ABC}(\mathbf{BC})^{\mathsf{T}}$

2. Compute the following matrix multiplications. Each problem should be completed twice using the two indicated perspectives of matrix multiplication (#1: element, #2: layer, #3: column, #4: row).

a) #1,2: $\begin{bmatrix} 1 & 0 \\ 3 & 1 \end{bmatrix}\begin{bmatrix} 0 & 5 \\ 2 & 2 \end{bmatrix}$

b) #2,4: $\begin{bmatrix} -3 & 2 \\ -2 & 3 \end{bmatrix}\begin{bmatrix} 1 & 0 \\ 0 & 2 \end{bmatrix}$

c) #3,4: $\begin{bmatrix} 11 & -5 \\ 9 & -13 \end{bmatrix}\begin{bmatrix} 3 & 1 \\ -8 & .5 \end{bmatrix}$

d) #1,4: $\begin{bmatrix} 1 & 0 \\ 0 & 2 \end{bmatrix}\begin{bmatrix} a & b \\ c & d \end{bmatrix}$

e) #2,3: $\begin{bmatrix} 2 & 2 \\ 1 & 3 \end{bmatrix}\begin{bmatrix} 10 & 1 \\ -5 & 4 \end{bmatrix}$

f) #1,3: $\begin{bmatrix} a & 0 \\ b & 0 \end{bmatrix}\begin{bmatrix} 2 & 3 \\ 4 & 1 \end{bmatrix}$

g) #2,3: $\begin{bmatrix} a & b \\ 0 & 0 \end{bmatrix} \begin{bmatrix} 2 & 3 \\ 4 & 1 \end{bmatrix}$

h) #1,2: $\begin{bmatrix} 1 & 0 & 4 \\ 0 & 1 & 1 \\ 3 & 3 & 0 \end{bmatrix} \begin{bmatrix} -2 & -3 & -1 \\ -1 & -9 & 3 \\ 0 & 1 & 5 \end{bmatrix}$

i) #2,3: $\begin{bmatrix} a & 0 & 1 \\ 0 & b & 0 \\ 1 & 0 & c \end{bmatrix} \begin{bmatrix} a & b & c \\ 1 & 2 & 3 \\ 0 & 0 & 1 \end{bmatrix}$

3. Compute the following matrix-vector products, if the operation is valid.

a) $\begin{bmatrix} 2 & 0 \\ 0 & 3 \end{bmatrix} \begin{bmatrix} 2 \\ 3 \end{bmatrix}$

b) $\begin{bmatrix} 2 \\ 3 \end{bmatrix}^{\mathrm{T}} \begin{bmatrix} 2 & 0 \\ 0 & 3 \end{bmatrix}$

c) $\begin{bmatrix} 2 & 1 \\ 2 & 3 \end{bmatrix} \begin{bmatrix} 2 \\ 3 \end{bmatrix}$

d) $\begin{bmatrix} 2 \\ 3 \end{bmatrix}^{\mathrm{T}} \begin{bmatrix} 2 & 1 \\ 2 & 3 \end{bmatrix}$

e) $\begin{bmatrix} 0 & 1 & 0 \\ 0 & 0 & 1 \\ 1 & 0 & 0 \end{bmatrix} \begin{bmatrix} a \\ b \\ c \end{bmatrix}$

f) $\begin{bmatrix} 1 & 0 & 1 \\ 0 & -4 & 0 \\ 1 & 0 & 1 \end{bmatrix} \begin{bmatrix} 5 \\ 2 \\ 1 \end{bmatrix}$

g) $\begin{bmatrix} 1 \\ 2 \\ 5 \end{bmatrix} \begin{bmatrix} 1 & 0 & 1 \\ 0 & -4 & 0 \\ 1 & 0 & 1 \end{bmatrix}$

h) $\begin{bmatrix} 3 \\ 3 \\ 2 \end{bmatrix}^{\mathrm{T}} \begin{bmatrix} 1 & 3 & 2 \\ 6 & 1 & 5 \\ 3 & 5 & 0 \end{bmatrix}$

4. Consider square matrices **A** and **B**, with nonzero values at all elements. What assumptions on symmetry would make the following equalities hold (note: the operations might also be impossible under any assumptions)? Provide a proof or example for each.

a) AB = A^{T}B^{T}

b) AB = (AB)^{T}

c) AB = AB^{T}

d) AB = A^{T}B

e) AB = B^{T}A

f) AB = (BA)^{T}

5. In section 6.7 you learned that the product of two symmetric matrices is generally not symmetric. That was for standard multiplication; is the *Hadamard product* of two symmetric matrices symmetric? Work through your reasoning first, then test your hypothesis on the following matrix pair.

$$\begin{bmatrix} 2 & 5 & 7 \\ 5 & 3 & 6 \\ 7 & 6 & 4 \end{bmatrix}, \begin{bmatrix} a & d & f \\ d & b & e \\ f & e & c \end{bmatrix}$$

6. For the following pairs of matrices, vectorize and compute the vector dot product, then compute the Frobenius inner product as $tr(\mathbf{A}^T\mathbf{B})$.

a) $\begin{bmatrix} a & b \\ c & d \end{bmatrix}, \begin{bmatrix} 1 & 2 \\ 3 & 4 \end{bmatrix}$

b) $\begin{bmatrix} 0 & 5 \\ 7 & -2 \end{bmatrix}, \begin{bmatrix} 1 & 0 \\ 13 & 14 \end{bmatrix}$

c) $\begin{bmatrix} 4 & -5 & 8 \\ 1 & -1 & 2 \\ -2 & 2 & -4 \end{bmatrix}, \begin{bmatrix} 4 & -5 & 8 \\ 1 & -1 & 2 \\ -2 & 2 & -4 \end{bmatrix}$

d) $\begin{bmatrix} a & b \\ c & d \end{bmatrix}, \begin{bmatrix} a & b \\ a & b \end{bmatrix}$

e) $\begin{bmatrix} a & b \\ c & d \end{bmatrix}, \begin{bmatrix} a & b \\ c & d \end{bmatrix}$

f) $\begin{bmatrix} 1 & 1 & 7 \\ 2 & 2 & 6 \\ 3 & 3 & 5 \end{bmatrix}, \begin{bmatrix} 1 & 0 \\ 0 & 1 \\ 1 & 1 \end{bmatrix}$

7. Implement the indicated multiplications for the following matrices.

$$\mathbf{A} = \begin{bmatrix} 3 & 0 & 0 \\ 0 & 2 & 0 \\ 0 & 0 & -1 \end{bmatrix}, \quad \mathbf{B} = \begin{bmatrix} 2 & 0 & 0 \\ 0 & 5 & 0 \\ 0 & 0 & 3 \end{bmatrix}, \quad \mathbf{C} = \begin{bmatrix} 2 & 1 & 3 \\ 0 & 4 & 1 \\ 2 & 2 & 3 \end{bmatrix}$$

a) AB   b) AC   c) BC   d) CA

e) CB   f) BCA   g) ACB   h) ABC

6.13 Answers

1. **a)** no   **b)** yes: 4×3

    c) no   **d)** yes: 4×4

    e) no   **f)** yes: 2×4

    g) yes: 4×4 **h)** no

    i) yes: 2×2 **j)** yes: 3×3

    k) no   **l)** no

    m) yes: 3×3 **n)** no

    o) yes: 3×4 **p)** yes: 3×3

    q) no   **r)** yes: 2×3

2. **a)** $\begin{bmatrix} 0 & 5 \\ 2 & 17 \end{bmatrix}$ **b)** $\begin{bmatrix} -3 & 4 \\ -2 & 6 \end{bmatrix}$ **c)** $\begin{bmatrix} 73 & 8.5 \\ 131 & 2.5 \end{bmatrix}$

    d) $\begin{bmatrix} a & b \\ 2c & 2d \end{bmatrix}$ **e)** $\begin{bmatrix} 10 & 10 \\ -5 & 13 \end{bmatrix}$ **f)** $\begin{bmatrix} 2a & 3a \\ 2b & 3b \end{bmatrix}$

    g) $\begin{bmatrix} 2a+4b & 3a+b \\ 0 & 0 \end{bmatrix}$ **h)** $\begin{bmatrix} -2 & 1 & 19 \\ -1 & -8 & 8 \\ -9 & -36 & 6 \end{bmatrix}$ **i)** $\begin{bmatrix} a^2 & ab & ac+1 \\ b & 2b & 3b \\ a & b & 2c \end{bmatrix}$

3. **a)** $\begin{bmatrix} 4 \\ 9 \end{bmatrix}$ **b)** $\begin{bmatrix} 4 & 9 \end{bmatrix}$ **c)** $\begin{bmatrix} 7 \\ 13 \end{bmatrix}$ **d)** $\begin{bmatrix} 10 & 11 \end{bmatrix}$

    e) $\begin{bmatrix} b \\ c \\ a \end{bmatrix}$ **f)** $\begin{bmatrix} 6 \\ -8 \\ 6 \end{bmatrix}$ **g)** invalid   **h)** $\begin{bmatrix} 27 & 22 & 21 \end{bmatrix}$

4. **a)** Both matrices symmetric.   **b) A = B**, both symmetric.
Or $\mathbf{A} = \mathbf{B}^{\mathrm{T}}$

c) B = B^{T}   **d) A = A^{T}**

e) No general rule   **f)** Both symmetric.

5. Yes, because the multiplication is done element-wise.

6.   **a)** $a+2b+3c+4d$ **b)** 63   **c)** 135

d) $a^2+b^2+ca+bd$ **e)** $a^2+b^2+c^2+d^2$ **f)** undefined

7.

a) $\begin{bmatrix} 6 & 0 & 0 \\ 0 & 10 & 0 \\ 0 & 0 & -3 \end{bmatrix}$ **b)** $\begin{bmatrix} 6 & 3 & 9 \\ 0 & 8 & 2 \\ -2 & -2 & -3 \end{bmatrix}$

c) $\begin{bmatrix} 4 & 2 & 6 \\ 0 & 20 & 5 \\ 6 & 6 & 9 \end{bmatrix}$ **d)** $\begin{bmatrix} 6 & 2 & -3 \\ 0 & 8 & -1 \\ 6 & 4 & -3 \end{bmatrix}$

e) $\begin{bmatrix} 4 & 5 & 9 \\ 0 & 20 & 3 \\ 4 & 10 & 9 \end{bmatrix}$ **f)** $\begin{bmatrix} 12 & 4 & -6 \\ 0 & 40 & -5 \\ 18 & 12 & -9 \end{bmatrix}$

g) $\begin{bmatrix} 12 & 15 & 27 \\ 0 & 40 & 6 \\ -4 & -10 & -9 \end{bmatrix}$ **h)** $\begin{bmatrix} 12 & 6 & 18 \\ 0 & 40 & 10 \\ -6 & -6 & -9 \end{bmatrix}$

6.14 Code challenges

1. Implement matrix multiplication between a 2×4 matrix and a 4×3 matrix, using the "layer perspective" in a for-loop. Confirm that you get the same result as when you compute matrix multiplication using @ (Python) or * (MATLAB).

2. Generate a 4×4 diagonal matrix and a 4×4 dense matrix of random numbers. Compute both standard and Hadamard multiplication between them. You already know that the resulting product matrices are not the same, but what about the diagonals of those two product matrices?

3. Consider $\mathbf{C}_1 = (\mathbf{A}^{\mathrm{T}} + \mathbf{A})/2$ and $\mathbf{C}_2 = \mathbf{A}^{\mathrm{T}}\mathbf{A}$ for some square nonsymmetric matrix $\mathbf{A}$. $\mathbf{C}_1$ and $\mathbf{C}_2$ are both symmetric and both formed from the same matrix, yet in general $\mathbf{C}_1 \neq \mathbf{C}_2$. Interestingly, if $\mathbf{A}$ is a diagonal matrix with all non-negative values, then $\mathbf{C}_1 = \mathbf{C}_2^{1/2}$. Show this in code using random numbers, and then explain why you get this result.

4. Let's explore the Cauchy-Schwarz inequality. Generate a random matrix $\mathbf{A}$ and a random vector $\mathbf{v}$, compute the norms of both sides of the inequality 6.27 (page 168), and show that the right-hand side is larger than the left-hand side.

6.15 Code solutions

1. **Note:** Showing equivalence between the two results is done by subtracting the matrices to get the zeros matrix (mathematically, this is $x = x \Rightarrow x - x = 0$). However, due to precision and rounding errors, the results might be very small numbers such as $1e-16$ (10^{-16}). You can consider numbers smaller than around $1e-15$ to be equal to zero.

Code block 6.13: Python

```
1  A = np.random.randn(2,4)
2  B = np.random.randn(4,3)
3  C1 = np.zeros((2,3))
4  for i in range(4):
5      C1 += np.outer(A[:,i],B[i,:])
6
7  C1 - A@B  # show equality
```

Code block 6.14: MATLAB

```
1  A = randn(2,4);
2  B = randn(4,3);
3  C1 = zeros(2,3);
4  for i=1:4
5      C1 = C1 + A(:,i)*B(i,:);
6  end
7  C1 - A*B  % show equality
```

2. The diagonals of the two product matrices are the same.

Code block 6.15: Python

```
1  D = np.diag(np.arange(1,5))
2  A = np.random.randn(4,4)
3  C1 = D*A
4  C2 = D@A
5  print(np.diag(C1))
6  print(np.diag(C2))
```

Code block 6.16: MATLAB

```
1  D = diag(1:4);
2  A = randn(4);
3  C1 = D.*A;
4  C2 = D*A;
5  [diag(C1) diag(C2)]
```

3. $C_1 = C_2^{1/2}$ sounds like an amazing and quirky property of matrix multiplication, but it's actually trivial because **A** is diagonal. The reason it works is the same reason that $x = \sqrt{x^2}$ for $x \geq 0$.

Code block 6.17: Python

```
1  A = np.diag(np.random.rand(3))
2  C1 = (A.T+A)/2
3  C2 = A.T@A
4  C1-np.sqrt(C2)
```

Code block 6.18: MATLAB

```
1  A = diag(rand(3,1));
2  C1 = (A'+A)/2;
3  C2 = A'*A;
4  C1-sqrt(C2)
```

4. The challenge isn't so challenging, but it's good excuse to gain experience coding with norms. My strategy for the inequality is to show that the right-hand side *minus* the left-hand side is positive. You can run the code multiples times to test different random numbers.

Code block 6.19: Python

```python
1  import numpy as np
2  m = 5
3  A = np.random.randn(m,m)
4  v = np.random.randn(m)
5  LHS = np.linalg.norm(A@v)
6  RHS = np.linalg.norm(A,ord='fro') *
7      np.linalg.norm(v)
8  RHS-LHS
```

Code block 6.20: MATLAB

```matlab
1  m = 5;
2  A = randn(m);
3  v = randn(m,1);
4  LHS = norm(A*v);
5  RHS = norm(A,'fro')*norm(v);
6  RHS-LHS
```

CHAPTER 7
MATRIX RANK

7.1 Six things to know about matrix rank

The rank of a matrix is a single number associated with that matrix, and is relevant for nearly all applications of linear algebra. Before learning about how to compute the rank, or even the formal definition of rank, it's useful to be exposed to a few key facts about matrix rank. In fact, you won't learn the formal methods to compute rank until the next few chapters; here we focus on the concept and interpretations of rank.

$\mathbb{N}$ is the set of natural numbers, a.k.a. the counting numbers. There is some debate about whether 0 is in the set of natural numbers; it's a philosophical issue that some people choose not to worry about.

1. The rank of the matrix is indicated by the letter r or by $rank(\mathbf{A})$, and is a non-negative integer. A matrix cannot have a rank of -2 or 4.7. A rank of 0 is possible, but most matrices have a rank > 0. If fact, only the zeros matrix can have a rank $= 0$.

2. The maximum possible rank of an $M{\times}N$ matrix is the smaller of M or N. That is,

$$r \in \mathbb{N}, s.t. \ 0 \leq r \leq \min\{M, N\} \tag{7.1}$$

3. Rank is a property of the entire matrix; it doesn't make sense to talk about the rank of the columns of the matrix, or the rank of the rows of the matrix. In the next chapter, you will learn about matrix spaces; it also doesn't make sense to talk about the rank of the null space of the matrix.

4. The figure below shows terminology for full-rank matrices, depending on their sizes.

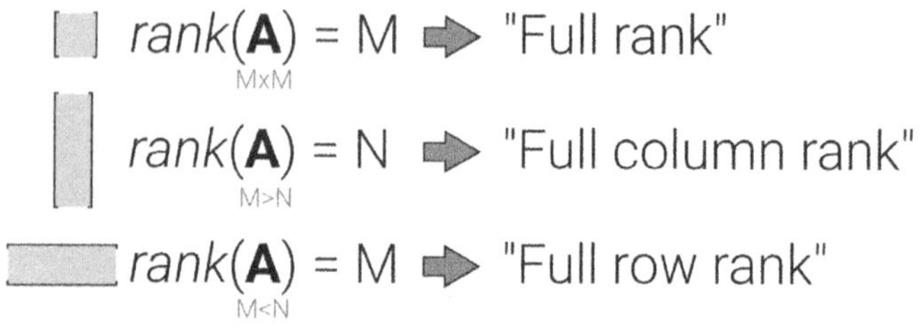

$rank(\mathbf{A}) = M \Rightarrow$ "Full rank"
MxM

$rank(\mathbf{A}) = N \Rightarrow$ "Full column rank"
M>N

$rank(\mathbf{A}) = M \Rightarrow$ "Full row rank"
M<N

Figure 7.1: Terminology for rank of matrices (boxes on left indicate matrix shapes).

If a matrix rank is less than the smaller of M or N, then it is variously called "reduced rank," "rank-deficient," "degenerate," "low-rank," or "singular." If you are the kind of person who copes with life's challenges by insulting others, then you might also apply the epithets "dummy" or "loser" matrix.

5. The rank indicates the number of dimensions of *information* contained in the matrix. This is not the same as the total number of columns or rows in the matrix. For example, the following matrix has 3 columns and 2 rows, but a rank of 1; notice that the columns form a linearly dependent set (as do the rows), and thus that any one column is a scalar multiple of any other column (same for the rows).

$$\begin{bmatrix} 1 & 3 & 4 \\ 3 & 9 & 12 \end{bmatrix}$$

6. There are several definitions of rank that you will learn throughout this book, and several algorithms for computing the rank. However, the key definition to keep in mind is that the **rank of a matrix is the largest number of columns that can form a linearly independent set**. This is exactly the same as **the largest number of rows that can form a linearly independent set**.

Reflection

Why all the fuss about rank? Why are full-rank matrices so important? There are some operations in linear algebra that are valid only for full-rank matrices (the matrix inverse being the most important). Other operations are valid on reduced-rank matrices (for example, eigendecomposition) but having full rank endows some additional properties. Furthermore, many computer algorithms return more reliable results when using full-rank compared to reduced-rank matrices. Indeed, one of the main goals of *regularization* in statistics and machine-learning is to increase numerical stability by ensuring that data matrices are full rank. So yeah, matrix rank is a big deal.

7.2 Interpretations of matrix rank

Algebraic interpretation   As mentioned in point 6 above, if you think of a matrix as comprising a set of vectors, then the rank of the matrix corresponds to the largest number of vectors that can form a linearly independent set. Remember that a set of vectors is linearly independent if no vector can be expressed as a linear combination of the other vectors.

The phrasing that seems correct here would be "the number of linearly independent columns" in the matrix, but of course you know that linear independence is a property of a *set* of vectors, not *individual* vectors within a set.

Below are a few matrices and their ranks. Although I haven't yet taught you any algorithms for computing rank, try to understand why each matrix has its associated rank based on the description above.

$$\begin{bmatrix} 1 \\ 2 \\ 4 \end{bmatrix}, \quad \begin{bmatrix} 1 & 3 \\ 2 & 6 \\ 4 & 12 \end{bmatrix}, \quad \begin{bmatrix} 1 & 3.1 \\ 2 & 6 \\ 4 & 12 \end{bmatrix}, \quad \begin{bmatrix} 1 & 3 & 2 \\ 6 & 6 & 1 \\ 4 & 2 & 0 \end{bmatrix}, \quad \begin{bmatrix} 1 & 1 & 1 \\ 1 & 1 & 1 \\ 1 & 1 & 1 \end{bmatrix}, \quad \begin{bmatrix} 0 & 0 & 0 \\ 0 & 0 & 0 \\ 0 & 0 & 0 \end{bmatrix}$$

r=1r=1r=2$$r=3$$r=1r=0

Geometric interpretation   Rank is the dimensionality of the subspace spanned by the columns (or the rows) of the matrix. This is not necessarily the same as the ambient dimensionality of the space containing the matrix. For example, consider the following vector (which we can also think of as a 3×1 matrix):

$$\mathbf{v} = \begin{bmatrix} 4 & 0 & 1 \end{bmatrix}^{\mathrm{T}}$$

This object lives in $\mathbb{R}^3$, although it spans only a 1D subspace (a line). The rank of this matrix is therefore 1. In fact, all vectors have a rank of 1, except for the zeros vector, which has a rank of 0.

Let's reinterpret vector $\mathbf{v}$: Instead of being a line in $\mathbb{R}^3$, let's consider it a row vector containing three elements in $\mathbb{R}^1$ (three points on the real number line). In this case, either of the non-zero elements can obtained by scaling the other. Again, this leads us to the conclusion that the rank is 1.

Here is another example:

$$\begin{bmatrix} 1 & 1 & -4 \\ 2 & -1 & 2 \end{bmatrix}$$

Let's start by thinking about the matrix as comprising three column vectors in $\mathbb{R}^2$. There are three vectors in ambient dimensionality of 2, so this set of vectors spans all of $\mathbb{R}^2$, which is a 2D plane (Figure 7.2, left panel). Thus, the rank is 2.

Now let's think about that matrix as comprising two row vectors in $\mathbb{R}^3$. Those two vectors are distinct, meaning they span a 2D plane embedded in ambient 3D space (Figure 7.2, right panel). Thus, the rank is 2.

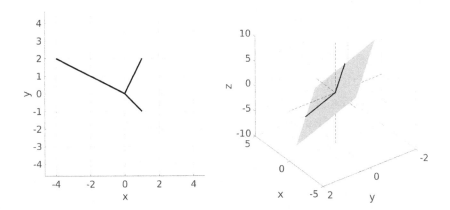

Figure 7.2: Geometrically, the rank of a matrix is the dimensionality of the subspaces spanned by either the columns (left) or the rows (right).

The point is that regardless of the perspective you take (a matrix as comprising columns or rows), the dimensionality of the subspace spanned by those vectors—and thus, the rank of the matrix—is the same. You can see in the example above that those subspaces might be very different (more on this in the next chapter!) but their dimensionalities are the same.

7.3 Computing matrix rank

Computing the matrix rank is, in modern applications, not trivial. In fact, beyond small matrices, computers cannot actually *compute* the rank of a matrix; they can only *estimate* the rank to a reasonable degree of certainty.

Nonetheless, computing the rank of small (and, if your linear algebra instructor is nice, integer-containing) matrices is not so difficult. There are several methods to compute the rank of a matrix. These methods all tap into the same underlying features of a matrix, but some methods are easier than others in some situations.

Below is a list of three methods to compute the rank of a matrix. At this point in the book, you can implement the first method; the other two methods rely on matrix operations that you will learn about in later chapters.

1. Count the largest number of columns (or rows) that can form a linearly independent set. This involves a bit of trial-and-error and a bit of educated guessing. You can follow the same tips for determining linear independence in Chapter 4 (page 95).
2. Count the number of pivots in the echelon or row-reduced echelon form of the matrix (Chapter 10).
3. Count the number of nonzero singular values from a singular value decomposition of the matrix (Chapter 16).

Code Except for your linear algebra exams, you will never compute matrix rank by hand. Fortunately, both Python and MATLAB have functions that return matrix rank.

Code block 7.1: Python

```
1  import numpy as np
2  A = np.random.randn(3,6)
3  r = np.linalg.matrix_rank(A)
```

```
1  A = randn(3,6);
2  r = rank(A)
```

Practice problems Compute the rank of the following matrices based on visual inspection.

a) $\begin{bmatrix} 1 & -2 \\ 2 & -4 \end{bmatrix}$
b) $\begin{bmatrix} 1 & 2 \\ 2 & 1 \end{bmatrix}$
c) $\begin{bmatrix} 1 & 4 \\ 5 & -220 \\ 5 & 5/2 \end{bmatrix}$
d) $\begin{bmatrix} 2 & -4 & 10 \\ 2 & 3 & -4 \\ 4 & 2 & 0 \end{bmatrix}$

Answers

a) $r = 1$ b) $r = 2$ c) $r = 2$ d) $r = 2$

7.4 Rank and scalar multiplication

I'll keep this brief: Scalar multiplication has no effect on the rank of a matrix, with one exception when the scalar is 0 (because this produces the zeros matrix, which has a rank of 0).

The reason why scalar multiplication has no effect is that the scalar simply stretches the information already present in the matrix; it does not transform, rotate, mix, unmix, change, combine, or create any new information.

Algebraically, scaling has no effect on rank because linear independence does not change if all vectors in the set are multiplied by the same scalar (of course, with the exception of 0).

I don't think this rule needs an equation, but in the interest of practicing my LaTeX skills:

$$rank(\alpha \mathbf{A}) = rank(\mathbf{A}), \quad \alpha \neq 0 \qquad (7.2)$$

Code There isn't any new code in this section, but I decided to add these code blocks to increase your familiarity with matrix rank.

You should confirm that the ranks of the random matrix and the scalar-multiplied matrix are the same.

Code block 7.3: Python

```
1  s = np.random.randn()
2  M = np.random.randn(3,5)
3  r1 = np.linalg.matrix_rank(M)
4  r2 = np.linalg.matrix_rank(s*M)
5  print(r1,r2)
```

Code block 7.4: MATLAB

```
1  s = randn;
2  M = randn(3,5);
3  r1 = rank(M);
4  r2 = rank(s*M);
5  disp([r1 r2])
```

7.5 Rank of added matrices

If you know the ranks of matrices $\mathbf{A}$ and $\mathbf{B}$, do you automatically know the rank of $\mathbf{A} + \mathbf{B}$? The short answer is No, you don't. However, knowing the ranks of the individual matrices will put an upper bound on the rank of $\mathbf{A} + \mathbf{B}$. Here's the rule:

$$rank(\mathbf{A} + \mathbf{B}) \leq rank(\mathbf{A}) + rank(\mathbf{B}) \tag{7.3}$$

I remember this rule is by thinking about adding together the simplest possible rank-1 matrices to create a rank-2 matrix:

$$\begin{bmatrix} 1 & 0 & 0 \\ 0 & 0 & 0 \\ 0 & 0 & 0 \end{bmatrix} + \begin{bmatrix} 0 & 0 & 0 \\ 0 & 1 & 0 \\ 0 & 0 & 0 \end{bmatrix} = \begin{bmatrix} 1 & 0 & 0 \\ 0 & 1 & 0 \\ 0 & 0 & 0 \end{bmatrix}$$

On the other hand, adding two rank-1 matrices does not guarantee a rank-2 matrix:

$$\begin{bmatrix} 1 & 0 & 0 \\ 0 & 0 & 0 \\ 0 & 0 & 0 \end{bmatrix} + \begin{bmatrix} -1 & 0 & 0 \\ 0 & 0 & 0 \\ 0 & 0 & 0 \end{bmatrix} = \begin{bmatrix} 0 & 0 & 0 \\ 0 & 0 & 0 \\ 0 & 0 & 0 \end{bmatrix}$$

With that in mind, here are some more examples. The ranks of the individual matrices are given in small subscripted numbers (*n.b.* non-standard notation used only in this chapter for convenience), but the ranks of the summed matrices are missing. You should compute them on your own, then check in the footnote[1] for the answers.

$$\begin{bmatrix} 1 & 2 & 3 \\ 3 & 4 & 1 \\ 5 & 9 & 1 \end{bmatrix}_3 + \begin{bmatrix} 0 & 3 & 5 \\ 1 & 0 & 4 \\ 3 & 3 & 0 \end{bmatrix}_3 = \begin{bmatrix} 1 & 5 & 8 \\ 4 & 4 & 5 \\ 8 & 12 & 1 \end{bmatrix} \qquad (7.4)$$

$$\begin{bmatrix} 1 & 2 & 0 \\ 3 & 4 & 0 \\ 5 & 9 & 0 \end{bmatrix}_2 + \begin{bmatrix} 0 & 0 & 5 \\ 0 & 0 & 4 \\ 0 & 0 & 1 \end{bmatrix}_1 = \begin{bmatrix} 1 & 2 & 5 \\ 3 & 4 & 4 \\ 5 & 9 & 1 \end{bmatrix} \qquad (7.5)$$

$$\begin{bmatrix} 1 & 1 & 1 \\ 2 & 2 & 2 \\ 3 & 3 & 0 \end{bmatrix}_2 + \begin{bmatrix} 0 & 0 & 0 \\ 0 & 0 & 0 \\ 0 & 0 & 0 \end{bmatrix}_0 = \begin{bmatrix} 1 & 1 & 1 \\ 2 & 2 & 2 \\ 3 & 3 & 0 \end{bmatrix} \qquad (7.6)$$

$$\begin{bmatrix} -1 & -4 & 2 \\ -4 & 2 & -1 \\ 9 & 4 & -3 \end{bmatrix}_3 + \begin{bmatrix} 1 & 4 & 0 \\ 4 & -2 & 0 \\ -9 & -4 & 0 \end{bmatrix}_2 = \begin{bmatrix} 0 & 0 & 2 \\ 0 & 0 & -1 \\ 0 & 0 & -3 \end{bmatrix} \qquad (7.7)$$

The rule shown in Equation 7.3 applies to matrix subtraction as well, because subtraction is the same thing as addition and multiplying the matrix by -1, and scalar multiplication doesn't change the rank of a matrix (see Equation 7.2).

Multiple constraints   There are multiple constraints on the rank of a matrix. For example, "Thing 2" to know about matrix rank was that the largest possible rank is the smaller of M or N (Equation 7.1). These constraints cannot be broken.

For example, imagine two 3×4 matrices, each with rank 3. The sum of those matrices cannot possibly have a rank of 6 (Equation 7.3), because 6 is greater than the matrix sizes. Thus, the largest possible rank of the summed matrix is 3 (the rank could be smaller than 3, depending on the values in the matrices).

---

[1] Top to bottom: 3, 3, 2, 1

Practice problems Determine the maximum possible rank of the following expressions, based on the following information (assume matrix sizes match for valid addition):
$rank(\mathbf{A}) = 4, \quad rank(\mathbf{B}) = 11, \quad rank(\mathbf{C}) = 14.$

   a) $\mathbf{A} + \mathbf{B}$ b) $(\mathbf{A} + \mathbf{B}) + 0\mathbf{C}$ c) $\mathbf{C} - 3\mathbf{A}$ d) $0((\mathbf{C} + \mathbf{A}) + 4\mathbf{A})$

Answers

   a) 15   b) 15   c) 18   d) 0

7.6 Rank of multiplied matrices

As with summed matrices, you cannot know the exact rank of a matrix $\mathbf{C} = \mathbf{AB}$ only by knowing the individual ranks of $\mathbf{A}$ and $\mathbf{B}$. But also as with summed matrices, there is a rule for knowing the maximum possible rank of the product matrix.

$$rank(\mathbf{AB}) \leq \min\{rank(\mathbf{A}), rank(\mathbf{B})\} \qquad (7.8)$$

In other words, the smallest rank of the individual matrices is the largest possible rank of the product matrix. Below are a few examples, and then I'll explain why this rule makes sense. These are the same pairs of matrices as in the previous section, so it's interesting to compare the results. (As in the previous section, ranks are listed in the subscripts, and the ranks of the products are listed in the footnote[2].)

$$\begin{bmatrix} 1 & 2 & 3 \\ 3 & 4 & 1 \\ 5 & 9 & 1 \end{bmatrix}_3 \begin{bmatrix} 0 & 3 & 5 \\ 1 & 0 & 4 \\ 3 & 3 & 0 \end{bmatrix}_3 = \begin{bmatrix} 11 & 12 & 13 \\ 7 & 12 & 31 \\ 12 & 18 & 61 \end{bmatrix} \qquad (7.9)$$

$$\begin{bmatrix} 1 & 2 & 0 \\ 3 & 4 & 0 \\ 5 & 9 & 0 \end{bmatrix}_2 \begin{bmatrix} 0 & 0 & 5 \\ 0 & 0 & 4 \\ 0 & 0 & 1 \end{bmatrix}_1 = \begin{bmatrix} 0 & 0 & 13 \\ 0 & 0 & 31 \\ 0 & 0 & 61 \end{bmatrix} \qquad (7.10)$$

$$\begin{bmatrix} 1 & 1 & 1 \\ 2 & 2 & 2 \\ 3 & 3 & 0 \end{bmatrix}_2 \begin{bmatrix} 0 & 0 & 0 \\ 0 & 0 & 0 \\ 0 & 0 & 0 \end{bmatrix}_0 = \begin{bmatrix} 0 & 0 & 0 \\ 0 & 0 & 0 \\ 0 & 0 & 0 \end{bmatrix} \qquad (7.11)$$

$$\begin{bmatrix} -1 & -4 & 2 \\ -4 & 2 & -1 \\ 9 & 4 & -3 \end{bmatrix}_3 \begin{bmatrix} 1 & 4 & 0 \\ 4 & -2 & 0 \\ -9 & -4 & 0 \end{bmatrix}_2 = \begin{bmatrix} -35 & -4 & 0 \\ 13 & -16 & 0 \\ 52 & 40 & 0 \end{bmatrix} \qquad (7.12)$$

How to understand this rule? You can think about it in terms of the column space of the matrix $\mathbf{C} = \mathbf{AB}$. "Column space" is a concept you'll learn more about in the next chapter, but basically it's the subspace spanned by the columns of a matrix. Think of the jth column of $\mathbf{C}$ as being the matrix-vector product of matrix $\mathbf{A}$ and the jth column in $\mathbf{B}$:

$$\mathbf{A}\mathbf{b}_j = \mathbf{c}_j \qquad (7.13)$$

This means that each column of $\mathbf{C}$ is a linear combination of columns of $\mathbf{A}$ with the weights defined by the corresponding column in $\mathbf{B}$. In other words, each column of $\mathbf{C}$ is in the subspace spanned by the columns of $\mathbf{A}$.

One definition of rank is the dimensionality of the column space of a matrix. And because the column space of $\mathbf{C}$ is fully within the column space of $\mathbf{A}$, the dimensionality of $\mathbf{C}$'s column space cannot be larger than that of $\mathbf{A}$. $\mathbf{C}$'s column space could be smaller, depending on the numbers in $\mathbf{B}$, but the rank of $\mathbf{A}$ provides an upper boundary.

---

[2]Top to bottom: 3, 1, 0, 2

The same argument can be made for matrix **B** by considering **C** to be built up row-wise instead of column-wise.

Practice problems Determine the maximum possible rank of the following expressions, based on the following information (assume valid matrix sizes):
$rank(\mathbf{A}) = 4$, $rank(\mathbf{B}) = 11$, $rank(\mathbf{C}) = 14$.

   a) **AB**   b) **(AB)C**   c) **3CA**   d) **(C + A)A**

Answers

   a) 4   b) 4   c) 4   d) 4

Rank of $\mathbf{A}$, $\mathbf{A}^{\mathsf{T}}$, $\mathbf{A}^{\mathsf{T}}\mathbf{A}$, and $\mathbf{A}\mathbf{A}^{\mathsf{T}}$

The key take-home message from this section is that these four matrices—$\mathbf{A}$, $\mathbf{A}^{\mathsf{T}}$, $\mathbf{A}^{\mathsf{T}}\mathbf{A}$, and $\mathbf{A}\mathbf{A}^{\mathsf{T}}$—all have exactly the same rank.

You already know that $\mathbf{A}$ and $\mathbf{A}^{\mathsf{T}}$ have the same rank because of property 3 in the first section of this chapter: the rank is a property of the matrix; it does not reflect the columns or the rows separately. Thus, transposing a matrix does not affect its rank.

Proving that $\mathbf{A}^{\mathsf{T}}\mathbf{A}$ and $\mathbf{A}\mathbf{A}^{\mathsf{T}}$ have the same rank as that of $\mathbf{A}$ takes a little more work. I'm going to present two explanations here. Unfortunately, both of these explanations rely on some concepts that I will introduce later in the book. So if you find these explanations confusing, then please ear-mark this page and come back to it later.

I know it's a bit uncomfortable to rely on concepts before learning about them, but it often happens in math (and in life in general) that a purely monotonic progression is impossible.

Proof 1: The rank-nullity theorem The first proof relies on a discussion of matrix null spaces, which you will learn more about in the next chapter. Briefly, the null space of a matrix is the set of all vectors $\mathbf{y}$ such that $\mathbf{Ay} = \mathbf{0}$ (excluding the trivial case of $\mathbf{y} = \mathbf{0}$). The proof involves showing that $\mathbf{A}^T\mathbf{A}$ and $\mathbf{A}$ have the same null space dimensionality, which means that they must have the same rank. We start by proving that $\mathbf{A}$ and $\mathbf{A}^T\mathbf{A}$ have the same null space.

$$\mathbf{Ay} = \mathbf{0} \tag{7.14}$$

$$\mathbf{A}^T\mathbf{Ay} = \mathbf{A}^T\mathbf{0} \tag{7.15}$$

$$\mathbf{A}^T\mathbf{Ay} = \mathbf{0} \tag{7.16}$$

Equations 7.14 and 7.16 show that any vector in the null space of $\mathbf{A}$ is also in the null space of $\mathbf{A}^T\mathbf{A}$. This proves that the null space of $\mathbf{A}^T\mathbf{A}$ is a subset of the null space of $\mathbf{A}$. That's half of the proof, because we also need to show that any vector in the null space of $\mathbf{A}^T\mathbf{A}$ is also in the null space of $\mathbf{A}$.

$$\mathbf{A}^T\mathbf{Ay} = \mathbf{0} \tag{7.17}$$

$$\mathbf{y}^T\mathbf{A}^T\mathbf{Ay} = \mathbf{y}^T\mathbf{0} \tag{7.18}$$

$$(\mathbf{Ay})^T(\mathbf{Ay}) = 0 \tag{7.19}$$

$$\|\mathbf{Ay}\| = 0 \tag{7.20}$$

Equations 7.17 and 7.20 together show that any vector in the null space of $\mathbf{A}^T\mathbf{A}$ is also in the null space of $\mathbf{A}$.

Now we've proven that $\mathbf{A}^T\mathbf{A}$ and $\mathbf{A}$ have the same null spaces. Why does that matter? You will learn in the next chapter that the row space (the set of all possible weighted combinations of the rows) and the null space together span all of $\mathbb{R}^N$, and so if the null spaces are the same, then the row spaces must have the same dimensionality (this is called the rank-nullity theorem). And the rank of a matrix is the dimensionality of the row space, hence, the ranks of $\mathbf{A}^T\mathbf{A}$ and $\mathbf{A}$ are the same.

Proving this for $\mathbf{A}\mathbf{A}^T$ follows the same proof as above, except you start from $\mathbf{y}^T\mathbf{A} = \mathbf{0}$ instead. I encourage you to reproduce the proof with a pen and some paper.

Proof 2: The singular value decomposition   This explanation relies on another definition of rank, which is the number of non-zero singular values. Briefly, the singular value decomposition (SVD) involves representing a matrix as the product of three other matrices: $\mathbf{A} = \mathbf{U}\mathbf{\Sigma}\mathbf{V}^T$. $\mathbf{\Sigma}$ is a diagonal matrix that contains the singular values. The SVD of $\mathbf{A}^T\mathbf{A}$ is

$$\mathbf{A}^T\mathbf{A} = (\mathbf{U}\mathbf{\Sigma}\mathbf{V}^T)^T\mathbf{U}\mathbf{\Sigma}\mathbf{V}^T \tag{7.21}$$

$$= \mathbf{V}\mathbf{\Sigma}\mathbf{U}^T\mathbf{U}\mathbf{\Sigma}\mathbf{V}^T \tag{7.22}$$

$$= \mathbf{V}\mathbf{\Sigma}^2\mathbf{V}^T \tag{7.23}$$

$\mathbf{U}$ is an orthogonal matrix, so $\mathbf{U}^T\mathbf{U} = \mathbf{I}$. Don't worry if these equations seem mysterious—that's the whole point of Chapter 16! The important point for now is that the rank of a matrix is the number of non-zero diagonal elements in $\mathbf{\Sigma}$, and that is exactly the same as the number of non-zero diagonal elements in $\mathbf{\Sigma}^2$. Thus, $\mathbf{A}$ and $\mathbf{A}^T\mathbf{A}$ have the same rank.

Let's see an example. The following page shows a 2×3 rank-1 matrix, and then that matrix transposed and multiplied by its transpose. You can confirm via visual inspection that the ranks of all these matrices are 1.

$$\mathbf{A} = \begin{bmatrix} 1 & 3 & 4 \\ 3 & 9 & 12 \end{bmatrix} \qquad rank(\mathbf{A}) = 1$$

$$\mathbf{A}^{\mathrm{T}} = \begin{bmatrix} 1 & 3 \\ 3 & 9 \\ 4 & 12 \end{bmatrix} \qquad rank(\mathbf{A}^{\mathrm{T}}) = 1$$

$$\mathbf{A}^{\mathrm{T}}\mathbf{A} = \begin{bmatrix} 10 & 30 & 40 \\ 30 & 90 & 120 \\ 40 & 120 & 160 \end{bmatrix} \qquad rank(\mathbf{A}^{\mathrm{T}}\mathbf{A}) = 1$$

$$\mathbf{A}\mathbf{A}^{\mathrm{T}} = \begin{bmatrix} 26 & 78 \\ 78 & 234 \end{bmatrix} \qquad rank(\mathbf{A}\mathbf{A}^{\mathrm{T}}) = 1$$

7.8 Rank of random matrices

A "random matrix" is a matrix that contains elements drawn at random. The elements of random matrices can come from various distributions, such as normal (Gaussian), uniform, Poisson, etc. Random matrices have some interesting properties, and there are entire theories built around random matrices.

The interesting property of random matrices that is most relevant for this book—and for using computers to explore concepts in linear algebra—is that they are basically always full rank. Almost any time you populate a matrix with random numbers, you can assume that that matrix will have its maximum possible rank (there are some exceptions described below).

Why is this the case? When you generate random numbers on computers—particularly floating-point precision random numbers—it is simply mindbogglingly unlikely that linear dependencies in the columns will *just happen* to arise. Here is an example of a 4×4 matrix of random numbers I generated in MATLAB using the function

```
randn:
```

$$\begin{bmatrix} -0.74441379927393025450754748817417 & 1.5153140904140030675861794069556 & 0.42176561501130205300569286919199 & 1.2551266421924042582247693646037 \\ -0.72646775218459369583001716819126 & -0.34072242399389618405791679833783 & 0.38661683336351230400040890344826 & 0.76957649534037353422633032096201 \\ -1.6869109322256918837051301764548 & 0.46106281417989597448681138303073 & -0.15846403504882577983892133488553 & 1.373587622180848745223613605048744 \\ 0.18966220087431615026751785535453 & 0.44733585004922499228641186164168 & 0.69627165982078986772307871433441 & -1.4775625702739539426033843483310 \end{bmatrix}$$

Apologies for making the font so small. The point isn't for you to read the actual numbers; the point is for you to appreciate that the probability of linear dependencies leading to a reduced-rank matrix is infinitesimal. Thus, whenever you create random matrices on computers, you can assume that their rank is their *maximum possible* rank.

On the other hand, matrices are not guaranteed to be full-rank simply by virtue of having randomly drawn numbers. Reduced-rank random matrices occur when the numbers are drawn from a restricted range. For example, the following matrix was generated by random numbers drawn from the population {0,1} and has a rank of 2.

$$\begin{bmatrix} 0 & 0 & 0 & 0 \\ 0 & 0 & 0 & 0 \\ 1 & 0 & 1 & 1 \\ 1 & 1 & 0 & 0 \end{bmatrix}$$

Thus, matrices populated with floating-point random numbers have maximum possible rank. This is useful because it allows you to create matrices with arbitrary rank, which in turn will unlock many opportunities for exploring linear algebra in code. Code challenge 1 will guide you through the process.

7.9 Full-rank matrices via "shifting"

Full-rank square matrices are absolutely fabulous to work with. But many matrices used in practical applications are rank-deficient. So what's a data-scientist to do?

One solution is to transform a rank-deficient matrix into a full-rank matrix through "shifting," which you learned about in section 5.8. As a quick reminder: shifting a matrix means to add a multiple of the identity matrix $(\mathbf{A} + \lambda\mathbf{I} = \tilde{\mathbf{A}})$, which adds a small quantity to the diagonal elements without changing the off-diagonal elements.

In statistics and machine learning, one of the main reasons to shift a matrix is to transform a reduced-rank matrix into a full-rank matrix. Remarkably, this feat can be accomplished while making only tiny (and usually practically insignificant) changes to the information contained in the matrix.

To show how this is possible, I'll start with an extreme example that shows how shifting a matrix can transform it into a full-rank matrix. What is the value of λ in the equation below?

$$\begin{bmatrix} 0 & 0 & 0 \\ 0 & 0 & 0 \\ 0 & 0 & 0 \end{bmatrix} + \lambda \begin{bmatrix} 1 & 0 & 0 \\ 0 & 1 & 0 \\ 0 & 0 & 1 \end{bmatrix} = \begin{bmatrix} 1 & 0 & 0 \\ 0 & 1 & 0 \\ 0 & 0 & 1 \end{bmatrix} \tag{7.24}$$

I'm sure you calculated that $\lambda = 1$, and shifting trivially moved the matrix rank from 0 to 3. On the other hand, usually the goal of shifting a matrix is to change the information contained in the matrix as little as possible, and I've clearly violated that principle here.

Let's go for a less extreme example:

$$\begin{bmatrix} 1 & 3 & -19 \\ 5 & -7 & 59 \\ -5 & 2 & -24 \end{bmatrix} + .01 \begin{bmatrix} 1 & 0 & 0 \\ 0 & 1 & 0 \\ 0 & 0 & 1 \end{bmatrix} = \begin{bmatrix} 1.01 & 3 & -19 \\ 5 & -6.99 & 59 \\ -5 & 2 & -23.99 \end{bmatrix} \tag{7.25}$$

The ranks of these matrices are, respectively, 2, 3, and 3. And unlike with example 7.24, the matrices $\tilde{\mathbf{A}}$ and $\mathbf{A}$ are really close to each other: All the off-diagonal elements are identical, and the diagonal elements differ by a mere .01, which, for this matrix, corresponds to a change of less than 1% on the diagonal elements.

One final (again, somewhat extreme) example:

$$\begin{bmatrix} 1 & 3 & -19 \\ 5 & -7 & 59 \\ -5 & 2 & -24 \end{bmatrix} + 10^3 \begin{bmatrix} 1 & 0 & 0 \\ 0 & 1 & 0 \\ 0 & 0 & 1 \end{bmatrix} = \begin{bmatrix} 1001 & 3 & -19 \\ 5 & 993 & 59 \\ -5 & 2 & 976 \end{bmatrix} \quad (7.26)$$

Again, the ranks are 2, 3, and 3. But let's think about what we've done: By setting λ to be large relative to the values in $\mathbf{A}$, we've pushed the matrix to be close to a scaled version of the identity matrix (in fact, we could even say that that matrix is $10^3\mathbf{I}$ plus some flotsam and jetsam).

This leads to an interesting observation about matrix "shifting": When λ is close to 0, $\tilde{\mathbf{A}}$ is close to $\mathbf{A}$, and as λ gets large (relative to the values in matrix $\mathbf{A}$), $\tilde{\mathbf{A}}$ moves towards $\lambda\mathbf{I}$.

In the context of statistics and machine learning, "shifting" is also called *regularization* or *matrix smoothing*. It is an important procedure for multivariate analyses such as principal components analysis and generalized eigendecomposition (which are the mathematical backbones of data compression and linear discriminant analyses).

An important question—and an area of ongoing research and testing in data science—is determining the optimal λ for a given matrix and a given application. I'll introduce one method, called "shrinkage regularization," in chapter 19.

7.10 Difficulties in computing rank in practice

I'd like to give you some sense of why it is difficult to compute the rank of large matrices, from both an algebraic and geometric interpretation.

I wrote above that one way to compute the rank of a matrix is to count the number of non-zero singular values. You haven't yet learned about singular values, but it is sufficient for now to know that an $M \times N$ matrix has $\min\{M, N\}$ singular values.

Computers suffer from rounding errors that lead to uncertainties in distinguishing very small numbers from true zero. Oftentimes, numbers smaller than around 10^{-15} are considered to be zero plus computer rounding error (the exact exponent depends on your computer's precision).

So let's say the computer estimates a singular value to be 3×10^{-15}; is this a true non-zero singular value that happens to be really small, or is this actually zero but with rounding error? Your computer software (MATLAB or Python) will define some threshold for considering a small singular value equal to zero. But that threshold is arbitrary, and a rounding error could be randomly on either side of that boundary. Therefore, rounding error plus an arbitrary threshold can influence the reported rank of the matrix. We'll come back to this issue—including a discussion of how that threshold is set—in Chapter 16.

Code The standard computer algorithm for computing rank is to count the number of singular values above a threshold. The purpose of this code block is for you to inspect the source code for computing rank. Even if you don't understand each line of the code, you should be able to see the following operations: (1) compute the SVD of the matrix, (2) define a "tolerance" (the threshold for identifying a number as being significantly nonzero), (3) count the number of singular values above this tolerance.

Code block 7.5: Python

```
1   ??np.linalg.matrix_rank
```

Code block 7.6: MATLAB

```
1   edit rank
```

Geometry Now let's think about difficulties in computing rank geometrically. Imagine you have a 3×3 matrix that represents some data you collected from a satellite. The columns are in $\mathbb{R}^3$, and let's imagine that you know for a fact that the three vectors all lie on a 2D plane. So you know for a fact, based on the design of the satellite's sensors, that the rank of the data matrix must be 2.

But the sensors on the satellite are not perfect, and there is a tiny, tiny bit of noise that corrupts the signal. So in fact, if you would look at the subspace spanned by the columns of the matrix at "eye level," you would expect to see the vectors perfectly lying in a plane. Instead, however, you see the vectors pointing ever-so-slightly above or below that plane (Figure 7.3).

Your computer would tell you that the rank of this data matrix is 3, which you know is actually due to sensor noise. So you might want your rank-estimating-algorithm to ignore some small amount of noise, based on what you know about the data contained in the matrix.

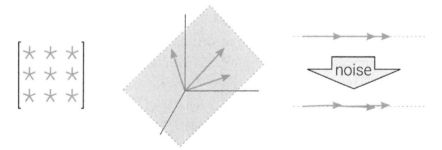

Figure 7.3: A 3×3 matrix representing a 2D plane in $\mathbb{R}^3$ may be counted as a rank-3 matrix in the presence of a small amount of noise. The diagrams at right illustrate three arrows on the plane (dotted line), from the perspective of looking directly across the surface of that plane.

7.11 Rank and span

In Chapter 4, you learned that an important question in linear algebra is whether a vector is in the span of another set of vectors. (Recall that a vector $\mathbf{v}$ is in the span of a set of vectors S if $\mathbf{v}$ can be written as a weighted combination of the vectors in S.)

I wrote that there are several algorithms that can answer that question, but that you hadn't yet learned the necessary concepts. We can now re-interpret this problem in the context of matrices and rank.

There is an entire section about this procedure in the next chapter (section 8.3), including a deeper explanation and diagrams. However, I believe that you are now knowledgeable enough to be introduced to the augment-rank algorithm. If you're struggling with understanding why the following procedure tells us whether a vector is in the span of a set of vectors, then don't worry—it means you have something to look forward to in the next chapter!

Repetition facilitates comprehension, especially when knowledge increases between each repetition.

1. Put the vectors from set S into a matrix $\mathbf{S}$.
2. Compute the rank of $\mathbf{S}$. Call that rank r_1.
3. Augment $\mathbf{S}$ by $\mathbf{v}$, thus creating $\mathbf{S_v} = \mathbf{S} \sqcup \mathbf{v}$
4. Compute the rank of $\mathbf{S_v}$. Call that rank r_2.
5. If $r_2 > r_1$, then $\mathbf{v}$ is *not* in the span of S.
   If $r_2 = r_1$, then $\mathbf{v}$ *is* in the span of S.
   If $r_2 < r_1$, then check your math or code for a mistake :(

1. Compute the rank of the following matrices based on visual inspection.

$$\text{a) } \begin{bmatrix} 1 & 2 & 2 \\ 2 & 4 & 4 \\ 4 & 8 & 8 \end{bmatrix} \quad \text{b) } \begin{bmatrix} 1 & 2 & 2 \\ 2 & 4 & 4 \\ 4 & 8 & 9 \end{bmatrix} \quad \text{c) } \begin{bmatrix} 2 & 1 & 0 \\ 1 & 2 & 0 \\ 0 & 0 & 3 \end{bmatrix} \quad \text{d) } \begin{bmatrix} 1 & 3 & 5 \\ 0 & 8 & 3 \\ 0 & 0 & 23 \end{bmatrix}$$

2. Compute the rank of the result of the following operations.

$$\mathbf{A} = \begin{bmatrix} 2 & 4 & 3 \\ 0 & 1 & 3 \end{bmatrix}, \quad \mathbf{B} = \begin{bmatrix} -2 & -1 & 3 \\ 6 & -7 & 7 \end{bmatrix}$$

   a) $\mathbf{A}$ b) $\mathbf{B}$ c) $\mathbf{A} + \mathbf{B}$ d) $\mathbf{A}\mathbf{A}^{\mathbf{T}}$

   e) $\mathbf{A}^{\mathbf{T}}\mathbf{A}$ f) $\mathbf{A}\mathbf{B}^{\mathbf{T}}$ g) $(\mathbf{A}\mathbf{B}^{\mathbf{T}})^{\mathbf{T}}$ h) $2\mathbf{A}\mathbf{A}^{\mathbf{T}}$

3. For the following matrices, what value of λ would give each matrix rank $m - 1$?

$$\text{a) } \begin{bmatrix} 1 & 3 \\ 1 & \lambda \end{bmatrix} \quad \text{b) } \begin{bmatrix} 0 & 0 \\ 0 & \lambda \end{bmatrix} \quad \text{c) } \begin{bmatrix} 1 & 2 & \lambda \\ 1 & 2 & 2 \\ 1 & 2 & 2 \end{bmatrix} \quad \text{d) } \begin{bmatrix} 0 & 1 & 0 \\ 0 & 2 & \lambda \\ 1 & 0 & 3 \end{bmatrix}$$

4. Determine the maximum possible rank of the following operations.

   $\mathbf{A} \in \mathbb{R}^{2 \times 3}, \quad \mathbf{B} \in \mathbb{R}^{3 \times 3}, \quad \mathbf{C} \in \mathbb{R}^{3 \times 4}, \quad \mathbf{D} \in \mathbb{R}^{3 \times 4}$

   a) $\mathbf{A}$ b) $\mathbf{B}$ c) $\mathbf{C}$ d) $\mathbf{D}$

   e) $\mathbf{C}^{\mathbf{T}}\mathbf{B}$ f) $\mathbf{C}^{\mathbf{T}}\mathbf{C}$ g) $\mathbf{A}\mathbf{D}$ h) $\mathbf{C}\mathbf{D}$

   i) $\mathbf{B} + \mathbf{B}$ j) $\mathbf{C} + \mathbf{D}$ k) $\mathbf{B}\mathbf{A}^{\mathbf{T}}\mathbf{A}\mathbf{C}$ l)$\mathbf{B}\mathbf{A}^{\mathbf{T}}\mathbf{A}\mathbf{C}+\mathbf{D}$

Answers

1. a) $r = 1$ b) $r = 2$ c) $r = 3$ d) $r = 3$

2. a) 2   b) 2   c) 2   d) 2

    e) 2   f) 2   g) 2   h) 2

3. a) $\lambda = 3$ b) $\lambda \neq 0$ c) $\lambda \neq 2$ d) $\lambda = 0$

4. a) 2   b) 3   c) 3   d) 3

    e) 3   f) 3   g) 2   h) invalid!

    i) 3   j) 3   k) 2   l) 3

7.14 Code challenges

1. The goal of this code challenge is to create random matrices with any arbitrary rank (though still limited by the constraints presented in this chapter). In particular, combine standard matrix multiplication (previous chapter) with the rule about rank and matrix multiplication (Equation 7.8) to create reduced-rank matrices comprising random numbers (hint: think about the "inner dimensions" of matrix multiplication).

2. The goal of this code challenge is to explore the tolerance level of your computer for computing the rank of matrices with tiny values. Start by creating the 5×5 zeros matrix and confirm that its rank is 0. Then add a 5×5 random numbers matrix scaled by machine-epsilon, which is the computer's estimate of its numerical precision due to round-off errors. Now the rank of that summed matrix will be 5. Finally, keep scaling down the machine-epsilon until the rank of the summed matrix is 0. You can also compute the Frobenius norm to get a sense of the magnitude of the values in the matrix.

7.15 Code solutions

1. When multiplying two random matrices that are $(M{\times}N){\times}(N{\times}K)$ where $M > N$ and $K > N$, then the product $M \times K$ matrix will have rank-N. The code below shows how to create a rank-2 random matrix. I encourage you to generalize this code so that the parameters M, N, and k are soft-coded.

Code block 7.7: Python

```
1  A = np.random.randn(9,2)
2  B = np.random.randn(2,16)
3  C = A@B
```

Code block 7.8: MATLAB

```
1  A = randn(9,2);
2  B = randn(2,16);
3  C = A*B;
```

2. On the laptop that I'm using while writing this exercise, I got rank-5 matrices down to scaling factors of around 10^{-307}.

Code block 7.9: Python

```
1  Z = np.zeros((5,5))
2  N = np.random.randn(5,5)
3  ZN = Z + N*np.finfo(float).eps*1e-307
4  print(np.linalg.matrix_rank(Z))
5  print(np.linalg.matrix_rank(ZN))
6  print(np.linalg.norm(ZN,'fro'))
```

Code block 7.10: MATLAB

```
1  Z = zeros(5);
2  N = randn(5)*eps*1e-307;
3  ZN = Z + N;
4  rank(Z)
5  rank(ZN)
6  norm(ZN,'fro')
```

. Rank

CHAPTER 8
MATRIX SPACES

START THIS CHAPTER HAPPY

"Matrix spaces" are the same concept as vector subspaces, but are defined by different features of a matrix instead of a set of vectors. This chapter ties together concepts of vector subspaces, basis, linear independence, and span.

Remarkably, this entire chapter can be summarized as trying to answer the following two questions about matrix-vector multiplication and a vector $\mathbf{b} \neq \mathbf{0}$:

$$\mathbf{Ax} = \mathbf{b}\,? \tag{8.1}$$

$$\mathbf{Ay} = \mathbf{0}\,? \tag{8.2}$$

In other words, the questions are: (8.1) Is there a weighted combination of columns of $\mathbf{A}$ that produces vector $\mathbf{b}$ with the weights given by vector $\mathbf{x}$? And (8.2) Is there a weighted combination of columns of $\mathbf{A}$ that produces the zeros vector with the weights given by vector $\mathbf{y}$ (for $\mathbf{y} \neq \mathbf{0}$)?

As you work through this chapter, try to think about how each concept fits into these questions. At the end of the chapter, I will provide a philosophical discussion of the meaning of these two questions.

Column space of a matrix

"Column space" sounds like a fancy and exotic term, but in fact, you already know what a column space is: The *column space* of a matrix is the subspace spanned by all columns of that matrix. In other words, think of a matrix as a set of column vectors, and the subspace spanned by that set of vectors as the column space of the matrix.

Column space is also sometimes called the *range* or the *image* of a matrix.

The column space is indicated using the notation $C(\mathbf{A})$. Here is a formal definition.

Column space of a matrix

$$C(\mathbf{A}) = \{\beta_1 a_1 + ... \beta_n a_n, \quad \beta \in \mathbb{R}\} \tag{8.3}$$

$$C(\mathbf{A}) = span(a_1, ..., a_n) \tag{8.4}$$

The two equations above show two different, and equally accept-able, ways to express the same concept.

The main difference between a subspace spanned by a set of vectors vs. the column space of a matrix is conceptual: a set of vectors is a collection of separate objects, whereas a matrix is one unit; it can be convenient to talk about particular groups of elements in a matrix as if they were column vectors. But the matrix elements that form columns always are also part of rows, and they are also individual elements. That fluid level of reorganization isn't possible with sets.

The column space of an $M \times N$ matrix is in $\mathbb{R}^M$. Don't be confused and think that the column space is in $\mathbb{R}^N$ because there are N columns; each of those N columns has M elements, hence, $C(\mathbf{A}) \in \mathbb{R}^M$. If the rank of the matrix is $r = M$, then the column space spans all of $\mathbb{R}^M$; if the rank is $r < M$, then the column space is an r-dimensional subspace of $\mathbb{R}^M$.

Also relevant here is the distinction between basis and span. The columns of a matrix *span* a subspace, but they may or may not be a *basis* for that subspace. Remember that a set of vectors is a basis for a subspace only if that set is linearly independent.

Consider the two matrices below; their column spaces are identical, but the columns of the left matrix form a basis for that subspace, whereas the columns of the right matrix do not.

$$\begin{bmatrix} 3 & 9 \\ 7 & 5 \\ 1 & 8 \\ 2 & 7 \\ 9 & 6 \end{bmatrix}, \quad \begin{bmatrix} 3 & 9 & 9 \\ 7 & 5 & 5 \\ 1 & 8 & 8 \\ 2 & 7 & 7 \\ 9 & 6 & 6 \end{bmatrix}$$

Let's try a few examples. For each of the matrices below, determine (1) the dimensionality of the ambient space in which the column space is embedded, (2) the dimensionality of the column space, and (3) whether the columns form a basis for the column space.

$$\mathbf{B} = \begin{bmatrix} 1 & 2 & 4 \\ 0 & 4 & 4 \\ 4 & 1 & 9 \\ 6 & 0 & 12 \\ 1 & 1 & 3 \end{bmatrix}, \quad \mathbf{C} = \begin{bmatrix} 1 & 2 & 3 & 5 \\ 0 & 8 & 13 & 21 \\ 0 & 0 & 34 & 55 \\ 0 & 0 & 0 & 89 \end{bmatrix}, \quad \mathbf{D} = \begin{bmatrix} 1 & 5 & -3 & 4 \\ 2 & 6 & -2 & 4 \\ 3 & 7 & -1 & 4 \\ 4 & 8 & 0 & 4 \\ 5 & 9 & 1 & 4 \\ 6 & 10 & 2 & 4 \\ 7 & 11 & 3 & 4 \end{bmatrix}$$

The column spaces of matrices $\mathbf{B}$, $\mathbf{C}$, and $\mathbf{D}$ live in ambient dimensionalities, respectively, of 5, 4, and 7 (an alternative phrasing is that $C(\mathbf{B}) \in \mathbb{R}^5$, $C(\mathbf{C}) \in \mathbb{R}^4$, $C(\mathbf{D}) \in \mathbb{R}^7$); this is determined simply by counting the number of elements in the columns, which is M.

The dimensionalities of the column spaces is a bit more work to compute, because it involves determining the largest number of columns that can form a linearly independent set of vectors, which is the same thing as the rank of the matrix. Some trial-and-error guesswork plus a bit of arithmetic, should lead you to the answers of 2, 4, and 2.

Once you know the dimensionality of the column space, determining whether the columns form a basis for the column space is easy: The columns form a basis for the column space if the subspace dimensionality is the same as the number of columns. Thus, the answers for the three matrices are No, Yes, and No. It is possible to use the columns to create basis sets for the column spaces. For example, the first two columns of matrix $\mathbf{B}$ can be used as a basis set for $C(\mathbf{B})$.

As a quick reminder, there is an infinite number of basis vectors for the column space of a matrix; the columns themselves are an easy-to-compute basis, but they are not necessarily the best basis; in fact, one of the goals of the singular value decomposition is to provide an orthogonal basis set for the column space of the matrix.

8.2 The column space of A and AA^T

Interestingly, $\mathbf{A}$ and $\mathbf{AA}^T$ have the same column space. Let's first confirm that the dimension of their ambient spaces are the same: Matrix $\mathbf{A}$ is size $M \times N$, so $C(\mathbf{A}) \in \mathbb{R}^M$. Matrix $\mathbf{AA}^T$ is size $(M \times N) \times (N \times M) = M \times M$, and therefore is also $\in \mathbb{R}^M$. This doesn't prove that their column spaces are the same, but it is a prerequisite. (For example, it should now be obvious that $\mathbf{A}$ and $\mathbf{A}^T\mathbf{A}$ cannot possibly have the same column space if $M \neq N$).

Now let's see why the column spaces must be equal. Recall from section 6.1 that the "column perspective" of matrix multiplication states that multiplication is a linear weighted combination of the columns of the left matrix, where the weights come from the columns in the right matrix. Thus, $\mathbf{AA}^T$ is simply a linear weighted combination of the columns of $\mathbf{A}$, which means it is in the span of the column space of $\mathbf{A}$.

Let's see this in an example. I'm going to write out the multiplication $\mathbf{AA}^T$ using the column perspective.

$$\begin{bmatrix} 0 & 10 \\ 3 & 7 \\ 5 & 3 \end{bmatrix} \begin{bmatrix} 0 & 3 & 5 \\ 10 & 7 & 3 \end{bmatrix} = \begin{bmatrix} 0\begin{bmatrix} 0 \\ 3 \\ 5 \end{bmatrix} + 10\begin{bmatrix} 10 \\ 7 \\ 3 \end{bmatrix} & 3\begin{bmatrix} 0 \\ 3 \\ 5 \end{bmatrix} + 7\begin{bmatrix} 10 \\ 7 \\ 3 \end{bmatrix} & 5\begin{bmatrix} 0 \\ 3 \\ 5 \end{bmatrix} + 3\begin{bmatrix} 10 \\ 7 \\ 3 \end{bmatrix} \end{bmatrix}$$

Notice that each column in $\mathbf{AA}^T$ is simply a linear weighted combination of the columns of $\mathbf{A}$. This is an important observation because linear combinations of vectors in some subspace always stay in that subspace (indeed, that is the definition of subspace!). This shows that the column space of $\mathbf{AA}^T$ is a subset of the column space of $\mathbf{A}$.

Next we rely on the fact that $\mathbf{AA}^T$ and $\mathbf{A}$ have the same rank (see rank-nullity theorem, page 191), which means the dimensionalities of their column spaces are the same. If the column space of $\mathbf{AA}^T$ is a subset of the column space of $\mathbf{AA}^T$ and those two subspaces have the same dimensionality, then they must be equal.

There is another explanation of why $\mathbf{AA}^{\mathrm{T}}$ and $\mathbf{A}$ have the same subspace, which relies on the singular value decomposition. More on this in chapter 16!

On the other hand, $\mathbf{A}$ and $\mathbf{AA}^{\mathrm{T}}$ generally do not have exactly the same *columns*. So, the columns of those two matrices span the same subspace, but can have different basis sets.

8.3 Determining whether $\mathbf{v} \in C(\mathbf{A})$

This section is a deeper discussion of the algorithm presented in section 7.11. As a reminder, one of the important questions in linear algebra is whether a certain vector is in the column space of a matrix.

Let's start with an example. Consider the following matrix and vectors.

$$\mathbf{A} = \begin{bmatrix} 2 & 1 \\ 4 & 4 \\ 0 & 0 \end{bmatrix}, \qquad \mathbf{v} = \begin{bmatrix} 4 \\ 12 \\ 0 \end{bmatrix}, \; \mathbf{w} = \begin{bmatrix} 4 \\ 1 \\ 1 \end{bmatrix}$$

First, notice that the column space of $\mathbf{A}$ is a 2D plane embedded in $\mathbb{R}^3$. This is the case because the two columns form a linearly independent set (it is not possible to obtain one column by a scaled version of the other).

Now onto the question at hand: Is vector $\mathbf{v}$ in the column space of matrix $\mathbf{A}$? Formally, this is written as $\mathbf{v} \in C(\mathbf{A})$ or $\mathbf{v} \notin C(\mathbf{A})$. This is not a trivial question: We're asking whether a vector in 3D happens to lie on an infinitely thin plane.

For vector $\mathbf{v}$, the answer is Yes, $\mathbf{v} \in C(\mathbf{A})$, because it can be expressed as a linear combination of the columns in matrix $\mathbf{A}$. A bit of guesswork will lead to you to coefficients of (1,2) for the columns to produce the vector $\mathbf{v}$:

$$1\begin{bmatrix} 2 \\ 4 \\ 0 \end{bmatrix} + 2\begin{bmatrix} 1 \\ 4 \\ 0 \end{bmatrix} = \begin{bmatrix} 4 \\ 12 \\ 0 \end{bmatrix} \tag{8.5}$$

One of the beautiful features of linear algebra is that it allows expressing a large number of equations in a compact form. We can do that here by putting the column coefficients (1,2) into a vector, and then re-writing equation 8.5 as a matrix-vector multiplication of the form $\mathbf{Ax} = \mathbf{v}$:

$$\begin{bmatrix} 2 & 1 \\ 4 & 4 \\ 0 & 0 \end{bmatrix}\begin{bmatrix} 1 \\ 2 \end{bmatrix} = \begin{bmatrix} 4 \\ 12 \\ 0 \end{bmatrix} \quad \Rightarrow \quad \mathbf{Ax} = \mathbf{v} \tag{8.6}$$

Whenever you see a matrix equation, the first thing you should do is confirm that the matrix sizes allow for a valid equation. Here we have matrix sizes $(3 \times 2) \times (2 \times 1) = (3 \times 1)$. That works.

Now let's consider vector $\mathbf{w}$. It should take only a moment's inspection to see that $\mathbf{w}$ cannot be expressed as a linear combination of columns in $\mathbf{A}$, because $w_3 = 1$ cannot be created from linear combinations of 0, therefore $\mathbf{w} \notin C(\mathbf{A})$.

We could also write
$\mathbf{Ax} \neq \mathbf{w}, \ \forall \mathbf{x} \in \mathbb{R}^{N}$

The "augment-rank" algorithm to determine whether $\mathbf{v} \in C(\mathbf{A})$
I've mentioned this algorithm twice in previous chapters; the novel part here is the application to determining whether a vector is in the column space of a matrix.

Start by creating a matrix $\mathbf{B} = \mathbf{A} \sqcup \mathbf{v}$ (that is, augment the matrix with the vector). Then compute the ranks of these two matrices ($\mathbf{B}$ and $\mathbf{A}$). There are two possible outcomes: (1) the ranks are the same, which means that $\mathbf{v} \in C(\mathbf{A})$; or (2) the rank of $\mathbf{B}$ is one higher than the rank of $\mathbf{A}$, which means that $\mathbf{v} \notin C(\mathbf{A})$.

Why is this the case? You can think about it geometrically: If $\mathbf{v}$ is in the column space of $\mathbf{A}$, then the vector is sitting somewhere in

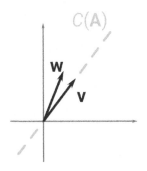

Figure 8.1: The dashed gray line represents $C(\mathbf{M}) \in \mathbb{R}^2$. Then $\mathbf{v} \in C(\mathbf{M})$ and $\mathbf{w} \notin C(\mathbf{M})$

the subspace, hence, no new geometric directions are obtained by including vector $\mathbf{v}$. In contrast, if $\mathbf{v}$ is outside the column space, then it points off in some other geometric dimension that is not spanned by the column space; hence, $\mathbf{B}$ has one extra geometric dimension not contained in $\mathbf{A}$, and thus the rank is one higher. This is depicted in Figure 8.1.

You can also think about it algebraically: If $\mathbf{v}$ can be obtained by a linear weighted combination of columns in $\mathbf{A}$, then augmenting $\mathbf{A}$ by $\mathbf{v}$ is necessarily creating a linearly dependent set, thus the rank cannot possible increase.

A corollary of this method is that if $\mathbf{A}$ is full rank square matrix (that is, rank$=M$), then $\mathbf{v}$ is necessarily in the column space, because it is not possible to have a subspace with more than M dimensions in $\mathbb{R}^M$.

This algorithm only tells you *whether* a vector is in the column of a matrix. It doesn't reveal *how* to combine the columns of the matrix to express that vector. For that, you can apply a procedure called Gaussian elimination, which is a major topic of Chapter 10. In the practice problems below, you can use a bit of trial-and-error and educated guessing to find the coefficients.

Practice problems Determine whether the following vectors are in the column space of the accompanying matrices, and, if so, the coefficients on the columns to reproduce the vector.

a) $\begin{bmatrix} 1 \\ 2 \end{bmatrix}, \begin{bmatrix} 0 & 1 \\ 1 & 0 \end{bmatrix}$

b) $\begin{bmatrix} 1 \\ 2 \\ 0 \end{bmatrix}, \begin{bmatrix} 0 & 1 & 1 \\ 1 & 0 & 0 \\ 3 & 3 & 0 \end{bmatrix}$

c) $\begin{bmatrix} 1 \\ 2 \\ 0 \end{bmatrix}, \begin{bmatrix} 0 & 1 \\ 1 & 0 \\ 3 & 3 \end{bmatrix}$

Answers

a) yes. (2,1)

b) yes. (2,-2,3)

c) no.

8.4 Row space of a matrix

The *row space* of a matrix, indicated by $R(\mathbf{A})$, is the same concept as the column space, except it refers to the subspace spanned by the rows. This means it is also the same thing as the column space of the matrix transpose, in other words, $R(\mathbf{A}) = C(\mathbf{A}^{\mathrm{T}})$. Therefore, there isn't really anything new in this section compared to section 8.1.

The primary difference is the way that you ask the question whether a given vector is in the row space of the matrix. In particular, this changes how you multiply the matrix and the vector: Instead of matrix-vector multiplication as with the column space ($\mathbf{A}\mathbf{x} = \mathbf{v}$), you have to put the row vector on the left side of the matrix, like this: $\mathbf{x}^{\mathrm{T}}\mathbf{A} = \mathbf{v}^{\mathrm{T}}$. Now the weighting vector $\mathbf{x}$, sometimes also called the coefficients vector, is a row vector on the left, meaning that we are taking weighted combinations of *rows* of $\mathbf{A}$ instead of columns.

An example: The row space of the matrix $\begin{bmatrix} 1 & 2 & 0 & -3 \end{bmatrix}$ is a line in $\mathbb{R}^4$. This is quite a different conceptualization from the column space of that matrix, which is all of $\mathbb{R}^1$. (Though notice that the dimensionalities are the same.)

You can apply a slightly modified version of the augment-rank algorithm to determine whether a vector is in the row space of a matrix: Place the vector as a new *row* in the matrix and then compute the rank of that row-augmented matrix.

Note that for a square full-rank matrix, $C(\mathbf{A}) = R(\mathbf{A}) = \mathbb{R}^{\mathrm{N}}$.

Practice problems Determine whether the following vectors are in the row space of the accompanying matrices, and, if so, the coefficients on the rows to reproduce the vector.

a) $\begin{bmatrix} \pi \\ 0 \end{bmatrix}^{\mathrm{T}}, \begin{bmatrix} 0 & 1 \\ 0 & 1 \end{bmatrix}$

b) $\begin{bmatrix} 1 \\ 1 \\ 1 \end{bmatrix}^{\mathrm{T}}, \begin{bmatrix} 0 & 1 & 1 \\ 2 & 1 & 1 \\ 0 & 0 & 0 \end{bmatrix}$

c) $\begin{bmatrix} 1 \\ 2 \\ 0 \end{bmatrix}^{\mathrm{T}}, \begin{bmatrix} 0 & 1 \\ 1 & 0 \\ 3 & 3 \end{bmatrix}$

Answers

a) no.

b) yes. (.5,.5,0)

c) wrong sizes!

Row spaces of A and $\mathrm{A^T A}$

Simply put, $\mathbf{A}$ and $\mathbf{A^T A}$ have the same row spaces ($R(\mathbf{A}) = R(\mathbf{A^T A})$). The arguments, explanations, and implications are exactly the same as with the column spaces discussed in section 8.2.

One new concept I will add here is that the fact that $R(\mathbf{A}) = R(\mathbf{A^T A})$ can be an example of dimensionality reduction: both of those matrices have the same row space, but $\mathbf{A^T A}$ might be a smaller matrix (that is, it might have fewer numbers), and therefore be computationally easier to work with.

Null space of a matrix

The null space is also sometimes called the *kernel* of the matrix.

You might be wondering what "null" refers to—you know what columns and rows are, but what is the "null" of a matrix? The null space of a matrix is like the basement of a cheesy horror movie: Not every house has a basement, but if there is one, anyone who goes into it won't come out. Likewise, not all matrices have a null space, but if a matrix has a null space and a vector goes into it, that vector can never return.

More formally, the null space of a matrix is indicated as $N(\mathbf{A})$ and is defined as the subspace containing all of the vectors that satisfy the following equation:

$$\mathbf{Ay} = \mathbf{0} \tag{8.7}$$

This means that there is a linear combination of the columns in matrix $\mathbf{A}$ that produces a column vector of zeros, and the elements of vector $\mathbf{y}$ specify those weightings.

When can Equation 8.7 be satisfied? Let us count the ways:

1. When $\mathbf{y} = \mathbf{0}$. This is the trivial case, and we ignore trivial cases in linear algebra.
2. When not all elements in $\mathbf{y}$ are zero, and the specific numbers in $\mathbf{y}$ and $\mathbf{A}$ align in just the right way that the matrix-vector product is the zeros vector. This is the non-trivial case, and our primary concern here.

Let's see an example to make this more concrete. See if you can come up with a vector (that is, find x and y) that satisfies the equation.

$$\begin{bmatrix} 1 & 2 \\ 4 & 8 \end{bmatrix} \begin{bmatrix} x \\ y \end{bmatrix} = \begin{bmatrix} 0 \\ 0 \end{bmatrix} \tag{8.8}$$

Did you come up with the vector $[\text{-}2 \ 1]^T$? That satisfies the equation and therefore is in the null space of that matrix (thus: $\mathbf{y} \in N(\mathbf{A})$).

But that's not the only vector that satisfies that equation—perhaps your solution was $[2 \ \text{-}1]^T$ or $[\text{-}1 \ .5]^T$ or $[\text{-}2000 \ 1000]^T$. I'm sure you see where this is going: There is an infinite number of vectors in the null space of this matrix, and all of those vectors are scaled versions of each other. In other words:

$$N\left(\begin{bmatrix} 1 & 2 \\ 4 & 8 \end{bmatrix} \right) = \left\{ \sigma \begin{bmatrix} -2 \\ 1 \end{bmatrix}, \quad \sigma \in \mathbb{R} \right\} \tag{8.9}$$

As mentioned earlier, the zeros vector also satisfies the equation, but that's a trivial solution and we ignore it.

Here is the complete definition of the null space of a matrix:

Null space of a matrix

$$N(\mathbf{A}) = \{\lambda \mathbf{y} \mid \mathbf{A}\mathbf{y} = \mathbf{0}, \quad \lambda \in \mathbb{R}\} - \{\mathbf{y} = \mathbf{0}\} \qquad (8.10)$$

(Aside on math notation: The | indicates "such that" and the minus sign excludes **0** from the set.)

Now let's try another example:

$$\begin{bmatrix} 1 & 2 \\ 4 & 7 \end{bmatrix} \begin{bmatrix} x \\ y \end{bmatrix} = \begin{bmatrix} 0 \\ 0 \end{bmatrix} \qquad (8.11)$$

Can you find a (non-trivial) vector in the null space? The answer is No, you cannot. There is no way to combine the columns to produce the zeros vector. It is colloquially said that this matrix "has no null space," although a more appropriate phrasing would be that the null space of this matrix is the empty set (again, the trivial zeros vector is ignored):

$$N\left(\begin{bmatrix} 1 & 2 \\ 4 & 7 \end{bmatrix}\right) = \{\} \qquad (8.12)$$

Did you notice anything about the two matrices in equations 8.8 and 8.11? Perhaps you noticed that the matrix in 8.8 was singular (rank=1) while the matrix in 8.11 was full rank (rank=2). This is no coincidence—full-rank square matrices and full-column-rank matrices necessarily have an empty null space, whereas reduced-rank and reduced-column-rank matrices necessarily have a non-empty null space. You'll learn more about why this is in a few pages.

The previous examples used square matrices; below are two examples of rectangular matrices so you can see that null space is not just for squares. The hard work of finding the vector $\mathbf{y}$ is already done, so pay attention to the sizes: the null space is all about linear weighted combinations of the N columns, which are in $\mathbb{R}^M$, and the vector that contains the weightings for the columns is $\mathbf{y} \in \mathbb{R}^N$, corresponding to the dimensionality of the row space.

$$\begin{bmatrix} 1 & 2 \\ 1 & 2 \\ 1 & 2 \\ 1 & 2 \end{bmatrix} \begin{bmatrix} -2 \\ 1 \end{bmatrix} = \begin{bmatrix} 0 \\ 0 \\ 0 \\ 0 \end{bmatrix}, \qquad \begin{bmatrix} 1 & 1 & 1 & 1 & -4 \\ 2 & 2 & 2 & 2 & -8 \end{bmatrix} \begin{bmatrix} 1 \\ 1 \\ 1 \\ 1 \\ 1 \end{bmatrix} = \begin{bmatrix} 0 \\ 0 \end{bmatrix}$$

There is a deterministic relationship between the rank of a matrix, its size, and the dimensionality of the four matrix spaces. We will return to this in section 8.10.

Practice problems Find a vector in the null space of each matrix, if there is one.

a) $\begin{bmatrix} 1 & 0 \\ 4 & 0 \\ 2 & 0 \\ 1 & 0 \end{bmatrix}$
b) $\begin{bmatrix} 1 & 2 & 3 \\ 3 & 1 & 4 \\ 4 & 4 & 8 \end{bmatrix}$
c) $\begin{bmatrix} 1 & 2 & 3 \\ 3 & 1 & 5 \\ 4 & 4 & 8 \end{bmatrix}$
d) $\begin{bmatrix} -5 & 5 & 5 \\ -3 & 7 & 15 \end{bmatrix}$

Answers

a) $\begin{bmatrix} 0 \\ 1 \end{bmatrix}$
b) $\begin{bmatrix} 1 \\ 1 \\ -1 \end{bmatrix}$
c) Empty null space
d) $\begin{bmatrix} 2 \\ 3 \\ -1 \end{bmatrix}$

Practice problems For each combination of matrix and vectors, determine whether neither, one, or both vectors are in the null space of the matrix.

a) $\begin{bmatrix} 1 & 1 \\ 2 & 1 \\ 4 & 0 \end{bmatrix}, \begin{bmatrix} -1 \\ 1 \end{bmatrix}, \begin{bmatrix} -2 \\ -1 \end{bmatrix}$
b) $\begin{bmatrix} 0 & 0 & 0 \\ 0 & 0 & 0 \\ 0 & 0 & 1 \end{bmatrix}, \begin{bmatrix} 1 \\ 1 \\ 0 \end{bmatrix}, \begin{bmatrix} 0 \\ 1 \\ 0 \end{bmatrix}$
c) $\begin{bmatrix} 1 & 2 & 3 \\ 3 & 1 & 5 \\ 4 & 4 & 8 \\ 0 & 4 & 2 \end{bmatrix}, \begin{bmatrix} 0 \\ 1 \\ 0 \\ 2 \end{bmatrix}, \begin{bmatrix} 1 \\ -2 \\ -1 \\ 0 \end{bmatrix}$

Answers

a) Neither
b) Both
c) Wrong sizes!

Left-null space There is a complementary space to the null space, called the *left-null space*, which is the same concept but with a row vector on the left of the matrix instead of a column vector on the right of the matrix. The resulting zeros vector is also a row vector. It looks like this:

$$\mathbf{y}^{\mathrm{T}}\mathbf{A} = \mathbf{0}^{\mathrm{T}} \qquad (8.13)$$

The left-null space can be thought of as the "regular" null space of the matrix transpose. This becomes apparent when transposing both sides of Equation 8.13.

The "regular" null space is formally the "right null space," but this is implied when referring to the "null space."

$$(\mathbf{y}^\mathrm{T}\mathbf{A})^\mathrm{T} = \mathbf{0}^\mathrm{TT}$$

$$\mathbf{A}^\mathrm{T}\mathbf{y} = \mathbf{0} \tag{8.14}$$

Considering the left-null space as the (right) null space of the matrix transpose is analogous to how $R(\mathbf{A}) = C(\mathbf{A}^\mathrm{T})$. This also means that the two null spaces are equal when the matrix is symmetric:

This result is not terribly surprising, but it is relevant for finding null space basis vectors via the SVD.

$$N(\mathbf{A}) = N(\mathbf{A}^\mathrm{T}), \quad \text{if } \mathbf{A} = \mathbf{A}^\mathrm{T} \tag{8.15}$$

Let's think about the dimensionality of the left-null space. It should be intuitive that it will mirror the null space. I'll start by showing the left-null spaces of the two rectangular matrices used above, and then discuss the rule. Notice that the null-space vector is now on the left of the matrix.

$$\begin{bmatrix} -1 & -1 & 1 & 1 \end{bmatrix} \begin{bmatrix} 1 & 2 \\ 1 & 2 \\ 1 & 2 \\ 1 & 2 \end{bmatrix} = \begin{bmatrix} 0 & 0 \end{bmatrix} \tag{8.16}$$

$$\begin{bmatrix} -2 & 1 \end{bmatrix} \begin{bmatrix} 1 & 1 & 1 & 1 & -4 \\ 2 & 2 & 2 & 2 & -8 \end{bmatrix} = \begin{bmatrix} 0 & 0 & 0 & 0 \end{bmatrix} \tag{8.17}$$

Here's the rule: For an $M \times N$ matrix, the row space is in ambient $\mathbb{R}^N$ and the left-null space is in ambient $\mathbb{R}^M$. Again, this is sensible because the left-null space provides a weighting of all the rows to produce the zeros row vector. There are M rows and so a null space vector must have M elements.

Look closely at Equation 8.16: Is that vector the *only* vector in the left-null space? I'm not referring to scaled version of that vector; I mean that there are more vectors in the left-null space that are separate from the one I printed. How many more (non-trivial) vectors can you identify?

MATRIX SPACES

Practice problems Find a vector in the left-null space of each matrix, if there is one. Notice that these matrices appeared in the practice problems on page 217; are the answers the same?

a) $\begin{bmatrix} 1 & 0 \\ 4 & 0 \\ 2 & 0 \\ 1 & 0 \end{bmatrix}$
b) $\begin{bmatrix} 1 & 2 & 3 \\ 3 & 1 & 4 \\ 4 & 4 & 8 \end{bmatrix}$
c) $\begin{bmatrix} 1 & 2 & 3 \\ 3 & 1 & 5 \\ 4 & 4 & 8 \end{bmatrix}$
d) $\begin{bmatrix} -5 & 5 & 5 \\ -3 & 7 & 15 \end{bmatrix}$

Answers

a) $\begin{bmatrix} 1 & 0 & -1 & 1 \end{bmatrix}$
b) $\begin{bmatrix} -8 & -4 & 5 \end{bmatrix}$
c) Empty left null space
d) Empty left null space

Code Python and MATLAB will return basis vectors for the null space of a matrix (if it has one). How do they solve this seemingly magical feat? They use the singular value decomposition! However, you'll have to wait several more chapters to understand why the SVD reveals bases for the null space.

Code block 8.1: Python

```
1  import numpy as np
2  from scipy.linalg import null_space
3  A = np.random.randn(3,4)
4  null_space(A)
```

Code block 8.2: MATLAB

```
1  A = randn(3,4);
2  null(A)
```

Geometric interpretation of the null space

Now that you know the horror-movie analogy (the evil basement from which no unsuspecting visitors return) and the algebraic definition ($\mathbf{Ay} = \mathbf{0}$), this is a good time to learn the geometric perspective of the null space.

Recall that a matrix times a vector produces another vector. We'll stick to $\mathbb{R}^2$ here so that everything can be easily visualized. Consider the following matrix and vectors.

$$\mathbf{M} = \begin{bmatrix} 1 & 2 \\ 2 & 4 \end{bmatrix}, \qquad \mathbf{u} = \begin{bmatrix} -1 \\ 1 \end{bmatrix}, \qquad \mathbf{y} = \begin{bmatrix} -2 \\ 1 \end{bmatrix}$$

Matrix $\mathbf{M}$ is singular and has a non-empty, 1-dimensional, null space. $\mathbf{u}$ is *not* in the matrix's null space, and $\mathbf{y}$ *is* in the null space (please do the matrix-vector multiplications in your head to confirm).

You can think of matrix $\mathbf{M}$ as a transformation matrix that warps vector $\mathbf{y}$ into vector $\mathbf{My}$. Figure 8.2 shows what that looks like.

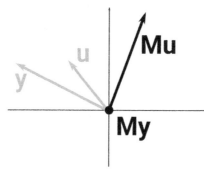

Figure 8.2: Depiction of vectors $\mathbf{y} \in N(\mathbf{M})$ and $\mathbf{u} \notin N(\mathbf{M})$. The vectors on their own are not remarkable; however, when multiplied by the matrix, y becomes the zeros vector (dot at the origin), whereas u is some other (non-zeros) vector.

Figure 8.2 shows that when you multiply a vector in the null space by that matrix, the resulting "vector" is just a point at the origin. And that's basically the end of the line for this matrix-vector product $\mathbf{My}$—it cannot do anything else but sit in the origin. Just like the basement of a horror movie: Once you go in, you never come out. There is no escape. There is no possible other matrix $\mathbf{A}$ such that $\mathbf{AMy} \neq \mathbf{0}$. In other words, the matrix entered its null space and became a singularity at the origin; no other matrix can bring it back from the abyss.

On the other hand, because matrix multiplication is not commutative, $\mathbf{AMy} \neq \mathbf{MAy}$. Try this yourself: Come up with a matrix $\mathbf{A}$ and prove to yourself that $\mathbf{MAy} \neq \mathbf{0}$. This will work for nearly any matrix as long as $\mathbf{A}$ is not the identity or the zeros matrices. Just pick four random integers and it will almost certainly work.

And this brings me to the final point I want to make in this section:

There is nothing special about vector **y**, and there is nothing special about matrix **M**. Instead, what is special is their *combination*, that $\mathbf{y} \in N(\mathbf{M})$. $\mathbf{MAy} \neq \mathbf{0}$ because **y** is not in the null space of matrix **A**, and vector **Ay** is not in the null space of matrix **M** (it could be if **A** is the identity matrix, the zeros matrix, or has **y** as an eigenvector, but that is galactically unlikely when populating **A** with random integers).

Practice problems For the following matrices, find a basis for the column space and a basis for the left-null space. Then draw those two basis vectors on the same Cartesian plot (one plot per matrix). Do you notice anything about the plots?

a) $\begin{bmatrix} 1 & 2 \\ 2 & 4 \end{bmatrix}$
b) $\begin{bmatrix} -3 & 1 \\ 6 & -2 \end{bmatrix}$

Answers In both cases, the column space and the left-null space are orthogonal to each other. You can easily confirm that in these examples by computing the dot products between the basis vectors. That's not just some quirky effect of these specific matrices; that's a general principle, and you will soon learn the reason why. (You can repeat this exercise for the row space and the null space and arrive at the same conclusion.)

8.8 Orthogonal subspaces, orthogonal complements

The four subspaces of a matrix—the column space, row space, null space, and left-null space—come in two pairs of *orthogonal complements*. Before explaining what that means and why it's important, I need to take a brief aside and explain the concepts of orthogonal subspaces and orthogonal complements.

You already know what it means for two lines to be orthogonal to each other (dot product of zero; meet at a right angle); what does it mean for two *subspaces* to be orthogonal? Let me start by mentioning something that's pretty obvious when you think about it: If a pair of vectors is orthogonal, then any scalar-vector multiplication will also be orthogonal.

$$\mathbf{v} \perp \mathbf{w} \quad \Rightarrow \quad \sigma\mathbf{v} \perp \lambda\mathbf{w}, \quad \sigma, \lambda \in \mathbb{R} \qquad (8.18)$$

The reason why Equation 8.18 is obvious is that if $\mathbf{v}^\mathsf{T}\mathbf{w} = 0$ then any scalar times 0 is still 0.

Now let's take this one step further: Imagine that two vectors $\mathbf{v_1}$ and $\mathbf{v_2}$ are each orthogonal to $\mathbf{w}$. They don't have to be orthogonal to each other. Here's an example:

$$\mathbf{v_1} = \begin{bmatrix} 1 \\ 1 \\ 2 \end{bmatrix}, \quad \mathbf{v_2} = \begin{bmatrix} 2 \\ 2 \\ 6 \end{bmatrix}, \quad \mathbf{w} = \begin{bmatrix} -1 \\ 1 \\ 0 \end{bmatrix},$$

Take a moment to confirm that $\mathbf{v_1}$ and $\mathbf{v_2}$ are each individually orthogonal to $\mathbf{w}$, and that they are *not* orthogonal to each other.

Now we can combine this concept with Equation 8.18 to write a new equation:

$$(\alpha_1 \mathbf{v_1} + \alpha_2 \mathbf{v_2}) \perp \beta \mathbf{w} \tag{8.19}$$

This equation says that *any linear combination* of $\mathbf{v_1}$ and $\mathbf{v_2}$ is orthogonal to any scaled version of $\mathbf{w}$.

Each side of Equation 8.19 is consistent with the definition of a vector subspace (Equation 4.1, page 84). Thus, we have just extended the notion of orthogonality from vectors to subspaces (hence: $V \perp W$). The interpretation is that any linear combination of vectors in subspace V is orthogonal to any linear combination of vectors in subspace W.

In this example, V is a 2D subspace and W is a 1D subspace, and they are both embedded in ambient $\mathbb{R}^3$. Two subspaces can be orthogonal only if they are in the same ambient dimensionality, because orthogonality is defined by dot products, and dot products are defined only for vectors with the same dimensionality.

Here is the formal definition of orthogonal subspaces:

Orthogonal subspaces

Subspaces S and M are orthogonal subspaces if

$$\forall \mathbf{v} \in S \text{ and } \forall \mathbf{w} \in M, \quad \mathbf{v} \perp \mathbf{w} \tag{8.20}$$

Read aloud, this definition is "For any vector **v** in subspace S, and for any vector **w** in subspace W, vector **v** is orthogonal to vector **w**.

Can you think of a geometric example of two orthogonal subspaces? You might initially think about two planes in $\mathbb{R}^3$ intersecting in a perpendicular line, like Figure 8.3.

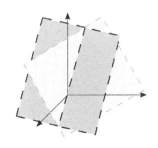

Figure 8.3: Two 2D subspaces in $\mathbb{R}^3$ cannot be orthogonal subspaces.

But alas, no, these planes are not orthogonal subspaces. The line of intersection between these two planes is a vector that is contained in both subspaces. And a vector that appears is both subspaces is clearly not orthogonal to itself. Of course, there can be many vectors in one plane that are orthogonal to many vectors in the other plane, but for the two subspaces to be orthogonal, *every possible vector* needs to be orthogonal.

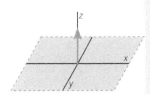

Figure 8.4: A 1D subspace can be an orthogonal complement to a 2D subspace in $\mathbb{R}^3$.

In fact, in $\mathbb{R}^3$ it is impossible for two *planes* to be orthogonal subspaces: They are 2D objects, and two 2D objects cannot possibly be orthogonal in a 3D space. A plane and a line, however, can be orthogonal complements if the line is orthogonal to the plane. The simplest example of this is the plane defined by the XY axis, and a line on the Z axis (Figure 8.4).

Orthogonal complements This leads us to *orthogonal complements*. The idea of orthogonal complements is that any ambient space $\mathbb{R}^N$ can be decomposed into two subspaces W and V such that $W \cup V$ spans all of $\mathbb{R}^N$ and $W \perp V$. In other words, the entire ambient space is carved into subspaces that are mutually orthogonal and that meet only at the origin (all subspaces meet at the origin).

Don't confuse complement with compliment! (Although both are things you should do for your significant other.)

"Mutually orthogonal" means that a vector cannot be in both subspaces. Thus, any vector in $\mathbb{R}^N$ that is not in W must be in V, and if it's in V then it must be orthogonal to any vector in W.

Orthogonalities of the matrix spaces

Now that you know what orthogonal subspaces and orthogonal complements are, let's get back to the task at hand, which is discussing how the four subspaces of a matrix are paired into two orthogonal complements.

Orthogonality of the column space and the left-null space A vector is orthogonal to the column space of a matrix if the following equation is satisfied:

$$\mathbf{y} \perp C(\mathbf{A}) \tag{8.21}$$

What does it mean for vector $\mathbf{y}$ to be orthogonal to the column space of $\mathbf{A}$? It means that $\mathbf{y}$ is orthogonal to each column individually, and therefore that $\mathbf{y}$ is orthogonal to all possible linear combinations of the columns.

We can re-write this statement as the following matrix-vector equation:

$$\mathbf{A}^{\mathrm{T}}\mathbf{y} = \mathbf{0} \tag{8.22}$$

Note: $\mathbf{0} \in \mathbb{R}^{N}$.

Remarkably, we've just re-derived Equation 8.13 (see also Equation 8.14), which was the definition of the left-null space. That's pretty neat, because we started from the question of a vector that is orthogonal to the *column space*, and we ended up re-discovering the *left-null space*.

What is the justification for transposing the matrix? Because the *columns* of $\mathbf{A}$ are the *rows* of $\mathbf{A}^{\mathrm{T}}$ (Figure 8.5), the multiplication $\mathbf{A}^{\mathrm{T}}\mathbf{y}$ involves the dot product between vector $\mathbf{y}$ and each column of $\mathbf{A}$. The question at hand here is whether we can find a vector $\mathbf{y}$ that has a dot product of zero with each column in $\mathbf{A}$.

$$\begin{bmatrix} a & b & c \\ a & b & c \\ a & b & c \end{bmatrix}^{\mathrm{T}} = \begin{bmatrix} a & a & a \\ b & b & b \\ c & c & c \end{bmatrix}$$

Figure 8.5: The columns of A are the rows of $\mathbf{A}^{\mathrm{T}}$.

The orthogonality of the column space and left-null space is a big deal, because we're talking about entire subspaces, not just individual vectors. A vector is a mere finite object, but subspaces are infinite expanses. Thus, the column space and the left-null space are orthogonal complements, and so together they must fill up the entire ambient space of $\mathbb{R}^M$.

$$C(\mathbf{A}) \cup N(\mathbf{A}^{\mathrm{T}}) \iff \mathbb{R}^M \qquad (8.23)$$

Let me explain that again so it's clear: For any given $M{\times}N$ matrix, *every* vector in $\mathbb{R}^M$ is either in the column space or in the left-null space. No vector can be in both (because they are orthogonal subspaces) except for the trivial zeros vector. Therefore, the column space and the left-null space together span all of $\mathbb{R}^M$.

Analogously, if someone asks you if you want ice cream with sprinkles, ice cream without sprinkles, or no ice cream, then those mutually exclusive options literally account for every imaginable thing in the universe.

OK, perhaps not a perfect analogy, but the point is that I like sprinkles without ice cream.

One implication of Equation 8.23 is that if the column space of the matrix spans all of $\mathbb{R}^M$, then the left-null space must be empty, because only the zeros vector can be orthogonal to an entire ambient space.

A visual example This is all quite theoretical; a visualizable example should help internalize the concept. Below are two matrices; Please take a moment to find bases for the column and left-null spaces of each matrix, then graph those vectors and compute the dot product between them. Then look at the next page to see my solution. No cheating!

$$\mathbf{B} = \begin{bmatrix} 1 & 1 \\ 2 & 2 \end{bmatrix}, \quad \mathbf{D} = \begin{bmatrix} 1 & 1 \\ 2 & 3 \end{bmatrix}$$

I chose the following as bases:

$$C(\mathbf{B}) = \left\{ \begin{bmatrix} 1 \\ 2 \end{bmatrix} \right\}, \qquad N(\mathbf{B}^{\mathrm{T}}) = \left\{ \begin{bmatrix} -2 \\ 1 \end{bmatrix} \right\}$$

$$C(\mathbf{D}) = \left\{ \begin{bmatrix} 1 & 1 \\ 2 & 3 \end{bmatrix} \right\}, \quad N(\mathbf{D}^{\mathrm{T}}) = \left\{ [\,] \right\}$$

The easiest way to choose a basis for the column space is to take the first r columns, where r is the rank of the matrix (make sure that those columns form a linearly independent set). Of course, this isn't necessarily *the best* basis set; it's just *the easiest* for small matrices.

Figure 8.6 shows these vectors, with black lines for the column space basis vectors and gray lines for the left-null space basis vectors.

Matrix **D** has an empty null space, which I've depicted as a dot at the origin of the graph. It's visually apparent that the column spaces are orthogonal to their respective left-null spaces.

Figure 8.6: Basis vectors for the column and null spaces of matrices B and D.

The orthogonality of $C(\mathbf{A})$ and $N(\mathbf{A}^{\mathrm{T}})$ will lead us to an important discovery about matrix subspace dimensionalities. That's the main topic of the next section. But first, I want to discuss the other pair of complementary matrix spaces, which are the row space and the null space.

Orthogonality of the row space and the null space There isn't
a lot to say here that isn't written above. Just swap "column"
with "row" and "left-null space" with "null space." I will briefly walk
through the reasoning as above but using slightly different notation,
for variety.

The idea is to find a vector that is orthogonal to all rows in $\mathbf{A}$, in
other words, $\mathbf{y} \perp R(\mathbf{A})$.

We can express this by writing that the dot product between each
row of the matrix (indicated as $\mathbf{a}_m$ below) and the vector $\mathbf{y}$ is 0.

$$\mathbf{a}_1\mathbf{y} = 0$$

$$\mathbf{a}_2\mathbf{y} = 0$$

$$\vdots$$

$$\mathbf{a}_m\mathbf{y} = 0$$

And then we simply collect all of these individual equations into
one compact matrix equation, which is, of course, the definition of
the null space.

$$\mathbf{A}\mathbf{y} = \mathbf{0}$$

As with the column and left-null spaces, the row space and null
space are orthogonal complements that together span all of $\mathbb{R}^N$:

$$C(\mathbf{A}^T) \cup N(\mathbf{A}) \; \Leftrightarrow \; \mathbb{R}^N \tag{8.24}$$

Any vector in $\mathbb{R}^N$ is either in the row space or in the null space.
The only vector that can be in both spaces is the N-element zeros
vector.

8.10 Dimensionalities of matrix spaces

The dimensionalities of the column space, the row space, and the
two null spaces are all interconnected.

First, I want to reiterate that "dimension" is not the same thing as "rank." The rank is a property of a matrix, and it's the same regardless of whether you are thinking about rows, columns, or null spaces. The ambient dimensionality differs between rows and columns for non-square matrices.

On the other hand, the dimensionality of the *subspaces spanned* by the column space and the row space is the same, and those equal the rank of the matrix. An example of this dissociation is the following 3×3, rank-2 matrix. To its right are the rank and dimensionalities ($dim()$ indicates the dimensionality) of two of its subspaces.

$$\mathbf{A} = \begin{bmatrix} 1 & 0 & 3 \\ 0 & 4 & 5 \\ 2 & 0 & 6 \end{bmatrix}, \qquad \begin{array}{c} \mathbf{A} \in \mathbb{R}^{3 \times 3} \\ rank(\mathbf{A}) = 2 \\ dim(N(\mathbf{A})) = 1 \\ dim(C(\mathbf{A})) = 2 \end{array}$$

The null space contains one basis vector, which means it has dimensionality of one, while the column and row spaces each has dimensionalities of 2 (notice that row 3 is a multiple of row 1). The rank of the matrix is also 2.

You can see in this example that the dimensionality of the column space plus the dimensionality of the left-null space adds up to the ambient dimensionality $\mathbb{R}^3$.

Two more examples and then I'll present the rules: If the column space is 2D and embedded in $\mathbb{R}^2$, then the column space already covers the entire ambient space, which means there's nothing for the left-null space to capture; the left-null space *must* therefore be the empty set. Here's a matrix to illustrate this point; note that the left-null is empty, because there is no way to combine the rows of the matrix (or, the columns of the matrix transpose) to get a vector of zeros.

$$\begin{bmatrix} 1 & 1 \\ 2 & 3 \end{bmatrix}$$

Final example: The 2×2 zeros matrix has columns in ambient $\mathbb{R}^2$, but the column space is empty; it contains nothing but a point at the origin. It is 0-dimensional. Therefore, its orthogonal complement must fill up the entirety of $\mathbb{R}^2$. This tells us that the left-null space must be 2-dimensional. What is a basis set for that left-null space? Literally any independent set of vectors can be a basis set. A common choice in this situation is the identity matrix, but that's because it's convenient, not because it's the only basis set.

The story is the same for the row space and the null space, so I will just re-state it briefly: The row space lives in ambient $\mathbb{R}^N$ but can span a lower-dimensional subspace depending on the elements in the matrix. The orthogonal complement—the null space—fills up whatever directions in $\mathbb{R}^N$ are not already spanned by the row space. If the matrix is full-row rank, then the row space already spans all of $\mathbb{R}^N$ and therefore the null space must be empty.

The formulas   Here you go:

$$\underbrace{C(\mathbf{A}) \cup N(\mathbf{A}^{\mathrm{T}})}_{\mathbb{R}^M} \qquad \underbrace{R(\mathbf{A}) \cup N(\mathbf{A})}_{\mathbb{R}^N}$$

And with numbered equations in a grey box:

Subspace dimensionalities

$$dim(C(\mathbf{A})) + dim(N(\mathbf{A}^{\mathrm{T}})) = M \qquad (8.25)$$

$$dim(R(\mathbf{A})) + dim(N(\mathbf{A})) = N \qquad (8.26)$$

One more relevant formula: The rank of the matrix is the dimensionality of the column space, which is the same as the dimensionality of the row space:

$$rank(\mathbf{A}) = dim(C(\mathbf{A})) = dim(R(\mathbf{A})) \qquad (8.27)$$

8.11 More on $\mathbf{Ax} = \mathbf{b}$ and $\mathbf{Ay} = 0$

These two equations are simple yet profound. It is no understatement to write that *most people learn linear algebra because they want to know how to solve these equations.* You might not realize that this is what you want to solve, but most of applied linear algebra boils down to solving one of these two equations.

Let's start with $\mathbf{Ax} = \mathbf{b}$. In this category of problems, you know *a priori* the matrix $\mathbf{A}$ and the vector $\mathbf{b}$, and the goal of the analysis is to find the vector $\mathbf{x}$. Basically all linear models in statistics and machine learning can be expressed using this form.

The letters might look different, though. For example, in statistics, the common form is $\mathbf{X}\beta = \mathbf{y}$, where $\mathbf{X}$ is called the "design matrix," β is called the "regression coefficients," and $\mathbf{y}$ is called the "observed data." You will learn more about those terms and what they mean in Chapter 14. But you can see that the general form is the same.

There are two questions that you ask with an $\mathbf{Ax} = \mathbf{b}$ problem:

1. **Does it have a solution?** You already know the answer to that question: The equation has an exact solution when $\mathbf{b}$ is in the column space of $\mathbf{A}$. In that case, the coefficients in vector $\mathbf{x}$ tell you the weightings of the columns in $\mathbf{A}$ in order

to produce vector **b**. If vector **b** is not in the column space of matrix **A**, then that leads to the second question:

2. **What is the closest approximation to an exact solution?** This changes the equation to $\mathbf{Ax} = \hat{\mathbf{b}}$, where **x** and $\hat{\mathbf{b}}$ are selected such that (1) $\hat{\mathbf{b}}$ is in the column space of **A** and **x** are the coefficients, and (2) $\hat{\mathbf{b}}$ is as close as possible to the original **b**. This is obtained through the "least squares solution," which is the backbone of statistics, model fitting, machine learning, and many other areas of applied mathematics.

Now I'd like to tell you more about $\mathbf{Ay} = \mathbf{0}$. It may seem strange that someone would be so interested in finding the null space of a matrix, considering that the null space is the "black hole of no return." In practice, people are not interested in this matrix **A** *per se*; instead, they are interested in a shifted version of this matrix, expressed as $(\mathbf{A} - \lambda\mathbf{I})\mathbf{y} = \mathbf{0}$.

The solution to this equation (vector **y**) is called an eigenvector of the matrix, and λ is its associated eigenvalue. Eigenvectors reveal directions in the matrix that have special properties, such as robustness to geometric transformations or maximizing covariance in a dataset. In different contexts, the solution to $\mathbf{Ay} = \mathbf{0}$ is called Principal Components Analysis, generalized eigendecomposition, singular value decomposition, Fisher linear discriminant analysis, Rayleigh quotient, and many other names. These analyses play central roles in machine-learning applications and multivariate signal processing.

I hope this helps put things in perspective. It's not the case that *every* problem in linear algebra boils down to one of these two equations. But as you proceed in your adventures through the jungle of linear algebra, please keep these two equations in mind; the terminology may differ across fields, but the core concepts are the same.

1. For each matrix-vector pair, determine whether the vector is in the column space of the matrix, and if so, the coefficients that map the vector into that column space.

a) $\begin{bmatrix} 1 & 0 \\ 0 & 1 \end{bmatrix}, \begin{bmatrix} 2 \\ 3 \end{bmatrix}$

b) $\begin{bmatrix} 1 & 0 \\ 2 & 0 \end{bmatrix}, \begin{bmatrix} 3 \\ 1 \end{bmatrix}$

c) $\begin{bmatrix} 1 & 0 \\ 2 & 0 \end{bmatrix}, \begin{bmatrix} 3 \\ 0 \end{bmatrix}$

d) $\begin{bmatrix} 1 & 1 \\ 3 & 1 \\ 0 & 1 \end{bmatrix}, \begin{bmatrix} 2 \\ 2 \\ 0 \end{bmatrix}$

e) $\begin{bmatrix} 1 & 1 \\ 3 & 1 \\ 0 & 1 \end{bmatrix}, \begin{bmatrix} 2 \\ 2 \end{bmatrix}$

f) $\begin{bmatrix} 1 & 2 \\ 2 & 1 \end{bmatrix}, \begin{bmatrix} -3 \\ 3 \end{bmatrix}$

g) $\begin{bmatrix} 0 & 0 & 1 \\ 0 & 1 & 0 \\ 1 & 0 & 0 \end{bmatrix}, \begin{bmatrix} 3 \\ 6 \\ 4 \end{bmatrix}$

h) $\begin{bmatrix} -1 & 5 & 2 \\ -7 & 9 & 8 \\ -1 & 4 & \pi \end{bmatrix}, \begin{bmatrix} 0 \\ 0 \\ 0 \end{bmatrix}$

2. Same as the previous exercise but for the row space.

a) $\begin{bmatrix} 1 & 0 \\ 0 & 1 \end{bmatrix}, \begin{bmatrix} 2 \\ 3 \end{bmatrix}^{\mathrm{T}}$

b) $\begin{bmatrix} 1 & 0 \\ 2 & 0 \end{bmatrix}, \begin{bmatrix} 3 \\ 0 \end{bmatrix}^{\mathrm{T}}$

c) $\begin{bmatrix} 1 & 6 \\ 2 & 12 \end{bmatrix}, \begin{bmatrix} 2 \\ 9 \end{bmatrix}^{\mathrm{T}}$

d) $\begin{bmatrix} 1 & 0 & 1 \\ 2 & 2 & 0 \end{bmatrix}, \begin{bmatrix} 1 \\ -2 \\ 3 \end{bmatrix}^{\mathrm{T}}$

3. For each matrix-set pair, determine whether the vector set can form a basis for the column space of the matrix.

a) $\begin{bmatrix} 1 & 0 \\ 2 & 0 \end{bmatrix}, \left\{ \begin{bmatrix} 3 \\ 1 \end{bmatrix}, \begin{bmatrix} 1 \\ 0 \end{bmatrix} \right\}$

b) $\begin{bmatrix} 1 & 1 \\ 2 & 1 \end{bmatrix}, \left\{ \begin{bmatrix} 3 \\ 1 \end{bmatrix}, \begin{bmatrix} 4 \\ 4 \end{bmatrix} \right\}$

c) $\begin{bmatrix} 3 & 6 \\ 0 & 0 \\ 1 & 2 \end{bmatrix}, \left\{ \begin{bmatrix} 1 \\ 0 \\ 1/3 \end{bmatrix} \right\}$ 　　　　**d)** $\begin{bmatrix} 0 & 0 & 3 \\ 2 & 0 & 0 \end{bmatrix}, \left\{ \begin{bmatrix} 1 \\ 0 \end{bmatrix}, \begin{bmatrix} 0 \\ 1 \end{bmatrix} \right\}$

e) $\begin{bmatrix} e^{\pi} & 3^e \\ \sqrt[3]{3.7} & e^{e^2} \end{bmatrix}, \left\{ \begin{bmatrix} -3 \\ -2 \end{bmatrix}, \begin{bmatrix} -1 \\ 2 \end{bmatrix} \right\}$

4. Determine whether the following matrices have a null space. If so, provide basis vector(s) for that null space.

a) $\begin{bmatrix} 1 & 0 \\ 2 & 0 \end{bmatrix}$ 　　**b)** $\begin{bmatrix} 1 & 0 \\ 2 & 2 \end{bmatrix}$ 　　**c)** $\begin{bmatrix} 4 & 3 \\ 1 & 1 \\ 0 & 5 \end{bmatrix}$ 　　**d)** $\begin{bmatrix} 3 & 1 & 5 \\ 4 & 1 & 0 \end{bmatrix}$

5. Fill in the blanks (*dim*=dimensionality) for matrix $\mathbf{A} \in \mathbb{R}^{2 \times 3}$

a) $dim(C(\mathbf{A})) = 0, \ dim(N(\mathbf{A}^{\mathsf{T}})) = $ _____

b) $dim(C(\mathbf{A})) = 1, \ dim(N(\mathbf{A}^{\mathsf{T}})) = $ _____

c) $dim(C(\mathbf{A})) = 2, \ dim(N(\mathbf{A}^{\mathsf{T}})) = $ _____

d) $dim(C(\mathbf{A})) = 3, \ dim(N(\mathbf{A}^{\mathsf{T}})) = $ _____

e) $dim(N(\mathbf{A})) = 0, \ dim(R(\mathbf{A})) = $_____

f) $dim(N(\mathbf{A})) = 1, \ dim(R(\mathbf{A})) = $_____

g) $dim(N(\mathbf{A})) = 2, \ dim(R(\mathbf{A})) = $_____

h) $dim(N(\mathbf{A})) = 3, \ dim(R(\mathbf{A})) = $_____

1. a) $\begin{bmatrix} 2 \\ 3 \end{bmatrix}$ b) not in column space

   c) not in column space   d) not in column space

   e) sizes don't match   f) $\begin{bmatrix} 3 \\ -3 \end{bmatrix}$

   g) $\begin{bmatrix} 4 \\ 6 \\ 3 \end{bmatrix}$ h) $\begin{bmatrix} 0 \\ 0 \\ 0 \end{bmatrix}$

2. a) $\begin{bmatrix} 2 \\ 3 \end{bmatrix}^{\mathrm{T}}$ b) $\begin{bmatrix} 1 \\ 1 \end{bmatrix}^{\mathrm{T}}$

   c) Not in the row space   d) $\begin{bmatrix} 3 \\ -1 \end{bmatrix}^{\mathrm{T}}$

3. a) No. Any column space basis must be a single vector that is a multiple of $[1\ 2]^{\mathrm{T}}$.

   b) Yes: $C(\mathbf{M}) = \mathbb{R}^2$, so any independent set of two vectors can be a basis.

   c) Yes

   d) Yes

   e) Yes for the same reason as (b).

4. a) $\begin{bmatrix} 0 \\ 1 \end{bmatrix}$ b) No null space

c) No null space

d) $\begin{bmatrix} 1 \\ -4 \\ 1/5 \end{bmatrix}$

5. **a)** 2

b) 1

c) 0

d) Trick question; $dim(C(\mathbf{A}))$ cannot be greater than 2.

e) Trick question; $dim(N(\mathbf{A}))$ must be >0.

f) 2

g) 1

h) 0

8.14 Code challenges

1. Create two 4×4 random numbers matrices, each with rank=3 (consult the code challenge from Chapter 7 for how to do this). Call those matrices **A** and **B**. Then find a vector in the null space of **A** (vector **n**). Finally, show that **BAn** is the zeros vector while **ABn** is not.

2. The goal of this code challenge is to confirm the subspace dimensionalities expressed on page 229. Create a 16×11 matrix with rank=9. Then identify bases for the left- and right-null spaces and determine their dimensionalities. Confirm that the dimensionality of the left-null space plus the dimensionality of the column space is 16 (the ambient dimensionality of the column space), and that the dimensionality of the null space plus the dimensionality of the row space is 11 (the ambient dimensionality of the row space).

8.15 Code solutions

1. The goal here is to see that once you've entered the null space of a matrix (**An**), you can never come back; and that matrix **b** rotates **n** such that **Bn** is no longer in the null space of **A**.

Code block 8.3: Python

```
1  import numpy as np
2  from scipy.linalg import null_space
3  A = np.random.randn(4,3)@np.random.randn(3,4)
4  B = np.random.randn(4,3)@np.random.randn(3,4)
5  n = null_space(A)
6  print(B@A@n)
7  print(A@B@n)
```

Code block 8.4: MATLAB

```
1  A = randn(4,3)*randn(3,4);
2  B = randn(4,3)*randn(3,4);
3  n = null(A);
4  B*A*n
5  A*B*n
```

2. Recall that the dimensionality of the row space equals that of the column space, which equals the rank of the matrix.

Code block 8.5: Python

```
1  A = np.random.randn(16,9) @
2       np.random.randn(9,11)
3  rn = null_space(A)
4  ln = null_space(A.T)
5  r  = np.linalg.matrix_rank(A)
6  print(rn.shape[1]+r)
7  print(ln.shape[1]+r)
```

```
1  A = randn(16,9)*randn(9,11);
2  rn = null(A);
3  ln = null(A');
4  r  = rank(A);
5  size(rn,2)+r
6  size(ln,2)+r
```

CHAPTER 9

COMPLEX NUMBERS IN LINEAR ALGEBRA

Complex numbers are used in theoretical and applied mathematics, for example in signal processing (e.g., the Fourier transform). Complex numbers play a small but important role in linear algebra, and you'll need to be at least a little bit comfortable working with complex numbers, for example when learning about eigendecomposition. The goal of this chapter is to introduce you to complex numbers and how certain linear algebra operations are adapted to matrices containing complex numbers.

If you are comfortable with the interpretation, graphing, and arithmetic of complex numbers, feel free to skim through the next several pages; section 9.5 is where we return to linear algebra.

9.1 Complex numbers and $\mathbb{C}$

You've probably heard this story before: A long, long time ago, mathematicians scratched their heads about how to solve equations like $x^2 + 1 = 0$. The answer, of course, is $x = \pm\sqrt{-1}$, but this is not a sensible answer (or so the elders thought) because no number times itself can give a negative number. Confused and concerned, they adopted the symbol $i = \sqrt{-1}$ and called it "imaginary" because it was the best term their imaginations could come up with.

Fun fact: Gauss and many other people despised the term "imaginary," instead arguing that "lateral" would be better. I (and many others) whole-heartedly agree, but unfortunately "imaginary" remains standard terminology.

The imaginary operator was, for a long time, just a quirky exception. It was Karl Friederich Gauss (yes, *that* Gauss) who had the brilliant insight that the imaginary operator was not merely an exceptional case study in solving one kind of equation, but instead, that the imaginary unit was the basis of an entirely different *dimension* of numbers. These numbers were termed "complex" and had both a "real" part and an "imaginary" part. Thus was born the complex plane as well as the field of complex numbers, $\mathbb{C}$.

Gauss was interested in complex numbers because he was developing what is now known as the Fundamental Theory of Algebra. The FTA, as it is sometimes abbreviated, states that an nth order algebraic equation has exactly n roots. That is, an equation of the form:

$$a_0 x^0 + a_1 x^1 + ... + a_n x^n = 0 \qquad (9.1)$$

has exactly n solutions for x (remember that $x^0 = 1$). The thing is that these solutions might be complex-valued. This important result is the reason why you can get complex-valued eigenvalues from real-valued matrices. More on this in Chapter 15. For now, let's review complex numbers.

9.2 What are complex numbers?

You learned in school that numbers exist on a line, with zero in the middle, negative numbers on the left, and positive numbers on the right, like in Figure 9.1

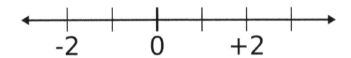

Figure 9.1: The real numbers, all lined up.

The idea of complex numbers is to extend this framework from a one-dimensional *line* to a two-dimensional *plane.* So now there are two axes for numbers, and each complex number is a coordinate in that plane. The horizontal axis is called the *real axis* (often abbreviated *Re*) and the vertical axis is called the *imaginary axis* (often abbreviated *Im*).

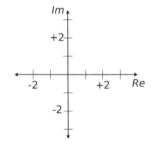

Figure 9.2: The complex numbers, all planed up.

Don't lose sleep over what complex numbers *really mean*, whether imaginary numbers have any physical interpretation, or whether intelligent life elsewhere in the universe would also come up with imaginary numbers (I think the answer is Yes, and I hope they call them "lateral numbers"). It doesn't matter. What does matter is that complex numbers are useful from a practical perspective, and they simplify many operations in both theoretical and applied mathematics.

Complex numbers are referred to using the real and imaginary axis coordinates, just like how you would refer to XY coordinates on a Cartesian axis. Figure 9.3 shows a few examples of complex numbers as geometric coordinates and their corresponding labels.

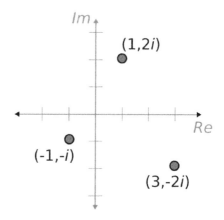

Figure 9.3: Example complex numbers on the complex plane.

A few remarks about indicating complex numbers in writing:

1. Complex numbers are always written using the real part first.
2. In between the two components could be a space, a comma, or a plus or minus sign. You might also see square brackets, parentheses, or nothing around the numbers. Variations include [a bi], (a,bi), [a+bi], a bi.
3. z is the go-to letter to indicate a complex number: $z =$ a+ib. After that, w is the next-best-thing.
4. You can position the i before or after the imaginary component: [a bi] or [a ib].
5. Most people use i to indicate the imaginary operator. Engineers tend to use j because they use i for electrical current. On the other hand, engineers write handwritten notes in ALL CAPS and start counting at 0, so let's not be too quick to adapt all engineering practices.
6. To avoid embarrassment at math parties, be careful to distinguish the following terms:
   - Complex number: A number that contains two parts, real and imaginary, like in the notational varieties above.
   - Imaginary number: A complex number with no real part: [0+ib] = ib.

- Imaginary operator: The symbol (i or j) that represents the square root of minus one ($\sqrt{-1}$), without any other numbers attached to it.
- Imaginary component: This is the real number that multiplies the imaginary operator. In the number a+ib, the imaginary component is b, not ib! Geometrically, this corresponds to the distance on the y-axis on a complex plane.

The reason why complex numbers are so useful is that they pack a lot of information into a compact representation. For the real number line, a number has only two pieces of information: its distance away from the zero and its sign (left or right of zero). A complex number contains more information: the real part; the imaginary part; the distance of the complex number to the origin; and the angle of the line from the origin to the complex number, relative to the positive real axis.

Complex vectors and complex matrices In some sense, complex matrices are really easy: They are just regular matrices except that the elements are drawn from $\mathbb{C}$ instead of $\mathbb{R}$, which in practice means that at least one matrix element has a non-zero imaginary part. (Technically, the number $4\,i0 \in \mathbb{C}$, but for practical purposes, we can say that there should be some non-zero imaginary components.) Below are a few examples.

$$\begin{bmatrix} 6 - i2 \\ 3 + i4 \end{bmatrix}, \quad \begin{bmatrix} 1 \\ 2 \\ 3 + i4 \\ i \end{bmatrix}, \quad \begin{bmatrix} 1 + 3i & 2 - 7i & -4 + i \\ 4 & 7 + 2i & 4i \end{bmatrix}, \quad \begin{bmatrix} 7 - 4i & 1 + i \\ 1 + i & 2 + 2i \end{bmatrix}$$

There is a minor abuse of notation in the matrices above: the number 1 is actually $1 + 0i$; likewise, the number $4i$ is really the number $0 + 4i$. But I and most other people omit the 0-valued components for visibility.

Complex vectors and matrices are confusing at first—many students mistakenly think that the left-most column *vector* above is a 2×2 *matrix*, and that the right-most 2×2 matrix is a 2×4 matrix. If ever you see i in a vector or matrix, be especially careful to inspect and correctly interpret the matrix.

Code There are several ways to create complex numbers in Python and MATLAB. The complex operator in Python is `1j` (or any other number and `j`). MATLAB accepts `1i` and `1j`. Be mindful that Python is more stringent about data types than is MATLAB. For example, try running the code below without the second input into the `np.zeros()` function.

Code block 9.1: Python

```
1  z = np.complex(3,4)
2  Z = np.zeros(2,dtype=complex)
3  Z[0] = 3+4j
```

Code block 9.2: MATLAB

```
1  z = complex(3,4);
2  Z = zeros(2,1);
3  Z(1) = 3+4i;
```

9.3 The complex conjugate

The *conjugate* of a complex number is simply that number with the sign of the imaginary part flipped. It is indicated using an overbar ($\bar{z}$) or using a superscripted asterisk (z^*). The equation below shows that the polar form of a complex number has the exponential multiplied by -1. If you are not familiar with polar notation, then don't worry about it—I include it here in the interest of completeness but it is not used in the rest of the chapter.

$$z^* = \bar{z} = \overline{a+bi} = \text{a-b}i \tag{9.2}$$

$$\bar{z} = \overline{re^{i\theta}} = re^{-i\theta} \tag{9.3}$$

Be mindful that the complex conjugate means to flip the sign of the imaginary component, not set it to be negative. Thus, if the imaginary component is already negative, then its conjugate would have a positive imaginary component: $\overline{a - bi} = a + bi$. Figure 9.4 depicts the geometric interpretation of the complex conjugate, which is to reflect the complex number across the real axis.

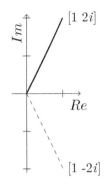

Figure 9.4: A complex number ([1 2i] and its complex conjugate ([1 -2i]).

Complex conjugate pairs A complex conjugate pair is a complex number and its conjugate, together forever, just like penguins. Here are a few examples; note that the magnitudes of the real and imaginary parts are the same; the only difference is the sign of the imaginary part.

$$z, \bar{z} = 4 + 2i, \ 4 - 2i$$

$$w, \bar{w} = 72 - 32i, \ 72 + 32i$$

$$u, \bar{u} = a + bi, \ a - bi$$

Complex conjugate pairs are featured in the "Complex conjugate root theorem," which states that if a polynomial with real-valued coefficients has at least one complex-valued root, then it has $2N$ complex roots that come in conjugate pairs. For example:

$$x^2 + 9 = 0 \qquad x = +3i, \ -3i$$

This should also be familiar from the quadratic equation: When $b^2 < 4ac$ then the roots come in conjugate pairs.

The quadratic equation:
$$x = \frac{-b \pm \sqrt{b^2 - 4ac}}{2a}$$

Code The complex conjugate is easy to implement. I'm using the opportunity to show you an additional way to create complex matrices.

Code block 9.3: Python

```python
1  r = np.random.randint(-3,4,size=3)
2  i = np.random.randint(-3,4,size=3)
3  Z = r+i*1j
4  print(Z)
5  print(Z.conj())
```

Code block 9.4: MATLAB

```matlab
1  r = randi([-3,3],1,3);
2  i = randi([-3,3],1,3);
3  Z = r+i*1j
4  conj(Z)
```

Practice problems Take the complex conjugate of the following numbers.

a) $3 + 4i$ b) $-6(-5-i)$ c) j d) 17

Answers

a) $3 - 4i$ b) $-6(-5+i)$ c) $-j$ d) 17

Reflection — Complex conjugate pairs are used in many areas of applied mathematics. For example, the most efficient way to compute a power spectrum from the Fourier transform is to multiply the complex-valued spectrum by its complex conjugate. More germane to this book: A matrix with entirely real-valued entries can have complex-valued eigenvalues; and when there are complex-valued eigenvalues, they always come in conjugate pairs.

9.4 Arithmetic with complex numbers

In this section, the scalars z and w refer to complex numbers, such that:

$$z = a + ib$$

$$w = c + id$$

Addition and subtraction Adding two complex numbers works the way you would think it should:

$$z + w = a + ib + c + id$$

$$= (a+c) + i(b+d)$$

In other words, sum the real parts, then sum the imaginary parts and attach the i. The only potential source of error here is misplacing the parentheses $(ib + d)$.

Subtraction works exactly the same way; just be careful that you are replacing the correct plus signs with a minus signs. Pay attention to the pluses and minuses here:

$$z - w = a + ib - (c + id)$$

$$= (a-c) + i(b-d)$$

Multiplication Multiplication of complex numbers, unfortunately, does *not* work the way you might initially expect. You might have expected (hoped) that you would separately multiply the two real parts and the two imaginary parts, and then put them together. Instead, you have to incorporate the cross-terms. Fortunately, though, the multiplication does follow algebraic rules you already know for expanding grouped terms.

$$zw = (a + ib)(c + id) \tag{9.4}$$

$$= ac + iad + ibc + i^2bd \tag{9.5}$$

$$= ac\text{-}bd + i(ad\text{+}bc) \tag{9.6}$$

Notice that $i^2bd = -bd$.

An interesting thing happens when you multiply a complex number by its conjugate. Observe:

$$z^*z = (a\text{+}bi)(a\text{-}bi)$$

$$= a^2 - (bi)^2 - abi + abi$$

$$= a^2 + b^2 \tag{9.7}$$

In addition to being practical, this is an important result, and equation 9.7 is used throughout complex linear algebra and signal processing. In the next section, you'll see how this property is related to the dot product with complex vectors.

Division Division is even weirder. There is a trick for doing division with complex numbers. I have no idea who invented it, but I suspect it was Gauss. That trick is to multiply both the numerator and the denominator by the complex conjugate of the denominator.

A rule in mathematics: *when in doubt, credit Gauss.*

$$\frac{z}{w} = \frac{a + ib}{c + id}$$

$$= \frac{(c - id)(a + ib)}{(c - id)(c + id)}$$

$$= \frac{(c - id)(a + ib)}{c^2 + d^2}$$

$$= \frac{(ca\text{+}db) + i(cb\text{-}da)}{c^2 + d^2}$$

Notice that the denominator becomes real-valued, which makes the fraction easier to work with. In the interest of learning-by-repetition, here is the concept again in compact form:

$$\frac{z}{w} = \frac{\overline{w}z}{\overline{w}w} \tag{9.8}$$

Reflection

> Why does the denominator have to be real-valued? I honestly have no idea. But all my math teachers and everyone who writes about math in books and on the Internet says that we should avoid having complex numbers in the denominator of a fraction. I don't condone conformity and I think it's important to question the status-quo, but on the other hand, you gotta pick your battles. This one isn't worth fighting.

Practice problems For the following two complex numbers, implement the indicated arithmetic operations.

$$z = 3 + 6i, \quad w = -2 - 5i$$

a) $2z + wz$
b) $w(z + \bar{z})$
c) $5z + 6w$
d) $5z + 6\overline{w}$
e) $\frac{(w+2)z}{w}$

Answers

a) $30 - 15i$
b) $-12 - 30i$
c) 3
d) $3 + 60i$
e) $(1 + 12i)\frac{15}{29}$

9.5 The Hermitian and complex dot products

The Hermitian transpose, often called simply the Hermitian, is a fancy term for a conjugate-and-transpose operation. It is indicated with a superscripted H instead of a T ($\mathbf{v}^H$). Sometimes you will also see the Hermitian indicated with a superscripted asterisk ($\mathbf{v}^*$) but this notation can lead to confusion because it can also indicate the conjugate (without transpose) of a vector. To be on the safe side, I will use an overbar on top of a vector ($\bar{\mathbf{v}}$) to indicate the conjugate of the elements in the vector without transposing that vector. Below is an example of a vector and its Hermitian.

$$\begin{bmatrix} 2 & 4 - i5 & 1 & 2 + i9 \end{bmatrix}^{H} = \begin{bmatrix} 2 \\ 4 + i5 \\ 1 \\ 2 - i9 \end{bmatrix}$$

Notice that nothing happened to the real-valued elements (first and third entries). For this reason, the Hermitian and "regular" transpose are identical operations for real-valued matrices.

Figure 9.5: The vector $\begin{bmatrix} 0 & i \end{bmatrix}$ has length=1, which the dot product formula must produce.

Dot product with complex vectors The dot product with complex vectors is exactly the same as as the dot product with real-valued vectors: element-wise multiply and sum.

However, in nearly all cases, the "regular" dot product is replaced with the Hermitian dot product, which simply means to implement the dot product as $\mathbf{z}^{H}\mathbf{w}$ instead of $\mathbf{z}^{T}\mathbf{w}$.

Why are complex vectors conjugated when computing the dot product? The answer will be obvious from a geometric perspective: Recall that the dot product of a vector with itself is the squared length of the line represented by that vector. Consider what happens when we compute the length of a complex vector that we know has length=1 (Figure 9.5):

$$\mathbf{v} = \begin{bmatrix} 0 \\ i \end{bmatrix}. \quad \begin{cases} \mathbf{v}^{T}\mathbf{v} = 0^2 + i^2 & = -1 \\ \mathbf{v}^{H}\bar{\mathbf{v}} = 0^2 + (-i)(-i) & = -1 \\ \mathbf{v}^{H}\mathbf{v} = 0^2 + (-i)(i) & = 1 \\ \mathbf{v}^{T}\bar{\mathbf{v}} = 0^2 + (i)(-i) & = 1 \end{cases}$$

Clearly, the third and fourth options provide accurate results. This example also shows that it doesn't matter which vector is conjugated, although the third option ($\mathbf{v}^{H}\mathbf{v}$) is generally preferred for typographical reasons.

Code The MATLAB dot() function always implements the Hermitian dot product, because conjugating real-valued numbers has no effect. In Python, however, you need to use vdot() instead of dot().

Code block 9.5: Python

```python
1  import numpy as np
2  v = [0,1j]
3  print(np.dot(v,v))
4  print(np.vdot(v,v))
```

Code block 9.6: MATLAB

```matlab
1  v = [0 1i];
2  dot(v,v)
```

Practice problems For the following vectors, implement the specified operations.

$$z = \begin{bmatrix} 1 \\ 3i \\ 4-2i \end{bmatrix}, w = \begin{bmatrix} i \\ 1-i \\ 0 \end{bmatrix},$$

a) $z^H(z+w)$

b) $\dfrac{z^H z}{w^H w}$

c) $2z + w \odot z$

Answers

a) $27 - 2i$

b) -10

c) $\begin{bmatrix} 2+i \\ 3+9i \\ 8-4i \end{bmatrix}$

Special complex matrices

Special complex matrices sometimes have different names from their real-valued counterparts. Below are two such matrices that you may encounter.

Hermitian matrices A Hermitian matrix is the complex-valued equivalent of something between a symmetric matrix $(\mathbf{A} = \mathbf{A}^T)$

and a skew-symmetric matrix $(\mathbf{A} = -\mathbf{A}^{\mathrm{T}})$.

A Hermitian matrix is defined as $\mathbf{A} = \mathbf{A}^{\mathrm{H}}$. Thus, the magnitudes of the real and imaginary parts are the same, but the signs of the imaginary parts are swapped. Below is an example; Please take a moment and mentally confirm that $\mathbf{A}^{\mathrm{H}} = \mathbf{A}$.

$$\begin{bmatrix} 2 & 3-2i & 2+2i \\ 3+2i & 5 & 8 \\ 2-2i & 8 & 9 \end{bmatrix} \tag{9.9}$$

Notice that the diagonal elements must be real-valued, because only real-valued numbers are equal to their complex conjugate ($a + 0i = a - 0i$). Notice also that Hermitian matrices may contain numbers with non-zero-valued imaginary parts.

Unitary matrix   For real-valued matrices, an "orthogonal matrix" is one for which its transpose is its inverse; thus, multiplying the matrix by its transpose gives the identity matrix ($\mathbf{Q}\mathbf{Q}^{\mathrm{T}} = \mathbf{I}$). Another way to phrase this is that each column in an orthogonal matrix is orthogonal with each other column, and that each column has unit magnitude. You'll learn more about these special matrices in Chapter 13.

A complex-valued matrix that has such properties is called a unitary matrix. Here is the typical example that is used to illustrate a unitary matrix:

$$\frac{1}{2}\begin{bmatrix} 1+i & 1-i \\ 1-i & 1+i \end{bmatrix}$$

You will have the opportunity to confirm that this matrix is indeed unitary in the code challenges.

There is a lot more that could be said about complex matrices in linear algebra. However, the topics introduced in this chapter cover what you will need to know for most linear algebra applications, including everything you need to know for the rest of this book.

Exercises

1. Implement the specified operations using the following variables.

$$w = 2 + 5i, \quad z = -i, \quad \mathbf{d} = \begin{bmatrix} 4 \\ 2 + 2i \\ -4i \end{bmatrix}, \quad \mathbf{R} = \begin{bmatrix} 3 & 4 & i \\ -2i & 0 & 0 \\ 4 & 1 & 1 \end{bmatrix}$$

a) $w\mathbf{d}$ **b)** $\mathbf{d}^H w \mathbf{d}$ **c)** $\mathbf{R}\mathbf{d}$ **d)** $\mathbf{R}^H \mathbf{R}\mathbf{d}$

e) wz **f)** wz^* **g)** $w\mathbf{d}\mathbf{R}$ **h)** $w\mathbf{d}^H \mathbf{R}$

1.

a) $\begin{bmatrix} 8 + 20i \\ -6 + 14i \\ 20 - 8i \end{bmatrix}$

b) $80 + 200i$

c) $\begin{bmatrix} 24 + 8i \\ -8i \\ 18 - 2i \end{bmatrix}$

d) $\begin{bmatrix} 160 + 16i \\ 114 + 30i \\ 26 - 26i \end{bmatrix}$

e) $5 - 2i$

f) $-5 + 2i$

g) Wrong sizes!

h) $\begin{bmatrix} -44 + 64i & 12 + 88i & -40 + 16i \end{bmatrix}$

Code challenges

1. On page 252 I showed an example of a unitary matrix. Confirm that this is unitary by showing that $\mathbf{U}^H\mathbf{U} = \mathbf{I}$. Also confirm that $\mathbf{U}^T\mathbf{U} \neq \mathbf{I}$.

2. In Chapter 6 you learned two methods (additive and multiplicative) to create a symmetric matrix from a non-symmetric matrix. What happens when you apply those methods to complex matrices? To find out, generate a 3×3 matrix of complex random numbers. Then apply those two methods to generate two new matrices, and test whether those matrices are (1) symmetric, (2) Hermitian, or (3) neither.

9.10 Code solutions

1. Both Python and MATLAB allow you to implement Hermitian and regular transpose operations. Be careful that you are implementing the correct version! Notice that the method .H in Python requires converting the matrix into a matrix object.

Code block 9.7: Python

```
1  U = .5*np.array([ [1+1j,1-1j],[1-1j,1+1j] ])
2  print(U@np.matrix(U).H)
3  U@U.T
```

Code block 9.8: MATLAB

```
1  U = .5*[1+1i 1-1i; 1-1i 1+1i];
2  U'*U
3  transpose(U)*U
```

2. Both methods for creating symmetric matrices ($\mathbf{A} + \mathbf{A}^T$ and $\mathbf{A}^T\mathbf{A}$) work for complex matrices, except that the resulting matrices are Hermitian, not symmetric. As mentioned earlier, be mindful that you are taking the Hermitian transpose, not the "regular" transpose. Python does not have a built-in function to test whether a matrix is Hermitian, but subtracting two equal matrices will produce the zeros matrix.

Code block 9.9: Python

```
1  r = np.random.randn(3,3)
2  i = np.random.randn(3,3)
3  A = np.matrix( r+i*1j )
4  A1 = A+A.H
5  A2 = A@A.H
6  print(A1-A1.H)
7  print(A2-A2.H)
```

Code block 9.10: MATLAB

```
1  A = complex(randn(3,3),randn(3,3));
2  A1 = A+A';
3  A2 = A*A';
4  ishermitian(A1)
5  ishermitian(A2)
```

COMPLEX NUMBERS

CHAPTER 10
SYSTEMS OF EQUATIONS

One of the many great things about linear algebra—which I've written in previous chapters but is particularly germane to this chapter—is that it can provide compact notation for large collections of mathematical expressions, equations, variables, data, and so on.

In this chapter you will learn how to represent systems of equations using matrices and vectors, and how to solve those systems using linear algebra operations. This knowledge will be central to a range of applications including matrix rank, the inverse, and least-squares statistical model fitting.

What is an equation? It is a statement of equality, typically with one or more unknown. For example:

$$2x = 6$$

To be sure, this single equation does not need matrices and vectors. In fact, using matrices to solve one equation simply creates gratuitous confusion. On the other hand, consider the following *system* of equations.

$$2x + 3y - 5z = 8$$

$$-2y + 2z = -3$$

$$5x - 4z = 3$$

You can imagine an even larger system, with more variables and more equations. It turns out that this system can be represented compactly using the form $\mathbf{Ax} = \mathbf{b}$. And this isn't just about saving space and ink—converting a system of many equations into one matrix equation leads to new and efficient ways of solving those equations. Are you excited to learn? Let's begin.

10.1 Algebra and geometry of equations

Algebraic equations have an associated picture. The number of variables (unknowns) in the equation determines the number of dimensions in the corresponding graph. For example, the equation

$$2x + 3 = 11 \tag{10.1}$$

has the solution $x = 4$, which can be visualized as a point on the number line:

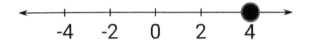

Figure 10.1: A graph of the solution to Equation 10.1.

Here is an equation with two variables:

$$2y = x + 4 \tag{10.2}$$

And I'm sure you know that the geometric translation of this equation is a line in a 2D space. You probably also know that any point on this line is a valid solution to the equation.

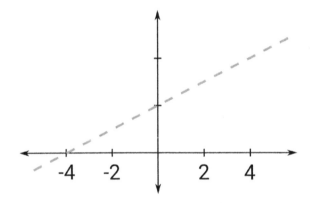

Figure 10.2: A graph of the solution to Equation 10.2.

An equation with 3 variables has an associated 3D graph, and so on.

So far, we been talking about individual equations. What do *systems* of equations look like? Consider the following system of two equations and two variables.

$$\left\{ \begin{array}{l} y = x/2 + 2 \\ y = -x + 4 \end{array} \right\} \tag{10.3}$$

If one 2-variable equation is a line, then a system of two 2-variable equations is two lines. Figure 10.3 shows the picture.

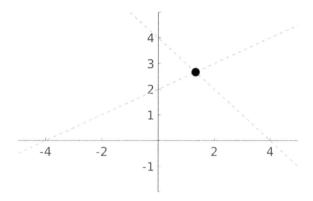

Figure 10.3: A graph of the solution to the system of equations 10.3.

Now things are starting to get interesting. The point on the graph where the two lines intersect is the solution to both equations. In this case, that point is $(x, y) = (4/3, 8/3)$. Try this yourself by plugging those values into both equations in system 10.3. You can also try points that are on one line but not the other; you will find that those pairs of numbers will solve only one of the equations. Try, for example, (0,4) and (-4,0).

When learning about equations in high school, you learned that any arithmetic operation performed on one side of the equation must be done to the other. For example, in the equation $x = 4$, you may multiply both sides by 8 ($8 \times x = 8 \times 4$), but it is not allowed to multiply only one side by 8.

With a system of equations, you still have the same rule, although you don't have to apply the same operation to all equations in the system. But having a system of equations allows you to do something more: You may add and subtract entire equations from each other (this is analogous to multiplying the left-hand side by "8" and the right-hand side by "4×2"). Let's try this with Equation 10.3. I will transform the first equation to be itself minus the second equation:

$$\left\{ \begin{array}{c} 0y = 3x/2 - 2 \\ y = -x + 4 \end{array} \right\} \tag{10.4}$$

Next, I will replace the second equation by itself plus two times the original first equation:

$$\left\{ \begin{array}{c} 0y = 3x/2 - 2 \\ 3y = 0x + 8 \end{array} \right\} \tag{10.5}$$

At a superficial glance, system 10.5 looks really different from system 10.3. What does the graph of this "new" system look like? Let's see:

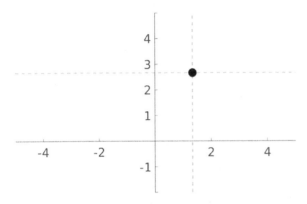

Figure 10.4: A graph of the solution to the system of equations 10.5. Compare with Figure 10.3.

The amazing thing here is that *the solution stays the same, even though the lines are different.* The same can be said of the algebraic equations (10.3 and 10.5): They look different, but the solution to the system remains the same before and after we subtracted equations from each other.

So the conclusion here is that you can take a system of equations, scalar multiply individual equations, and add and subtract equations from each other, to your heart's delight. The individual equations—and the lines representing those equations—will change, but the point of intersection will remain exactly the same (of course, this statement breaks down if you scalar-multiply by 0, so let's exclude this trivial annoyance).

Now let me explain why this concept is powerful. Consider the system of equations 10.6. Take a moment to try to find the solution to this system (that is, the (x, y) pair that satisfies both equations); try it based on visual inspection without writing anything down and without adding or subtracting the equations from each other.

$$\left\{ \begin{array}{rcr} 2x + 3y = & 8 \\ -2x + 2y = & -3 \end{array} \right\} \qquad (10.6)$$

Did you get it? It's actually pretty difficult to solve in your head. Now I will add the first equation to the second; try again to solve the system without writing anything down.

$$\left\{ \begin{array}{rcl} 2x + 3y = & 8 \\ 5y = & 5 \end{array} \right\} \qquad (10.7)$$

Suddenly, this new second equation is much easier to solve. You see immediately that $y = 1$, and then you can plug that into the first equation to get $x = 5/2 = 2.5$. Thus, the solution is now easier to calculate because the second equation decouples y from x. This is the principle of row reduction and Gaussian elimination, which you will learn about later in this chapter.

Do all systems have a common algebraic solution and unique geometric crossing? No, definitely not. A system of equations will have (1) one intersecting point like in the examples above, (2) no points in common, or (3) an infinite number of points in common. We'll get to this discussion later on in this chapter. First you need to learn how to convert a system of equations into a matrix-vector equation.

10.2 Matrices representing systems of equations

Converting a system of equations into a matrix equation is straightforward, and requires understanding the three components that together define a system of equations:

1. **Variables**: These are the unknowns that you want to solve for. They are typically labeled x, y, ..., or x_1, x_2, ...

2. **Coefficients**: These are the numbers that multiply the variables. There is one coefficient per variable. If the variable is sitting by itself, then the coefficient is 1; if the variable is not present, then the coefficient is 0.
3. **Constants**: These are the numbers that do not multiply variables. Every equation has one constant (which might be 0).

Sometimes, these components are easy to spot. For example, in the equation

$$2x + 3y - 4z = 5 \qquad (10.8)$$

The variables are (x, y, z), the corresponding coefficients are $(2, 3, -4)$, and the constant is 5. In other equations, you might need to do a bit of arithmetic to separate the components:

$$2(x + 3y) - z - 5 = 1 \qquad (10.9)$$

The variables are still (x, y, z), the coefficients are $(2, 6, -1)$, and the constant is 6.

Components to matrices Once you've identified the components of a system, you put those components into matrices:

1. The coefficients go into the coefficients matrix, with columns corresponding to variables and with rows corresponding to equations.
2. The variables go into a column vector that right-multiplies the coefficients matrix. Importantly, the order of variables in this vector must match the order of variables in the columns of the matrix.
3. The coefficients matrix and variables vector are on the left-hand side of the equation. The constants go into a column vector on the right-hand side of the equation, with the number of elements in the vector corresponding to the number of equations. Of course, the nth element in the constants vector must correspond to the nth equation in the coefficients matrix.

For an example, let's work with the following system of equations:

$$\begin{cases} 2x + 3y - 5z = 8 \\ -2y + 2z + 2 = -1 \end{cases} \qquad (10.10)$$

Observe how this system is translated into matrices and vectors. In particular, observe how the coefficients, variables, and constants are organized:

$$\begin{bmatrix} 2 & 3 & -5 \\ 0 & -2 & 2 \end{bmatrix} \begin{bmatrix} x \\ y \\ z \end{bmatrix} = \begin{bmatrix} 8 \\ -3 \end{bmatrix} \qquad (10.11)$$

Be mindful that one or more variables might be missing from an equation, in which case you must put zeros in the correct locations of the coefficients matrix. Also note that all numbers unattached to variables are combined into one constant.

Take a minute to work through the matrix-vector multiplication to convince yourself that Equation 10.11 is an accurate representation of the system of equations in 10.10.

You can see that converting a system of equations into a matrix equation is not terribly difficult. But it does require vigilance, because a simple mistake here can have dire consequences later on. For example, consider the following system:

$$\begin{cases} 2x + 3y - 5z = 8 \\ 5x = 2 \end{cases} \qquad (10.12)$$

If you are converting this system into matrices while simultaneously Facebooking, savoring Vietnamese coconut coffee, and watching reruns of *Rick and Morty*, you might end up with the following matrix:

$$\begin{bmatrix} 2 & 3 & -5 \\ 0 & 0 & 5 \end{bmatrix} \begin{bmatrix} x \\ y \\ z \end{bmatrix} = \begin{bmatrix} 8 \\ 2 \end{bmatrix}$$

This is wrong because the second equation is actually now implemented as $5z = 2$ whereas the original equation was $5x = 2$. When

there is potential for confusion, re-write the set of equations with
all the variables vertically aligned, using 0's where appropriate:

$$
\begin{aligned}
2x + 3y - 5z &= 8 \\
5x &= 2
\end{aligned}
\quad \Rightarrow \quad
\begin{aligned}
2x + 3y - 5z &= 8 \\
5x + 0y + 0z &= 2
\end{aligned}
$$

Practice problems (1 of 2)   Convert the following systems of equations into their matrix form.

a) $\begin{cases} 2x + 3y + 75z = 8 \\ \quad\;\; -2y + 2z = -3 \end{cases}$

b) $\begin{cases} x - z/2 = 1/3 \\ 3y + 6z = 4/3 \end{cases}$

c) $\begin{cases} s - t = 6 \\ u + v = 1 \\ t + u = 0 \\ 2v + 3t = 10 \end{cases}$

d) $\begin{cases} x + y = 2 \\ x - y = 0 \end{cases}$

Answers

a) $\begin{bmatrix} 2 & 3 & 75 \\ 0 & -2 & 2 \end{bmatrix} \begin{bmatrix} x \\ y \\ z \end{bmatrix} = \begin{bmatrix} 8 \\ -3 \end{bmatrix}$

b) $\begin{bmatrix} 1 & 0 & -1/2 \\ 0 & 3 & 6 \end{bmatrix} \begin{bmatrix} x \\ y \\ z \end{bmatrix} = \frac{1}{3} \begin{bmatrix} 1 \\ 4 \end{bmatrix}$

c) $\begin{bmatrix} 1 & -1 & 0 & 0 \\ 0 & 0 & 1 & 1 \\ 0 & 1 & 1 & 0 \\ 0 & 3 & 0 & 2 \end{bmatrix} \begin{bmatrix} s \\ t \\ u \\ v \end{bmatrix} = \begin{bmatrix} 6 \\ 1 \\ 0 \\ 10 \end{bmatrix}$

d) $\begin{bmatrix} 1 & 1 \\ 1 & -1 \end{bmatrix} \begin{bmatrix} x \\ y \end{bmatrix} = \begin{bmatrix} 2 \\ 0 \end{bmatrix}$

Practice problems (2 of 2)   Convert the following matrix-vector products into their "long-form"
equations (i.e., the opposite of the previous exercises).

a) $\begin{bmatrix} 1 & 0 & 2 \\ 0 & 1 & 1 \end{bmatrix} \begin{bmatrix} x \\ y \end{bmatrix} = \begin{bmatrix} 1 \\ 5 \end{bmatrix}$

b) $\begin{bmatrix} 1 & 0 \\ 0 & 1 \end{bmatrix} \begin{bmatrix} j \\ k \end{bmatrix} = \begin{bmatrix} 10 \\ 9 \end{bmatrix}$

c) $\begin{bmatrix} 7 & 7 & 8 & 8 & 6 & 7 \\ 1 & 0 & 9 & 1 & 2 & 0 \end{bmatrix} \begin{bmatrix} q \\ w \\ e \\ r \\ t \\ y \end{bmatrix} = \begin{bmatrix} 9 \\ 9 \end{bmatrix}$

d) $\begin{bmatrix} 1 & 3 \\ 2 & 4 \\ 3 & 4 \\ 4 & 2 \end{bmatrix} \begin{bmatrix} s \\ t \end{bmatrix} = \begin{bmatrix} 5 \\ 4 \\ 6 \\ 2 \end{bmatrix}$

Answers

a) Not a valid equation!

b) $\begin{cases} j = 10 \\ k = 9 \end{cases}$

c) $\begin{cases} 7q + 7w + 8e + 8r + 6t + 7y = 9 \\ 1q + 9e + r + 2t = 9 \end{cases}$

d) $\begin{cases} s + 3t = 5 \\ 2s + 4t = 4 \\ 3s + 4t = 6 \\ 4s + 2t = 2 \end{cases}$

$$\begin{bmatrix} \text{Sometimes, the biggest challenge in data analysis and} \\ \text{modeling is figuring out how to represent a problem us-} \\ \text{ing equations; the rest is usually just a matter of alge-} \\ \text{bra and number-crunching. Indeed, the translation from} \\ \text{real-world problem to matrix equation is rarely trivial and} \\ \text{sometimes impossible. In this case, representing a system} \\ \text{of equations as matrix-vector multiplication leads to the} \\ \text{compact and simplified notation: } \mathbf{Ax = b}. \text{ And this form} \\ \text{leads to an equally compact solution via the least-squares} \\ \text{algorithm, which is a major topic of Chapter 14.} \end{bmatrix}$$

10.3 Row reduction, echelon form, and pivots

Row reduction may initially seem like a tangent from representing and solving systems of equations, however, it provides the computational backbone of solving systems of equations.

Row reduction involves modifying rows of a matrix while leaving many key properties of the matrix intact. It is based on the principle that you learned about in section 10.1: in a system of equations, individual equations can be scalar-multiplied, added, and subtracted. Thus, row reduction involves linearly combining the rows of a matrix, with the goal of transforming a matrix into a form that facilitates subsequent inspection and analyses.

"Transforming the matrix to facilitate analyses" basically means increasing the number of zeros in the matrix. Zeros are great in matrices: the more zeros a matrix has, the easier and faster it is to work with. Thus, think of row reduction as a method to re-organize the information in a matrix in a way that increases the number of zero-valued entries.

So how does row reduction work? It's exactly the same procedure we applied in Equation 10.6 (page 264): Replace rows in the matrix with linear combinations of other rows in the same matrix. Let's start with an example.

Consider the matrix defined by the coefficients in the equation system 10.6 (the constants vector is omitted for now; after learning the mechanism of row reduction, you'll learn how to incorporate the right-hand side of the equations). Notice that by adding the first row to the second row, we get a zero in the (2,1) position.

$$\begin{bmatrix} 2 & 3 \\ -2 & 2 \end{bmatrix} \xrightarrow{R_1 + R_2} \begin{bmatrix} 2 & 3 \\ 0 & 5 \end{bmatrix} \qquad (10.13)$$

The arrow with $R_1 + R_2$ indicates the operation that was performed, in this case, adding row 1 to row 2.

These two matrices are not the same, but they are related to each other by a simple linear operation that could be undone if we keep track of which rows were added to which other rows. That linear operation increased the number of zeros in the matrix from none to one, and so is consistent with our goal. In this case, the linear transformation converted the original matrix into an upper-triangular matrix, which, in the parlance of row reduction, is called the *echelon form* of the matrix.

Echelon form   One of the main goals of row reduction is to convert a dense matrix into its echelon form. A matrix is in its echelon form when the following two criteria are satisfied:

Sometimes also called *row echelon form*.

1. The first non-zero number in each row is to the right of the first non-zero numbers in the rows above.
2. Rows of all zeros are below rows with at least one non-zero element.

The matrices below are all in echelon form:

$$\begin{bmatrix} 2 & 4 & 5 \\ 0 & 1 & 3 \\ 0 & 0 & 9 \end{bmatrix}, \begin{bmatrix} 4 & 3 & 0 \\ 0 & 0 & 2 \\ 0 & 0 & 0 \end{bmatrix}, \begin{bmatrix} 2 & 5 & 0 & 0 \\ 0 & 0 & 2 & 0 \\ 0 & 0 & 0 & 9 \end{bmatrix}, \begin{bmatrix} 4 & 1 \\ 0 & 1 \\ 0 & 0 \\ 0 & 0 \end{bmatrix}$$

Notice how each of these matrices conforms to the two criteria: the first non-zero term in each row is to the right of the first non-zero term in the rows above, and rows of all zeros are on the bottom.

Obviously, most matrices are not already in their echelon form. This is where row reduction comes in: Apply row reduction to a matrix until it reaches echelon form. (Some matrices need to have rows swapped; we'll deal with this situation later.)

Let's try an example with a 3×3 matrix. The goal is to find the multiples of some rows to add to other rows in order to obtain the echelon form of the matrix. It's often easiest to start by clearing out the bottom row using multiples of the top row(s).

$$
\begin{bmatrix} 1 & 2 & 2 \\ -1 & 3 & 0 \\ 2 & 4 & -3 \end{bmatrix} \xrightarrow{-2R_1+R_3} \begin{bmatrix} 1 & 2 & 2 \\ -1 & 3 & 0 \\ 0 & 0 & -7 \end{bmatrix} \xrightarrow{R_1+R_2} \begin{bmatrix} 1 & 2 & 2 \\ 0 & 5 & 2 \\ 0 & 0 & -7 \end{bmatrix}
$$

As with many operations in linear algebra (and math in general), the procedure is easy to implement in small examples with carefully chosen integer numbers. Computers can take care of the arithmetic for harder problems, but it's important that you understand the procedure.

One of the nice features of the echelon form is that linear dependencies in the columns and rows reveal themselves. In the example above, you can immediately see that the third column cannot be formed from a linear combination of the first two. It is similarly straightforward to use the presence of zeros to convince yourself that the first row cannot be created by combinations of the other two rows (for example, nothing times zero can produce the 1 in the top-left element). So, this matrix comprises a set of linearly independent columns (and rows), which means this is a rank-3 (full-rank) matrix.

Watch what happens to the echelon form when there are linear dependencies.

$$
\begin{bmatrix} 1 & 2 & 2 \\ -1 & 3 & 0 \\ 2 & 4 & 4 \end{bmatrix} \xrightarrow{-2R_1+R_3} \begin{bmatrix} 1 & 2 & 2 \\ -1 & 3 & 0 \\ 0 & 0 & 0 \end{bmatrix} \xrightarrow{R_1+R_2} \begin{bmatrix} 1 & 2 & 2 \\ 0 & 5 & 2 \\ 0 & 0 & 0 \end{bmatrix}
$$

When the columns (or rows) of a matrix form a linearly dependent set, the echelon form of the matrix has at least one row of zeros.

In fact, this is one way to compute the rank of a matrix: Transform it to its echelon form, and count the number of rows that contain at least one non-zero number. That count is the rank of the matrix. I'll have more to say about the relationship between rank and row reduction in a later section, but this statement (rank is the number of non-zeros rows in the echelon form) is the main idea.

Practice problems Convert the following matrices into their echelon form.

a) $\begin{bmatrix} 1 & 0 & 2 \\ 2 & 1 & 1 \end{bmatrix}$
b) $\begin{bmatrix} 1 & 2 \\ 0 & 1 \\ 2 & 1 \end{bmatrix}$
c) $\begin{bmatrix} 2 & 2 & 1 \\ 4 & 0 & 1 \\ 3 & 1 & 1 \end{bmatrix}$

Answers

a) $\begin{bmatrix} 1 & 0 & 2 \\ 0 & 1 & -3 \end{bmatrix}$
b) $\begin{bmatrix} 1 & 2 \\ 0 & 1 \\ 0 & 0 \end{bmatrix}$
c) $\begin{bmatrix} 2 & 2 & 1 \\ 0 & -4 & -1 \\ 0 & 0 & 0 \end{bmatrix}$

A few tips for row reduction Row reduction is admittedly kindof a weird procedure when you first start doing it. But after you solve several problems, it will start to feel more natural. Here are a few tips that might help you avoid difficult arithmetic. These are not steps that you always implement; these are strategies to keep in mind that might make things easier.

1) Divide an entire row by a scalar to make the left-most non-zero number equal 1.

$$\begin{bmatrix} 3 & 6 & 9 \\ 1 & 1 & 1 \\ 2 & 1 & 1 \end{bmatrix} \xrightarrow{R_1/3} \begin{bmatrix} 1 & 2 & 3 \\ 1 & 1 & 1 \\ 2 & 1 & 1 \end{bmatrix}$$

2) Multiply a row by a scalar to facilitate eliminating elements.

$$\begin{bmatrix} 3 & 6 & 9 \\ 1 & 1 & 1 \\ 1 & 1 & 2 \end{bmatrix} \xrightarrow{-R_1+3R_3} \begin{bmatrix} 3 & 6 & 9 \\ 1 & 1 & 1 \\ 0 & -3 & -3 \end{bmatrix}$$

3) Multiply a row by a scalar to get rid of difficult fractions.

$$\begin{bmatrix} 3 & 6 & 9 & 2 \\ 1 & 1 & 2 & 4 \\ 0 & 0 & 2/3 & 17/6 \end{bmatrix} \xrightarrow{6R_3} \begin{bmatrix} 3 & 6 & 9 & 2 \\ 1 & 1 & 2 & 4 \\ 0 & 0 & 4 & 17 \end{bmatrix}$$

Keeping track of row reduction Although the matrices change during row reduction, those changes are reversible if you keep track of them. Let's continue working with the 2×2 matrix from a few pages ago:

$$\mathbf{A} = \begin{bmatrix} 2 & 3 \\ -2 & 2 \end{bmatrix}$$

It's trivial that $\mathbf{IA} = \mathbf{A}$. But what would happen if we change the identity matrix just a bit? Let's see:

This is no longer the identity matrix, so I'll call it $\mathbf{R}$ for *reduction*.

$$\mathbf{RA} = \begin{bmatrix} 1 & 0 \\ 0 & 2 \end{bmatrix} \begin{bmatrix} 2 & 3 \\ -2 & 2 \end{bmatrix} = \begin{bmatrix} 2 & 3 \\ -4 & 4 \end{bmatrix}$$

What we've done here is keep row 1 the same and double row 2. But how do we linearly combine rows? Well, if changing the diagonal elements affects only the corresponding row, then we need to change the off-diagonal elements to combine rows. To replace row-2 with row-1 plus row-2, you put a 1 in the (2,1) position of the $\mathbf{R}$ matrix:

$$\mathbf{RA} = \begin{bmatrix} 1 & 0 \\ 1 & 1 \end{bmatrix} \begin{bmatrix} 2 & 3 \\ -2 & 2 \end{bmatrix} = \begin{bmatrix} 2 & 3 \\ 0 & 5 \end{bmatrix}$$

More generally, to multiply the ith row by σ and add it to the jth row, you enter σ into the (i, j) entry of the identity matrix to form an $\mathbf{R}$ matrix.

Each nth step of row reduction has its own $\mathbf{R_n}$ matrix, each one to the left of $\mathbf{A}$ and any previously applied $\mathbf{R}$ matrices. Depending on why you are implementing row reduction, you might not need to keep track of the transformation matrices, but it is important to understand that every echelon matrix $\mathbf{E}$ is related to its original form $\mathbf{A}$ through a series of transformation matrices:

$$\mathbf{E} = \mathbf{R_n R_{n-1} ... R_1 A} \tag{10.14}$$

This also shows how row reduction does not actually entail losing information in the matrix, or even fundamentally changing the information in the matrix. Instead, we are merely applying a sequence of linear transformations to *reorganize* the information in the matrix. (That said, row reduction without storing the $\mathbf{R}$ matrices does involve information-loss; whether that matters depends on the goal of row-reduction. More on this point later.)

Exchanging rows in a matrix   In the examples of row reduction thus far, the matrices "just so happened" to be constructed such that each row had nonzero elements to the right of nonzero elements in higher rows (criteria #1 of an echelon form matrix). This is not guaranteed to happen, and sometimes rows need to be exchanged. Row exchanges have implications for several matrix properties.

Exchanging rows of a matrix is a linear transformation—sometimes called a *permutation* because we are permuting the row order—which means it can be expressed as a matrix multiplication. The way to accomplish it is by first manipulating the identity matrix with how you want the rows to be exchanged (let's call this matrix $\mathbf{P}$ for permutation), then left-multiplying the to-be-permuted matrix by $\mathbf{P}$.

For example, if you want to exchange the first and second rows of a 3×3 matrix, create matrix $\mathbf{P}$, which is the identity matrix with the first two rows exchanged, then left-multiply by this permutation matrix.

$$\mathbf{PA} = \begin{bmatrix} 0 & 1 & 0 \\ 1 & 0 & 0 \\ 0 & 0 & 1 \end{bmatrix} \begin{bmatrix} 1 & 2 & 3 \\ 4 & 5 & 6 \\ 7 & 8 & 9 \end{bmatrix} = \begin{bmatrix} 4 & 5 & 6 \\ 1 & 2 & 3 \\ 7 & 8 & 9 \end{bmatrix} \tag{10.15}$$

Important: This is a good illustration of how matrix multiplication is non-commutative. Watch what happens when the same permutation matrix right-multiplies $\mathbf{A}$.

$$\mathbf{AP} = \begin{bmatrix} 1 & 2 & 3 \\ 4 & 5 & 6 \\ 7 & 8 & 9 \end{bmatrix} \begin{bmatrix} 0 & 1 & 0 \\ 1 & 0 & 0 \\ 0 & 0 & 1 \end{bmatrix} = \begin{bmatrix} 2 & 1 & 3 \\ 5 & 4 & 6 \\ 8 & 7 & 9 \end{bmatrix} \tag{10.16}$$

Thus: left-multiply for row exchanges, right-multiply for column-exchanges (this is also why the **R**'s are on the left). To help you remember this, I'm going to recycle a mnemonic I introduced in the chapter on matrix multiplications (box 6.3, page 151):

Order of matrices for transforming rows vs. columns

P**R**e-multiply to transform **R**ows

P**O**st-multiply to transform c**O**lumns.

If you are confused about why **PA** and **AP** are so different, you might consider reviewing section 6.1 on thinking about matrix multiplication as linear combinations of rows vs. columns.

Now we can add to our general formula for transforming a matrix to its echelon form (Equation 10.14) to include row exchanges.

$$\mathbf{E} = \mathbf{R_n R_{n-1} ... R_1 P A} \tag{10.17}$$

(You might need additional permutation matrices, in which case they would be called $\mathbf{P_1}$, $\mathbf{P_2}$, and so on.)

The permutation matrix is the mechanism to keep track of the transformations you apply to the matrix. As I wrote above, in many cases, you don't need to keep track of these transformation matrices; you can simply swap rows as needed.

Let's see an example of reducing a matrix to its echelon form that requires a row swap.

$$
\begin{bmatrix} 2 & 1 & 4 \\ 4 & 2 & 9 \\ 8 & 5 & 3 \end{bmatrix}
\xrightarrow{-4R_1+R_3}
\begin{bmatrix} 2 & 1 & 4 \\ 4 & 2 & 9 \\ 0 & 1 & -9 \end{bmatrix}
\xrightarrow{-R_1+R_2}
\begin{bmatrix} 2 & 1 & 4 \\ 0 & 0 & 1 \\ 0 & 1 & -9 \end{bmatrix}
$$

Notice that the right-most matrix is *not* in its echelon form, because the leading non-zero term in the third row is to the left of the leading non-zero term in the second row. Swapping the second and third rows will set things right, and we'll have our proper echelon form.

Row swapping has implications for the sign of the determinant, which is a number associated with a square matrix that is zero for all singular square matrices and non-zero for full-rank matrices. You'll learn more about determinants in the next chapter, including the effect of row swaps. I mention it here to create a space in your brain for this information to be slotted in. To quell suspense: Each row swap flips the sign of the determinant but does not change its magnitude.

Pivots   In mechanics, a pivot is a point around which something rotates or moves. The pivot is an important part of a moving system; think of the fulcrum of a see-saw. Pivots in a matrix are similarly important, because they reveal several key properties of a matrix.

After putting the matrix into echelon form, the pivots are the left-most non-zero elements in each row. Not every row has a pivot, and not every column has a pivot. A zero cannot be a pivot even if it's in a position that could be a pivot. That's because pivots are used as a denominator in row-reduction, and terrible things happen when you divide by zero. In the following matrix, the gray boxes highlight the pivots.

$$\begin{bmatrix} \boxed{a} & b & c & d & e \\ 0 & \boxed{f} & g & h & i \\ 0 & 0 & 0 & \boxed{j} & k \\ 0 & 0 & 0 & 0 & 0 \end{bmatrix}$$

The pivots of a matrix are generally not visible before transforming to echelon form. That is to say, you cannot determine the pivots of a matrix without first converting it into its echelon form.

Code   There are no dedicated functions in Python or in MATLAB to apply row reduction to obtain the echelon form of a matrix. This is because the echelon form of a matrix is non-unique, meaning you can obtain many distinct $\mathbf{E}$ matrices for any given $\mathbf{A}$ matrix (of course, the $\mathbf{R}$ and $\mathbf{P}$ matrices will differ for different $\mathbf{E}$ matrices).

You'll learn more about the non-uniqueness of the echelon form in a few pages.

However, there is a way to obtain *an* echelon form of a matrix—and the corresponding $\mathbf{R}$ and $\mathbf{P}$ matrices—through a procedure called LU decomposition. "LU" stands for lower-upper, and is a decomposition that represents a matrix as the product of two triangular matrices. There are several algorithms of LU decomposition, one of which is conceptually similar to Gaussian elimination. I won't go into a lengthy discussion of LU decomposition here, but the idea in the context of the echelon form of a matrix is the following:

$$\mathbf{LU} = \mathbf{PA} \tag{10.18}$$

$$\mathbf{E} = \mathbf{U} \tag{10.19}$$

$$\mathbf{R_n}\mathbf{R_{n-1}}...\mathbf{R_1} = \mathbf{L}^{-1} \tag{10.20}$$

Code block 10.1: Python

```
1  from scipy.linalg import lu
2  P,L,U = lu(A)
```

Code block 10.2: MATLAB

```
1  [L,U,P] = lu(A);
```

Practice problems Use row reduction to transform the matrix into its echelon form, and then identify the pivots.

a) $\begin{bmatrix} 1 & 2 & 2 & 4 \\ 2 & 0 & 3 & 2 \\ 8 & 0 & 4 & 0 \end{bmatrix}$
b) $\begin{bmatrix} 2 & 0 & 1 \\ 1 & 1 & 2 \\ 3 & 1 & 3 \end{bmatrix}$
c) $\begin{bmatrix} 3 & 2 & 1 \\ 3 & 2 & 7 \\ 9 & 6 & 3 \\ 1 & 1 & 1 \end{bmatrix}$

Answers Echelon form is shown; pivots are highlighted.

a) $\begin{bmatrix} \boxed{1} & 2 & 2 & 4 \\ 0 & \boxed{-4} & -1 & -6 \\ 0 & 0 & \boxed{-8} & -8 \end{bmatrix}$
b) $\begin{bmatrix} \boxed{2} & 0 & 1 \\ 0 & \boxed{1} & 1.5 \\ 0 & 0 & 0 \end{bmatrix}$
c) $\begin{bmatrix} \boxed{3} & 2 & 1 \\ 0 & \boxed{1} & 2 \\ 0 & 0 & \boxed{6} \\ 0 & 0 & 0 \end{bmatrix}$

Pivot-counting and rank The rank of a matrix is the number of pivots in the echelon form of that matrix. Let's think about why this is the case.

During row reduction, any row that can be created using a linear weighted combination of other rows in the matrix will turn into a row of zeros. We could phrase this another way: If row reduction produces a zeros row, then it means that some linear combination of row vectors equals the zeros vector. This is literally the definition of linear dependence (Equation 4.6, page 94).

But this only proves that row reduction can distinguish a reduced-rank matrix from a full-rank matrix. How do we know that the number of pivots equals the rank of the matrix?

One way to think about this is using the theorem presented in Chapter 8, that the rank of a matrix is the dimensionality of the row space. Row reduction makes the dimensionality of the row space crystal clear, because all rows that can be formed by other rows are zeroed out. Any remaining rows necessarily form a linearly independent set, and the rank of a matrix is the largest number of rows that can form a linearly independent set. Each non-zeros row in the echelon form contains exactly one pivot; hence, the number of pivots in a matrix equals the number of non-zeros rows in the echelon form of the matrix, which equals the dimensionality of the row space (and thus also the dimensionality of the column space), which equals the rank.

For this same reason, row reduction reveals a basis set for the row space: You simply take all the non-zeros rows.

So the echelon form "cleans up" the matrix to reveal the dimensionality of the row space and therefore the rank of the matrix. And the "cleaning" process happens by moving information around in the matrix to increase the number of zero-valued elements.

Practice problems Use row reduction to compute the rank of the following matrices by counting pivots.

a) $\begin{bmatrix} 0 & 0 & 0 & 0 \\ 0 & 0 & 0 & 0 \\ 0 & 0 & 0 & 0 \end{bmatrix}$

b) $\begin{bmatrix} 3 & 3 & 5 \\ -4 & 4 & 0 \\ 5 & 1 & 5 \\ 6 & 2 & 1 \end{bmatrix}$

c) $\begin{bmatrix} 2 & 4 & 6 \\ 5 & 3 & 2 \end{bmatrix}$

Answers Echelon form is shown; pivots are highlighted.

a) Easy: no pivots!
$r = 0$

b) $\begin{bmatrix} \boxed{1} & 1 & 5/3 \\ 0 & \boxed{6} & 5 \\ 0 & 0 & \boxed{30} \\ 0 & 0 & 0 \end{bmatrix}, r = 3$

c) $\begin{bmatrix} \boxed{1} & 2 & 3 \\ 0 & \boxed{7} & 13 \end{bmatrix}, r = 2$

Non-uniqueness of the echelon form Did you always get the *exact* same echelon matrices that I got in all the exercises above? You might have, but you might also have gotten some slightly different results.

The echelon form of a matrix is non-unique. This means that a given matrix can have multiple—equally valid—associated echelon-form matrices. That's because of row-swapping and row-scalar multiplications. Take any echelon matrix, pick a row at random, and multiply that randomly selected row by some random scalar. There is literally no end to the possible matrices you can create this way, and they will all be the echelon form of the original matrix (assuming no arithmetic mistakes).

On the other hand, some features of the infinite number of echelon form matrices for a given matrix are constant. In particular, the number of pivots will always be the same (although the numerical values of the pivots may differ), as will the number of zeros rows (this is obvious, because the number of zeros rows is $M - r$, where M is the number of rows and r is the rank).

10.4 Gaussian elimination

Gaussian elimination is an application of row reduction to solving a system of equations. Let us return to the system presented in Equation 10.6, which I'll reproduce here:

$$\left\{ \begin{array}{rcr} 2x + 3y = & 8 \\ -2x + 2y = & -3 \end{array} \right\} \tag{10.6}$$

We discovered that it's difficult to solve this system because of the multiple x and y terms. So far in this chapter, you learned how to convert this system into a matrix equation, and then you learned how to apply row reduction to transform a matrix into its echelon form.

Now we're going to extend this procedure by a little bit. In particular, we will do the following:

1. Augment the coefficients matrix by the constants vector.
2. Row-reduce to echelon form.
3. Apply back-substitution to solve the system.

Step 1 produces the following matrix:

$$\left[\begin{array}{cc|c} 2 & 3 & 8 \\ -2 & 2 & -3 \end{array} \right] \tag{10.21}$$

When implementing row reduction, make sure to apply the row operations to the entire row, not just the numbers from the coefficients matrix. Step 2 will produce the following matrix:

$$\left[\begin{array}{cc|c} 2 & 3 & 8 \\ 0 & 5 & 5 \end{array} \right] \tag{10.22}$$

Before moving on to step 3, I'm going to simplify this matrix by replacing row 2 with itself divided by 5.

$$\left[\begin{array}{cc|c} 2 & 3 & 8 \\ 0 & 1 & 1 \end{array} \right] \tag{10.23}$$

Now we're ready for step 3. What is "back substitution"? This means mapping the matrix-vector equation back into a "long-form" system of equations, and then solving the system from the bottom row to the top row.

$$\left\{ \begin{array}{c} 2x + 3y = 8 \\ y = 1 \end{array} \right\} \qquad (10.24)$$

Take a moment to compare system 10.24 to matrix 10.23, and make sure you see how they map onto each other.

Now the solution to this system is easy to compute, and you can understand where the name "back-substitution" comes from: Starting from the bottom row and moving upwards, substitute variables in each equation until you've solved for all the variables. In this case, we already see that $y = 1$, and substituting that into the first equation leads to $x = 5/2$.

As I mentioned in the outset of this chapter, row manipulations change the equations and the corresponding graphs, but *the solution stays the same*. Therefore, it's a good idea to substitute the solution we discovered here back into the original system (Equation 10.6) to confirm that the solution solves the system. This is an important test, because if the solution from Gaussian elimination does not work for the original system, then you've made a mistake somewhere, either in row reduction or in the arithmetic during back-substitution.

Are you impressed by Gaussian elimination? Perhaps you are now thinking that this is the pinnacle of using linear algebra to solve systems of equations, and it couldn't possibly get better than this. Well, prepare to be proven wrong!

Practice problems Perform Gaussian elimination to solve the following systems of equations.

a) $\begin{cases} 2x - 3z = -8 \\ y + 4z + 3x = 25 \\ -z + x = -2 \end{cases}$

b) $\begin{cases} 3y + x + 2z = 36.5 \\ 2x + 6y - 2z = -29 \\ y + z = 18 \\ 14x - z = -24 \end{cases}$

Answers

a) $\begin{cases} x = 2 \\ y = 3 \\ z = 4 \end{cases}$

b) $\begin{cases} x = -.5 \\ y = 1 \\ z = 17 \end{cases}$

Reflection

Before the Internet age, communication among scientists was slow, difficult, and limited. Geographical distances and language barriers exacerbated the problem. I'm not a math historian, but I did read up a bit about the history of the term "Gaussian elimination." Apparently, the method was known to Chinese mathematicians even before Christ was born. Gauss himself did not discover the method, but improved it, along with better notation, from Newton (who might have discovered it independently of the Chinese). The attribution to Gauss was made in the 20th century, 100 years after his death. He could neither correct the record nor inappropriately take credit.

10.5 Row-reduced echelon form

Often abbreviated RREF, this is row reduction taken to the extreme. The goal here is to continue with row reduction after converting a matrix to its echelon form, until it becomes a matrix where all pivots have a value of 1, and each pivot is the only non-zero element in its column. Here is the procedure to get a matrix into its row-reduced echelon form.

1. Transform a matrix into its echelon form as described earlier.

2. For each row that contains a pivot:

    a) Divide that row by its pivot, which converts the pivot into the number 1.

    b) Apply row-reduction but work upwards instead of downwards. That is, use row-reduction to produce zeros in the elements above the pivot. Continue "upwards row-reduction" until the pivot is the only non-zero element in its column.

It is often useful to apply step 2 from the bottom row of the matrix to the top. Thus, to obtain the echelon form of the matrix, you work from the top row down to the bottom; and to obtain the RREF, you work from the bottom row (or the last row with pivots if there are rows of zeros) back up to the top.

Below are a few examples of matrices and their row-reduced echelon forms; notice that all pivots have a value of one and that the pivot is the only non-zero entry in its column.

Linear dependencies in the columns produce zeros row(s) and pivotless column(s).

$$\begin{bmatrix} 1 & 2 & 3 \\ 4 & 5 & 6 \\ 7 & 8 & 9 \end{bmatrix} \Rightarrow \begin{bmatrix} 1 & 0 & -1 \\ 0 & 1 & 2 \\ 0 & 0 & 0 \end{bmatrix}$$

A wide matrix with independent rows becomes $\mathbf{I}$ augmented by other numbers.

$$\begin{bmatrix} 5 & 2 & 1 & 0 & 4 \\ 4 & 1 & 5 & 6 & 3 \\ 2 & 1 & 9 & 0 & 4 \end{bmatrix} \Rightarrow \begin{bmatrix} 1 & 0 & 0 & 3.4 & -.03 \\ 0 & 1 & 0 & -8.6 & 1.967 \\ 0 & 0 & 1 & .2 & .233 \end{bmatrix}$$

A tall matrix with linearly independent columns has $\mathbf{I}$ on top and zeros underneath.

$$\begin{bmatrix} 1 & 2 \\ 6 & 2 \\ 4 & 7 \\ 1 & 7 \end{bmatrix} \Rightarrow \begin{bmatrix} 1 & 0 \\ 0 & 1 \\ 0 & 0 \\ 0 & 0 \end{bmatrix}$$

A full-rank square matrix transforms into $\mathbf{I}$.

$$\begin{bmatrix} 1 & 2 & 3 \\ 4 & 1 & 2 \\ 6 & 4 & 2 \end{bmatrix} \Rightarrow \begin{bmatrix} 1 & 0 & 0 \\ 0 & 1 & 0 \\ 0 & 0 & 1 \end{bmatrix}$$

At this point, you might be concerned that transforming a matrix into its RREF is non-unique, meaning that many different matrices will become the same row-reduced echelon matrix. That's true: although each matrix has a unique RREF (that is, there is exactly one RREF associated with a matrix), many different matrices can lead to the same RREF. For example, all square full-rank matrices have the identity matrix as their RREF.

However, you already know how to keep track of the progression from the original matrix to its RREF: Put each step of row reduction and row swaps into transformation matrices, as described earlier in this chapter. On the other hand, the usual goal of RREF is to solve a system of equations, and that solution is the same for the original matrix, the echelon form, and the RREF. Thus, in practice, you will probably not need to worry about saving the intermediate transformation matrices.

Code Computing the RREF of a matrix is easy. In Python, you must first convert the matrix (which is likely to be stored as a numpy array) into a sympy matrix.

Code block 10.3: Python

```
1  import numpy as np
2  import sympy as sym
3  A = np.random.randn(2,4)
4  sym.Matrix(A).rref()
```

Code block 10.4: MATLAB

```
1  A = randn(2,4);
2  rref(A)
```

Practice problems Reduce these matrices to their RREF.

a) $\begin{bmatrix} 4 & 8 & 4 & 3 \\ 0 & 1 & 8 & 0 \\ 2 & 7 & 0 & 8 \end{bmatrix}$
b) $\begin{bmatrix} 4 & 0 & 2 \\ 8 & 1 & 7 \\ 4 & 8 & 0 \\ 3 & 0 & 8 \end{bmatrix}$
c) $\begin{bmatrix} 13 & 7 & 4 & 7 \\ 5 & 3 & 2 & 3 \\ 2 & 1 & 1 & 1 \end{bmatrix}$

Answers

a) $\begin{bmatrix} 1 & 0 & 0 & -3 \\ 0 & 1 & 0 & 2 \\ 0 & 0 & 1 & -1/4 \end{bmatrix}$
b) $\begin{bmatrix} 1 & 0 & 0 \\ 0 & 1 & 0 \\ 0 & 0 & 1 \\ 0 & 0 & 0 \end{bmatrix}$
c) $\begin{bmatrix} 1 & 0 & 0 & 0 \\ 0 & 1 & 0 & 1 \\ 0 & 0 & 1 & 0 \end{bmatrix}$

10.6 Gauss-Jordan elimination

Gauss-Jordan elimination is like a super-charged version of Gaussian elimination. It's basically the same procedure that was described on page 279, except you modify step 2: Instead of row-reducing the coefficients-constants augmented matrix to its echelon form, you row-reduce the matrix to its RREF. The idea is that the row reduction takes a bit longer, but the back-substitution becomes *much* easier. I will continue with the example show previously. We arrived at the following matrix:

$$\left[\begin{array}{cc|c} 2 & 3 & 8 \\ 0 & 1 & 1 \end{array}\right] \tag{10.25}$$

Now let's continue with upwards row reduction to get all pivots equal to 1 and the only non-zero elements in their columns:

$$\left[\begin{array}{cc|c} 2 & 3 & 8 \\ 0 & 1 & 1 \end{array}\right] \xrightarrow{-3R_2+R_1} \left[\begin{array}{cc|c} 2 & 0 & 5 \\ 0 & 1 & 1 \end{array}\right] \xrightarrow{.5R_1} \left[\begin{array}{cc|c} 1 & 0 & 5/2 \\ 0 & 1 & 1 \end{array}\right]$$

Now we map the right-most matrix above back onto their equations:

$$\left\{\begin{array}{c} x = 5/2 \\ y = 1 \end{array}\right\}$$

OK, so now it's time for back-substitution... except you don't need to do any back-substitution! All the work is done for you; you simply read off the solutions right from the equations.

Practice problems Implement Gauss-Jordan elimination to solve the following systems of equations.

a) $\left\{\begin{array}{l} 3x + 10y = 62 \\ -x + 3y = 11 \end{array}\right\}$

b) $\left\{\begin{array}{l} 3x + 10y = 11.5 \\ -x + 3y = -1.3 \end{array}\right\}$

c) $\left\{\begin{array}{l} 4x - 6y + 3z = 1 \\ 5z + 2y + x = 8 \\ 3y + x - 4z = 0 \end{array}\right\}$

Answers

a) $\left\{\begin{array}{l} x = 4 \\ y = 5 \end{array}\right\}$

b) $\left\{\begin{array}{l} x = 5/2 \\ y = 2/5 \end{array}\right\}$

c) $x = y = z = 1$

Reflection

Math has many life-lessons if you look at it in the right way. The wisdom in this chapter is the following: Try to solve a problem (system of equations) with no preparation or organization, and you will spend a lot of time with little to show except stress and frustration. Do some preparation and organization (Gaussian elimination) and you can solve the problem with a bit of dedication and patience. And if you spend a lot of time preparing and strategizing before even starting to solve the problem (Gauss-Jordan elimination), the solution may simply reveal itself with little additional work. You'll be left with a deep sense of satisfaction and you will have earned your Mojito on the beach.

10.7 Possibilities for solutions

All of the example systems shown so far in this chapter have had a unique solution. But this is not always the case. In fact, there are three possibilities:

1. The system has no solutions.
2. The system has exactly one unique solution.
3. The system has an infinite number of solutions.

This might be more intuitive to understand geometrically. Figure 10.5 shows how the three possibilities would look (this is for a system with two equations and two variables, but this generalizes to higher dimensions).

Let's consider each possibility in turn.

No solution (Figure 10.5A) Geometrically, the lines for the different equations never touch. In 2D that means that lines are parallel;

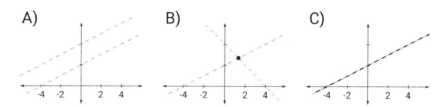

Figure 10.5: The three possibilities of solutions to systems of equations.

in higher dimensions there are other possibilities, but still the lines do not have a common meeting point. Here is an example of a system without a solution:

$$\left\{ \begin{array}{l} y = x/2 + 2 \\ y = x/2 + 4 \end{array} \right\} \tag{10.26}$$

It's clear from the equations that there is no common solution. Of course, each equation on its own can be solved, but the *system* of equations is inconsistent. Here's what the coefficients-constants matrix and its RREF look like:

$$\begin{bmatrix} -.5 & 1 & | & 2 \\ -.5 & 1 & | & 4 \end{bmatrix} \Rightarrow \begin{bmatrix} 1 & -2 & 0 \\ 0 & 0 & 1 \end{bmatrix}$$

Do you spot the problem? Let's map the RREF back onto a system of equations:

$$\left\{ \begin{array}{r} y - 2x = 0 \\ 0 = 1 \end{array} \right\} \tag{10.27}$$

Notwithstanding some silly "proofs" that require division by zero[1], we generally do not accept the conclusion that $0 = 1$. Therefore, this system is inconsistent; it has no solution.

Unique solution (Figure 10.5B) This is the case for the examples we've worked through earlier in this chapter. The system has exactly one solution and you can use Gaussian elimination to find it.

---

[1]For example: https://www.pleacher.com/mp/mhumor/onezero2.html

Infinite solutions (Figure 10.5C)   Geometrically, this means that the two equations are collinear; they are in the same subspace. Here's a system that would produce Figure 10.5C:

$$\left\{ \begin{array}{c} y = x/2 + 2 \\ 2y = x + 4 \end{array} \right\} \tag{10.28}$$

Notice that the second equation is the first multiplied by 2. And here is that system's corresponding matrix and RREF, and below that, the mapping back into a system of equations:

$$\left[\begin{array}{cc|c} -.5 & 1 & 2 \\ -1 & 2 & 4 \end{array} \right] \quad \Rightarrow \quad \left[\begin{array}{ccc} 1 & -2 & -4 \\ 0 & 0 & 0 \end{array} \right]$$

$$\left\{ \begin{array}{c} y - 2x = 4 \end{array} \right\} \tag{10.29}$$

Yeah, it's not really a "system" anymore, unless you want to include an extra equation that reads $0 + 0 = 0$.

So what is the solution to this equation? There are many. Pick whatever you want for x and then solve for y. Or pick whatever you want for y and solve for x.

Reflection

$$\left[\begin{array}{l} \text{An important aspect of life is balancing priorities, which} \\ \text{is basically like trying to find a solution that satisfies mul-} \\ \text{tiple equations. As you now know, a system of equations} \\ \text{has (1) zero solutions, (2) exactly one solution, or (3) an} \\ \text{infinite number of equally good solutions. So if life is all} \\ \text{about balancing equations, then it seems that one of these} \\ \text{three possibilities is correct:} \\ \text{1. Life has no purpose.} \\ \text{2. Life has exactly one purpose.} \\ \text{3. Life has an infinite number of equally good purposes.} \end{array} \right]$$

In Chapter 8 you learned about matrix spaces and subspaces, and in this chapter you learned about how to reorganize the contents of a matrix by linear combinations of rows. Row-reduction has implications for the span of matrix subspaces, which you will learn in this section.

To quell suspense, the main take-home message here is that row reduction does not affect the row space of the matrix, but it can drastically affect the column space of the matrix; on the other hand, the dimensionalities of the matrix subspaces do not change. Now let's work through this methodically.

Let's talk about rank first. You already know that rank is a property of the *matrix*, not of the rows or the columns. The rank doesn't change before vs. after row-reduction. In fact, row-reduction makes the rank easier to compute (count the pivots).

Next let's think about the row space. That doesn't change after row reduction. To understand why, think about the definition of a subspace and the process of row reduction: A subspace is defined as all possible linear combinations of a set of vectors. That means that you can take any constant times any vector in the subspace, add that to any other constant times any other vector in the subspace, and the resulting vector will still be in the subspace.

Now think about the process of row reduction: you take some constant times one row and add it to another row. That is entirely consistent with the algebraic definition of a subspace. So you can do row-reduction to your heart's delight and you will never leave the initial subspace.

The only characteristic of the row space that *could* change is the basis vectors: If you take the rows of the matrix (possibly sub-selecting to get a linearly independent set) as a basis for the row space, then row reduction will change the basis vectors. But those are just different vectors that span the same space; the subspace spanned by the rows is unchanged before, during, and after row reduction.

Now let's talk about the column space. The column space actually can change during row reduction. Let me first clarify that the *dimensionality* of the column space does not change with row reduction. The dimensionality will stay the same because the dimensionality of the row space, and the rank of the matrix, are unaffected by row reduction.

But what can change is the actual subspace that is spanned by the columns. This can happen when the column space occupies a lower-dimensional subspace of the ambient space in which the columns live. The reason is that *row* reduction involves changing entire *rows* at a time; individual elements of a column will change while other elements in the same column stay the same. I believe that one clear example will suffice for understanding. Below you can see a matrix and its RREF.

Anyway, the rows tend to be a poor choice for basis vectors. You will understand why when you learn about the SVD.

$$\mathbf{M} = \begin{bmatrix} 1 & 2 \\ 3 & 7 \\ 9 & 1 \end{bmatrix}, \quad rref(\mathbf{M}) = \begin{bmatrix} 1 & 0 \\ 0 & 1 \\ 0 & 0 \end{bmatrix} \quad (10.30)$$

The two columns form a linearly independent set in both matrices (clearly seen in both, though easier to see in the RREF), so we can take the columns as bases for the column spaces. In both matrices, the column space is a 2D plane embedded in a 3D ambient space.

But are they the *same* plane, i.e., the *same* subspace? Not at all! They intersect at the origin, and they have a line in common (that is, there is a 1D subspace in both 2D subspaces), but otherwise they are very different from each other—before RREF it was a tilted plane and after RREF it's the XY plane at Z=0 (Figure 10.6).

On the other hand, keep in mind that row reduction is not *necessarily guaranteed* to change the column space. Consider the following matrix and its RREF:

$$\begin{bmatrix} 1 & 2 \\ 3 & 7 \end{bmatrix} \quad \Rightarrow \quad \begin{bmatrix} 1 & 0 \\ 0 & 1 \end{bmatrix}$$

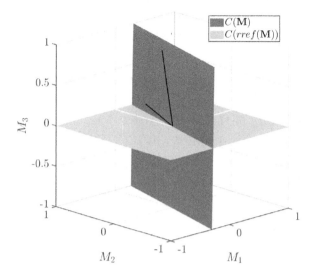

Figure 10.6: A graph of the column spaces before and after RREF for matrix M (Equation 10.30). Column vectors are drawn on top of the planes (unit-normalized for visualization).

It's a full-rank matrix and its RREF is the identity matrix. The column space spans all of $\mathbb{R}^2$ both before and after row reduction. Now this situation is analogous to the row space: The elements in the columns are different but the subspaces spanned by those columns are exactly the same.

Again, the take-home messages in this section are that row reduction (1) does not affect the rank or the dimensionalities of the matrix subspaces, (2) does not change the row space, and (3) can (but does not necessarily) change the column space.

Exercises

1. Reduce the following matrices to their echelon form. Highlight the pivots.

a)
$$\begin{bmatrix} 2 & 0 & -1 & -1 \\ 1 & -2 & -2 & 5 \\ -3 & 5 & -4 & -1 \\ 0 & -3 & -1 & -3 \end{bmatrix}$$

b)
$$\begin{bmatrix} 2 & 1 & 3 & -1 \\ -5 & -6 & -5 & 3 \\ -3 & -4 & -3 & 2 \\ -1 & -2 & -1 & 1 \end{bmatrix}$$

2. Given the following matrix sizes and ranks, determine the number of zeros rows in the row-reduced echelon form.

a) $\mathbb{R}^{2\times3}, r = 2$ b) $\mathbb{R}^{3\times2}, r = 2$ c) $\mathbb{R}^{7\times7}, r = 7$

d) $\mathbb{R}^{7\times7}, r = 3$ e) $\mathbb{R}^{7\times2}, r = 2$ f) $\mathbb{R}^{2\times7}, r = 2$

g) $\mathbb{R}^{6\times7}, r = 0$ h) $\mathbb{R}^{4\times4}, r = 4$

3. Use row reduction to determine whether the following systems have zero, one, or an infinite number of solutions. You don't need to solve the system.

a) $\begin{cases} 4x - 3y + 3z = 4 \\ 5x + y + z = 7 \\ x + 4y - 2z = 1 \end{cases}$ b) $\begin{cases} 4x - 3y + 3z = 4 \\ 5x + y + z = 7 \\ x + 4y - 2z = 3 \end{cases}$ c) $\begin{cases} 4x - 3y + 3z = 4 \\ 5x + y + z = 7 \\ 2x + 4y - 2z = 1 \end{cases}$

4. Solve the following systems of equations, by converting the equations in a matrix equation and then apply Gaussian elimination and back-substitution (or Gauss-Jordan elimination).

a) $\begin{cases} 2x + 4y - 6z = -15 \\ y - 4z = -8 \\ x + 6z = 10 \end{cases}$ b) $\begin{cases} 3z + y - x = 12 \\ -2y + 10x - z = 12 \\ 9x - y + 2z = 24 \\ 4x + 3y + 2z = 22 \end{cases}$

Answers

1.
a) $\begin{bmatrix} \boxed{1} & -2 & -2 & 5 \\ 0 & \boxed{4} & 3 & -11 \\ 0 & 0 & \boxed{-37} & 45 \\ 0 & 0 & 0 & \frac{1554}{29} \end{bmatrix}$

b) $\begin{bmatrix} \boxed{1} & 2 & 1 & -1 \\ 0 & \boxed{-3} & 1 & 1 \\ 0 & 0 & \boxed{2} & -1 \\ 0 & 0 & 0 & 0 \end{bmatrix}$

2. **a)** 0 **b)** 1 **c)** 0 **d)** 4

 e) 5 **f)** 0 **g)** 6 **h)** 0

3. **a)** No solutions **b)** ∞ solutions **c)** One solution

4. **a)** $x = 1, y = -2, z = 3/2$ **b)** $x = 2, y = 2, z = 4$

1. How do you think I came up with the sample systems of equations in this chapter? Is it because I'm a super-duper-math-genius? Unfortunately, that's definitely not the case. But I am a decent coder. And in this code challenge, you will learn the age-old secret of creating your own systems of equations. Below is an explanation of the procedure; your task is to write code to implement it. To start with, use three equations and three variables (x, y, and z).

   1. Create a vector that contains the values of the variables, which is actually the numbers that you want to solve for in the equations. For example, if you pick $x = 3$ and $y = -4$, then the vector of solutions is $\mathbf{x} = [3 \ -4]$.
   2. Make up the expressions with random coefficients—but don't worry about the solution (the constants). For example, $2x - 3z$.
   3. Create the coefficients matrix like what you learned in section 10.2. Let's call this matrix $\mathbf{A}$.
   4. Compute the constants as $\mathbf{Ax}$.

   And voilà! You now have all the pieces of a system of equations. If you want to create systems that have zero, one, or infinite solutions, you will need to make some minor adjustments to the above procedure (e.g., by changing a coefficient after already solving for the constants).

2. The margin notes in section 10.5 described patterns in the RREF of a matrix that depend on the size of the matrix. The idea is that every RREF is essentially the identity matrix, possibly with some additional rows of zeros or columns of non-zero numbers. Write code to explore these possibilities. In particular, create random numbers matrices that are (1) square, (2) wide, or (3) tall; and then compute and examine the RREF of those matrices.

10.12 Code solutions

1. Hint: You can actually skip from step 1 directly to step 3; step 2 is useful if you plan on writing out the full equations. To create a system with no solutions, start by creating a system with one solution, and then manually change one of the numbers. To create a system with infinite solutions, start by creating a system with one solution, and remove at least one equation from the system.

Code block 10.5: Python

```
1  import numpy as np
2  A = np.array([[2,0,-3],[3,1,4],[1,0,-1]])
3  x = [2,3,4]
4  b = A@x
```

Code block 10.6: MATLAB

```
1  A = [ 2 0 -3; 3 1 4; 1 0 -1];
2  x = [2 3 4]';
3  b = A*x;
```

2. The code below shows an example of a wide matrix (3×6).

Code block 10.7: Python

```
1  import numpy as np
2  import sympy as sym
3  A = np.random.randn(3,6)
4  sym.Matrix(A).rref()[0]
```

Code block 10.8: MATLAB

```
1  rref(randn(3,6))
```

CHAPTER 11
MATRIX DETERMINANT

Four things to know about determinants

Thing 1: only for square matrices The determinant is defined only for square matrices. Any time you hear or read the word "determinant," you can immediately start thinking about square $(M \times M)$ matrices. Therefore, all of the matrices in this chapter are square.

Thing 2: a matrix has one determinant The determinant is a scalar that contains information about the matrix. The determinant is unique in the sense that a matrix has exactly one determinant (of course, many different matrices can have the same numerical value as their determinant, but it is not possible for one matrix to have multiple distinct determinants). You might already be thinking about other numbers that characterize a matrix, like rank or dimensionality. The determinant is not the same thing as the rank, although it is related to the rank, which is the next thing to know.

Thing 3: zero for singular matrices The determinant is zero for a non-invertible matrix—a matrix with rank $r < M$. You can also say that a matrix with linear dependencies in the columns or in the rows has a determinant of zero. In fact, when you learn about computing the inverse in the next chapter, you'll learn that you should compute the determinant of a matrix before even starting to compute the inverse.

Thing 4: notation The determinant is indicated using single-vertical lines around the matrix letter, by printing the contents of the matrix with vertical lines instead of square brackets, or by using $det(\mathbf{A})$. Single vertical lines are used to disambiguate the determinant ($|\mathbf{A}|$) from the magnitude or norm ($\|\mathbf{A}\|$). The Greek character Δ is also commonly used to indicate the determinant.

Thus:

$$det(\mathbf{A}) \quad = \quad |\mathbf{A}| \quad = \quad \begin{vmatrix} 1 & 2 & 3 \\ 4 & 5 & 6 \\ 7 & 8 & 9 \end{vmatrix} \quad = \quad \Delta$$

There are several applications of the determinant. The two applications used in this book are computing the inverse (and determining whether a matrix has an inverse) (Chapter 12), and uncovering the eigenvalues of a matrix (Chapter 15). A third application is in geometry: If a matrix contains the vertices of a polygon, then the absolute value of the determinant measures the volume of that polygon. I won't discuss this application here.

The determinant is really difficult to compute for large matrices ("large" is a subjective term, but for calculating the determinant, I'd consider anything larger than 4×4 to be large). In fact, computers are unable to compute the determinant reliably for large matrices. You'll see this yourself in the code challenges for this chapter.

However, there are handy short-cuts for computing the determinant of 2×2 and 3×3 matrices. Therefore, I will introduce these short-cuts first, and then present the "full" determinant formula thereafter.

11.2 Determinant of a 2×2 matrix

The determinant of a 2×2 matrix equals the product of the diagonal minus the product of the off-diagonal.

Don't be seduced by the simplicity of this equation—this short-cut works only for 2×2 matrices.

Equation for the determinant of a 2×2 matrix.

$$det\left(\begin{bmatrix} a & b \\ c & d \end{bmatrix}\right) = \begin{vmatrix} a & b \\ c & d \end{vmatrix} = ad - bc \qquad (11.1)$$

Here are a few examples with real numbers.

$$\begin{vmatrix} 1 & 2 \\ 0 & 1 \end{vmatrix} = 1 \times 1 - 2 \times 0 = 1 \tag{11.2}$$

$$\begin{vmatrix} 5 & -3 \\ -4 & 2 \end{vmatrix} = 5 \times 2 - (-3 \times -4) = -2 \tag{11.3}$$

$$\begin{vmatrix} 1 & 2 \\ 2 & 4 \end{vmatrix} = 1 \times 4 - 2 \times 2 = 0 \tag{11.4}$$

Notice that the first two matrices have a rank of 2 (and, thus, the columns form a linearly independent set), while the third matrix has a rank of 1. And that the determinant was non-zero for the first two matrices and zero for the third matrix.

That is no coincidence: Every reduced-rank matrix has a determinant of zero. Indeed, one definition of a singular matrix is a matrix with a determinant of zero. Thus, $ad = bc$ for *every* singular 2×2 matrix.

To understand why a 2×2 matrix must have $\Delta = 0$, consider a matrix of letters with one column a scalar multiple of the other, i.e., linear dependence in the columns:

$$\begin{bmatrix} a & \lambda a \\ c & \lambda c \end{bmatrix}$$

And now we compute the determinant of this matrix:

$$\Delta = ac\lambda - a\lambda c \tag{11.5}$$

$$= 0$$

Thus, the determinant of a 2×2 matrix with linear dependencies in the columns is necessarily 0. Take a moment to re-do this example but setting the linear dependency in the rows instead of the columns.

Practice problems Determine whether the following determinants are correct, and, if not, compute the true determinant.

a) $\begin{vmatrix} 3 & 1 \\ 2 & 1 \end{vmatrix} = 1$ b) $\begin{vmatrix} 3 & 4 \\ 1 & 1 \end{vmatrix} = -1$ c) $\begin{vmatrix} 1 & 9 \\ 6 & 1 \end{vmatrix} = -3$ d) $\begin{vmatrix} 9 & 1 \\ 6 & 1 \end{vmatrix} = -3$

e) $\begin{vmatrix} 1 & 9 \\ 0 & 0 \end{vmatrix} = 0$ f) $\begin{vmatrix} 1 & 5 \\ 3 & 15 \end{vmatrix} = 15$ g) $\begin{vmatrix} 1 & 5 \\ 3 & 0 \end{vmatrix} = -8$ h) $\begin{vmatrix} -1 & 2 \\ 4 & -5 \end{vmatrix} = -3$

Answers

a) Correct b) Correct c) No, $\Delta = -53$ d) No, $\Delta = 3$

e) Correct f) No, $\Delta = 0$ g) No, $\Delta = -15$ h) Correct

Determinant and transpose The determinant is robust to the transpose operation. In other words, $det(\mathbf{A}) = det(\mathbf{A}^{\mathrm{T}})$. This is because the determinant is a property of the *matrix*, not of the rows or the columns. This is easy to prove:

$$\begin{vmatrix} a & b \\ c & d \end{vmatrix} = ad - bc \qquad (11.6)$$

$$\begin{vmatrix} a & c \\ b & d \end{vmatrix} = ad - cb \qquad (11.7)$$

Notice that the difference between the matrix and its transpose is simply the swapping of c and d. Scalar multiplication is commutative, and thus the determinant is unaffected by the transpose.

This proof is valid only for 2×2 matrices because Equation 11.1 is a short-cut for 2×2 matrices. However, this property does generalize to any sized square matrix. We will revisit this concept when learning about 3×3 matrices.

11.3 The characteristic polynomial

An interpretation of Equation 11.1 is that we transform a matrix into an equation with the matrix elements on one side of the equation, and the determinant on the other side. Let me write that explicitly, using Δ to indicate the determinant:

$$ab - cd = \Delta \qquad (11.8)$$

This is interesting because it means that we can solve for a particular matrix element if we know the determinant. Let's see an example:

$$\begin{vmatrix} 2 & 7 \\ 4 & \lambda \end{vmatrix} = 4 \quad \Rightarrow \quad 2\lambda - 28 = 4 \quad \Rightarrow \quad 2\lambda = 32 \quad \Rightarrow \quad \lambda = 16$$

So we start with the knowledge that the matrix determinant is 4 and then we can solve for a unique matrix element λ that makes the equation true. Let's try another example:

$$\begin{vmatrix} \lambda & 1 \\ 3 & \lambda \end{vmatrix} = 1 \quad \Rightarrow \quad \lambda^2 - 3 = 1 \quad \Rightarrow \quad \lambda^2 = 4 \quad \Rightarrow \quad \lambda = \pm 2$$

Notice how the equation worked out: There were two λs on the diagonal, which produced a second-order polynomial equation, and thus there were two solutions. So in this case, there is no *single* λ that satisfies our determinant equation; instead, there are two equally acceptable solutions. That's no surprise: The Fundamental Theorem of Algebra tells us that an nth order polynomial has exactly n roots (though they might be complex-valued).

Now I want to push this idea one step further. Instead of having only λ on the diagonal of the matrix, let's have both a real number and an unknown. I'm also assuming that the matrix below is singular, which means I know that its determinant is zero.

$$\begin{vmatrix} 1 - \lambda & 3 \\ 3 & 1 - \lambda \end{vmatrix} = 0 \quad \Rightarrow \quad (1 - \lambda)^2 - 9 = 0 \qquad (11.9)$$

$$\Rightarrow \quad \lambda^2 - 2\lambda - 8 = 0$$

$$\Rightarrow \quad (\lambda + 2)(\lambda - 4) = 0$$

$$\Rightarrow \quad \lambda = -2, 4$$

There are two possible values of λ, which means there are two distinct matrices that solve this equation. Those two matrices are shown below (obtained by plugging in λ). It should take only a quick glance to confirm that both matrices have $\Delta = 0$ (which is the same thing as saying that both matrices are reduced-rank).

$$\lambda = -2 \quad \Rightarrow \quad \begin{bmatrix} 3 & 3 \\ 3 & 3 \end{bmatrix}$$

$$\lambda = 4 \quad \Rightarrow \quad \begin{bmatrix} -3 & 3 \\ 3 & -3 \end{bmatrix}$$

Does subtracting a constant from the diagonal of a square matrix sound familiar? In fact, what we did in this example is *shift the matrix* by $-\lambda\mathbf{I}$. Therefore, we could rewrite Equation 11.9 as

$$det\left(\begin{bmatrix} 1 & 3 \\ 3 & 1 \end{bmatrix} - \lambda\mathbf{I} \right) = 0 \qquad (11.10)$$

Now I will replace that specific matrix with a letter so that it generalizes to any square matrix of any size. That gives us the *characteristic polynomial* of the matrix.

The characteristic polynomial of a matrix.

$$det\left(\mathbf{A} - \lambda\mathbf{I} \right) \qquad (11.11)$$

The characteristic polynomial is a big deal. For one thing, it allows us to represent a matrix in terms of a polynomial expression, and polynomials have a lot of great properties in mathematics.

But more importantly for our purposes in this book, when the characteristic polynomial is set to zero (that is, when we assume the determinant of the shifted matrix is 0), the λ's—the roots of the polynomial—are the eigenvalues of the matrix. Pretty neat, eh? More on this in Chapter 15. For now, we're going to continue our explorations of determinants of larger matrices.

Practice problems Which value(s) of λ would make the following matrices singular (that is, have a determinant of zero)?

a) $\begin{bmatrix} 1 & 2 \\ 4 & \lambda \end{bmatrix}$ b) $\begin{bmatrix} 0 & 14 \\ \lambda & 4 \end{bmatrix}$ c) $\begin{bmatrix} 4 & 1 \\ 1 & \lambda \end{bmatrix}$ d) $\begin{bmatrix} 10 & 1 \\ 3-\lambda & 1 \end{bmatrix}$

e) $\begin{bmatrix} 6 & 2 \\ 5 & 3\lambda \end{bmatrix}$ f) $\begin{bmatrix} \lambda & 4 \\ 1 & \lambda \end{bmatrix}$ g) $\begin{bmatrix} \lambda & 18 \\ 1/2 & \lambda \end{bmatrix}$ h) $\begin{bmatrix} 5-\lambda & -1/3 \\ -3 & 5-\lambda \end{bmatrix}$

Answers

a) $\lambda = 8$ b) $\lambda = 0$ c) $\lambda = 1/4$ d) $\lambda = -7$
e) $\lambda = 5/9$ f) $\lambda = \pm 2$ g) $\lambda = \pm 3$ h) $\lambda = 6, 4$

11.4 Determinant of a 3×3 matrix

There is also a short-cut to determine the determinant of a 3×3 matrix, which involves adding the products of the right-going diagonals and subtracting the products of the left-going diagonals.

It's easiest to understand visually. There are two ways to think about the procedure, one that "wraps around" the matrix and one that augments the matrix with the first two columns (Figure 11.1). Of course, these aren't really *different* methods, just different ways of interpreting the same procedure. Whichever picture you find easier to remember is the one you should focus on.

I hope you find the pictures intuitive and memorable. Trying to memorize the algebraic equation is a terrible idea, but it's printed below for completeness.

Determinant of 3×3 matrix.

$$\begin{vmatrix} a & b & c \\ d & e & f \\ g & h & i \end{vmatrix} = aei + bfg + cdh - ceg - bdi - afh \quad (11.12)$$

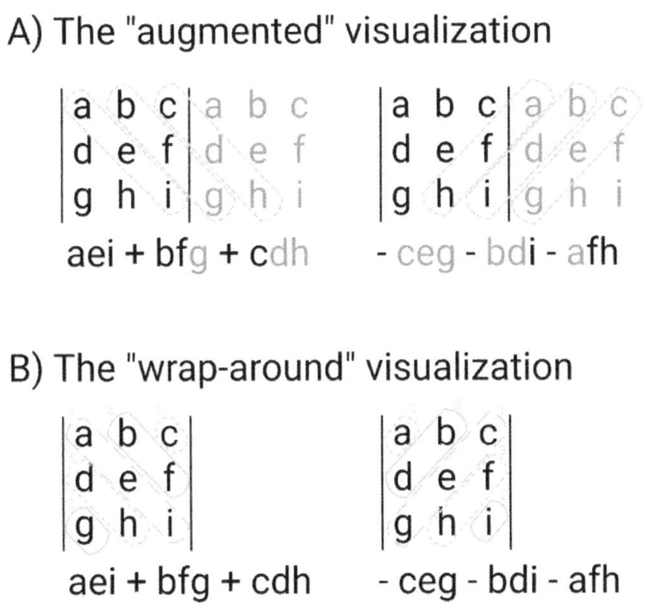
A) The "augmented" visualization
a b c a b c
d e f d e f
g h i g h i
aei + bfg + cdh
a b c a b c
d e f d e f
g h i g h i
- ceg - bdi - afh
B) The "wrap-around" visualization
a b c
d e f
g h i
aei + bfg + cdh
a b c
d e f
g h i
- ceg - bdi - afh

Figure 11.1: Two visualizations of the short-cut for computing the determinant of a 3×3 matrix.

Let's see a few examples with numbers.

$$\begin{vmatrix} 1 & 3 & 5 \\ 2 & 4 & 2 \\ 1 & 2 & 3 \end{vmatrix} = 1{\cdot}4{\cdot}3 + 3{\cdot}2{\cdot}1 + 5{\cdot}2{\cdot}2 - 5{\cdot}4{\cdot}1 - 3{\cdot}2{\cdot}3 - 1{\cdot}2{\cdot}2 = 38 - 44 = -4$$

$$\begin{vmatrix} 0 & 3 & -9 \\ -6 & 0 & 1 \\ 8 & 0 & 1 \end{vmatrix} = 0{\cdot}0{\cdot}1 + 3{\cdot}1{\cdot}8 + 9{\cdot}6{\cdot}0 - 9{\cdot}0{\cdot}8 + 3{\cdot}6{\cdot}1 - 0{\cdot}1{\cdot}0 = 24 + 18 = 42$$

$$\begin{vmatrix} 1 & 3 & 5 \\ 2 & 4 & 2 \\ 3 & 7 & 7 \end{vmatrix} = 1{\cdot}4{\cdot}7 + 3{\cdot}2{\cdot}3 + 5{\cdot}2{\cdot}7 - 5{\cdot}4{\cdot}3 - 3{\cdot}2{\cdot}7 - 1{\cdot}2{\cdot}7 = 116 - 116 = 0$$

The third example has a determinant of zero, which means the matrix is singular (reduced-rank). It's singular because the columns (or rows) form a dependent set. Can you guess by visual inspection how the columns are linearly related to each other? It might be easier to see from looking at the rows.

Let's now demonstrate that the determinant of a 3×3 reduced-rank matrix must be 0. Like with the example of the 2×2 matrix, we'll accomplish this by creating a matrix with letters such that one column is a multiple of another column.

$$\begin{bmatrix} a & b & \lambda a \\ d & e & \lambda d \\ g & h & \lambda g \end{bmatrix}$$

The determinant, after some algebraic handiwork, is found to be zero (parentheses added for visual clarity).

$$\Delta = ae\lambda g + b\lambda dg + \lambda adh - \lambda aeg - bd\lambda g - a\lambda dh \qquad (11.13)$$

$$= (\lambda aeg - \lambda aeg) + (\lambda bdg - \lambda bdg) + (\lambda adh - \lambda adh)$$

$$= 0$$

It is worth taking a few moments to go through this demonstration assuming a linear dependency in the rows.

Practice problems   Determine whether the following determinants are correct.

a) $\begin{vmatrix} 1 & 1 & 2 \\ 2 & 2 & 1 \\ 4 & 3 & 0 \end{vmatrix} = -2$
   b) $\begin{vmatrix} 1 & 1 & 2 \\ 4 & 3 & 0 \\ 2 & 2 & 1 \end{vmatrix} = -3$
   c) $\begin{vmatrix} 1 & 2 & 4 \\ 1 & 2 & 3 \\ 2 & 1 & 0 \end{vmatrix} = -3$
   d) $\begin{vmatrix} 1 & -2 & 3 \\ -4 & 5 & -6 \\ 7 & -8 & 9 \end{vmatrix} = 8$

Answers

a) No, $\Delta = -3$ b) No, $\Delta = +3$ c) Correct   d) No, $\Delta = 0$

Practice problems   Which value(s) of λ would make the following matrices singular?

a) $\begin{bmatrix} 0 & 1 & 1 \\ 0 & 4 & 7 \\ 0 & 3 & \lambda \end{bmatrix}$
   b) $\begin{bmatrix} 1 & 0 & -3 \\ -4 & -11 & 1 \\ 3 & \lambda & 0 \end{bmatrix}$

c) $\begin{bmatrix} 1 & 1 & 1 \\ 2 & 2 & 3 \\ 3 & \lambda & 4 \end{bmatrix}$
   d) $\begin{bmatrix} 1-\lambda & 0 & 4 \\ -4 & 3-\lambda & 4 \\ 0 & 0 & 5-\lambda \end{bmatrix}$

Answers

a) any λ b) $\lambda = 9$
c) $\lambda = 3$ d) $\lambda = 1, 3, 5$

Determinant and transpose   We can now show that the determinant of a 3×3 matrix is the same before and after transposing. It takes slightly longer to prove than for the 2×2 case, but is still worth the effort. The ordering of the terms is different, but the individual products are the same, as are their signs.

$$\begin{vmatrix} a & b & c \\ d & e & f \\ g & h & i \end{vmatrix} = aei + bfg + cdh - ceg - bdi - afh \qquad (11.14)$$

$$\begin{vmatrix} a & d & g \\ b & e & h \\ c & f & i \end{vmatrix} = aei + dhc + gbf - gec - dbi - ahf \qquad (11.15)$$

11.5 Full procedure to compute the determinant

It turns out that the aforediscussed tricks for computing the determinants of 2×2 and 3×3 matrices are simplifications of the full procedure to compute the determinant of any sized matrix. In this section you will learn that full procedure. It gets really complicated really quickly, so I will illustrate it using a 4×4 matrix, and then you'll see how this simplifies to the smaller matrices.

In general, the procedure is to multiply the ith element of the first row of the matrix by the determinant of the 3×3 submatrix created by excluding the ith row and i^{th} column. That gives four numbers. You then add the 1st and 3rd, and subtract the 2nd and 4th. Figure 11.2 shows the operation.

$$\begin{vmatrix} a & b & c & d \\ e & f & g & h \\ i & j & k & l \\ m & n & o & p \end{vmatrix} = a \times \begin{vmatrix} f & g & h \\ j & k & l \\ n & o & p \end{vmatrix} - b \times \begin{vmatrix} e & g & h \\ i & k & l \\ m & o & p \end{vmatrix} + c \times \begin{vmatrix} e & f & h \\ i & j & l \\ m & n & p \end{vmatrix} - d \times \begin{vmatrix} e & f & g \\ i & j & k \\ m & n & o \end{vmatrix}$$

Figure 11.2: The procedure for computing the determinant of a 4×4 matrix. Note the alternating plus and minus signs.

Thus, computing the determinant of a 4×4 matrix actually requires computing four 3×3 determinants. Interestingly, you can modify

Note: There are some fancy linear algebra terms here like *minors matrix* and *cofactors* that will be introduced in the next chapter.

this procedure to go column-wise rather than row-wise. That is, multiply each element of the first column by the determinant of the submatrix created by excluding that element's row. Alternatively: Transpose the matrix and apply the procedure illustrated in Figure 11.2.

Now let's see what happens when we apply this same procedure to a 3×3 matrix (Figure 11.3).

$$\begin{vmatrix} a & b & c \\ d & e & f \\ g & h & i \end{vmatrix} = a\begin{vmatrix} e & f \\ h & i \end{vmatrix} - b\begin{vmatrix} d & f \\ g & i \end{vmatrix} + c\begin{vmatrix} d & e \\ g & h \end{vmatrix}$$

$$= a(ei-fh) - b(di-fg) + c(dh-eg)$$

$$= aei-afh - (bdi-dfg) + cdh-ceg$$

$$= aei + bfg + cdh - ceg - bdi - afh$$

Figure 11.3: The procedure for computing the determinant of a 3×3 matrix. Note the alternating plus and minus signs. And notice that the end result is the same as the shortcut in Equation 11.12.

Now it's your turn: apply the full procedure to a 2×2 matrix. (The determinant of a scalar is simply that scalar, thus, $det(-4) = -4$.) You will arrive at the familiar $ad - bc$.

The full procedure scales up to any sized matrix. But that means that computing the determinant of a 5×5 matrix requires computing 5 determinants of 4×4 submatrices, and each of those submatrices must be broken down into 3×3 submatrices. Honestly, I could live 1000 years and die happy without ever computing the determinant of a 5×5 matrix by hand.

Practice problems Compute the determinant of the following matrices (lots of zeros in these matrices... you're welcome).

a) $\begin{bmatrix} 0 & -1 & 2 & 0 \\ 1 & 2 & 0 & 5 \\ 0 & 3 & -4 & 0 \\ 1 & 0 & 2 & 0 \end{bmatrix}$
b) $\begin{bmatrix} 0 & 0 & -3 & 3 \\ 6 & 0 & 0 & -1 \\ 0 & 0 & -4 & 0 \\ -1 & -1 & -3 & 2 \end{bmatrix}$
c) $\begin{bmatrix} 0 & -1 & 0 & 0 \\ 1 & 2 & 0 & 5 \\ 0 & 3 & 0 & 0 \\ 1 & 0 & 0 & 0 \end{bmatrix}$

Answers

a) -10 b) 72 c) 0

11.6 Determinant of a triangular matrix

Here's the key take-home of this section: *The determinant of a triangular matrix is equal to the product of its diagonal elements.*

There are three kinds of triangular matrices: upper-triangular, lower-triangular, and diagonal. Thus, computing the determinant of even a large triangular matrix is pretty easy.

In fact, for some matrices, it's easier to apply row reduction to get the matrix into its echelon form and then compute the determinant as the product of the diagonal. HOWEVER, be aware that row exchanges and row-scalar-multiplication affect the determinant, as you will learn in subsequent sections.

| Useful tip for exams!

Why is this shortcut true? Let's start by proving it for upper-triangular 2×2 matrices:

$$\begin{vmatrix} a & b \\ 0 & d \end{vmatrix} = ad - b0 = ad \qquad (11.16)$$

You can now prove this for lower-triangular and diagonal matrices.

The proof for 3×3 matrices is comparable but involves slightly more algebra. The expression below draws from Equation 11.12 but sets the lower-triangular elements to zero.

$$\begin{vmatrix} a & b & c \\ 0 & e & f \\ 0 & 0 & i \end{vmatrix} = aei + bf0 + c00 - ce0 - b0i - af0 = aei \quad (11.17)$$

Again, I will leave it to you to adapt Equation 11.17 to lower-triangular and diagonal matrices. You will discover that the result is the same: The determinant equals the product of the diagonals.

Finally, let's inspect the 4×4 case. Figure 11.4 is a modified version of Figure 11.2 with $e = i = f = m = n = o = 0$.

$$\begin{vmatrix} a & b & c & d \\ 0 & f & g & h \\ 0 & 0 & k & l \\ 0 & 0 & 0 & p \end{vmatrix} = a \times \begin{vmatrix} f & g & h \\ 0 & k & l \\ 0 & 0 & p \end{vmatrix} - b \times \begin{vmatrix} 0 & g & h \\ 0 & k & l \\ 0 & 0 & p \end{vmatrix} + c \times \begin{vmatrix} 0 & f & h \\ 0 & 0 & l \\ 0 & 0 & p \end{vmatrix} - d \times \begin{vmatrix} 0 & f & g \\ 0 & 0 & k \\ 0 & 0 & 0 \end{vmatrix}$$

Figure 11.4: The full determinant formula with an upper-triangular 4×4 matrix.

The remarkable result here is that three of the four submatrices are singular (notice the columns of zeros). The only non-singular matrix is the first, which itself is a diagonal matrix, and which multiplies the first diagonal element of the original matrix. In other words, after following this rather complicated formula, the determinant of the matrix simplifies to $\Delta = afkp$.

In mathematics, proofs don't necessarily lead to intuition. The reason *why* the determinant equals the product of the diagonals for any triangular matrix is this: All-but-one of the individual terms in the determinant formula have at least one element from the upper-triangle and at least one element from the lower-triangle. The one exception is the term defined by the main diagonal.

Code Computing the determinant is simple in Python and in MATLAB. However, the determinant is a numerically unstable computation for large matrices, which will be demonstrated in the code challenges.

```
1  import numpy as np
2  A = np.random.randn(3,3)
3  np.linalg.det(A)
```

```
1  A = randn(3,3);
2  det(A)
```

11.7 Determinant and row reduction

The procedures involved in row reduction (swapping rows, adding multiples of rows to other rows, and multiplying a row by a constant) have implications for the determinant of the matrix. Let's explore each of these three operations in turn.

Row swapping Curiously enough, swapping the rows of a matrix flips the sign of the determinant, without affecting the magnitude of the determinant. Let's start with a simple example of the identity matrix with and without rows swapped:

As sure as the sun rises, the determinant of the identity matrix of any size is 1.

$$\begin{vmatrix} 1 & 0 \\ 0 & 1 \end{vmatrix} = 1 \times 1 - 0 \times 0 = 1$$

$$\begin{vmatrix} 0 & 1 \\ 1 & 0 \end{vmatrix} = 0 \times 0 - 1 \times 1 = -1$$

Now let's try with a full matrix comprising letters.

$$\begin{vmatrix} a & b \\ c & d \end{vmatrix} = ad - cb$$

$$\begin{vmatrix} c & d \\ a & b \end{vmatrix} = cb - da = -(ab - cd)$$

With a 2×2 matrix, there is only one possible way to swap rows. Let's try this again with the 3×3 identity matrix. We can see what happens with multiple row swaps.

$$\begin{vmatrix} 1 & 0 & 0 \\ 0 & 1 & 0 \\ 0 & 0 & 1 \end{vmatrix} = 1{\cdot}1{\cdot}1 + 0{\cdot}0{\cdot}0 + 0{\cdot}0{\cdot}0 - 0{\cdot}1{\cdot}0 - 0{\cdot}0{\cdot}1 - 1{\cdot}0{\cdot}0 = 1$$

$$\begin{vmatrix} 0 & 1 & 0 \\ 1 & 0 & 0 \\ 0 & 0 & 1 \end{vmatrix} = 0{\cdot}0{\cdot}1 + 1{\cdot}0{\cdot}0 + 0{\cdot}1{\cdot}0 - 0{\cdot}0{\cdot}0 - 1{\cdot}1{\cdot}1 - 0{\cdot}0{\cdot}0 = -1$$

$$\begin{vmatrix} 0 & 1 & 0 \\ 0 & 0 & 1 \\ 1 & 0 & 0 \end{vmatrix} = 0{\cdot}0{\cdot}0 + 1{\cdot}1{\cdot}1 + 0{\cdot}0{\cdot}0 - 0{\cdot}0{\cdot}1 - 1{\cdot}0{\cdot}0 - 0{\cdot}1{\cdot}0 = 1$$

Thus, each row swap reverses the sign of the determinant. Two row swaps therefore "double-reverses" the sign. More generally, an odd number of row swaps effectively multiplies the sign of the determinant by -1, whereas an even number of row swaps preserves the sign of the determinant.

One more example with a matrix of letters.

$$\begin{vmatrix} a & b & c \\ d & e & f \\ g & h & i \end{vmatrix} = aei + bfg + cdh - ceg - bdi - afh \qquad (11.18)$$

$$\begin{vmatrix} d & e & f \\ a & b & c \\ g & h & i \end{vmatrix} = bdi + ceg + afh - bfg - aei - cdh \qquad (11.19)$$

$$= -(aei + bfg + cdh - ceg - bdi - afh)$$

$$\begin{vmatrix} d & e & f \\ g & h & i \\ a & b & c \end{vmatrix} = cdh + aei + bfg - afh - ceg - bdi \qquad (11.20)$$

Adding multiples of rows Adding a multiple of one row to another is the most common operation in row reduction. Let's see what happens when we replace row 1 by row 1 plus row 2 (spoiler alert: the determinant is unchanged):

$$\begin{vmatrix} a+c & b+d \\ c & d \end{vmatrix} = (a+c)d - (b+d)c$$

$$= ad + cd - (bc + dc)$$

$$= ad - bc \qquad (11.21)$$

Let's try this again with a $3{\times}3$ matrix to make sure our conclusion isn't based on a quirk of the $2{\times}2$ case:

$$\begin{vmatrix} a+g & b+h & c+i \\ d & e & f \\ g & h & i \end{vmatrix}$$

$$= (a+g)ei + (b+h)fg + (c+i)dh - (c+i)eg - (b+h)di - (a+g)fh$$

$$= aei + gei + bfg + hfg + cdh + idh - ceg - ieg - bdi - hdi - afh - gfh$$

$$= aei + bfg + cdh - ceg - bdi - afh \qquad (11.22)$$

It's not immediately visually obvious that the "extra" terms will cancel, but notice that there are identical terms with opposite signs and with letters in a different order (for example: $+gei$ and $-ieg$). Canceling those terms will bring us back to the familiar determinant formula. It's as we never added any rows in the first place.

Now you know *that* the determinant is unaffected by adding rows to each other. *Why* does this happen? In Equation 11.21, the copy of row 2 embedded in row 1 adds, and then subtracts, the added elements ($+cd$ and $-dc$). Same story for Equation 11.22: The "extra terms" come from the products of the right-going diagonals with the added elements (gei, hfg, idh) (consult back to Figure 11.1 on page 303), and then those same "extra terms" are subtracted off from the left-going diagonals (ieg, hdi, gfh).

The previous paragraph will provide an answer to the next question: What about adding *multiples* of one row to another? In the two examples above, I only showed a row being added to another row, but row reduction often involves scalar-multiplying rows and adding them. It turns out that scalar multiplying does not change our conclusion: combining rows has no effect on the determinant. The reason is that the multiple is simply a different constant that gets added and then subtracted to the determinant formula.

Let's think through this using example 11.22. Instead of adding row 3 to row 1, let's add 4 times row 3 to row 1. The first row of the new matrix then becomes [$(a + 4g)$ $(b + 4h)$ $(c + 4i)$]. Well, $4g$ is still just a constant, so we might as well give it a new variable name g'. Thus, the first element becomes $(a + g')$. Same for the other two elements of the first row: $(b + h')$ and $(c + i')$. Then the opposite-signed terms in Equation 11.22 are, for example, $g'ei$ and $-ieg'$. Those still cancel out.

Finally, we can address subtracting rows: Subtracting rows is the same thing as adding rows with one row scalar-multiplied by -1. For this reason, subtracting rows has the same impact on the determinant as adding rows: None whatsoever.

Row-scalar multiplication   What happens to the determinant when you multiply an entire row by a scalar? Notice the difference from the discussion above: Here we are concerned with multiplying only one row by a scalar; we are not combining multiple rows by addition or subtraction.

The answer is that multiplying a row by some scalar β scales the determinant by β. Let's see an example in our favorite lettered 2×2 matrix.

$$\begin{vmatrix} \beta a & \beta b \\ c & d \end{vmatrix} = \beta ad - \beta bc = \beta(ad - bc) \tag{11.23}$$

How does this generalize to scaling rows by different values? Let's find out:

$$\begin{vmatrix} \beta a & \beta b \\ \gamma c & \gamma d \end{vmatrix} = \beta a\gamma d - \beta b\gamma c = \beta\gamma(ad - bc) \tag{11.24}$$

In other words, any scalar that multiplies an entire row, scales the determinant by the same amount.

This scales up to any sized matrix, which is easy to confirm in the 3×3 case:

$$\begin{vmatrix} a & b & c \\ d & e & f \\ \zeta g & \zeta h & \zeta i \end{vmatrix} = ae\zeta i + bf\zeta g + cd\zeta h - ce\zeta g - bd\zeta i - af\zeta h$$

$$= \zeta(aei + bfg + cdh - ceg - bdi - afh) \quad (11.25)$$

The reason why this happens is that each term in the determinant formula contains exactly one element from each row in the matrix. Therefore, multiplying an entire row by a scalar means that every term in the formula contains that scalar, and it can thus be factored out.

Summary Following is the high-level summary of this section; it's really easy to memorize, but of course you needed the previous pages to explain *why* these are true.

$$\begin{aligned} \text{Row swap} \quad &\to \quad \Delta = -\Delta \\ \text{Add rows} \quad &\to \quad \Delta = \Delta \\ \text{Scale row by } \beta \quad &\to \quad \Delta = \Delta\beta \end{aligned}$$

11.8 Determinant & matrix-scalar multiplication

The previous section might have led you to wonder what happens to the determinant of a scalar-multiplication over the entire matrix. That is, what is the relationship between $|\mathbf{A}|$ and $|\beta\mathbf{A}|$?

One way to think about this is that matrix-scalar multiplication is the same thing as row-scalar multiplication, repeated for all rows and using the same scalar. So if multiplying one row by a scalar β scales the determinant by β, then multiplying two rows by β scales the determinant by $\beta\beta = \beta^2$. Generalizing this to all M rows of a matrix leads to the following formula:

$$det(\beta\mathbf{A}) = \beta^M det(\mathbf{A}), \quad \mathbf{A} \in \mathbb{R}^{M \times M} \tag{11.26}$$

It is also insightful to think about this from an element perspective of matrix-scalar multiplication.

$$\beta \begin{vmatrix} a & b \\ c & d \end{vmatrix} = \begin{vmatrix} \beta a & \beta b \\ \beta c & \beta d \end{vmatrix} = \beta a \beta d - \beta b \beta c = \beta^2 (ad - bc) \tag{11.27}$$

You can see that each term in the determinant formula brings β^2, which can be factored out. Let's see how this looks for a 3×3 matrix.

$$\beta \begin{vmatrix} a & b & c \\ d & e & f \\ g & h & i \end{vmatrix} = \begin{vmatrix} \beta a & \beta b & \beta c \\ \beta d & \beta e & \beta f \\ \beta g & \beta h & \beta i \end{vmatrix}$$

$$= \beta^3 aei + \beta^3 bfg + \beta^3 cdh - \beta^3 ceg - \beta^3 bdi - \beta^3 afh$$

$$= \beta^3 (aei + bfg + cdh - ceg - bdi - afh) \tag{11.28}$$

You can consider how this works for the 4×4 case (refer to Figure 11.2): The determinant of each submatrix has a scalar of β^3, which then multiplies β times the element in the first row, leading to β^4.

Generalizing this to higher dimensions leads back to Equation 11.26.

11.9 Determinant in theory and in practice

As mentioned at the outset of this chapter, the determinant has several applications. Two of the most important applications—and the primary applications in this book—are computing the matrix inverse, and discovering the eigenvalues. Clearly, the determinant has an important role in linear algebra.

On the other hand, the determinant is difficult to compute for "large" matrices, due to numerical instabilities. Numerical instabilities in computers result from multiplying or dividing by very very small numbers, or very very large numbers. This is particularly problematic when the matrices have a high condition number (a concept you will learn about in Chapter 16 on the singular value decomposition), are close to singular, or are singular.

You will have the opportunity to examine this yourself in the code challenges at the end of this chapter. The main point is that the determinant is an important concept to understand for the *theory* of linear algebra, but you should avoid computing or using it directly when *implementing* linear algebra concepts on computers.

Exercises

1. Compute the determinant of the following matrices.

a) $\begin{bmatrix} a & a \\ b & c \end{bmatrix}$

b) $\begin{bmatrix} 5 & 2 \\ 10 & 4 \end{bmatrix}$

c) $\begin{bmatrix} 5 & 10 \\ 2 & 4 \end{bmatrix}$

d) $\begin{bmatrix} 50 & 7 \\ 7 & 1 \end{bmatrix}$

e) $\begin{bmatrix} 2 & \sqrt{e^{-\pi/314}} \\ 0 & 8 \end{bmatrix}$

f) $\begin{bmatrix} -2 & 6 \\ -4 & 11 \end{bmatrix}$

g) $\begin{bmatrix} 100 & \sqrt{599} \\ \sqrt{599} & 6 \end{bmatrix}$

h) $\begin{bmatrix} 13 & 34 \\ 5 & 13 \end{bmatrix}$

i) $\begin{bmatrix} 1 & 0 & 0 \\ 0 & 13 & 34 \\ 0 & 5 & 13 \end{bmatrix}$

j) $\begin{bmatrix} 1 & 1 & 0 \\ 6 & -5 & 4 \\ 2 & 0 & -9 \end{bmatrix}$

k) $\begin{bmatrix} 0 & 2 & 3 \\ 1 & -78 & 17 \\ 0 & 1 & 2 \end{bmatrix}$

l) $\begin{bmatrix} 1 & -78 & 17 \\ 0 & 2 & 3 \\ 0 & 1 & 2 \end{bmatrix}$

m) $\begin{bmatrix} 0 & 1 & 2 \\ 1 & -78 & 17 \\ 0 & 2 & 3 \end{bmatrix}$

n) $\begin{bmatrix} 1 & -2 & 3 \\ -4 & 5 & -6 \\ 7 & -8 & 9 \end{bmatrix}$

o) $\begin{bmatrix} 0 & 1 & 2 & 0 \\ -4 & 0 & 3 & 1 \\ 3 & -3 & 0 & 0 \\ 6 & 0 & -2 & -2 \end{bmatrix}$

2. Apply row-reduction to obtain the echelon form of these matrices, and then compute the determinant as the product of the diagonal. Keep track of row-swaps and row-scalar multiplications.

a) $\begin{bmatrix} 2 & 3 \\ 4 & 5 \end{bmatrix}$

b) $\begin{bmatrix} 3 & 4 \\ 1 & 3 \end{bmatrix}$

c) $\begin{bmatrix} 1 & 3 & -2 \\ 3 & 5 & 6 \\ 2 & 4 & 3 \end{bmatrix}$

d) $\begin{bmatrix} 0 & 2 & -4 \\ 3 & -2 & 7 \\ 3 & 2 & -1 \end{bmatrix}$

3. Does having a zero in the main diagonal necessarily give a matrix $\Delta = 0$? The correct answer is "it depends"; now you need to figure out what it depends on, and why that is. Then create an example matrix with all zeros on the diagonal but with $\Delta \neq 0$.

1.   **a)** $a(c-b)$ **b)** 0 **c)** 0

     d) 1 **e)** 16 **f)** 2

     g) 1 **h)** -1 **i)** -1

     j) 107 **k)** -1 **l)** $+1$

     m) 1 **n)** 0 **o)** -24

2. These answers show the echelon form and the determinant of the original matrix. Notice that the determinant of the original matrix is not necessarily the same thing as the the product of the diagonals of the echelon form of the matrix (depending on row manipulations).

     a) $\begin{bmatrix} 2 & 3 \\ 0 & -1 \end{bmatrix}, \Delta = -2$ **b)** $\begin{bmatrix} 1 & 3 \\ 0 & -5 \end{bmatrix}, \Delta = 5$

     c) $\begin{bmatrix} 1 & 3 & -2 \\ 0 & -2 & -6 \\ 0 & 0 & 1 \end{bmatrix}, \Delta = -4$ **d)** $\begin{bmatrix} 3 & 2 & -1 \\ 0 & -4 & 8 \\ 0 & 0 & 0 \end{bmatrix}, \Delta = 0$

3. The determinant of a matrix is zero if at least one diagonal element is zero only if the matrix is triangular (upper-triangular, lower-triangular, or diagonal). This is because the determinant of a triangular matrix is equal to the product of the diagonal elements. Here is an example of a matrix with a diagonal of zeros and $\Delta = 4$:

$$\begin{bmatrix} 0 & 0 & 1 \\ 1 & 0 & 0 \\ 2 & 1 & 0 \end{bmatrix}$$

Code challenges

1. Write code that illustrates Equation 11.26. Your code should generate a 4×4 matrix comprising integers between 0 and 10, then generate a random integer β between -10 and -1, and then print out the left- and right-hand sides of Equation 11.26.

2. We will now demonstrate the numerical instabilities of the determinant. Implement the following in code:

1. Create a matrix of normally distributed random numbers.
2. Ensure that the matrix is reduced-rank.
3. Compute the absolute value of the determinant (we are interested in whether the determinant deviates from zero; the sign doesn't matter).

Run these three steps in a double for-loop: One over matrix sizes ranging from 3×3 to 30×30, and a second that repeats the three steps 100 times. This is equivalent to repeating a scientific experiment multiple times.

Finally, make a plot of the average determinant as a function of the matrix size. In theory, all of these determinants should be zero! The figure below shows my result. I show the y-axis in log-scale because the determinants grow exponentially.

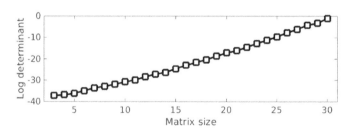

Figure 11.5: Average determinant magnitudes of singular matrices of different sizes.

11.13 Code solutions

1. Note that upper bounds in Python are usually (though not always) specified as exclusive, meaning that an upper bound parameter of "11" will produce random numbers up to 10.

Code block 11.3: Python

```
1  import numpy as np
2  A = np.random.randint(0,11,(4,4))
3  b = np.random.randint(-10,1)
4  print(np.linalg.det(b*A),
5        b**4*np.linalg.det(A))
```

Code block 11.4: MATLAB

```
1  A = randi([0 10],4);
2  b = randi([-10 -1],1);
3  [det(b*A) b^4*det(A)]
```

2. One easy way to create a singular matrix is to set column 1 equal to column 2.

Code block 11.5: Python

```python
1  import numpy as np
2  import matplotlib.pyplot as plt
3
4  ns = np.arange(3,31)
5  iters = 100
6  dets = np.zeros((len(ns),iters))
7
8  for ni in range(len(ns)):
9    for i in range(iters):
10     A = np.random.randn(ns[ni],ns[ni])
11     A[:,0] = A[:,1]
12     dets[ni,i]=np.abs(np.linalg.det(A))
13
14 plt.plot(ns,np.log(np.mean(dets,axis=1)))
15 plt.xlabel('Matrix size')
16 plt.ylabel('Log determinant');
```

Code block 11.6: MATLAB

```matlab
1  ns = 3:30;
2  iters = 100;
3  dets = zeros(length(ns),iters);
4
5  for ni=1:length(ns)
6      for i=1:iters
7          A = randn(ns(ni));
8          A(:,1) = A(:,2);
9          dets(ni,i) = abs(det(A));
10     end
11 end
12
13 plot(ns,log(mean(dets,2)),'s-')
14 xlabel('Matrix size')
15 ylabel('Log determinant')
```

CHAPTER 12
MATRIX INVERSE

START THIS CHAPTER HAPPY

As usual, I will begin this chapter with some general conceptual introductions, and then we'll get into the details.

12.1 Concepts and applications

In section 6.11 I wrote that matrix division *per se* doesn't exist, however, there is a conceptually similar operation, which involves multiplying a matrix by its inverse. By way of introduction to the matrix inverse, I'm going to start with the "scalar inverse." Solve for x in this equation.

$$3x = 1 \tag{12.1}$$

Obviously, $x = 1/3$. How did you solve this equation? I guess you divided both sides of the equation by 3. But let me write this in a slightly different way:

$$3x = 1$$

$$3^{-1}3x = 3^{-1}1$$

$$1x = 3^{-1}$$

$$x = \frac{1}{3}$$

I realize that this is a gratuitously excessive number of steps to write out explicitly, but it does illustrate a point: To separate the 3 from the x, we multiplied by 3^{-1}, which we might call the "inverse of 3." And of course, we had to do this to both sides of the equation. Thus, $3 \times 3^{-1} = 1$. A number times its inverse is 1. The number 1 is special because it is the multiplicative identity.

What about the following equation; can you solve for x here?

$$0x = 1$$

Nope, you cannot solve for x here, because you cannot compute $0/0$. There is no number that can multiply 0 to give 1. The lesson here is that not all numbers have inverses.

OK, now let's talk about the *matrix* inverse. The matrix inverse is a matrix that multiplies another matrix such that the product is the identity matrix. The identity matrix is important because it is the matrix analog of the number 1—the multiplicative identity ($\mathbf{AI} = \mathbf{A}$). Here it is in math notation:

$$\mathbf{A}^{-1}\mathbf{A} = \mathbf{I} \qquad (12.2)$$

Now let me show you an example of using the matrix inverse. In the equations below, imagine that $\mathbf{A}$ and $\mathbf{b}$ are known and $\mathbf{x}$ is the vector of unknowns that we want to solve for.

$$\mathbf{A}\mathbf{x} = \mathbf{b} \qquad (12.3)$$

$$\mathbf{A}^{-1}\mathbf{A}\mathbf{x} = \mathbf{A}^{-1}\mathbf{b} \qquad (12.4)$$

$$\mathbf{I}\mathbf{x} = \mathbf{A}^{-1}\mathbf{b} \qquad (12.5)$$

$$\mathbf{x} = \mathbf{A}^{-1}\mathbf{b} \qquad (12.6)$$

IMPORTANT: Because matrix multiplication is non-commutative (that is, $\mathbf{AB} \neq \mathbf{BA}$), you need to be mindful to multiply both sides of the equation by the matrix inverse on the same side. For example, the following equation is *invalid*:

This was already mentioned in section 6.2 but it's important enough to repeat.

$$\mathbf{A}^{-1}\mathbf{A}\mathbf{x} = \mathbf{b}\mathbf{A}^{-1} \qquad (12.7)$$

This equation is **WRONG** because the inverse pre-multiplies on the left-hand side of the equation but post-multiplies on the right-hand side of the equation. As it turns out, post-multiplying by $\mathbf{A}^{-1}$:

$$\mathbf{A}\mathbf{x}\mathbf{A}^{-1} = \mathbf{b}\mathbf{A}^{-1} \qquad (12.8)$$

is invalid for this equation, because both $\mathbf{A}\mathbf{x}$ and $\mathbf{b}$ are column vectors. Thus, the sizes do not permit matrix post-multiplication.

Inverting the inverse Because the inverse is unique (you'll learn the proof of this claim later), it can be undone. Thus, the inverse of an inverse is the original matrix. That is:

$$(\mathbf{A}^{-1})^{-1} = \mathbf{A} \qquad (12.9)$$

Transpose and inverse   Equation 12.9 is reminiscent of double-transposing a matrix ($\mathbf{A}^{\mathrm{TT}} = \mathbf{A}$). Although the transpose and inverse are completely different operations, they do have a special relationship: The transpose of the inverse equals the inverse of the transpose.

$$(\mathbf{A}^{-1})^{\mathrm{T}} = (\mathbf{A}^{\mathrm{T}})^{-1} = \mathbf{A}^{-\mathrm{T}} \tag{12.10}$$

Actually, what I wrote above ("transpose and inverse are completely different") is true only for most matrices. There is a special kind of matrix, called an orthogonal matrix, for which the inverse equals the transpose. More about this in the next chapter!

Conditions for invertibility   You saw above that not all numbers have an inverse. Not all matrices have inverses either. In fact, many (or perhaps most) matrices that you will work with in practical applications are not invertible. Remember that square matrices without an inverse are variously called singular, reduced-rank, or rank-deficient.

A matrix has a full inverse matrix if the following criteria are met:

1. It is square
2. It is full-rank

So the full matrix inverse exists only for square matrices. What does a "full" matrix inverse mean? It means you can put the inverse on either side of the matrix and still get the identity matrix:

$$\mathbf{A}\mathbf{A}^{-1} = \mathbf{A}^{-1}\mathbf{A} = \mathbf{I} \tag{12.11}$$

Thus, the full matrix inverse is one of the few exceptions to matrix multiplication commutivity.

Some rectangular matrices have a "one-sided" inverse, if certain conditions are met. One-sided inverses are non-commutative, for example $\mathbf{A}\mathbf{A}^{-1} = \mathbf{I}$ but $\mathbf{A}^{-1}\mathbf{A} \neq \mathbf{I}$. For this reason, the "full inverse" is also sometimes called the "two-sided inverse." You'll learn about one-sided inverses starting on page 339; until then, please assume that all matrices are square.

Remember to LIVE EVIL   As a quick reminder:

$$(\mathbf{ABC})^{-1} = \mathbf{C}^{-1}\mathbf{B}^{-1}\mathbf{A}^{-1} \qquad (12.12)$$

However, this is not as simple as it sounds: It is possible for the matrix product $(\mathbf{ABC})$ to be invertible while the individual matrices are not invertible.

Uniqueness of the matrix inverse   Every inverse is unique, meaning that if a matrix has an inverse, it has exactly one inverse. I'll show two proofs for this claim; both proofs rely on the same assumptions, and both work by contradiction. The assumptions are:

1. Matrix $\mathbf{A}$ is invertible.
2. $\mathbf{B}$ is an inverse of $\mathbf{A}$.
3. $\mathbf{C}$ is also an inverse of $\mathbf{A}$, distinct from $\mathbf{B}$ (thus, $\mathbf{B} \neq \mathbf{C}$).

Assumptions 2 and 3 can be written out mathematically:

$$\mathbf{AB} = \mathbf{I} \qquad (12.13)$$

$$\mathbf{AC} = \mathbf{I} \qquad (12.14)$$

Next I'm going to pre-multiply both equations by $\mathbf{A}^{-1}$:

$$\mathbf{A}^{-1}\mathbf{AB} = \mathbf{A}^{-1}\mathbf{I} \quad \Rightarrow \quad \mathbf{B} = \mathbf{A}^{-1} \qquad (12.15)$$

$$\mathbf{A}^{-1}\mathbf{AC} = \mathbf{A}^{-1}\mathbf{I} \quad \Rightarrow \quad \mathbf{C} = \mathbf{A}^{-1} \qquad (12.16)$$

From the equations to the right of the arrow, we must conclude that $\mathbf{B} = \mathbf{C}$. However, our assumption was that $\mathbf{B} \neq \mathbf{C}$. The conclusion was inconsistent with the assumption, therefore the assumption is wrong. This proves that all inverses of a given matrix are equal.

The second proof is shorter; notice that each subsequent expression is based on adding or removing the identity matrix, expressed as the matrix times its inverse:

$$\mathbf{C} = \mathbf{CI} = \mathbf{CAB} = \mathbf{IB} = \mathbf{B} \qquad (12.17)$$

Again, the conclusion is that any two matrices that claim to be the inverse of the same matrix must be equal to each other.

Inverse of a symmetric matrix The inverse of a symmetric matrix is itself symmetric. That is, if $\mathbf{A} = \mathbf{A}^\mathrm{T}$ then $\mathbf{A}^{-1} = \mathbf{A}^{-\mathrm{T}}$.

To prove this claim, we start from two assumptions: That the matrix $\mathbf{A}$ is symmetric, and that it has an inverse. The strategy here is to transpose the inverse equation and then do a bit of algebra. Here's math tip: Write down the first equation, close the book, and see if you can discover the proof on your own.

$$\mathbf{A}^{-1}\mathbf{A} = \mathbf{I} \tag{12.18}$$

$$(\mathbf{A}^{-1}\mathbf{A})^\mathrm{T} = \mathbf{I}^\mathrm{T} \tag{12.19}$$

$$\mathbf{A}^\mathrm{T}\mathbf{A}^{-\mathrm{T}} = \mathbf{I} \tag{12.20}$$

$$\mathbf{A}\mathbf{A}^{-\mathrm{T}} = \mathbf{I} \tag{12.21}$$

$$\mathbf{A}\mathbf{A}^{-\mathrm{T}} = \mathbf{A}\mathbf{A}^{-1} \tag{12.22}$$

In the previous page, we proved that if a matrix has an inverse, it has one unique inverse. Therefore, Equation 12.22 brings us to our final conclusion that if the matrix is symmetric, its inverse is also symmetric.

Avoid the inverse when possible! The last thing I want to discuss before teaching you how to compute the matrix inverse is that the matrix inverse is great *in theory*. When doing abstract paper-and-pencil work, you can invert matrices as much as you want, regardless of their size and content (assuming they are square and full-rank). But in practice, computing the inverse of a matrix on a computer is difficult and can be wrought with numerical inaccuracies and rounding errors.

Thus, in practical computer applications of linear algebra, you should avoid using the explicit inverse unless it is absolutely necessary.

Computer scientists have worked hard over the past several decades to develop algorithms to solve problems that—on paper—require the inverse, without actually computing the inverse. The details of those algorithms are beyond the scope of this book. Fortunately, they are implemented in low-level libraries called by MATLAB, Python, C, and other numerical processing languages. This is good news, because it allows you to focus on understanding the conceptual aspects of the inverse, while letting your computer deal with the number-crunching.

Computing the matrix inverse There are several algorithms to compute the matrix inverse. In this book, you will learn three: MCA (minors, cofactors, adjugate), row-reduction, and SVD. You will learn about the first two algorithms in this chapter, and you'll learn about the SVD method in Chapter 16. But there are convenient short-cuts for computing the inverses of a diagonal matrix and a 2×2 matrix, and that's where we'll start.

12.2 Matrix inverse of a diagonal matrix

Diagonal matrices have an extremely easy-to-compute inverse: Simply invert each diagonal element and ignore the off-diagonal zeros.

$$\mathbf{A} = \begin{bmatrix} a & 0 & 0 \\ 0 & b & 0 \\ 0 & 0 & c \end{bmatrix} \tag{12.23}$$

$$\mathbf{A}^{-1} = \begin{bmatrix} 1/a & 0 & 0 \\ 0 & 1/b & 0 \\ 0 & 0 & 1/c \end{bmatrix} \tag{12.24}$$

$$\mathbf{A}\mathbf{A}^{-1} = \mathbf{A}^{-1}\mathbf{A} = \begin{bmatrix} a/a & 0 & 0 \\ 0 & b/b & 0 \\ 0 & 0 & c/c \end{bmatrix} \tag{12.25}$$

This example is for a 3×3 matrix for visualization, but the principle holds for any number of dimensions.

This inverse procedure also shows one reason why singular matrices are not invertible: A singular diagonal matrix has at least one diagonal element equal to zero. If you try to apply the above short-cut, you'll end up with an element of $0/0$.

The universe would be a lovely place—and linear algebra would be a much easier subject—if all matrix inverses were as easy and intuitive to compute as the short-cut for diagonal matrices (invert each matrix element). However, it takes only one example to show that this doesn't work when there is a single off-diagonal non-zero element. We start with an almost-diagonal matrix $\mathbf{A}$, and another matrix $\tilde{\mathbf{A}}$ that is obtained by reciprocating each non-zero matrix element.

$$\mathbf{A} = \begin{bmatrix} 3 & 0 & 2 \\ 0 & 1/2 & 0 \\ 0 & 0 & 4 \end{bmatrix}, \qquad \tilde{\mathbf{A}} = \begin{bmatrix} 1/3 & 0 & 1/2 \\ 0 & 2 & 0 \\ 0 & 0 & 1/4 \end{bmatrix}$$

$$\mathbf{A}\tilde{\mathbf{A}} = \begin{bmatrix} 1 & 0 & 2 \\ 0 & 1 & 0 \\ 0 & 0 & 1 \end{bmatrix} \tag{12.26}$$

$$\tilde{\mathbf{A}}\mathbf{A} = \begin{bmatrix} 1 & 0 & 8/3 \\ 0 & 1 & 0 \\ 0 & 0 & 1 \end{bmatrix} \tag{12.27}$$

You can see that $\tilde{\mathbf{A}}$ is definitely not the inverse of $\mathbf{A}$, because their product is not the identity matrix.

Before learning the full formula for computing the matrix inverse, let's spend some time learning another short-cut for the inverse that works on 2×2 matrices.

12.3 Matrix inverse for a 2×2 matrix

The famous shortcut for computing the inverse of a 2×2 matrix has four steps:

1. Compute the determinant and check whether $\Delta = 0$.
2. Swap the diagonal elements.
3. Multiply the off-diagonal elements by -1.
4. Divide all matrix elements by Δ.

The reason why you start the procedure by computing the determinant is that the matrix has no inverse if the determinant is zero. Thus, if step 1 gives an answer of zero, then you don't need to apply the remaining steps. You'll see an example of this soon, but let's start with an invertible matrix.

$$\begin{bmatrix} 1 & 2 \\ 2 & 3 \end{bmatrix}^{-1} = \frac{1}{-1} \begin{bmatrix} 3 & -2 \\ -2 & 1 \end{bmatrix} = \begin{bmatrix} -3 & 2 \\ 2 & -1 \end{bmatrix}$$

Multiplying the right-most and left-most matrices above will prove that one is the inverse of the other. As I wrote earlier, a square invertible matrix has a full inverse, meaning the order of multiplication doesn't matter.

$$\begin{bmatrix} 1 & 2 \\ 2 & 3 \end{bmatrix} \begin{bmatrix} -3 & 2 \\ 2 & -1 \end{bmatrix} = \begin{bmatrix} 1 & 0 \\ 0 & 1 \end{bmatrix}$$

$$\begin{bmatrix} -3 & 2 \\ 2 & -1 \end{bmatrix} \begin{bmatrix} 1 & 2 \\ 2 & 3 \end{bmatrix} = \begin{bmatrix} 1 & 0 \\ 0 & 1 \end{bmatrix}$$

Here is the general formula for the 2×2 inverse.

Formula for the inverse of a 2×2 matrix

$$\begin{bmatrix} a & b \\ c & d \end{bmatrix} = \frac{1}{ad - bc} \begin{bmatrix} d & -b \\ -c & a \end{bmatrix} \qquad (12.28)$$

Now watch what happens when we try to invert a rank-1 matrix.

$$\begin{bmatrix} 1 & 2 \\ 2 & 4 \end{bmatrix} = \frac{1}{4 - 4} \begin{bmatrix} & \\ & \end{bmatrix}$$

You can stop the computation as soon as you see that the determinant, which goes into the denominator, is zero. This is one explanation for why a singular matrix (with $\Delta = 0$) has no inverse.

Below are two more examples of matrices and their inverses, and a check that the multiplication of the two yields $\mathbf{I}$.

$$\begin{bmatrix} 3 & 1 \\ 2 & 1 \end{bmatrix}^{-1} = \frac{1}{1} \begin{bmatrix} 1 & -1 \\ -2 & 3 \end{bmatrix} \quad \Rightarrow \quad \begin{bmatrix} 3 & 1 \\ 2 & 1 \end{bmatrix} \begin{bmatrix} 1 & -1 \\ -2 & 3 \end{bmatrix} = \begin{bmatrix} 1 & 0 \\ 0 & 1 \end{bmatrix}$$

Hint: Sometimes it's easier to leave the determinant as a scalar, rather than to divide each element.

$$\begin{bmatrix} 2 & 7 \\ 3 & -8 \end{bmatrix}^{-1} = \frac{1}{-37} \begin{bmatrix} -8 & -7 \\ 3 & 2 \end{bmatrix} \quad \Rightarrow \quad \frac{1}{-37} \begin{bmatrix} -8 & -7 \\ 3 & 2 \end{bmatrix} \begin{bmatrix} 2 & 7 \\ 3 & -8 \end{bmatrix} = \begin{bmatrix} 1 & 0 \\ 0 & 1 \end{bmatrix}$$

Practice problems Compute the inverse (if it exists) of the following matrices.

a) $\begin{bmatrix} 1 & 4 \\ 4 & 4 \end{bmatrix}$ b) $\begin{bmatrix} 2 & 1/2 \\ 3 & 1/3 \end{bmatrix}$ c) $\begin{bmatrix} 2 & 1/2 \\ 3 & 3/4 \end{bmatrix}$ d) $\begin{bmatrix} -9 & 3 \\ -9 & -8 \end{bmatrix}$

Answers

a) $\frac{1}{3} \begin{bmatrix} -1 & 1 \\ 1 & -1/4 \end{bmatrix}$ b) $\frac{-1}{6/5} \begin{bmatrix} 1/3 & -1/2 \\ -3 & 2 \end{bmatrix}$ c) No inverse. d) $\frac{1}{99} \begin{bmatrix} -8 & -3 \\ 9 & -9 \end{bmatrix}$

12.4 The MCA algorithm

The short-cut for a 2×2 matrix above is actually just a special case of the MCA algorithm. This full procedure for computing the matrix inverse is not really difficult, but it is rather time-consuming. There are three steps.

The MCA algorithm bears no explicit connection to the late-and-great Adam Yauch.

M: Compute the *minors matrix*, a matrix of determinants of submatrices.

C: Compute the *cofactors matrix*, the Hadamard multiplication of the minors matrix with an alternating grid of $+1$ and -1.

A: Compute the *adjugate matrix*, the transpose of the cofactors matrix, divided by the determinant.

(OK, it's technically 4 steps if you consider dividing by the determinant its own full step. But MCA sounds better than MCAD.)

Let's go through each of these steps in more detail.

Minors matrix The minors matrix is a matrix in which each element $m_{i,j}$ of the matrix is the determinant of the matrix excluding the ith row and the jth column. Thus, for each element in the matrix, cross out that row and that column, and compute the determinant of the remaining matrix. That determinant goes into the matrix element under consideration. It's easier to understand visually (Figure 12.1).

This should sound familiar from the formula for computing the determinant of a 4×4 matrix.

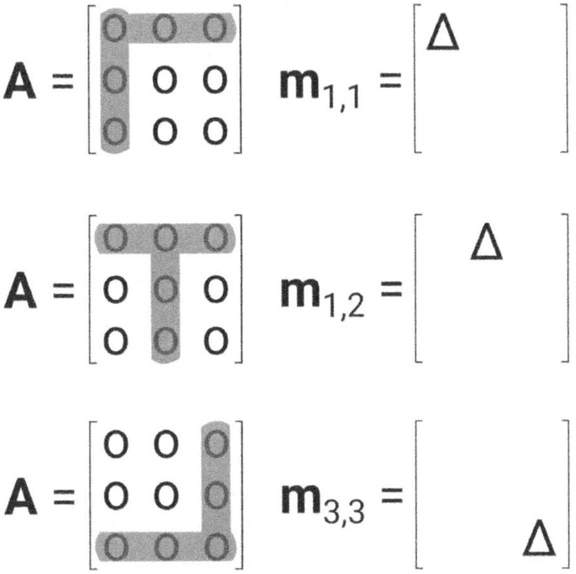

Figure 12.1: Each element $m_{i,j}$ of the minors matrix is the determinant of the submatrix formed from excluding row i and column j from the original matrix.

The matrices on the following page illustrate creating a minors matrix $\mathbf{M}$ from a 3×3 matrix $\mathbf{A}$. Pick a few elements of the minors matrix to confirm that you can reproduce those values from the determinants of submatrices in matrix $\mathbf{A}$.

$$\mathbf{A} = \begin{bmatrix} 2 & 1 & 1 \\ 0 & 4 & 2 \\ 1 & 3 & 2 \end{bmatrix}, \quad m_{1,1} = \begin{bmatrix} & 2 & \\ & & \\ & & \end{bmatrix} \tag{12.29}$$

$$m_{1,2} = \begin{bmatrix} & -2 & \\ & & \\ & & \end{bmatrix} \tag{12.30}$$

$$\mathbf{M} = \begin{bmatrix} 2 & -2 & -4 \\ -1 & 3 & 5 \\ -2 & 4 & 8 \end{bmatrix} \tag{12.31}$$

The minors matrix is the most time-consuming part of the MCA algorithm. It's also the most tedious. Don't rush through it.

Practice problems Compute the minors matrix of the following matrices.

a) $\begin{bmatrix} 1 & 2 \\ 3 & 4 \end{bmatrix}$

b) $\begin{bmatrix} 1 & 2 & 3 \\ 4 & 5 & 6 \\ 7 & 8 & 9 \end{bmatrix}$

c) $\begin{bmatrix} 3 & 4 & 1 \\ 0 & 2 & 3 \\ 5 & 4 & 1 \end{bmatrix}$

Answers

a) $\begin{bmatrix} 4 & 3 \\ 2 & 1 \end{bmatrix}$

b) $-3 \begin{bmatrix} 1 & 2 & 1 \\ 2 & 4 & 2 \\ 1 & 2 & 1 \end{bmatrix}$

c) $\begin{bmatrix} -10 & -15 & -10 \\ 0 & -2 & -8 \\ 10 & 9 & 6 \end{bmatrix}$

Cofactors matrix The cofactors matrix is the Hadamard product of the minors matrix with a matrix of alternating signs. Let's call that matrix $\mathbf{G}$ for grid: The matrix is a grid of $+1$s and -1s, starting with $+1$ for the upper-left element. Below are a few examples of $\mathbf{G}$ matrices. They look like checkerboards (or chessboards, depending on your level of board game sophistication) (Figure 12.2).

$$\begin{bmatrix} + & - \\ - & + \end{bmatrix}, \quad \begin{bmatrix} + & - & + \\ - & + & - \\ + & - & + \end{bmatrix}, \quad \begin{bmatrix} + & - & + & - \\ - & + & - & + \\ + & - & + & - \\ - & + & - & + \end{bmatrix}$$

The formula that defines each element of the **G** matrix is

$$g_{i,j} = -1^{i+j} \qquad (12.32)$$

where i and j refer, respectively, to row and column index. Try out a few examples to see how this formula produces the alternating grids above. For example, the $(1,1)$ position is $-1^{1+1} = 1$ while the $(1,2)$ position is $-1^{1+2} = -1$. That said, I think it's easier to remember what the matrix looks like rather than memorizing the formula.

Finally, the cofactors matrix: $\mathbf{C} = \mathbf{G} \odot \mathbf{M}$. Using the example matrix from the previous page,

Figure 12.2: Simple and elegant. Linear algebra is truly inspiring.

$$\mathbf{C} = \begin{bmatrix} 2 & 2 & -4 \\ 1 & 3 & -5 \\ -2 & -4 & 8 \end{bmatrix}$$

Be mindful of the signs: The sign of each cofactors matrix element depends both on the sign of the determinant, and on the sign of the **G** matrix. That is, of course, obvious from your elementary school arithmetic, but most mistakes in higher mathematics are arithmetic...

Practice problems   Compute the cofactors matrix of the following matrices.

a) $\begin{bmatrix} 1 & 2 \\ 3 & 4 \end{bmatrix}$
b) $\begin{bmatrix} 1 & 2 & 3 \\ 4 & 5 & 6 \\ 7 & 8 & 9 \end{bmatrix}$
c) $\begin{bmatrix} 3 & 4 & 1 \\ 0 & 2 & 3 \\ 5 & 4 & 1 \end{bmatrix}$

Answers

a) $\begin{bmatrix} 4 & -3 \\ -2 & 1 \end{bmatrix}$
b) $-3 \begin{bmatrix} 1 & -2 & 1 \\ -2 & 4 & -2 \\ 1 & -2 & 1 \end{bmatrix}$
c) $\begin{bmatrix} -10 & 15 & -10 \\ 0 & -2 & 8 \\ 10 & -9 & 6 \end{bmatrix}$

Adjugate matrix   At this point, all the hard work is behind you. The adjugate matrix is simply the transpose of the cofactors matrix, scalar-multiplied by the inverse of the determinant of the matrix (*note*: it's the determinant of the original matrix, not the minors or cofactors matrices). Again, if the determinant is zero, then this step will fail because of the division by zero.

Assuming the determinant is not zero, the adjugate matrix is the inverse of the original matrix.

Let's continue working with the matrix in the examples above.

$$\mathbf{A}^{-1} = \frac{1}{2} \begin{bmatrix} 2 & 1 & -2 \\ 2 & 3 & -4 \\ -4 & -5 & 8 \end{bmatrix}$$

And now let's test that this matrix really is the inverse of our original matrix:

$$\begin{bmatrix} 2 & 1 & 1 \\ 0 & 4 & 2 \\ 1 & 3 & 2 \end{bmatrix} \frac{1}{2} \begin{bmatrix} 2 & -1 & -2 \\ -2 & 3 & 4 \\ -4 & 5 & 8 \end{bmatrix} = \frac{1}{2} \begin{bmatrix} 2 & 0 & 0 \\ 0 & 2 & 0 \\ 0 & 0 & 2 \end{bmatrix}$$

Now that you know the full MCA formula, we can apply this to a 2×2 matrix. You can see that the "short-cut" in the previous section is just a simplification of this procedure.

Original matrix : $\begin{bmatrix} 4 & 2 \\ 3 & 2 \end{bmatrix}$

Minors matrix : $\begin{bmatrix} 2 & 3 \\ 2 & 4 \end{bmatrix}$

Cofactors matrix : $\begin{bmatrix} 2 & -3 \\ -2 & 4 \end{bmatrix}$

Adjugate matrix : $\frac{1}{2} \begin{bmatrix} 2 & -2 \\ -3 & 4 \end{bmatrix}$

Practice problems Compute the adjugate matrices of the following matrices (in case you haven't noticed: you've already computed the minors and cofactors matrices above).

a) $\begin{bmatrix} 1 & 2 \\ 3 & 4 \end{bmatrix}$

b) $\begin{bmatrix} 1 & 2 & 3 \\ 4 & 5 & 6 \\ 7 & 8 & 9 \end{bmatrix}$

c) $\begin{bmatrix} 3 & 4 & 1 \\ 0 & 2 & 3 \\ 5 & 4 & 1 \end{bmatrix}$

Answers

a) $\frac{1}{-2}\begin{bmatrix} 4 & -2 \\ -3 & 1 \end{bmatrix}$

b) $\frac{-3}{0}\begin{bmatrix} 1 & -2 & 1 \\ -2 & 4 & -2 \\ 1 & -2 & 1 \end{bmatrix}$

c) $\frac{1}{20}\begin{bmatrix} -10 & 0 & -10 \\ 15 & -2 & -9 \\ 10 & 8 & 6 \end{bmatrix}$

Practice problems Apply the MCA algorithm to the following matrices to derive their inverses, when they exist.

a) $\begin{bmatrix} 1 & 1 \\ 1 & 4 \end{bmatrix}$

b) $\begin{bmatrix} 2 & 2 & 4 \\ 4 & 2 & 5 \\ 1 & 2 & 1 \end{bmatrix}$

c) $\begin{bmatrix} 1 & -5 & 4 \\ -1 & -15 & 6 \\ 2 & 0 & 3 \end{bmatrix}$

Answers

a) $3\begin{bmatrix} 4 & -1 \\ -1 & 1 \end{bmatrix}$

b) $10\begin{bmatrix} -8 & 6 & 2 \\ 1 & -2 & 6 \\ 6 & -2 & -4 \end{bmatrix}$

c) No inverse!

Code The code challenges at the end of this chapter will provide the opportunity to implement the MCA algorithm in code. Below you can see how easy it is to call the inverse functions in Python and MATLAB.

Code block 12.1: Python

```
1  import numpy as np
2  A = np.random.randn(3,3)
3  Ai = np.linalg.inv(A)
4  A@Ai
```

Code block 12.2: MATLAB

```
1  A = randn(3,3);
2  Ai = inv(A);
3  A*Ai
```

12.5 Inverse via row reduction

This is a conceptually very different method for obtaining the inverse of a square matrix, but the result will be the same as the MCA method. The idea is to augment the matrix with the identity matrix and then perform row reduction to get the matrix into its RREF form. This will lead to one of two possible outcomes:

- Row reduction transforms the original matrix to the identity matrix, in which case the augmented matrix is the inverse (Equation 12.33).

- Row reduction does not produce the identity matrix, in which case the matrix is singular and therefore has no inverse.

Row reduction method of computing the inverse

$$rref\left(\left[\mathbf{A} \mid \mathbf{I}\right]\right) \Rightarrow \left[\mathbf{I} \mid \mathbf{A}^{-1}\right] \qquad (12.33)$$

Let's start with an example:

$$\begin{bmatrix} 1 & 2 \\ 3 & 4 \end{bmatrix} \Rightarrow \left[\begin{array}{cc|cc} 1 & 2 & 1 & 0 \\ 3 & 4 & 0 & 1 \end{array}\right] \xrightarrow{-3R_1+R_2} \left[\begin{array}{cc|cc} 1 & 2 & 1 & 0 \\ 0 & -2 & -3 & 1 \end{array}\right]$$

$$\xrightarrow{R_2+R_1} \left[\begin{array}{cc|cc} 1 & 0 & -2 & 1 \\ 0 & -2 & -3 & 1 \end{array}\right] \xrightarrow{-1/2R_2} \left[\begin{array}{cc|cc} 1 & 0 & -2 & 1 \\ 0 & 1 & 3/2 & -1/2 \end{array}\right]$$

You can confirm that the augmented part of the final matrix is the same as the inverse we computing from the MCA algorithm in the practice problems in the previous section.

We know that a singular matrix has no inverse. Let's see what happens when we apply the row-reduction method to a rank-1 matrix.

$$\begin{bmatrix} 1 & 2 \\ 3 & 6 \end{bmatrix} \Rightarrow \left[\begin{array}{cc|cc} 1 & 2 & 1 & 0 \\ 3 & 6 & 0 & 1 \end{array}\right] \xrightarrow{-3R_1+R_2} \left[\begin{array}{cc|cc} 1 & 2 & 1 & 0 \\ 0 & 0 & -3 & 1 \end{array}\right]$$

That's the end of the line. We cannot row reduce anymore, and yet we have not gotten the identity matrix on the left. This system is inconsistent, and ergo, this matrix has no inverse.

Practice problems Use row reduction to compute the inverse of the following matrices, or to discover that the matrix is singular. Then multiply each matrix by its inverse to make sure you've gotten the correct result.

a) $\begin{bmatrix} -4 & 7 \\ 3 & -8 \end{bmatrix}$

b) $\begin{bmatrix} 1 & 0 & 2 \\ 1 & 2 & 1 \\ 1 & 0 & 1 \end{bmatrix}$

c) $\begin{bmatrix} 1 & 0 & 2 & 5 \\ 3 & 0 & 0 & 1 \\ 0 & 4 & 5 & 0 \\ 5 & 8 & 2 & -17 \end{bmatrix}$

d) $\begin{bmatrix} 1 & 0 & 2 & 5 \\ 3 & 0 & 0 & 1 \\ 0 & 4 & 5 & 0 \\ 0 & 3 & 4 & 0 \end{bmatrix}$

Answers

a) $\frac{1}{11} \begin{bmatrix} -8 & -7 \\ -3 & -4 \end{bmatrix}$

b) $\begin{bmatrix} -1 & 0 & 2 \\ 0 & 1/2 & -1/2 \\ 1 & 0 & -1 \end{bmatrix}$

c) No inverse.

d) $14 \begin{bmatrix} -1 & 5 & -6 & 8 \\ 0 & 0 & 56 & -70 \\ 0 & 0 & -42 & 56 \\ 3 & -1 & 18 & -24 \end{bmatrix}$

Code The code below shows the row-reduction method, and then compares that to the inverse function.

Code block 12.3: Python

```
1  import numpy as np
2  import sympy as sym
3  A  = np.random.randn(3,3)
4  Acat = np.concatenate((A,np.eye(3,3)),axis=1)
5  Ar = sym.Matrix(Acat).rref()[0]  # RREF
6  Ar = Ar[:,3:]  # keep inverse
7  Ai = np.linalg.inv(A)
8  Ar−Ai
```

```
1  A = randn(3);
2  Ar = rref([A eye(3)]);
3  Ar = Ar(:,4:end);
4  Ai = inv(A);
5  Ar-Ai
```

Why does it work? Equation 12.33 almost seems like magic. (In fairness, much of mathematics seems like magic before you become familiar with it... and a lot of it continues to seem like magic even after years of experience.) In fact, the reason why this method works is fairly straightforward, and involves thinking about Equation 12.33 in terms of solving a system of equations.

In Chapter 10, you learned that you can solve the equation $\mathbf{Ax} = \mathbf{b}$ by performing Gauss-Jordan elimination on the augmented matrix $[\mathbf{A}|\mathbf{b}]$. If there is a solution—that is, if $\mathbf{b}$ is in the column space of $\mathbf{A}$—then row reduction produces the augmented matrix $[\mathbf{I}|\mathbf{x}]$.

Here we follow the same reasoning, but the vector $\mathbf{b}$ is expanded to the matrix $\mathbf{I}$. That is, we want to solve $\mathbf{AX} = \mathbf{I}$, where $\mathbf{X}$ is the inverse of $\mathbf{A}$. It might be easier to think about this in terms of columns of the identity matrix. I'll use $\mathbf{e}_i$ to indicate the ith column of the identity matrix. And I'll use a 3×3 matrix in the interest of concreteness, but the procedure is valid for a matrix of any size.

$$\mathbf{Ax}_1 = \begin{bmatrix} 1 \\ 0 \\ 0 \end{bmatrix} \quad \Rightarrow \quad rref([\,\mathbf{A}\mid\mathbf{e}_1\,]) \quad \Rightarrow \quad [\,\mathbf{I}\mid\mathbf{x}_1\,] \qquad (12.34)$$

$$\mathbf{Ax}_2 = \begin{bmatrix} 0 \\ 1 \\ 0 \end{bmatrix} \quad \Rightarrow \quad rref([\,\mathbf{A}\mid\mathbf{e}_2\,]) \quad \Rightarrow \quad [\,\mathbf{I}\mid\mathbf{x}_2\,] \qquad (12.35)$$

$$\mathbf{Ax}_3 = \begin{bmatrix} 0 \\ 0 \\ 1 \end{bmatrix} \quad \Rightarrow \quad rref([\,\mathbf{A}\mid\mathbf{e}_3\,]) \quad \Rightarrow \quad [\,\mathbf{I}\mid\mathbf{x}_3\,] \qquad (12.36)$$

Each equation individually finds $\mathbf{x}_i$, which is the vector that represents the weighting of the columns in $\mathbf{A}$ in order to obtain the vector $\mathbf{e}_i$, which is one column of the identity matrix. As long as the column space of $\mathbf{A}$ spans all of $\mathbf{R}^M$, there is guaranteed to be a solution to each of the systems of equations. And $C(\mathbf{A})$ spans the entire ambient space when $\mathbf{A}$ is full-rank.

Thus, when breaking the problem down into individual column vectors, there is nothing new compared to what you learned in Chapter 10. The only addition here is to collect all of these separate steps together into one matrix equation: $\mathbf{AX} = \mathbf{I}$.

Reflection

The matrix inverse is a funny thing. Conceptually, it's one of the most important matrix operations in linear algebra and its applications. And yet, computer programs go to great lengths to avoid explicitly computing it unless absolutely necessary. *So why*, you might wonder, *should I suffer through learning how to compute it when I can type* inv *on a computer?* For the same reason that you need to learn how to compute 3+4 without a calculator: You will never really learn math unless you can do it without a computer. Frustrating but true.

12.6 The left inverse for tall matrices

I wrote on page 324 that only square matrices can have a full inverse. That's true, but it applies only to a *full*, a.k.a. two-sided, inverse. Rectangular matrices can have a *one-sided* inverse. The goal of this section is to derive the one-sided left inverse, explain how to interpret it, and define the conditions for a rectangular matrix to have a left inverse.

Let's start with a tall matrix, so dimensions $M > N$. We'll call this matrix $\mathbf{T}$ for tall. Although this matrix is not invertible, we can, with a bit of creativity, come up with another matrix (actually, the product of several matrices) that will left-multiply $\mathbf{T}$ to produce the identity matrix. The key insight to get us started is that $\mathbf{T}^{\mathrm{T}}\mathbf{T}$ is a square matrix. In fact, $\mathbf{T}^{\mathrm{T}}\mathbf{T}$ is invertible if $rank(\mathbf{T}) = N$ (more on this condition later). If $\mathbf{T}^{\mathrm{T}}\mathbf{T}$ is invertible, then it has an inverse.

Yes, I realize that there is an absurd number of "T"s in these equations.

$$(\mathbf{T}^{\mathrm{T}}\mathbf{T})^{-1}(\mathbf{T}^{\mathrm{T}}\mathbf{T}) = \mathbf{I} \qquad (12.37)$$

If this expression looks strange, then just imagine rewriting it as:

$$\mathbf{C} = \mathbf{T}^{\mathrm{T}}\mathbf{T}$$

$$\mathbf{C}^{-1}\mathbf{C} = \mathbf{I} \qquad (12.38)$$

Here's the thing about Equation 12.37: The first set of parentheses is necessary because we are inverting the product of two matrices (neither of those matrices is individually invertible!). However, the second set of parentheses is not necessary; they're there just for aesthetic balance. By removing the unnecessary parentheses and re-grouping, some magic happens: the product of three matrices that can left-multiply $\mathbf{T}$ to produce the identity matrix.

The left inverse

$$\underbrace{(\mathbf{T}^{\mathrm{T}}\mathbf{T})^{-1}\mathbf{T}^{\mathrm{T}}}_{\text{Left inverse}} \mathbf{T} = \mathbf{I} \qquad (12.39)$$

Here is another way to look at it:

$$\mathbf{T}^{\text{-L}} = (\mathbf{T}^{\mathrm{T}}\mathbf{T})^{-1}\mathbf{T}^{\mathrm{T}}$$

$$\mathbf{T}^{\text{-L}}\mathbf{T} = \mathbf{I}$$

where $\mathbf{T}^{\text{-L}}$ indicates the left inverse. (This is non-standard notation, used here only to facilitate comprehension.)

Why is this called a "one-sided" inverse? Let's see what happens when we put the left inverse on the right side of the matrix:

$$\mathbf{T}(\mathbf{T}^{\mathrm{T}}\mathbf{T})^{-1}\mathbf{T}^{\mathrm{T}} \neq \mathbf{I}$$

The left-hand side of this equation is actually valid, in the sense that all the sizes match to make the multiplications work. But the result will not be the identity matrix. You'll see numerical examples later. The point is that this is a *left* inverse.

Conditions for validity Now let's think about the conditions for the left inverse to be valid. Looking back to Equation 12.38, matrix $\mathbf{C}$ (which is actually $\mathbf{T}^T\mathbf{T}$) is invertible if it is full rank, meaning $rank(\mathbf{C}) = N$. When is $\mathbf{T}^T\mathbf{T}$ a full-rank matrix? Recall from section 7.7 that a matrix times its transpose has the same rank as the matrix on its own. Thus, $\mathbf{T}^T\mathbf{T}$ is full-rank if $\mathbf{T}$ has a rank of N, meaning it is full column-rank.

And this leads us to the two conditions for a matrix to have a left inverse:

1. It is tall (more rows than columns, $M > N$).
2. It is full column rank (rank=N).

Enough talk. Let's see an example.

$$\mathbf{T} = \begin{bmatrix} 1 & 2 \\ 1 & 3 \\ 1 & 4 \end{bmatrix} \tag{12.40}$$

$$\mathbf{T}^T\mathbf{T} = \begin{bmatrix} 3 & 9 \\ 9 & 29 \end{bmatrix} \tag{12.41}$$

$$(\mathbf{T}^T\mathbf{T})^{-1} = \frac{1}{6}\begin{bmatrix} 29 & -9 \\ -9 & 3 \end{bmatrix} \tag{12.42}$$

$$\mathbf{T}^{-L} = (\mathbf{T}^T\mathbf{T})^{-1}\mathbf{T}^T = \frac{1}{6}\begin{bmatrix} 11 & 2 & -7 \\ -3 & 0 & 3 \end{bmatrix} \tag{12.43}$$

$$\mathbf{T}^{-L}\mathbf{T} = \frac{1}{6}\begin{bmatrix} 6 & 0 \\ 0 & 6 \end{bmatrix} \tag{12.44}$$

$$\mathbf{T}\mathbf{T}^{-L} = \begin{bmatrix} 5 & 2 & -1 \\ 2 & 2 & 2 \\ -1 & 2 & 5 \end{bmatrix} \tag{12.45}$$

Equation 12.44 shows that the pre-multiplying by the left inverse produces the identity matrix. In contrast, Equation 12.45 shows that *post*-multiplying by the left inverse definitely does not produce the identity matrix. This example also highlights that it is often useful to leave the determinant as a scalar outside the matrix to avoid dealing with difficult fractions during matrix multiplications.

Practice problems Compute the left inverse of the following matrices.

a) $\begin{bmatrix} 3 & 0 \\ 0 & 2 \\ 0 & 4 \end{bmatrix}$
b) $\begin{bmatrix} 1 & 1 \\ 1 & 2 \\ 2 & 3 \end{bmatrix}$
c) $\begin{bmatrix} 1 & 2 \\ 1 & 2 \\ 1 & 2 \end{bmatrix}$

Answers Matrices below are $(\mathbf{T}^{\mathsf{T}}\mathbf{T})^{-1}\mathbf{T}^{\mathsf{T}}$

a) $\frac{1}{10} \begin{bmatrix} 10/3 & 0 & 0 \\ 0 & 1 & 2 \end{bmatrix}$
b) $\frac{1}{3} \begin{bmatrix} 5 & -4 & 1 \\ -3 & 3 & 0 \end{bmatrix}$
c) No left inverse!

12.7 The right inverse for wide matrices

You can probably guess where we're going in this section: wide matrices (that is, more columns than rows) do not have a left inverse. However, they can have a right inverse. I encourage you to try to discover the right inverse, as well as the conditions for a matrix to have a right inverse, on your own before continuing to read the rest of this section. To make things easier for you, I'll leave the rest of this page blank...

Did you figure it out? The reasoning is the same as for the left inverse. The key difference is that you *post*-multiply by the transposed matrix instead of *pre*-multiplying by it. Let's call this matrix $\mathbf{W}$ for wide.

Briefly: We start from $\mathbf{W}\mathbf{W}^{\mathrm{T}}$, and then right-multiply by $(\mathbf{W}\mathbf{W}^{\mathrm{T}})^{-1}$. That leads us to the following:

The right inverse

$$\mathbf{W}\underbrace{\mathbf{W}^{\mathrm{T}}(\mathbf{W}\mathbf{W}^{\mathrm{T}})^{-1}}_{\text{Right inverse}} = \mathbf{I} \qquad (12.46)$$

Again, if you find the multitude of matrices confusing, then you can substitute the three-matrix product for another matrix:

$$\mathbf{W}^{\text{-R}} = \mathbf{W}^{\mathrm{T}}(\mathbf{W}^{\mathrm{T}}\mathbf{W})^{-1}$$

$$\mathbf{W}\mathbf{W}^{\text{-R}} = \mathbf{I}$$

The conditions for a matrix to have a right inverse are:

1. It is wide (more columns than rows, $M < N$).
2. It is full row rank (rank=M).

As with the left-inverse, putting the *right* inverse on the *left* of matrix $\mathbf{W}$ is a valid matrix multiplication, but will not produce the identity matrix.

And finally, an example with numbers.

$$\mathbf{W} = \begin{bmatrix} 1 & 0 & 4 \\ 2 & -3 & 1 \end{bmatrix} \tag{12.47}$$

$$\mathbf{W}\mathbf{W}^{\mathrm{T}} = \begin{bmatrix} 17 & 6 \\ 6 & 14 \end{bmatrix} \tag{12.48}$$

$$(\mathbf{W}\mathbf{W}^{\mathrm{T}})^{-1} = \frac{1}{202} \begin{bmatrix} 14 & -6 \\ -6 & 17 \end{bmatrix} \tag{12.49}$$

$$\mathbf{W}^{\text{-R}} = \mathbf{W}^{\mathrm{T}}(\mathbf{W}\mathbf{W}^{\mathrm{T}})^{-1} = \frac{1}{202} \begin{bmatrix} 2 & 28 \\ 18 & -51 \\ 50 & -7 \end{bmatrix} \tag{12.50}$$

$$\mathbf{W}^{\text{-R}}\mathbf{W} = \frac{1}{202} \begin{bmatrix} 58 & -84 & 36 \\ -84 & 153 & 21 \\ 36 & 21 & 193 \end{bmatrix} \tag{12.51}$$

$$\mathbf{W}\mathbf{W}^{\text{-R}} = \frac{1}{202} \begin{bmatrix} 202 & 0 \\ 0 & 202 \end{bmatrix} \tag{12.52}$$

Practice problems Compute the right inverse of the following matrices.

a) $\begin{bmatrix} 3 & 0 & 0 \\ 0 & 2 & 4 \end{bmatrix}$ b) $\begin{bmatrix} 1 & 0 & 3 \\ -2 & 0 & 4 \end{bmatrix}$ c) $\begin{bmatrix} 1 & 3 & 2 \\ 2 & 6 & 4 \end{bmatrix}$

Answers Matrices below are $\mathbf{W}^{\mathrm{T}}(\mathbf{W}^{\mathrm{T}}\mathbf{W})^{-1}$

a) $\frac{1}{10} \begin{bmatrix} 10/3 & 0 \\ 0 & 1 \\ 0 & 2 \end{bmatrix}$ b) $\frac{1}{10} \begin{bmatrix} 4 & -3 \\ 0 & 0 \\ 2 & 1 \end{bmatrix}$ c) No right inverse!

Code The code below shows the left inverse for a tall matrix; it's your job to modify the code to produce the right-inverse for a wide matrix! (Note: In practice, it's better to compute the one-sided inverses via the Moore-Penrose pseudoinverse algorithm, but it's good practice to translate the formulas directly into code.)

```
1  import numpy as np
2  A = np.random.randn(5,3)
3  Al = np.linalg.inv(A.T@A)@A.T
4  Al@A
```

Code block 12.6: MATLAB

```
1  A = randn(5,3);
2  Al = inv(A'*A)*A';
3  Al*A
```

12.8 The pseudoinverse, part 1

This section is called "part 1" because I'm going to introduce you to the pseudoinverse here, but I'm not going to teach you how to compute it until section 16.12. That's not because I'm mean, and it's not because I'm testing your patience (which is, by the way, a virtue). Instead, it's because the algorithm to compute the Moore-Penrose pseudoinverse will seem incomprehensibly complicated if I present it here, whereas it will be intuitive and almost obvious in Chapter 16 after learning about the SVD.

The pseudoinverse is used when a matrix does not have a full inverse, for example if the matrix is square but rank-deficient. As I mentioned in the beginning of this chapter, a rank-deficient matrix does not have a true inverse. However, all matrices have a pseudoinverse, which is a matrix that will transform the rank-deficient matrix to something close-to-but-not-quite the identity matrix.

There are several algorithms to compute a pseudoinverse, but the most commonly used method is called the Moore-Penrose pseudoinverse. The original author names are often dropped, therefore, when you read or hear the term "pseudoinverse," it's safe to assume that it's the MP pseudoinverse.

Below is a list of important concepts about the pseudoinverse. This list contains claims that are justified and proven in Chapter 16.

1. It is indicated using a "dagger," asterisk, or plus sign in the superscript: $\mathbf{A}^\dagger$, $\mathbf{A}^*$, or $\mathbf{A}^+$.

2. The pseudoinverse multiplies the original matrix to approximate the identity matrix: $\mathbf{A}\mathbf{A}^\dagger \approx \mathbf{I}$.

3. There are several ways to create a matrix pseudoinverse, which means that a singular matrix can have several pseudoinverses (unlike the true inverse, which is unique). However, the MP pseudoinverse is unique, meaning that every matrix has exactly one MP pseudoinverse. The uniqueness of the MP pseudoinverse contributes to its popularity.

4. The pseudoinverse is sided, thus $\mathbf{A}\mathbf{A}^\dagger \neq \mathbf{A}^\dagger\mathbf{A}$. However, the pseudoinverse has the neat property that $\mathbf{A}\mathbf{A}^\dagger\mathbf{A} = \mathbf{A}$ (for square matrices).

5. For a full-rank matrix, the pseudoinverse is the same as the full inverse, that is, $\mathbf{A}^\dagger = \mathbf{A}^{-1}$.

6. For a tall full column-rank matrix, the pseudoinverse equals the one-sided left inverse. Same story for a wide full row-rank matrix and the right inverse.

Here is an example of a non-invertible square matrix, its pseudoinverse, and the products of those matrices.

$$\mathbf{A} = \begin{bmatrix} 1 & 2 & 1 \\ 1 & 3 & 1 \\ 2 & 5 & 2 \end{bmatrix}, \quad \mathbf{A}^\dagger = \frac{1}{6}\begin{bmatrix} 8 & -7 & 1 \\ -6 & 6 & 0 \\ 8 & -7 & 1 \end{bmatrix}$$

$$\mathbf{A}^\dagger\mathbf{A} = \frac{1}{2}\begin{bmatrix} 1 & 0 & 1 \\ 0 & 2 & 0 \\ 1 & 0 & 1 \end{bmatrix}, \quad \mathbf{A}\mathbf{A}^\dagger = \frac{1}{3}\begin{bmatrix} 2 & -1 & 1 \\ -1 & 2 & 1 \\ 1 & 1 & 2 \end{bmatrix}$$

You can see several properties of the pseudoinverse in this example, including that $\mathbf{A}\mathbf{A}^\dagger \neq \mathbf{A}^\dagger\mathbf{A}$ and that neither of these produces the identity matrix, although they both produce a matrix is that is sorta-kinda close to the identity.

Code The MP pseudoinverse is so important in applied linear algebra that numerical software developers have made it super-easy to implement. Notice that the matrix below is singular.

Code block 12.7: Python

```
1  import numpy as np
2  A = np.random.randn(3,3)
3  A[1,:] = A[0,:]
4  Api = np.linalg.pinv(A)
5  Api@A
```

Code block 12.8: MATLAB

```
1  A = randn(3,3);
2  A(2,:) = A(1,:);
3  Api = pinv(A);
4  Api*A
```

12.9
Exercises

1. Compute the inverse of the following matrices (when possible). For problems with a *, additionally compute $\mathbf{AA}^{-1}$ and $\mathbf{A}^{-1}\mathbf{A}$.

a) $\begin{bmatrix} 1 & 0 \\ 0 & 1 \end{bmatrix}$

b) $\begin{bmatrix} 4 & 0 \\ 0 & -2 \end{bmatrix}$

c) $*$ $\begin{bmatrix} 1 & 2 \\ 2 & 1 \end{bmatrix}$

d) $\begin{bmatrix} 3 & 2 \\ 6 & 4 \end{bmatrix}$

e) $*$ $\begin{bmatrix} 4 & -4 \\ 1 & 6 \end{bmatrix}$

f) $\begin{bmatrix} 1 & 0 & 0 \\ 0 & 1 & 2 \\ 0 & 2 & 1 \end{bmatrix}$

g) $*$ $\begin{bmatrix} 2 & 1 & 0 \\ 1 & 2 & 0 \\ 0 & 0 & 1 \end{bmatrix}$

h) $\begin{bmatrix} 2 & 1 & 0 \\ 1 & 2 & 0 \\ 7 & 6 & 0 \end{bmatrix}$

i) $\begin{bmatrix} 2 & 0 & 0 \\ 0 & 4 & 0 \\ 0 & 0 & 3 \end{bmatrix}$

j) $*$ $\begin{bmatrix} a & b \\ c & d \end{bmatrix}$

k) $\begin{bmatrix} 3 & 1 \\ 0 & b \end{bmatrix}$

l) $\begin{bmatrix} 2 & 1 & 0 & 6 \\ -1 & 0 & 4 & 0 \\ 2 & 0 & 3 & -4 \\ 0 & 1 & 0 & 4 \end{bmatrix}$

Hint: Law of Exponents:

$$x^n x^m = x^{n+m}$$

$$(x^n)^m = x^{nm}$$

2. The inverse of the inverse is the original matrix. Is that $\mathbf{A}^{-1}\mathbf{A}^{-1}$ or $(\mathbf{A}^{-1})^{-1}$? Think of an answer and then confirm it empirically using the matrix $\begin{bmatrix} 1 & 2 \\ 1 & 3 \end{bmatrix}$.

3. Use the row-reduction method to compute the inverse of the following matrices.

a) $\begin{bmatrix} a & b \\ c & d \end{bmatrix}$

b) $\begin{bmatrix} 1 & 7 \\ -2 & 4 \end{bmatrix}$

c) $\begin{bmatrix} 1 & 2 & 3 \\ 1 & 3 & 4 \\ 1 & 2 & 5 \end{bmatrix}$

d) $\begin{bmatrix} 1 & 2 & 3 \\ 1 & 3 & 4 \\ 2 & 5 & 7 \end{bmatrix}$

MATRIX INVERSE

4. For the following matrices and vectors, compute and use A_n^{-1} to solve for x in $A_n x = b_n$.

$$A_1 = \begin{bmatrix} 1 & 4 \\ 5 & 2 \end{bmatrix}, A_2 = \begin{bmatrix} 3 & -3 \\ 2 & 2 \end{bmatrix}, A_3 = \begin{bmatrix} 1 & 3 & 4 \\ 0 & 0 & 4 \\ 2 & 2 & 1 \end{bmatrix} A_4 = \begin{bmatrix} 9 & 0 & 1 \\ 3 & 1 & 0 \\ 0 & 6 & 1 \end{bmatrix}$$

$$b_1 = \begin{bmatrix} 4 \\ 1 \end{bmatrix}, b_2 = \begin{bmatrix} 6 \\ -3 \end{bmatrix}, b_3 = \begin{bmatrix} 1 \\ 3 \\ 8 \end{bmatrix} b_4 = \begin{bmatrix} 8 \\ 3 \\ 1 \end{bmatrix}$$

a) $A_1 x = b_1$ b) $A_1 x = b_2$ c) $A_2 x = b_1$ d) $A_2 x = b_2$

e) $A_3 x = b_3$ f) $A_3 x = b_4$ g) $A_4 x = b_2$ h) $A_4 x = b_4$

1.

a) $\begin{bmatrix} 1 & 0 \\ 0 & 1 \end{bmatrix}$

b) $\begin{bmatrix} 1/4 & 0 \\ 0 & -1/2 \end{bmatrix}$

c) $\frac{1}{3} \begin{bmatrix} -1 & 2 \\ 2 & -1 \end{bmatrix}$

d) No inverse!

e) $\frac{1}{28} \begin{bmatrix} 6 & 4 \\ -1 & 4 \end{bmatrix}$

f) $\frac{1}{3} \begin{bmatrix} 3 & 0 & 0 \\ 0 & -1 & 2 \\ 0 & 2 & -1 \end{bmatrix}$

g) $\frac{1}{3} \begin{bmatrix} 2 & -1 & 0 \\ -1 & 2 & 0 \\ 0 & 0 & 3 \end{bmatrix}$

h) No inverse!

i) $\begin{bmatrix} 1/2 & 0 & 0 \\ 0 & 1/4 & 0 \\ 0 & 0 & 1/3 \end{bmatrix}$

j) $\frac{1}{ad-bc} \begin{bmatrix} d & -b \\ -c & a \end{bmatrix}$

k) $\frac{1}{3b} \begin{bmatrix} b & -1 \\ 0 & 3 \end{bmatrix}$

l) $\frac{1}{-54} \begin{bmatrix} -16 & 6 & -8 & 16 \\ 44 & 24 & -32 & -98 \\ -4 & -12 & -2 & 4 \\ -11 & -6 & 8 & 11 \end{bmatrix}$

2. The correct expression for the inverse of the inverse is $(\mathbf{A}^{-1})^{-1}$. $\mathbf{A}^{-1}\mathbf{A}^{-1}$ would mean to matrix-multiply the inverse by itself, which is a valid mathematical operation but is not relevant here.

3. Matrices below are the inverses (the augmented side of the matrix).

a) $\frac{1}{ad-bc} \begin{bmatrix} d & -b \\ -c & a \end{bmatrix}$

b) $\frac{1}{18} \begin{bmatrix} 4 & -7 \\ 2 & 1 \end{bmatrix}$

c) $\frac{1}{2} \begin{bmatrix} 7 & -4 & -1 \\ -1 & 2 & -1 \\ -1 & 0 & 1 \end{bmatrix}$ **d)** Not invertible!

4. The strategy here is to compute the inverses of the four **A** matrices, then implement matrix-vector multiplication. Below are the inverses, and below that, the solutions to **x**.

$$\mathbf{A}_1^{-1} = \frac{1}{-18} \begin{bmatrix} 2 & -4 \\ -5 & 1 \end{bmatrix}, \quad \mathbf{A}_2^{-1} = \frac{1}{12} \begin{bmatrix} 2 & 3 \\ -2 & 3 \end{bmatrix},$$

$$\mathbf{A}_3^{-1} = \frac{1}{16} \begin{bmatrix} -8 & 5 & 12 \\ 8 & -7 & -4 \\ 0 & 4 & 0 \end{bmatrix}, \quad \mathbf{A}_4^{-1} = \frac{1}{27} \begin{bmatrix} 1 & 6 & -1 \\ -3 & 9 & 3 \\ 18 & -54 & 9 \end{bmatrix}$$

a) $18 \begin{bmatrix} -4 & 19 \end{bmatrix}^{\mathrm{T}}$ **b)** $18 \begin{bmatrix} -24 & 33 \end{bmatrix}^{\mathrm{T}}$

c) $12 \begin{bmatrix} 11 & -5 \end{bmatrix}^{\mathrm{T}}$ **d)** $12 \begin{bmatrix} 3 & -21 \end{bmatrix}^{\mathrm{T}}$

e) $16 \begin{bmatrix} 103 & -45 & 12 \end{bmatrix}^{\mathrm{T}}$ **f)** $16 \begin{bmatrix} -37 & 39 & 12 \end{bmatrix}^{\mathrm{T}}$

g) Invalid operation!   **h)** $27 \begin{bmatrix} 25 & 6 & -9 \end{bmatrix}^{\mathrm{T}}$

12.10 ANSWERS

12.11 Code challenges

1. Your task here is "simple": Implement the MCA algorithm to compute the matrix inverse. Consult the description in section 12.4. Test your algorithm by computing the inverse of random matrices and compare against the Python/MATLAB inv functions.

2. I wrote earlier that the algorithm underlying the MP pseudoinverse is only understandable after learning about the SVD. But that needn't stop us from exploring the pseudoinverse with code! The goal of this challenge is to illustrate that the pseudoinverse is the same as (1) the "real" inverse for a full-rank square matrix, and (2) the left inverse for a tall full-column-rank matrix.

12.12 Code solutions

1. This one might have been challenging, particularly if you are not an experienced coder.

Code block 12.9: Python

```
1   import numpy as np
2
3   # create matrix
4   m = 4
5   A = np.random.randn(m,m)
6   M = np.zeros((m,m))
7   G = np.zeros((m,m))
8
9   # compute minors matrix
10  for i in range(m):
11    for j in range(m):
12
13      # select rows and cols
14      rows = [True]*m
15      rows[i] = False
16
17      cols = [True]*m
18      cols[j] = False
19
20      M[i,j]=np.linalg.det(A[rows,:][:,cols])
21
22      # compute G
23      G[i,j] = (-1)**(i+j)
24
25  # compute C
26  C = M * G
27
28  # compute A
29  Ainv = C.T / np.linalg.det(A)
30  AinvI = np.linalg.inv(A)
31  AinvI-Ainv # compare against inv()
```

```
1    % create matrix
2    m = 4;
3    A = randn(m);
4    [M,G] = deal( zeros(m) );
5
6    % compute matrices
7    for i=1:m
8      for j=1:m
9
10         %% select rows,cols
11         rows = true(1,m);
12         rows(i) = false;
13
14         cols = true(1,m);
15         cols(j) = false;
16
17         %% compute M
18         M(i,j) = det( A(rows,cols) );
19
20         %% compute G
21         G(i,j) = (-1)^(i+j);
22      end
23   end
24
25   % compute C
26   C = M .* G;
27
28   % compute A
29   Ainv = C'/det(A);
30   AinvI = inv(A);
31   AinvI-Ainv  % compare against inv()
```

2. .

```
1   import numpy as np
2
3   # square matrix
4   A   = np.random.randn(5,5)
5   Ai  = np.linalg.inv(A)
6   Api = np.linalg.pinv(A)
7   Ai - Api  # test equivalence
8
9   # tall matrix
10  T   = np.random.randn(5,3)
11  Tl  = np.linalg.inv(T.T@T)@T.T  # left inv
12  Tpi = np.linalg.pinv(T)  # pinv
13  Tl - Tpi  # test equivalence
```

Code block 12.12: MATLAB

```
1   % square matrix
2   A   = randn(5);
3   Ai  = inv(A);
4   Api = pinv(A);
5   Ai - Api  % test equivalence
6
7   % tall matrix
8   T   = randn(5,3);
9   Tl  = inv(T'*T)*T';  % left inv
10  Tpi = pinv(T);  % pinv
11  Tl - Tpi  % test equivalence
```

CHAPTER 13
PROJECTIONS AND ORTHOGONALIZATION

START THIS CHAPTER HAPPY

The goal of this chapter is to introduce a framework for projecting one space onto another space (for example, projecting a point onto a line). This framework forms the basis for orthogonalization and for an algorithm called *linear least-squares*, which is the primary method for estimating parameters and fitting models to data, and is therefore one of the most important algorithms in applied mathematics, including control engineering, statistics, and machine learning. Along the way, we'll also re-discover the left inverse.

13.1 Projections in $\mathbb{R}^2$

We are going to discover a formula for projecting a point onto a line. From there, we can generalize the formula to projecting one space onto another space. Don't worry, it's easier than you might think.

We start with a vector **a**, a point b not on **a**, and a scalar β such that β**a** is as close to b as possible without leaving **a**. Figure 13.1 shows the situation. (Because we are working with standard-position vectors, it is possible to equate coordinate points with vectors.)

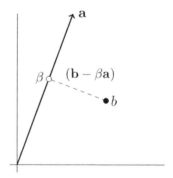

Figure 13.1: We need a formula to obtain the scalar β such that point βa is as close as possible to point b without leaving vector a.

The question is: Where do we place β so that the point β**a** is as close as possible to point b? You might have an intuition that β should be placed such that the line from β**a** to b is at a right angle to **a**. That's the right intuition (yes, that's a pun).

One way to think about this is to imagine that the line from $\beta\mathbf{a}$ to b is one side of a right triangle. Then the line from b to **a** is the hypotenuse of that triangle. Any hypotenuse is longer than the adjacent side, and so the shortest hypotenuse (i.e., the shortest distance from b to **a**) *is* the adjacent side.

We need an expression for the line from *point* b to *point* $\beta\mathbf{a}$. We can express this line as the subtraction of *vector* **b** (the vector from the origin to point b) and *vector* $\beta\mathbf{a}$ (the scaled version of vector **a**). Thus, the expression for the line is $(\mathbf{b} - \beta\mathbf{a})$.

Let's recap: We have established that the closest projection of b onto **a** involves the line that meets **a** at a right angle, and we have an expression for that line. Now our goal is to figure out the value of β. The geometric approach already provided the key insight, we just need to translate that into algebra. In particular, vectors $(\mathbf{b} - \beta\mathbf{a})$ and **a** are orthogonal, meaning they are perpendicular:

$$(\mathbf{b} - \beta\mathbf{a}) \perp \mathbf{a} \tag{13.1}$$

And that in turns means that the dot product between them is zero. Thus, we can rewrite Equation 13.1 as

$$(\mathbf{b} - \beta\mathbf{a})^{\mathrm{T}}\mathbf{a} = 0 \tag{13.2}$$

And that is the key insight that geometry provides us. From here, solving for β just involves a bit of algebra. It's a beautiful and important derivation, so I'll put all of it into a math box.

Orthogonal projection of a point onto a line

$$\mathbf{a}^{\mathrm{T}}(\mathbf{b} - \beta\mathbf{a}) = 0 \tag{13.3}$$

$$\mathbf{a}^{\mathrm{T}}\mathbf{b} - \beta\mathbf{a}^{\mathrm{T}}\mathbf{a} = 0$$

$$\beta\mathbf{a}^{\mathrm{T}}\mathbf{a} = \mathbf{a}^{\mathrm{T}}\mathbf{b}$$

$$\beta = \frac{\mathbf{a}^{\mathrm{T}}\mathbf{b}}{\mathbf{a}^{\mathrm{T}}\mathbf{a}} \tag{13.4}$$

Note that dividing both sides of the equation by $\mathbf{a}^{\mathrm{T}}\mathbf{a}$ is valid because it is a scalar quantity.

The technical term for this procedure is *projection*: We are projecting b onto the subspace defined by vector $\mathbf{a}$. This is commonly written as $proj_a(b)$.

(As an aside: It's tricky to remember whether projecting b onto $\mathbf{a}$ is written as $proj_a(b)$ or $proj_b(a)$. A memory trick here is that **the Subspace goes in the Subscript**. You've seen now several of these weird little mnemonics in this book, and there will be more. I hope they help you learn, or at least make you smile.)

Note that Equation 13.4 gives the scalar value β, not the actual point represented by the open circle in Figure 13.1. To calculate that vector $\beta\mathbf{a}$, simply replace β with its definition:

In the fraction, one $\mathbf{a}$ in the denominator doesn't cancel the multiplying $\mathbf{a}$, because the vector in the denominator is part of a dot product.

Projection of a point onto a line

$$proj_a(b) = \frac{\mathbf{a}^{\mathrm{T}}\mathbf{b}}{\mathbf{a}^{\mathrm{T}}\mathbf{a}}\mathbf{a} \qquad (13.5)$$

Let's work through an example with real numbers. We'll use the following vector and point.

$$\mathbf{a} = \begin{bmatrix} -2 \\ -1 \end{bmatrix}, \quad b = (3, -1)$$

If you draw these two objects on a 2D plane, you'll see that this example is different from that presented in Figure 13.1: The point is "behind" the line, so it will project negatively onto the vector. Let's see how this works out algebraically.

$$proj_a(b) = \frac{\begin{bmatrix} -2 \\ -1 \end{bmatrix}^{\mathrm{T}} \begin{bmatrix} 3 \\ -1 \end{bmatrix}}{\begin{bmatrix} -2 \\ -1 \end{bmatrix}^{\mathrm{T}} \begin{bmatrix} -2 \\ -1 \end{bmatrix}} \begin{bmatrix} -2 \\ -1 \end{bmatrix} = \frac{-6+1}{4+1} \begin{bmatrix} -2 \\ -1 \end{bmatrix} = -1 \begin{bmatrix} -2 \\ -1 \end{bmatrix}$$

Notice that $\beta = -1$. Thus, we are projecting "backwards" onto the vector (Figure 13.2). This makes sense when we think of $\mathbf{a}$ as being a basis vector for a 1D subspace that is embedded in $\mathbb{R}^2$.

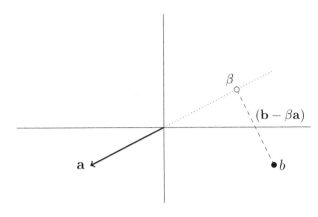

Figure 13.2: Example of projecting a point onto a line. The intersection βa is coordinate (2,1).

Practice problems Draw the following lines (**a**) and points (b). Draw the approximate location of the orthogonal projection of b onto **a**. Then compute the exact $\text{proj}_a(b)$ and compare with your guess.

a) $\mathbf{a} = \begin{bmatrix} -.5 \\ 2 \end{bmatrix}$, $b = (.5, 2)$ b) $\mathbf{a} = \begin{bmatrix} 0 \\ 2 \end{bmatrix}$, $b = (0, 1)$

c) $\mathbf{a} = \begin{bmatrix} 2 \\ 0 \end{bmatrix}$, $b = (0, -1)$ d) $\mathbf{a} = \begin{bmatrix} 1 \\ 2 \end{bmatrix}$, $b = (2, 1)$

Answers Answers below are the β; $\text{proj}_a(b)$ is β**a**.

a) $3.75/4.25$ b) $.5$
c) 0 d) $4/5$

Reflection

$\Bigg[$ *Mapping over magnitude*: Meditating on Equation 13.4 will reveal that it is a mapping between two vectors, scaled by the squared length of the "target" vector. It's useful to understand this intuition (*mapping over magnitude*), because many computations in linear algebra and its applications (e.g., correlation, convolution, normalization) involve some kind of mapping divided by some kind of magnitude or norm. $\Bigg]$

Now you know how to project a point onto a line, which is a 1D subspace. We're now going to extend this to projecting a point onto an N-D subspace.

We begin simply by replacing *vector* **a** (which is, by definition, a 1D subspace) to *matrix* **A**, the columns of which form a subspace with some dimensionality between 1 and the matrix rank (excluding the case of a zero-dimensional subspace from the zeros matrix; that would be boring).

Point b is still the same: We can conceptualize it as a coordinate in space, but we represent it using vector **b**, which is in $\mathbb{R}^M$, corresponding to the ambient dimensionality of the column space of **A**.

Because **A** has multiple columns, we also need to replace *scalar* β with a *vector*. I'll call that vector **x**.

Note the zeros vector here instead of the scalar 0 used above.

$$\mathbf{A}^\mathrm{T}(\mathbf{b} - \mathbf{A}\mathbf{x}) = \mathbf{0} \tag{13.6}$$

$$\mathbf{A}^\mathrm{T}\mathbf{b} - \mathbf{A}^\mathrm{T}\mathbf{A}\mathbf{x} = \mathbf{0}$$

$$\mathbf{A}^\mathrm{T}\mathbf{A}\mathbf{x} = \mathbf{A}^\mathrm{T}\mathbf{b} \tag{13.7}$$

Hmm... are we stuck here? When we restricted ourselves to a 1D subspace, **a** was a vector and therefore $\mathbf{a}^\mathrm{T}\mathbf{a}$ was a scalar, so we could divide both sides of the equation by that dot product. But now we have $\mathbf{A}^\mathrm{T}\mathbf{A}$, and as you know, there is no matrix division. Can you guess the solution that allows us to solve for **x**? The secret is revealed on the next page; see if you can derive a solution to our conundrum before looking ahead!

I'm sure you guessed it: Left-multiply by $(\mathbf{A}^T\mathbf{A})^{-1}$.

$$(\mathbf{A}^T\mathbf{A})^{-1}\mathbf{A}^T\mathbf{A}\mathbf{x} = (\mathbf{A}^T\mathbf{A})^{-1}\mathbf{A}^T\mathbf{b}$$

$$\mathbf{x} = (\mathbf{A}^T\mathbf{A})^{-1}\mathbf{A}^T\mathbf{b} \qquad (13.8)$$

I hope you see that we "accidentally" re-discovered the formula for the left inverse in Equation 13.8. This never ceases to amaze me: We started off with a completely different goal that seems to have nothing whatsoever to do with computing an inverse of a tall matrix, and yet we arrived at the left inverse as the way to project a point onto the column space of $\mathbf{A}$.

Indeed, one way of thinking about the one-sided inverse is that it projects a rectangular matrix onto the (square) identity matrix.

You can see that this equation involves inverting a matrix, which should immediately raise the question in your mind: What is the condition for this equation to be valid? The condition, of course, is that $\mathbf{A}^T\mathbf{A}$ is square and full-rank. And you know from the previous chapter that this is the case if $\mathbf{A}$ is already square and full-rank, or if it is tall and full column-rank.

It is insightful to think back to the geometric perspective: we are trying to project a point (also represented as the end-point of a vector in its standard position) $\mathbf{b}$ onto the column space of matrix $\mathbf{A}$. If $\mathbf{b}$ is in the column space of $\mathbf{A}$, then $\mathbf{x}$ indicates the combinations of columns in $\mathbf{A}$ that produce $\mathbf{b}$. Figure 13.3 shows a visualization of this idea for a 2D column space embedded in 3D ambient space (in other words, the matrix $\mathbf{A}$ has three rows and rank=2).

What happens if $\mathbf{b}$ is already inside the column space of $\mathbf{A}$? Geometrically, it means that $\|\mathbf{b} - \mathbf{A}\mathbf{x}\| = 0$, and consequently, that $\mathbf{b} = \mathbf{A}\mathbf{x}$. Plugging this into Equation 13.6 also makes sense algebraically.

We can also consider what happens when $\mathbf{A}$ is a square full-rank matrix: This guarantees that $\mathbf{b}$ is already in its column space, because the column space of $\mathbf{A}$ spans all of $\mathbb{R}^M$. In that case,

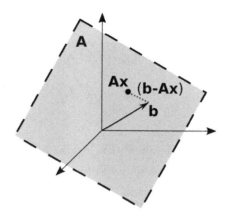

Figure 13.3: Visualization of projecting point b onto the 2D column subspace of A (grey patch). Assume that b is not in the column space of A, and vector (b − Ax), represented as the dotted line, is orthogonal to the column space. Thus, Ax is the vector inside the column space of A that minimizes the distance to b.

Equation 13.8 simplifies a bit:

$$\mathbf{x} = (\mathbf{A}^{\mathrm{T}}\mathbf{A})^{-1}\mathbf{A}^{\mathrm{T}}\mathbf{b}$$

$$\mathbf{x} = \mathbf{A}^{-1}\mathbf{A}^{-\mathrm{T}}\mathbf{A}^{\mathrm{T}}\mathbf{b}$$

$$\mathbf{x} = \mathbf{A}^{-1}\mathbf{b} \tag{13.9}$$

Practice problems Solve for $\mathbf{x}$ using Equation 13.8.

a) $\begin{bmatrix} 1 & 2 \\ 3 & 1 \\ 1 & 1 \end{bmatrix} \begin{bmatrix} x_1 \\ x_2 \end{bmatrix} = \begin{bmatrix} 5.5 \\ -3.5 \\ 1.5 \end{bmatrix}$

b) $\begin{bmatrix} -2 & 2 \\ 1 & 3 \end{bmatrix} \begin{bmatrix} x_1 \\ x_2 \end{bmatrix} = \begin{bmatrix} 12 \\ 46 \end{bmatrix}$

c) $\begin{bmatrix} 1 & 0 \\ 0 & 1 \\ 0 & 0 \end{bmatrix} \begin{bmatrix} x_1 \\ x_2 \end{bmatrix} = \begin{bmatrix} 2 \\ 1 \\ 1.2 \end{bmatrix}$

d) $\begin{bmatrix} 1 & 3 \\ 2 & 6 \\ 3 & 9 \end{bmatrix} \begin{bmatrix} x_1 \\ x_2 \end{bmatrix} = \begin{bmatrix} 4 \\ 8 \\ 11 \end{bmatrix}$

Answers

a) $\begin{bmatrix} -2.5 & 4 \end{bmatrix}^{\mathrm{T}}$

b) $\begin{bmatrix} 7 & 13 \end{bmatrix}^{\mathrm{T}}$

c) $\begin{bmatrix} 2 & 1 \end{bmatrix}^{\mathrm{T}}$

d) Doesn't work! ($\mathbf{A}^{\mathrm{T}}\mathbf{A}$ is singular)

[
Figures 13.2 and 13.3 provide the geometric intuition underlying the least-squares formula, which is the mathematical backbone of many analyses in statistics, machine-
learning, and AI. Stay tuned...
]

Code   You can implement Equation 13.8 based on what you learned
in the previous chapter. But that equation is so important and
is used so often that numerical processing software packages have
short-cuts for solving it. The Python code uses the numpy function
`lstsq`, which stands for least-squares.

Code block 13.1: Python

```
1  import numpy as np
2  A = [[1,2],[3,1],[1,1]]
3  b = [5.5,-3.5,1.5]
4  np.linalg.lstsq(A,b)[0]
```

Code block 13.2: MATLAB

```
1  A = [1 2; 3 1; 1 1];
2  b = [5.5 -3.5 1.5]';
3  A\b
```

13.3 Orthogonal and parallel vector components

In this section, you will learn how to decompose one vector into two
separate vectors that are orthogonal to each other, and that have a
special relationship to a third vector. This procedure will draw on
concepts you learned in Chapter 2 (adding and subtracting vectors)
and in the previous section (projecting onto vectors). And in turn,
it forms the basis for *orthogonalization*, which you'll learn about in
the following section.

Let's start with a picture so you understand our goal (in $\mathbb{R}^2$, of
course, because linear algebra always starts in $\mathbb{R}^2$). We begin with

two vectors, **w** and **v**. Let's call **w** the "target" vector, and **v** the "reference" vector.

The idea is that we want to break up **w** into two separate vectors, one of which is *parallel* to **w** and the other is *perpendicular* to **w**. In Figure 13.4, the component of vector **w** that is parallel to **v** is labeled $\mathbf{w}_{||\mathbf{v}}$ and the component that is perpendicular to **v** is labeled $\mathbf{w}_{\perp\mathbf{v}}$. The thin gray dashed lines illustrate that these two vector components sum to form the original vector **w**. In other words:

$$\mathbf{w} = \mathbf{w}_{\perp\mathbf{v}} + \mathbf{w}_{||\mathbf{v}} \tag{13.10}$$

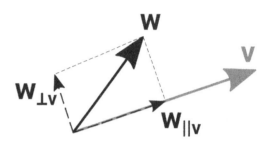

Figure 13.4: Decomposing vector w into components that are parallel and orthogonal to vector v.

Now that you have the picture, let's start deriving formulas and proofs. Don't worry, it'll be easier than you might think.

Parallel component If **w** and **v** have their tails at the same point, then the component of **w** that is parallel to **v** is simply collinear with **v**. In other words, $\mathbf{w}_{||\mathbf{v}}$ is a scaled version of **v**. Does this situation look familiar? If not, then you were either sleep-reading section 13.1, or you just opened to book to this page. Either way, it would behoove you to go back and re-read section 13.1. All we need to do here is project **w** onto **v**. Here's what that formula looks like:

$$\mathbf{w}_{||\mathbf{v}} = \mathrm{proj}_{\mathbf{v}}\mathbf{w} = \frac{\mathbf{w}^{\mathrm{T}}\mathbf{v}}{\mathbf{v}^{\mathrm{T}}\mathbf{v}}\mathbf{v} \tag{13.11}$$

This is just a modified version of Equation 13.5.

Perpendicular component How do we solve for $\mathbf{w}_{\perp\mathbf{v}}$? We don't need to do anything fancy; we simply revisit the fact that the vector

w is exactly decomposed into the sum of its perpendicular and parallel components (Equation 13.10). In particular, we already know **w**, and we just computed $\mathbf{w}_{||\mathbf{v}}$. A bit of middle-school algebra leads us to the solution:

$$\mathbf{w}_{\perp\mathbf{v}} = \mathbf{w} - \mathbf{w}_{||\mathbf{v}} \tag{13.12}$$

And this brings us to the full set of equations for decomposing a vector into two components relative to a target vector.

Decomposing a vector relative to another vector

$$\mathbf{w} = \mathbf{w}_{||\mathbf{v}} + \mathbf{w}_{\perp\mathbf{v}} \tag{13.13}$$

$$\mathbf{w}_{||\mathbf{v}} = \text{proj}_{\mathbf{v}}\mathbf{w} = \frac{\mathbf{w}^{\mathrm{T}}\mathbf{v}}{\mathbf{v}^{\mathrm{T}}\mathbf{v}}\mathbf{v} \tag{13.14}$$

$$\mathbf{w}_{\perp\mathbf{v}} = \mathbf{w} - \mathbf{w}_{||\mathbf{v}} \tag{13.15}$$

Here's a tip that might help you remember these formulas: Because $\mathbf{w}_{||\mathbf{v}}$ is parallel to **v**, it's really the same vector as **v** but scaled. Thus, $\mathbf{w}_{||\mathbf{v}} = \alpha\mathbf{v}$. Try to link the formulas to their geometric pictures rather than memorizing letters; the vector symbols (e.g., **w** and **v**) will change in different examples and textbooks.

We need to prove that $\mathbf{w}_{||\mathbf{v}}$ and $\mathbf{w}_{\perp\mathbf{v}}$ really are orthogonal to each other. The proof comes from taking the dot product between them, and then expanding then simplifying the results. Hopefully we'll find that the dot product is zero.

$$(\mathbf{w}_{||\mathbf{v}})^{\mathrm{T}}(\mathbf{w}_{\perp\mathbf{v}}) = \left(\frac{\mathbf{w}^{\mathrm{T}}\mathbf{v}}{\mathbf{v}^{\mathrm{T}}\mathbf{v}}\mathbf{v}\right)^{\mathrm{T}}\left(\mathbf{w} - \frac{\mathbf{w}^{\mathrm{T}}\mathbf{v}}{\mathbf{v}^{\mathrm{T}}\mathbf{v}}\mathbf{v}\right) \tag{13.16}$$

$$= \frac{\mathbf{w}^{\mathrm{T}}\mathbf{v}}{\mathbf{v}^{\mathrm{T}}\mathbf{v}}\mathbf{v}^{\mathrm{T}}\mathbf{w} - \frac{\mathbf{w}^{\mathrm{T}}\mathbf{v}}{\mathbf{v}^{\mathrm{T}}\mathbf{v}}\frac{\mathbf{w}^{\mathrm{T}}\mathbf{v}}{\mathbf{v}^{\mathrm{T}}\mathbf{v}}\mathbf{v}^{\mathrm{T}}\mathbf{v}$$

$$= \frac{(\mathbf{w}^{\mathrm{T}}\mathbf{v})^2}{\mathbf{v}^{\mathrm{T}}\mathbf{v}} - \frac{(\mathbf{w}^{\mathrm{T}}\mathbf{v})^2}{\mathbf{v}^{\mathrm{T}}\mathbf{v}}$$

$$= 0$$

That looks on first glance like a messy set of equations, but when keeping in mind that the dot product is a single number, I hope

If you squint, this proof looks like a flock of birds.

you will see that it's actually a straightforward proof. If you find it difficult to follow, then consider re-writing the proof using $\alpha = \mathbf{w}^{\mathrm{T}}\mathbf{v}$ and $\beta = \mathbf{v}^{\mathrm{T}}\mathbf{v}$.

Let's work through an example in $\mathbb{R}^2$, using vectors $\mathbf{v}=[2\ 3]^{\mathrm{T}}$ and $\mathbf{w}=[4\ 0]^{\mathrm{T}}$. And to make sure that you are learning concepts instead of memorizing strings of letters, I'll reverse the mapping, such that the goal is to decompose $\mathbf{v}$ into its parallel and perpendicular components relative to $\mathbf{w}$.

$$\mathbf{v}_{\|\mathbf{w}} = \frac{2\cdot4 + 3\cdot0}{4\cdot4 + 0\cdot0}\begin{bmatrix}4\\0\end{bmatrix} = \begin{bmatrix}2\\0\end{bmatrix}$$

$$\mathbf{v}_{\perp\mathbf{w}} = \begin{bmatrix}2\\3\end{bmatrix} - \begin{bmatrix}2\\0\end{bmatrix} = \begin{bmatrix}0\\3\end{bmatrix}$$

It's easily seen in this example that $\mathbf{v}_{\|\mathbf{w}}$ and $\mathbf{v}_{\perp\mathbf{w}}$ are orthogonal and that $\mathbf{v}_{\|\mathbf{w}} + \mathbf{v}_{\perp\mathbf{w}} = \mathbf{v}$. This example is also easy to map onto geometry (Figure 13.5).

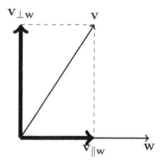

Figure 13.5: Example of decomposing vector v relative to vector w.

Now let's try an example in $\mathbb{R}^6$. We won't be able to visualize the results, but the algorithm and interpretation of the findings is the same. Again, given two vectors with the same dimensionality, we will decompose vector **a** into two components, one parallel to and one perpendicular to **b**.

$$\mathbf{a} = \begin{bmatrix} 2 \\ 3 \\ 5 \\ 0 \\ 1 \\ 2 \end{bmatrix}, \ \mathbf{b} = \begin{bmatrix} 0 \\ -2 \\ -2 \\ 5 \\ 5 \\ -6 \end{bmatrix}$$

$$\mathbf{a}_{\|\mathbf{b}} = \frac{2 \cdot 0 + 3 \cdot -2 + 5 \cdot -2 + 0 \cdot 5 + 1 \cdot 5 + 2 \cdot -6}{0 \cdot 0 + -2 \cdot -2 + -2 \cdot -2 + 5 \cdot 5 + 5 \cdot 5 + -6 \cdot -6} \begin{bmatrix} 0 \\ -2 \\ -2 \\ 5 \\ 5 \\ -6 \end{bmatrix} = \frac{-23}{94} \begin{bmatrix} 0 \\ -2 \\ -2 \\ 5 \\ 5 \\ -6 \end{bmatrix}$$

$$\mathbf{a}_{\perp\mathbf{b}} = \begin{bmatrix} 2 \\ 3 \\ 5 \\ 0 \\ 1 \\ 2 \end{bmatrix} - \frac{-23}{94} \begin{bmatrix} 0 \\ -2 \\ -2 \\ 5 \\ 5 \\ -6 \end{bmatrix} = \frac{94}{94} \begin{bmatrix} 2 \\ 3 \\ 5 \\ 0 \\ 1 \\ 2 \end{bmatrix} - \frac{23}{94} \begin{bmatrix} 0 \\ 2 \\ 2 \\ -5 \\ -5 \\ 6 \end{bmatrix} = \frac{1}{94} \begin{bmatrix} 188 \\ 236 \\ 424 \\ 115 \\ 209 \\ 50 \end{bmatrix}$$

You can confirm (on paper or computer) that the two vector components (1) sum to produce the original vector $\mathbf{a}$ and (2) are orthogonal to each other. In general, the arithmetic can become challenging in these problems, but that's the nature of linear algebra. The silver lining is that computers are really good at arithmetic, at least until you start working with really tiny numbers or really huge numbers.

Practice problems For the following pairs of vectors $(\mathbf{a}, \mathbf{b})$, decompose $\mathbf{a}$ into parallel and perpendicular components relative to $\mathbf{b}$. For $\mathbb{R}^2$ problems, additionally draw all vectors.

a) $\begin{bmatrix} 2 \\ 2 \end{bmatrix}, \begin{bmatrix} 0 \\ -3 \end{bmatrix}$
  b) $\begin{bmatrix} 1/2 \\ 0 \end{bmatrix}, \begin{bmatrix} -1 \\ 2 \end{bmatrix}$
  c) $\begin{bmatrix} 0 \\ 0 \\ 3 \end{bmatrix}, \begin{bmatrix} 2 \\ 4 \\ 0 \end{bmatrix}$

Answers Answers below are $\mathbf{a}_{\|\mathbf{b}}$ and $\mathbf{a}_{\perp\mathbf{b}}$.

a) $\begin{bmatrix} 0 \\ 2 \end{bmatrix}, \begin{bmatrix} 2 \\ 0 \end{bmatrix}$
  b) $\begin{bmatrix} .1 \\ -.2 \end{bmatrix}, \begin{bmatrix} .4 \\ .2 \end{bmatrix}$
  c) $\begin{bmatrix} 0 \\ 0 \\ 0 \end{bmatrix}, \begin{bmatrix} 0 \\ 0 \\ 3 \end{bmatrix}$

13.4 Orthogonal matrices

I introduced you to *orthogonal matrices* in section 5.5. Transforming a matrix into an orthogonal matrix is the main goal of the Gram-Schmidt procedure and QR decomposition, and so before discussing those operations I'd like to tell you more about the properties of orthogonal matrices.

Orthogonal matrices are typically indicated using the letter $\mathbf{Q}$. That's not the only letter given to matrices that are orthogonal, but any time you see matrix $\mathbf{Q}$ it is safe to assume that it is an orthogonal matrix.

There are two key properties of an orthogonal matrix:

1. All columns are pairwise orthogonal.
2. All columns have a magnitude of 1.

Here are these two properties translated into math:

$$\langle \mathbf{q}_i, \mathbf{q}_j \rangle = \begin{cases} 0, & \text{if } i \neq j \\ 1, & \text{if } i = j \end{cases} \tag{13.17}$$

In a linear algebra sense, Equation 13.17 is ugly because it can be written in a more compact and simultaneously more revealing manner:

Orthogonal matrix definition

$$\mathbf{Q}^T\mathbf{Q} = \mathbf{I} \tag{13.18}$$

If you're struggling to see the link between Equations 13.17 and 13.18, then think about matrix multiplication from the element perspective, and how each element in the product matrix is the dot product between the corresponding row of the left matrix and column of the right matrix.

This is a remarkable definition, because it matches the definition of the matrix inverse. That means that for a square matrix $\mathbf{Q}$ (I'll get to the rectangular case later),

$$\mathbf{Q}^T\mathbf{Q} = \mathbf{Q}\mathbf{Q}^T = \mathbf{Q}^{-1}\mathbf{Q} = \mathbf{Q}\mathbf{Q}^{-1} = \mathbf{I} \tag{13.19}$$

That's really convenient, because computing the inverse is a hassle and can be numerically unstable. But computing the transpose is trivial and always accurate.

Now for some examples. The trivial example of an orthogonal matrix is the identity matrix, because $\mathbf{I}^T\mathbf{I} = \mathbf{I}$. Here's a less trivial example:

$$\mathbf{Q} = \begin{bmatrix} 1 & -1 \\ 1 & 1 \end{bmatrix} \tag{13.20}$$

But wait a minute—it that really an orthogonal matrix? It conforms to the first property (orthogonal columns), but the columns both have a magnitude of $\sqrt{2}$. Thus, this matrix needs to be scaled:

$$\mathbf{Q} = \frac{1}{\sqrt{2}} \begin{bmatrix} 1 & -1 \\ 1 & 1 \end{bmatrix} \tag{13.21}$$

In fact, this is a special case of the general form for 2×2 $\mathbf{Q}$ matrices:

$$\mathbf{Q} = \begin{bmatrix} \cos(\theta) & -\sin(\theta) \\ \sin(\theta) & \cos(\theta) \end{bmatrix} \tag{13.22}$$

A bit of arithmetic will confirm the first property, and a bit of trigonometry will confirm the second property.

$$-\cos(\theta)\sin(\theta) + \sin(\theta)\cos(\theta) = 0 \tag{13.23}$$

$$\cos^2(\theta) + \sin^2(\theta) = (-\sin(\theta))^2 + \cos^2(\theta) = 1 \tag{13.24}$$

Rectangular Q The quick version here is that an orthogonal matrix does not need to be square, however, the transpose of a rectangular orthogonal matrices is only a one-sided inverse.

Consider the following matrix. Take a moment to prove to yourself that it is an orthogonal matrix.

$$\mathbf{Q} = \frac{1}{3} \begin{bmatrix} 2 & 1 \\ -2 & 2 \\ 1 & 2 \end{bmatrix}$$

Pre- and post-multiplying this matrix by its transpose shows that $\mathbf{Q}^{\mathrm{T}}$ is the left inverse of $\mathbf{Q}$.

$$\mathbf{Q}^{\mathrm{T}}\mathbf{Q} = \frac{1}{9} \begin{bmatrix} 2 & -2 & 1 \\ 1 & 2 & 2 \end{bmatrix} \begin{bmatrix} 2 & 1 \\ -2 & 2 \\ 1 & 2 \end{bmatrix} = \frac{1}{9} \begin{bmatrix} 9 & 0 \\ 0 & 9 \end{bmatrix} \tag{13.25}$$

$$\mathbf{Q}\mathbf{Q}^{\mathrm{T}} = \frac{1}{9} \begin{bmatrix} 2 & 1 \\ -2 & 2 \\ 1 & 2 \end{bmatrix} \begin{bmatrix} 2 & -2 & 1 \\ 1 & 2 & 2 \end{bmatrix} = \frac{1}{9} \begin{bmatrix} 5 & -2 & 4 \\ -2 & 8 & 2 \\ 4 & 2 & 5 \end{bmatrix} \tag{13.26}$$

This example is for a tall orthogonal matrix. Can we have a wide orthogonal matrix? Let's inspect $\mathbf{Q}^{\mathrm{T}}$ to find out (I'll rename it to $\tilde{\mathbf{Q}}$ for convenience).

$$\tilde{\mathbf{Q}} = \frac{1}{3} \begin{bmatrix} 2 & -2 & 1 \\ 1 & 2 & 2 \end{bmatrix} \tag{13.27}$$

Well, the second requirement (norm of 1) already fails. A scalar of $(3\sqrt{5})/5$ will work for the first and third columns but not the second column. You could rescale the columns differently, but this matrix will still fail the first test of orthogonality.

But this example doesn't show that a wide matrix *cannot* be orthogonal; it merely shows that the transpose of a tall orthogonal matrix is not necessarily orthogonal. Our question remains: Is a wide orthogonal matrix possible?

In a strict sense, the answer is No: A wide matrix cannot be an orthogonal matrix. That's because both properties of an orthogonal matrix (orthogonal columns, each with magnitude of 1) cannot simultaneously be satisfied. Let's think about why that is the case.

A wide matrix has size $M < N$ and its maximum possible rank is M, corresponding to the number of rows. Thus, the largest possible set of linearly independent columns is M; the rest of columns $r + 1$ through N can be expressed as some linear combination of the first M columns, and thus cannot possibly be orthogonal.

That said, wide matrices can be "almost orthogonal"—they can have interesting properties that almost meet the criteria of an orthogonal matrix. The wide $\mathbf{Q}$ matrix has at least one column of zeros, because the zeros vector is orthogonal to every other vector (meets the first criteria). But obviously the zeros vector does not have a magnitude of 1. Here is an example of such a wide matrix:

$$\mathbf{Q} = \frac{1}{\sqrt{5}} \begin{bmatrix} -2 & -1 & 0 \\ -1 & 2 & 0 \end{bmatrix} \tag{13.28}$$

You can see that all columns are pairwise orthogonal, but the third column has a norm of 0. This matrix transposed still provides a right inverse. However, it does not provide a left inverse.

$$\mathbf{Q}^{\mathsf{T}}\mathbf{Q} = \frac{1}{5}\begin{bmatrix} -2 & -1 \\ -1 & 2 \\ 0 & 0 \end{bmatrix}\begin{bmatrix} -2 & -1 & 0 \\ -1 & 2 & 0 \end{bmatrix} = \frac{1}{5}\begin{bmatrix} 5 & 0 & 0 \\ 0 & 5 & 0 \\ 0 & 0 & 0 \end{bmatrix} \tag{13.29}$$

$$\mathbf{Q}\mathbf{Q}^{\mathsf{T}} = \frac{1}{5}\begin{bmatrix} -2 & -1 & 0 \\ -1 & 2 & 0 \end{bmatrix}\begin{bmatrix} -2 & -1 \\ -1 & 2 \\ 0 & 0 \end{bmatrix} = \frac{1}{5}\begin{bmatrix} 5 & 0 \\ 0 & 5 \end{bmatrix} \tag{13.30}$$

Orthogonal matrices seem a bit magical. Are they exceedingly rare and nearly impossible to construct? Quite the opposite! And even better, you already know everything you need to create an orthogonal matrix. In the next section, you'll see how to put the pieces together.

Practice problems Determine the value of ζ that will produce orthogonal matrices.

a) $\zeta\begin{bmatrix} -1/2 & 1/2 \\ 1/2 & 1/2 \end{bmatrix}$

b) $\begin{bmatrix} 0 & 2^{-.5} & 2^{-.5} \\ 0 & 2^{-.5} & -2^{-.5} \\ \zeta & 0 & 0 \end{bmatrix}$

c) $\begin{bmatrix} \cos(\zeta) & -\sin(\zeta) & 0 \\ \sin(\zeta) & \cos(\zeta) & 0 \\ 0 & 0 & 1 \end{bmatrix}$

Answers Answers below are ζ.

a) $\sqrt{2}$

b) 1

c) any ζ

13.5 Orthogonalization via Gram-Schmidt

Let's say you have a set of vectors in $\mathbb{R}^N$ that is independent but not orthogonal. You can create a set of orthogonal vectors from the original vectors by applying the Gram-Schmidt process. Just follow the three-step plan (using vectors $\mathbf{v}_1$ through $\mathbf{v}_n$).

Procedure for creating a set of orthonormal vectors

1) Start with $\mathbf{v}_1$ and normalize to unit length: $\mathbf{v}_1^* = \dfrac{\mathbf{v}_1}{|\mathbf{v}_1|}$

For all remaining vectors in the set:

2) Orthogonalize $\mathbf{v}_k^*$ to all previous vectors (eq. 13.15)

3) Normalize $\mathbf{v}_k^*$ to unit length

The result of this procedure is a set of orthonormal vectors that, when placed as column vectors in a matrix, yield an orthogonal matrix $\mathbf{Q}$.

Let's start with an example using three vectors in $\mathbb{R}^2$. Before looking at the math, draw these three vectors on a 2D plane, and try to visualize how the resulting orthogonalized vectors might look.

$$\mathbf{v}_1 = \begin{bmatrix} 1 \\ 3 \end{bmatrix}, \ \mathbf{v}_2 = \begin{bmatrix} 1 \\ -1 \end{bmatrix}, \ \mathbf{v}_3 = \begin{bmatrix} -2 \\ 1 \end{bmatrix} \quad \Rightarrow \quad \mathbf{V} = \begin{bmatrix} 1 & 1 & -2 \\ 3 & -1 & 1 \end{bmatrix}$$

$$\mathbf{v}_1^* = \frac{1}{\sqrt{10}} \begin{bmatrix} 1 \\ 3 \end{bmatrix}$$

$\bigg|$ Normalize to unit vector

$$\mathbf{v}_2^* = \mathbf{v}_2 - \mathbf{v}_{2\|\mathbf{v}_1} = \begin{bmatrix} 1 \\ -1 \end{bmatrix} - \frac{1\cdot 1 + 3\cdot -1}{1\cdot 1 + 3\cdot 3} \begin{bmatrix} 1 \\ 3 \end{bmatrix} = \begin{bmatrix} 1 + 1/5 \\ -1 + 3/5 \end{bmatrix} = \frac{1}{5} \begin{bmatrix} 6 \\ -2 \end{bmatrix}$$

$\bigg|$ Orthogonalize to $\mathbf{v}_1$

$$\mathbf{v}_2^* = \frac{\sqrt{5}}{10\sqrt{2}} \begin{bmatrix} 6 \\ -2 \end{bmatrix}$$

$\bigg|$ Normalize to unit vector

$$\mathbf{v}_3^* = \mathbf{v}_3 - \mathbf{v}_{3\|\mathbf{v}_1^*} - \mathbf{v}_{3\|\mathbf{v}_2^*} = \begin{bmatrix} -2 \\ 1 \end{bmatrix} - \frac{10^{-1/2}\cdot -2 + 3\cdot 10^{-1/2}}{(10^{-1/2})^2 + (3\cdot 10^{-1/2})^2} \begin{bmatrix} 1 \\ 3 \end{bmatrix}$$

$\bigg|$ Orthogonalize to $\mathbf{v}_1^*$ and to $\mathbf{v}_2^*$

$$-\frac{6\sqrt{5}/10\sqrt{2}\cdot -2 + -2\sqrt{5}/10\sqrt{2}}{(6\sqrt{5}/10\sqrt{2})^2 + (-2\sqrt{5}/10\sqrt{2})^2} \begin{bmatrix} 6 \\ -2 \end{bmatrix}$$

$$= \begin{bmatrix} -2 \\ 1 \end{bmatrix} - \frac{10^{-1/2}}{\sqrt{10}} \begin{bmatrix} 1 \\ 3 \end{bmatrix} - \sqrt{5}\frac{\frac{-7\sqrt{5}}{5\sqrt{2}}}{10\sqrt{2}} \begin{bmatrix} 6 \\ -2 \end{bmatrix} = \begin{bmatrix} 0 \\ 0 \end{bmatrix}$$

Putting these vectors into a matrix yields

$$\mathbf{Q} = \begin{bmatrix} \dfrac{1}{\sqrt{10}} & \dfrac{3\sqrt{5}}{5\sqrt{2}} & 0 \\[2ex] \dfrac{3}{\sqrt{10}} & \dfrac{3\sqrt{5}}{10\sqrt{2}} & 0 \end{bmatrix}$$

A few notes about this example:

1. The arithmetic gets difficult quickly, doesn't it? I could have come up with numbers that worked out easier, but there are several important lessons here: (1) even seemingly simple problems can become complicated (a general challenge in life), (2) don't be intimidated by the complexity—take a deep breath, get some paper and a pencil, and work through your (math) problems with a positive and assertive attitude.

2. Note that each vector is orthogonalized to $\mathbf{v}^*_{k-1}$—the already-orthogonalized vector—*not* to the original $\mathbf{v}_{k-1}$.

3. Are you surprised with the result $\mathbf{v}^*_3 = \mathbf{0}$? You shouldn't be—it's not possible to have 3 orthogonal vectors in $\mathbb{R}^2$ or, in general, $n + 1$ orthogonal vectors in $\mathbb{R}^N$.

4. Numerical computing programs like MATLAB and Python will omit the final column of zeros, thus returning a true orthogonal matrix, even though it is not the same size as the original matrix. I'll write more about the sizes of orthogonalized matrices in a later section.

Figure 13.6 shows the column vectors of $\mathbf{V}$ and $\mathbf{Q}$. Aside from the intense arithmetic on the previous page, it is also geometrically obvious that $\mathbf{q}_3$ must be zeros, because it is not possible to have more than two orthogonal vectors in $\mathbb{R}^2$. This is an application of the theorem about the maximum number of vectors that can form a linearly independent set, which was introduced in section 4.6.

PROJECTIONS

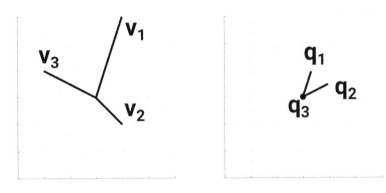

Figure 13.6: Lines show column vectors in matrix V (left) and Q (right). Note that vector q_3 is a dot at the origin.

Practice problems Produce orthogonal matrices using the Gram-Schmidt procedure.

a) $\begin{bmatrix} 1 & 3 \\ 1 & 4 \end{bmatrix}$

b) $\begin{bmatrix} 1 & 3 \\ -3 & 4 \end{bmatrix}$

c) $\begin{bmatrix} 3 & 3 \\ 4 & 4 \end{bmatrix}$

Answers

a) $\frac{1}{\sqrt{2}} \begin{bmatrix} 1 & -1 \\ 1 & 1 \end{bmatrix}$

b) $\frac{1}{\sqrt{10}} \begin{bmatrix} 1 & 3 \\ -3 & 1 \end{bmatrix}$

c) $\frac{1}{5} \begin{bmatrix} 3 & 0 \\ 4 & 0 \end{bmatrix}$

Reflection

The Gram-Schmidt procedure is numerically unstable, due to round-off errors that propagate forward to each subsequent vector and affect both the normalization and the orthogonalization. You'll see an example of this in the code challenges. Computer programs therefore use numerically stable algorithms that achieve the same conceptual result, based on modifications to the standard Gram-Schmidt procedure or alternative methods such as Givens rotations or Gaussian elimination.

13.6 QR decomposition

The Gram-Schmidt procedure transforms matrix $\mathbf{A}$ into orthogonal matrix $\mathbf{Q}$. Unless $\mathbf{A}$ is already an orthogonal matrix, $\mathbf{Q}$ will be different than $\mathbf{A}$, possibly very different. Thus, information is lost when going from $\mathbf{A} \to \mathbf{Q}$. Is is possible to recover the information that was lost in translation? Obviously, the answer is yes. And that's the idea of QR decomposition:

$$\mathbf{A} = \mathbf{QR} \tag{13.31}$$

The $\mathbf{Q}$ here is the same $\mathbf{Q}$ that you learned about above; it's the result of Gram-Schmidt orthogonalization (or other comparable but more numerically stable algorithm). $\mathbf{R}$ is like a "residual" matrix that contains the information that was orthogonalized out of $\mathbf{A}$. You already know how to create matrix $\mathbf{Q}$; how do you compute $\mathbf{R}$? Easy: Take advantage of the definition of orthogonal matrices:

QR decomposition is unrelated to QR codes.

$$\mathbf{Q}^{\mathrm{T}}\mathbf{A} = \mathbf{Q}^{\mathrm{T}}\mathbf{QR} \tag{13.32}$$

$$\mathbf{Q}^{\mathrm{T}}\mathbf{A} = \mathbf{R} \tag{13.33}$$

I'd like to show you an example, but because you already know how to compute $\mathbf{Q}$, I'll simply write the answer without details or fanfare; that will allow us to focus the discussion on $\mathbf{R}$.

$$\mathbf{A} = \begin{bmatrix} 1 & 0 \\ 1 & 1 \\ 0 & 1 \end{bmatrix}, \quad \Rightarrow \quad \mathbf{Q} = \begin{bmatrix} \sqrt{2}^{-1} & \sqrt{6}^{-1} \\ \sqrt{2}^{-1} & -\sqrt{6}^{-1} \\ 0 & -2\sqrt{6}^{-1} \end{bmatrix} \tag{13.34}$$

Following Equation 13.33, we compute $\mathbf{R}$.

$$\mathbf{R} = \mathbf{Q}^{\mathrm{T}}\mathbf{A} = \begin{bmatrix} \sqrt{2}^{-1} & \sqrt{2}^{-1} & 0 \\ \sqrt{6}^{-1} & -\sqrt{6}^{-1} & -2\sqrt{6}^{-1} \end{bmatrix} \begin{bmatrix} 1 & 0 \\ 1 & 1 \\ 0 & 1 \end{bmatrix} = \begin{bmatrix} \sqrt{2} & \sqrt{2}^{-1} \\ 0 & -\sqrt{6}/2 \end{bmatrix}$$

$$\tag{13.35}$$

In this example, $\mathbf{R}$ is an upper-triangular matrix. That's not just some happy coincidence. In fact, $\mathbf{R}$ will *always* be an upper-triangular matrix.

To understand why $\mathbf{R}$ must be upper-triangular, it's useful to keep your eye on Equation 13.33 while reviewing the mechanics of matrix multiplication. In particular, on page 144 I stated that the upper triangle of the product matrix (here that's $\mathbf{R}$) comprises dot products between *earlier* rows in the left matrix (here that's $\mathbf{Q}^{\mathrm{T}}$) with *later* columns in the right matrix ($\mathbf{A}$). In contrast, the lower triangle of the product matrix comprises dot products between *later* rows of the left matrix and *earlier* columns of the right matrix. (Also keep in mind that the rows of $\mathbf{Q}^{\mathrm{T}}$ are the columns of $\mathbf{Q}$.)

Because orthogonalization works column-wise from left-to-right, later columns in $\mathbf{Q}$ (i.e., rows of $\mathbf{Q}^{\mathrm{T}}$) are orthogonalized to earlier columns of $\mathbf{A}$, hence the lower triangle comes from pairs of vectors that have been orthogonalized. But the other way around is not the case: earlier columns in $\mathbf{Q}$ (earlier rows in $\mathbf{Q}^{\mathrm{T}}$) have not yet been orthogonalized to later columns of $\mathbf{A}$. And that's why $\mathbf{R}$ will always be upper-triangular.

Sizes of Q and R, given A   The sizes of $\mathbf{Q}$ and $\mathbf{R}$ depend on the size of $\mathbf{A}$, and on a parameter of the implementation.

Let's start with the square case, because that's easy: If $\mathbf{A}$ is a square matrix, then $\mathbf{Q}$ and $\mathbf{R}$ are also square matrices, of the same size as $\mathbf{A}$. This is true regardless of the rank of $\mathbf{A}$ (more on rank and QR decomposition below).

Now let's consider a tall matrix $\mathbf{A}$ ($M > N$). Computer algorithms can implement the "economy QR" or "full QR" decomposition. The economy QR is what you might expect based on the example in the previous page: $\mathbf{Q}$ will be the same size as $\mathbf{A}$, and $\mathbf{R}$ will be $N \times N$. However, it is possible to create a square $\mathbf{Q}$ from a tall $\mathbf{A}$. That's because the columns of $\mathbf{A}$ are in $\mathbb{R}^{M}$, so even if $\mathbf{A}$ has only N columns, there are $M - N$ more possible columns to create that will be orthogonal to the first M. Thus, the full QR decomposition of a tall matrix will have $\mathbf{Q} \in \mathbb{R}^{M \times M}$ and $\mathbf{R} \in \mathbb{R}^{M \times N}$. In other words, $\mathbf{Q}$ is square and $\mathbf{R}$ is the same size as $\mathbf{A}$.

Finally, we consider wide matrices. There is no economy QR for wide matrices, because **A** already has more columns than could form a linearly independent set. Thus, for a wide matrix **A**, the story is the same as for the full QR decomposition of a tall matrix: $\mathbf{Q} \in \mathbb{R}^{M \times M}$ and $\mathbf{R} \in \mathbb{R}^{M \times N}$.

Figure 13.7 provides a graphical overview of these sizes.

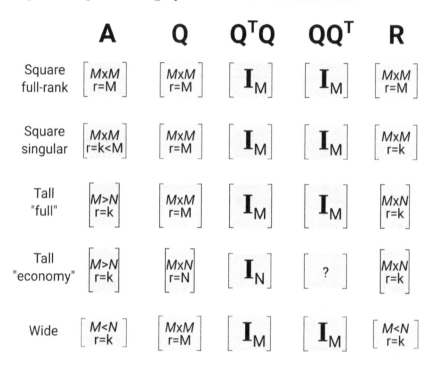

Figure 13.7: Representation of matrix sizes and ranks from QR decomposition for different possibilities of **A** (the different rows). When k is not specified relative to M, then $k \leq M$. The "?" indicates that the matrix elements depend on the values in **A** and **Q**, i.e., it is not the identity matrix.

Ranks of Q, R, and A   The **Q** matrix will always have its maximum possible rank (M or N depending on its size, as described above), even if **A** is not full rank.

It may seem surprising that the rank of **Q** can be higher than the rank of **A**, considering that **Q** is created from **A**. But consider this: If I give you a vector [-1 1], can you give me a different, orthogonal, vector? Of course you could: [1 1] (among others). Thus, new columns in **Q** can be created that are orthogonal to all previous columns. You can try this yourself in Python or MATLAB by taking the QR decomposition of $\mathbf{1}$ (the matrix of all 1's).

On the other hand, $\mathbf{R}$ will have the same rank as $\mathbf{A}$. First of all, because $\mathbf{R}$ is created from the product $\mathbf{Q}^T\mathbf{A}$, the maximum possible rank of $\mathbf{R}$ will be the rank of $\mathbf{A}$, because the rank of $\mathbf{A}$ is equal to or less than the rank of $\mathbf{Q}$. Now let's think about why the rank of $\mathbf{R}$ equals the rank of $\mathbf{A}$: Each diagonal element in $\mathbf{R}$ is the dot product between corresponding columns in $\mathbf{A}$ and $\mathbf{Q}$. Because each column of $\mathbf{Q}$ is orthogonalized to earlier columns in $\mathbf{A}$, the dot products forming the diagonal of $\mathbf{R}$ will be non-zero as long as each column in $\mathbf{A}$ is linearly independent of its earlier columns. On the other hand, if column k in $\mathbf{A}$ can be expressed as a linear combination of earlier columns in $\mathbf{A}$, then column k of $\mathbf{Q}$ is orthogonal to column k of $\mathbf{A}$, meaning that matrix element $R_{k,k}$ will be zero.

Code QR decomposition is easy to implement in Python and MATLAB. Computing the full vs. economy version requires an additional optional input. Confusingly, the default is Python is economy whereas the default in MATLAB is full.

Code block 13.3: Python

```
1  import numpy as np
2  A = np.random.randn(4,3)
3  Q,R = np.linalg.qr(A)
```

Code block 13.4: MATLAB

```
1  A = randn(4,3);
2  [Q,R] = qr(A);
```

Inverse via QR

I've mentioned before that you should avoid having computers explicitly compute the inverse unless it's necessary, because of the risk of inaccurate results due to numerical instabilities. The QR decomposition provides a more stable algorithm to compute the matrix inverse, compared to the MCA algorithm you learned about in the previous chapter. To begin, we simply write out the QR decomposition formula and then invert both sides of the equation:

$$\mathbf{A} = \mathbf{QR}$$

$$\mathbf{A}^{-1} = (\mathbf{QR})^{-1}$$

$$\mathbf{A}^{-1} = \mathbf{R}^{-1}\mathbf{Q}^{-1}$$

$$\mathbf{A}^{-1} = \mathbf{R}^{-1}\mathbf{Q}^{\mathrm{T}} \tag{13.36}$$

Well, we still need to compute the explicit inverse of $\mathbf{R}$, but if $\mathbf{A}$ is a dense matrix, then $\mathbf{R}^{-1}$ is easier and more stable to calculate than is $\mathbf{A}^{-1}$, because nearly half of the elements in $\mathbf{R}$ are zeros, and matrices with a lot of zeros are easy to work with.

13.8 Exercises

1. Without looking back at page 367, derive $\mathbf{w}_{\|\mathbf{v}}$ and $\mathbf{w}_{\perp\mathbf{v}}$ and prove that they are orthogonal.

2. Simplify the following operations, assuming $\mathbf{Q}, \mathbf{A} \in \mathbb{R}^{M \times M}$.

   a) $\mathbf{Q}^{-\mathrm{T}}$

   b) $\mathbf{QQ}^{\mathrm{T}}\mathbf{Q}^{-\mathrm{T}}\mathbf{Q}^{\mathrm{T}}\mathbf{Q}^{-1}\mathbf{QQ}^{-1}\mathbf{Q}^{\mathrm{T}}$

   c) $\mathbf{Q}^{-\mathrm{T}}\mathbf{QQQ}^{-1}\mathbf{AAQ}^{\mathrm{T}}\mathbf{QA}^{-1}$

3. In section 13.1, I defined the difference vector to be $(\mathbf{b} - \beta\mathbf{a})$. What happens if you define this vector as $(\beta\mathbf{a} - \mathbf{b})$? Do the algebra to see if the projection formula changes.

4. Why are orthogonal matrices called "pure rotation" matrices? It's not because they've never committed sins; it's because they rotate but do not scale any vector to which they are applied. Prove this claim by comparing $\|\mathbf{x}\|$ to $\|\mathbf{Qx}\|$. (Hint: It's easier to prove that the magnitudes-squared are equal.)

5. Determine whether the following are orthogonal matrices.

   a) $\begin{bmatrix} 1 & -\sqrt{3} \\ \sqrt{3} & 1 \end{bmatrix}$

   b) $\frac{1}{5}\begin{bmatrix} 3 & 4 & 0 \\ -4 & 3 & 0 \\ 0 & 0 & 5 \end{bmatrix}$

   c) $\begin{bmatrix} 1/\sqrt{2} & 1\sqrt{2} & 0 \\ -\sqrt{2}/6 & \sqrt{2}/6 & 2\sqrt{2}/3 \\ 2/3 & -2/3 & 2/3 \end{bmatrix}$

 **Answers**

1. You can check your proof on page 367.

2. a) $\mathbf{Q}$

    b) $(\mathbf{Q}^{\mathrm{T}})^2$

    c) $\mathbf{Q}^2\mathbf{A}$

3. It doesn't; you'll arrive at the same projection formula.

4. Here's the proof; the key result at the end is that $\|\mathbf{Qx}\| = \|\mathbf{x}\|$.

$$\|\mathbf{Qx}\|^2 = (\mathbf{Qx})^{\mathrm{T}}(\mathbf{Qx})$$
$$= \mathbf{x}^{\mathrm{T}}\mathbf{Q}^{\mathrm{T}}\mathbf{Qx}$$
$$= \mathbf{x}^{\mathrm{T}}\mathbf{x} = \|\mathbf{x}\|^2$$

5. a) No (but try a scaling factor)

    b) Yes

    c) No (but change the final element to $1/3$)

13.10 Code challenges

1. Use code to confirm the sizes of $\mathbf{Q}$ and $\mathbf{R}$ based on Figure 13.7.

2. Implement the Gram-Schmidt algorithm to compute $\mathbf{Q}$ from a matrix $\mathbf{A}$. You can check that your code is correct by (1) Confirming that $\mathbf{Q}^\mathrm{T}\mathbf{Q} = \mathbf{I}$ and (2) by computing $\mathbf{Q}$ from QR decomposition. I recommend starting with a square $\mathbf{A}$ so you don't need to worry about economy vs. full decomposition.

   Note: When you compare your $\mathbf{Q}$ against the output of QR decomposition, you might find that some columns have the same values but opposite sign. For example, perhaps your $\mathbf{Q}$ will have a column [1 2 3] whereas the $\mathbf{Q}$ from Python/MATLAB is [-1 -2 -3]. There are fundamental sign uncertainties in many decompositions. The short version of the reason is that the vectors are crafted to be basis vectors for 1D subspaces, and thus the sign of the vector is simply a scalar. This will be more clear after learning about eigenvectors.

3. Using your code above, compute $\mathbf{Q}$ on the following matrix (this was the example in section 13.5):

$$\begin{bmatrix} 1 & 1 & -2 \\ 3 & -1 & 1 \end{bmatrix}$$

   The first two columns of your $\mathbf{Q}$ should match $\mathbf{v}_1^*$ and $\mathbf{v}_2^*$ in the text. But you will not get a third column of zeros; it will be some other vector that has magnitude of 1 and is not orthogonal to the previous two columns (easily confirmed: $\mathbf{Q}^\mathrm{T}\mathbf{Q} \neq \mathbf{I}$). What on Earth is going on here?!?!

13.11 Code solutions

1. This one's easy, so I'm not giving you code! You simply need to create random matrices of various sizes, and check the sizes of the resulting **Q** and **R** matrices.

2. This is a tricky algorithm to implement. In fact, this exercise is one of the most difficult in this book.

Code block 13.5: Python

```
1   import numpy as np
2
3   m = 4
4   n = 4
5   A = np.random.randn(m,n)
6   Q = np.zeros((m,n))
7
8   for i in range(n):
9
10      Q[:,i] = A[:,i]
11
12
13      a = A[:,i]
14      for j in range(i):
15          q = Q[:,j]
16          Q[:,i]=Q[:,i]-np.dot(a,q)/np.dot(q,q)*q
17
18
19      Q[:,i] = Q[:,i] / np.linalg.norm(Q[:,i])
20
21
22   Q2,R = np.linalg.qr(A)
```

```
1  m = 4;
2  n = 4;
3  A = randn(m,n);
4  Q = zeros(m,n);
5
6  for i=1:n
7
8      Q(:,i) = A(:,i);
9
10
11     if i>1
12       a = A(:,i);
13       for j=1:i-1
14         q = Q(:,j);
15         Q(:,i) = Q(:,i) - (a'*q/(q'*q)) * q;
16       end
17     end
18
19
20     Q(:,i) = Q(:,i) / norm(Q(:,i));
21  end
22
23
24  [Q2,R] = qr(A);
```

3. The issue here is normalization of computer rounding errors. To see this, modify your algorithm so that column 3 of **Q** is *not* normalized.

You will find that both components of the third column have values close to zero, e.g., around 10^{-15}. That's basically zero plus computer round error. The normalization step is making mountains out of microscopic anthills. Congratulations, you have just discovered one of the reasons why the "textbook" Gram-Schmidt algorithm is avoided in computer applications!

CHAPTER 14
LEAST-SQUARES

START THIS CHAPTER HAPPY

14.1 Introduction

The physical and biological world that we inhabit is a really, really, *really* complicated place. There are uncountable dynamics and processes and individuals with uncountable and mind-bogglingly complex interactions. How can we make sense of this complexity? The answer is we can't: Humans are terrible at understanding such enormously complex systems.

So we do the next-best thing, which is to develop simplified models of the most important aspects of the system under investigation, while ignoring or abstracting away the aspects that are less relevant.

This process leads to a *model*, which is a set of equations that allows scientists to isolate and understand the principles of the system under investigation. Thus, the goal of building models is not to replicate *exactly* the system under investigation, but instead to identity a simplified and low-dimensional representation that actually can be understood by humans or simulated by computers.

On the other hand, there is a lot of diversity in nature, and models should be sufficiently generic that they can be applied to different datasets. This means that the models must be flexible enough that they can be adjusted to different datasets without having to create a brand new model for each particular dataset.

This is why models contain both *fixed features* and *free parameters*. The fixed features are components of the model that the scientist imposes, based on scientific evidence, theories, and intuition (a.k.a. random guesses). Free parameters are variables that can be adjusted to allow the model to fit any particular data set. And this brings us to the primary goal of model-fitting: Find values for these free parameters that make the model match the data as closely as possible.

Here is an example to make this more concrete. Let's say you want to predict how tall someone is. Your hypothesis is that height is a result of the person's sex (that is, male or female), their parents' height, and their childhood nutrition rated on a scale from 1-10. So, males tend to be taller, people born to taller parents tend to be taller, and people who ate healthier as children tend to be taller. Obviously, what really determines an adult's height is much more complicated than this, but we are trying to capture a few of the important factors in a simplistic way. We can then construct our model of height:

$$h = \beta_1 s + \beta_2 p + \beta_3 n + \epsilon \qquad (14.1)$$

where h is the person's height, s is the sex, p is the parents' height, and n is the childhood nutrition score. These are the fixed features of the model—they are in the model because I put them there, because I believe that they are important. On the other hand, it is obvious that these three factors do not exactly determine someone's height; hence, we include the ϵ as an "error term" or "residual" that captures all of the variance in height that the three other variables cannot explain.

But here's the thing: I don't know *how* important each of these factors is. So I specify that the model needs to include these terms, and I will let the data tell me how important each term is. That's why each fixed feature is scaled by a β parameter. Those βs are the free parameters. For example, if β_3 is large, then nutrition is very important for determining someone's adult height; and if β_3 is close to zero, then the data are telling me that childhood nutrition is not important for determining height.

Of course, that leads to the question of how you find the model parameters that make the model match the data as closely as possible. Randomly picking different values for the βs is a terrible idea; instead, we need an algorithm that will find the best parameters given the data. This is the idea of model fitting. The most commonly used algorithm for fitting models to data is **linear least-squares**, and that is what you will learn in this chapter.

14.2 The five steps of model-fitting

The process of model-fitting in statistics can be broken down into five steps.

Step 1   Determine an equation or set of equations that comprise your model. In practice, you would often use existing equations or slight modifications of existing equations. I already showed you an example above: Our hypothesis about important factors that predict height were converted into Equation 14.1.

Step 2   Work the data into the model. You get existing data from a database or by collecting data in a scientific experiment. Or you can simulate your own data. I made up the data in Table 14.1 for illustration purposes.

ID	Height	Sex	Parents' height	Nutrition
1	180	M	175	8
2	170	F	172	6
⋮	⋮	⋮	⋮	⋮
10	176	F	189	7

Table 14.1: Example data table. Height is in cm.

But this is not the format that we need the data in. We need to map the data in this table into the model. That means putting these numbers inside the equation from step 1. The first row of data, converted into an equation, would look like this:

$$180 = \beta_1 1 + \beta_2 175 + \beta_3 8$$

One row of data gives us one equation. But we have multiple rows, corresponding to multiple individuals, and so we need to create a set of equations. And because those equations are all linked, we can consider them a system of equations. That system will look like this:

Binary variables are often "dummy-coded," meaning that female=0 and male=1 (this mapping will make positive β correspond to taller adults).

$$\left\{ \begin{array}{l} 180 = \beta_1 1 + \beta_2 175 + \beta_3 8 \\ 170 = \beta_1 0 + \beta_2 172 + \beta_3 6 \\ \quad\quad\quad \vdots \\ 176 = \beta_1 0 + \beta_2 189 + \beta_3 7 \end{array} \right\} \quad\quad (14.2)$$

Notice that each equation follows the same "template" from Equation 14.1, but with the numbers taken from the data table. (The statistically astute reader will notice the absence of an intercept term, which captures expected value of the data when the predictors are all equal to zero. I'm omitting that for now, but will discuss it later.)

Step 3 The system of equations above should active your happy memories of working through Chapter 10 on solving systems of equations. Armed with those memories, you might have already guessed what step 3 is: convert the system of equations into a single matrix-vector equation. It's exactly the same concept that you learned previously: Split up the coefficients, variables, and constants, and put those into matrices and vectors.

$$\begin{bmatrix} 1 & 175 & 8 \\ 0 & 172 & 6 \\ 0 & 189 & 7 \end{bmatrix} \begin{bmatrix} \beta_1 \\ \beta_2 \\ \beta_3 \end{bmatrix} = \begin{bmatrix} 180 \\ 170 \\ 176 \end{bmatrix} \quad\quad (14.3)$$

In previous chapters, I would have called this $\mathbf{Ax} = \mathbf{b}$. The standard statistics lingo uses different letters, although the concepts and algorithms are the same. I'll explain the statistics terminology in a few pages, but for now, suffice it to say that this equation is now called $\mathbf{X}\boldsymbol{\beta} = \mathbf{y}$. $\mathbf{X}$ is the matrix of coefficients, $\boldsymbol{\beta}$ is the vector of the unknown free parameters that we want to solve for, and $\mathbf{y}$ is the vector of constants (in this example, height measured in cm).

Note that $\boldsymbol{\beta}$ here is a vector, although I have previously written that Greek characters indicate scalars.

Step 4 Solve for β, which is also called fitting the model, estimating the parameters, computing the best-fit parameters, or some other related terminology. The rest of the chapter is focused on this step.

Step 5 Statistically evaluate the model: is it a good model? How well does it fit the data? Does it generalize to new data or have we over-fit our sample data? Do all model terms contribute or should some be excluded? This step is all about inferential statistics, and it produces things like p-values and t-values and F-values. Step 5 is important for statistics applications, but is outside the scope of this book, in part because it relies on probability theory, not on linear algebra. Thus, step 5 is not further discussed here.

14.3 Terminology

It is unfortunate and needlessly confusing that statisticians and linear algebrists use different terminology for the same concepts. Terminological confusion is a common speed-bump to progress in science and cross-disciplinary collaborations. Nonetheless, there are worse things in human civilization than giving a rose two names. The table below introduces the terminology that will be used only in this chapter.

LinAlg	Stats	Description
$\mathbf{Ax} = \mathbf{b}$	$\mathbf{X}\beta = \mathbf{y}$	General linear model (GLM)
$\mathbf{A}$	$\mathbf{X}$	Design matrix (columns = independent variables, predictors, regressors)
$\mathbf{x}$	β	Regression coefficients or beta parameters
$\mathbf{b}$	$\mathbf{y}$	Dependent variable, outcome measure, data

Table 14.2: Translating between linear algebra and statistics terminology.

The final point I want to make here is about the term "linear" in linear least-squares. Linear refers to the way that the parameters are estimated; it is not a restriction on the model. The model may contain nonlinear terms and interactions; the restriction for linearity is that the coefficients (the free parameters) scalar-multiply their variables and sum to predict the dependent variable. Basically that just means that it's possible to transform the system of equations into a matrix equation. That restriction allows us to use linear algebra methods to solve for β; there are also nonlinear methods for estimating parameters in nonlinear models.

To make sure this point is clear, consider the following model, which contains two nonlinearities:

$$h = \beta_1 s + \beta_2 \sqrt{\beta_3} p + \beta_3 n^3 + \epsilon \qquad (14.4)$$

One nonlinearity is in the regressors ($\beta_2 \sqrt{\beta_3}$), and one is in a predictor (n^3). The latter is no problem; the former prevents linear least-squares from fitting this model (there are nonlinear alternatives that you would learn about in a statistics course).

14.4 Least-squares via left inverse

There is actually one solution to the general linear model equation, but it is insightful to arrive at that solution from different perspectives. In this and the next sections, we will start from algebra (this section), geometry (next section), and row-reduction (next-next section), and arrive at the same conclusion.

The problem we face is simple: Solve for β in $\mathbf{X}\beta = \mathbf{y}$. If $\mathbf{X}$ were a square matrix, we would obtain the solution by pre-multiplying both sides by $\mathbf{X}^{-1}$. However, design matrices are typically tall matrices, because there are typically many more observations than there are variables. Using our example of predicting height, we might have data from 1000 individuals and our model contains 3 predictors. Thus, $\mathbf{X}$ would be a 1000×3 matrix. (Deep learning applications often have wide matrices—more variables than observations—and this requires regularization and other tricks to make the problem solvable. But nearly all statistics applications involve tall design matrices.)

You know what the solution is: instead of the full inverse, we use the left-inverse. Thus, the solution to the least squares problem is:

$$\mathbf{X}\beta = \mathbf{y}$$

$$(\mathbf{X}^\mathrm{T}\mathbf{X})^{-1}\mathbf{X}^\mathrm{T}\mathbf{X}\beta = (\mathbf{X}^\mathrm{T}\mathbf{X})^{-1}\mathbf{X}^\mathrm{T}\mathbf{y}$$

$$\beta = (\mathbf{X}^\mathrm{T}\mathbf{X})^{-1}\mathbf{X}^\mathrm{T}\mathbf{y} \qquad (14.5)$$

When is Equation 14.5 a valid solution? I'm sure you guessed it—when $\mathbf{X}$ is full column-rank, which means the design matrix contains a linearly independent set of predictor variables. If the design matrix has repeated columns, or if one predictor variable can be obtained from a linear combination of other predictor variables, then $\mathbf{X}$ will be rank-deficient and the solution is not valid. In statistics lingo, this situation is called "multicollinearity."

When is the solution exact? I wrote in section 8.11 that one of the fundamental questions in linear algebra is whether some vector is in the column space of some matrix. Here you can see an application of that question. We want to know whether vector $\mathbf{y}$ is in the column space of matrix $\mathbf{X}$. They're both in $\mathbb{R}^M$, because they both have M elements in the columns, so it's a valid question to ask. But here's the thing: $\mathbf{y}$ has M elements and $\mathbf{X}$ has N columns, where $N \ll M$ (e.g., $M = 1000$ vs. $N = 3$). In this example, we are asking whether a specific vector is inside a 3D subspace embedded in ambient $\mathbb{R}^{1000}$.

The answer is nearly always *No*, $\mathbf{y} \notin C(\mathbf{X})$. Even for a good model, a tiny bit of noise in the data would push vector $\mathbf{y}$ out of the column space of $\mathbf{X}$. What to do here?

The solution is to think about a slightly different question: Is there a $\hat{\mathbf{y}}$ such that $\hat{\mathbf{y}}$ really is in the column space of $\mathbf{X}$? Then we would call the parameters $\hat{\beta}$. Obviously, some $\hat{\beta}$ and $\hat{\mathbf{y}}$ exist, and also obviously, we want to find the $\hat{\mathbf{y}}$ that is as close to $\mathbf{y}$ as possible. That leads to the full formulation of the general linear model and some related equations.

$$\mathbf{y} = \mathbf{X}\beta + \epsilon \tag{14.6}$$

$$\hat{\mathbf{y}} = \mathbf{y} + \epsilon \tag{14.7}$$

$$\hat{\mathbf{y}} = \mathbf{X}\hat{\beta} \tag{14.8}$$

ϵ is the residual, what you need to add to $\mathbf{y}$ to get it into the column space of the design matrix. The better the model fits the data, the closer $\mathbf{y}$ is to the column space of $\mathbf{X}$, and thus the smaller the ϵ. Keep in mind that ϵ is not in the data that you measured, and it's not in the model that you specify. Instead, it's what you need to add to $\mathbf{y}$ to reach the column space of $\mathbf{X}$.

There is more to say about this ϵ vector (section 14.7), but first I want to prove to you that the least squares equation minimizes ϵ. And to do that, we need to re-derive the least-squares solution from a geometric perspective.

14.5 Least-squares via orthogonal projection

Imagine an ambient $\mathbb{R}^M$ space, and a subspace inside that ambient space, whose basis vectors are the columns of the design matrix. I will illustrate this using a 2D subspace because it is easy to visualize (Figure 14.1), but the actual dimensionality of this subspace corresponds to the number of columns in the design matrix, which means the number of predictor variables in your statistical model.

The measured data in $\mathbf{y}$ form a vector in $\mathbb{R}^M$. As discussed in the previous chapter, it is sometimes easier to conceptualize $\mathbf{y}$ as a coordinate in space rather than a vector from the origin.

When working with real data, it is incredibly unlikely that $\mathbf{y}$ is exactly in the column space of $\mathbf{X}$. If fact, if $\mathbf{y} \in C(\mathbf{X})$, then probably the model is way too complicated or the data are way too simple. The goal of science is to understand things that are difficult to un-

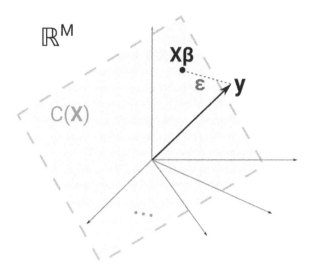

Figure 14.1: The geometry of least-squares via orthogonal projection.

n.b. I'm kindof joking here. Sortof.

derstand; if your model explains a phenomenon 100%, then it's not difficult to understand, and you should try to work on a harder problem.

But the column space *is* important because that is the mathematical representation of our theory of the world. So then the question is, What is the coordinate that is as close as possible to the data vector while still being inside the subspace? The answer to that question comes from the orthogonal projection of the vector onto the subspace. That orthogonal projection is vector $\epsilon = \mathbf{y} - \mathbf{X}\beta$, which is orthogonal to the column space of $\mathbf{X}$.

$$\mathbf{X}^{\mathrm{T}}\epsilon = 0 \tag{14.9}$$

$$\mathbf{X}^{\mathrm{T}}(\mathbf{y} - \mathbf{X}\beta) = 0 \tag{14.10}$$

$$\mathbf{X}^{\mathrm{T}}\mathbf{y} - \mathbf{X}^{\mathrm{T}}\mathbf{X}\beta = 0 \tag{14.11}$$

$$\mathbf{X}^{\mathrm{T}}\mathbf{X}\beta = \mathbf{X}^{\mathrm{T}}\mathbf{y} \tag{14.12}$$

$$\beta = (\mathbf{X}^{\mathrm{T}}\mathbf{X})^{-1}\mathbf{X}^{\mathrm{T}}\mathbf{y} \tag{14.13}$$

And amazingly (though perhaps not surprisingly), we've arrived back at the same solution as in the previous section.

We also see that the design matrix $\mathbf{X}$ and the residuals vector ϵ are orthogonal. Geometrically, that makes sense; statistically, it means that the prediction errors should be unrelated to the model, which is an important quality check of the model performance.

14.6 Least-squares via row-reduction

Now we're going to derive the least-squares formula again, this time using row-reduction and Gauss-Jordan elimination. It may seem gratuitous to have yet another derivation of least-squares, but this section will help link concepts across different chapters of this book, and therefore has high conceptual/educational value (IMHO).

Recall from Chapter 10 that we can solve a system of equations by performing row-reduction on a matrix of coefficients augmented by the constants. And then in Chapter 12 you saw how to apply that method to computing the matrix inverse. Let's see if we can apply that same concept here to solve for β in our statistical model.

$$\text{rref}([\,\mathbf{X}\mid\mathbf{y}\,]) \quad \Rightarrow \quad [\,\mathbf{I}\mid\beta\,] \tag{14.14}$$

Unfortunately, life does not always conform to expectations. Take a moment to think about the problem with the conclusion above.

The problem is not the augmented matrix: $\mathbf{X}$ and $\mathbf{y}$ both have M rows, so the augmenting is valid. And row-reduction is also valid. However, $[\,\mathbf{X}\mid\mathbf{y}\,]$ will have $N+1$ columns and will have a rank of $N+1 < M$. Thus, the actual outcome of RREF will be

$$\text{rref}([\,\mathbf{X}\mid\mathbf{y}\,]) \quad\Rightarrow\quad \begin{bmatrix}\mathbf{I}\\\mathbf{0}\end{bmatrix} \tag{14.15}$$

In other words, a tall matrix with the identity matrix $\mathbf{I_N}$ on top and all zeros underneath. This is not useful; we need to re-think this.

The solution comes from pre-multiplying the general linear model equation by $\mathbf{X}^{\mathrm{T}}$:

$$\mathbf{X}^{\mathrm{T}}\mathbf{X}\beta = \mathbf{X}^{\mathrm{T}}\mathbf{y} \tag{14.16}$$

Equation 14.16 is often called the "normal equation." (I know what you're thinking and I agree: it looks less normal than the equation we derived it from. But that's the terminology.)

Now we can go back to Gauss-Jordan and get a sensible result.

$$\text{rref}(\begin{bmatrix}\mathbf{X}^{\mathrm{T}}\mathbf{X}\mid\mathbf{X}^{\mathrm{T}}\mathbf{y}\end{bmatrix}) \quad\Rightarrow\quad [\,\mathbf{I}\mid\beta\,] \tag{14.17}$$

Let's think about the sizes. $\mathbf{X}^{\mathrm{T}}\mathbf{X}$ will be $N \times N$ and thus the augmented matrix will be of size $N \times (N+1)$, in other words, a wide, full row-rank, matrix. That will give us our desired β on the right.

The reason why this works comes from thinking about the row spaces of $\mathbf{X}$ and $\mathbf{X}^{\mathrm{T}}\mathbf{X}$. Remember from Chapter 8 (section 8.5) that these two matrices have the same row space, and that $\mathbf{X}^{\mathrm{T}}\mathbf{X}$ is a more compact representation of the space spanned by rows of $\mathbf{X}$. Furthermore, assuming that $\mathbf{X}$ has linearly independent columns (which is an assumption we've been making in this entire chapter), then $\mathbf{X}^{\mathrm{T}}\mathbf{X}$ spans all of $\mathbb{R}^{N}$, which means that any point in $\mathbb{R}^{N}$ is guaranteed to be in the column space of $\mathbf{X}^{\mathrm{T}}\mathbf{X}$. And $\mathbf{X}^{\mathrm{T}}\mathbf{y}$ is just some point in $\mathbb{R}^{N}$, so it's definitely going to be in the column space of $\mathbf{X}^{\mathrm{T}}\mathbf{X}$. Therefore, β contains the coefficients on the columns of matrix $\mathbf{X}^{\mathrm{T}}\mathbf{X}$ to get us exactly to $\mathbf{X}^{\mathrm{T}}\mathbf{y}$. Note that with the

Gauss-Jordan approach to solving least-squares using the normal equations, we never leave the N-dimensional subspace of $\mathbb{R}^N$, so the question of whether $\mathbf{y} \in C(\mathbf{X})$ doesn't even come up.

However, we still need to compute ϵ to make the GLM equation correct. The reason is that β is a solution to the normal equation, but we want to find the solution to $\mathbf{y}$, which is not the same thing as $\mathbf{X}^T\mathbf{y}$. Fortunately, that's an easy rearrangement of Equation 14.6:

$$\epsilon = \mathbf{X}\beta - \mathbf{y} \tag{14.18}$$

The statistical interpretation of Equation 14.18 is that the residual is the difference between the model-predicted values $(\mathbf{X}\beta)$ and the observed data $(\mathbf{y})$.

By the way, we can also arrive at the normal equations by starting from the known solution of the left-inverse, and then pre-multiplying by $\mathbf{X}^T\mathbf{X}$:

$$\beta = (\mathbf{X}^T\mathbf{X})^{-1}\mathbf{X}^T\mathbf{y}$$

$$\mathbf{X}^T\mathbf{X}\beta = (\mathbf{X}^T\mathbf{X})(\mathbf{X}^T\mathbf{X})^{-1}\mathbf{X}^T\mathbf{y} \tag{14.19}$$

$$\mathbf{X}^T\mathbf{X}\beta = \mathbf{X}^T\mathbf{y} \tag{14.20}$$

14.7 Model-predicted values and residuals

Let me bring your attention back to Figure 14.1. The data vector $\mathbf{y}$ is unlikely to be exactly in the column space of the design matrix $\mathbf{X}$, and vector ϵ gets us from the data into the subspace spanned by the design matrix. We also know that ϵ is defined as being orthogonal to the column space of $\mathbf{X}$.

Statistically, ϵ is the residual variance in the data that the model cannot account for. We can also write this as follows:

$$\epsilon = \mathbf{X}\beta - \mathbf{y} \tag{14.21}$$

When is the model a good fit to the data? It is sensible that the smaller ϵ is, the better the model fits the data. In fact, we don't really care about the exact *values* comprising ϵ (remember, there is one ϵ_i for each data value y_i); instead, we care about the norm of ϵ.

$$\|\epsilon\|^2 = \|\mathbf{X}\beta - \mathbf{y}\|^2 \tag{14.22}$$

Now we can re-frame the goal of model-fitting in a slightly different way: Find the values in vector β that minimize both sides of Equation 14.22. This is a standard optimization problem, and can be expressed as

$$\min_{\beta} \|\mathbf{X}\beta - \mathbf{y}\|^2 \tag{14.23}$$

The solution to this problem is obtained by computing the derivative and setting that equal to zero:

$$0 = \frac{d}{d\beta}\|\mathbf{X}\beta - \mathbf{y}\|^2 = 2\mathbf{X}^{\mathrm{T}}(\mathbf{X}\beta - \mathbf{y}) \tag{14.24}$$

$$0 = \mathbf{X}^{\mathrm{T}}\mathbf{X}\beta - \mathbf{X}^{\mathrm{T}}\mathbf{y} \tag{14.25}$$

$$\mathbf{X}^{\mathrm{T}}\mathbf{X}\beta = \mathbf{X}^{\mathrm{T}}\mathbf{y} \tag{14.26}$$

$$\beta = (\mathbf{X}^{\mathrm{T}}\mathbf{X})^{-1}\mathbf{X}^{\mathrm{T}}\mathbf{y} \tag{14.27}$$

And here we are, back at the same solution to least-squares that we've obtained already using three different approaches. And now I've slipped in a fourth method to derive the least-squares equation, using a bit of calculus and optimization. (If your calculus is rusty, then don't worry if the first equation is nebulous. The idea is to take the derivative with respect to β using the chain rule.)

14.8 Least-squares example

Doing statistics in the real-world is usually not so simple as defining the model, fitting the parameters to data, and then going out for sushi to celebrate a job-well-done. In practice, statisticians will often begin with simple models and then add complexity to the models as it becomes clear that the simple models are inappropriately simple for the data, and according to the available theoretical frameworks. I want to give you a taste of that process.

We begin with a set of numbers. Let's call it set D for data. We assume that the order is meaningful; perhaps these are data values from a signal being recorded over time.

$$D = \{-4, 0, -3, 1, 2, 8, 5, 8\}$$

I'm going to start by assuming that the signal has a constant value. Thus, my hypothesis at this point is that there is only one meaningful signal value, and the divergences at each time point reflect errors (for example, sensor noise). Thus, my model is:

$$d = \beta 1 + \epsilon \tag{14.28}$$

That was step 1. Step 2 is to work the data into the model. That will give a series of equations that looks like this:

$$\left\{ \begin{array}{rcl} -4 &=& \beta 1 \\ 0 &=& \beta 1 \\ -3 &=& \beta 1 \\ 1 &=& \beta 1 \\ 2 &=& \beta 1 \\ 8 &=& \beta 1 \\ 5 &=& \beta 1 \\ 8 &=& \beta 1 \end{array} \right\} \tag{14.29}$$

Why is there a "1" next to the β? My hypothesis is that a single number explains the data. But I don't know *a priori* what that number should be. That's what the β is for. Now, that number could be anything else, and β would scale to compensate. For example, let's say the average data value is 2. With the coefficient set to 1, then $\beta = 2$, which is easy to interpret. However, if I were to set the coefficient to 9.8, then $\beta = .20408....$ And then the interpretation would be that the average value of the signal is $\beta \times 9.8$. That is mathematically correct, but difficult and awkward to interpret. That's why we set the coefficient value to 1 (in a few pages, I will start calling this column the "intercept").

Now for step 3: Convert the set of equations into a matrix-vector equation.

$$\begin{bmatrix} 1 \\ 1 \\ 1 \\ 1 \\ 1 \\ 1 \\ 1 \\ 1 \end{bmatrix} \begin{bmatrix} \beta \end{bmatrix} = \begin{bmatrix} -4 \\ 0 \\ -3 \\ 1 \\ 2 \\ 8 \\ 5 \\ 8 \end{bmatrix} \tag{14.30}$$

Step 4 is to fit the model.

$$\beta = (\mathbf{X}^{\mathrm{T}}\mathbf{X})^{-1}\mathbf{X}^{\mathrm{T}}\mathbf{y} \tag{14.31}$$

$$\beta = 8^{-1} \times 17 \tag{14.32}$$

$$\beta = \frac{17}{8} = 2.125 \tag{14.33}$$

Did you notice what happened here? We ended up summing all the data points (dot product between the numbers and a vector of 1's) and dividing by the number of elements. That's literally the arithmetic mean. So we've re-derived the average from a statistics/linear algebra perspective, where our model is that the data are meaningfully characterized by a single number.

Another good reason to set the coefficients to 1.

It's always a good idea to visualize data and models. Let's see what they look like (Figure 14.2).

What do you think of the comparison of predicted and actual data shown in Figure 14.2? I think the model looks pretty awful, to be honest. The data clearly show an upward trend, which the model cannot capture. Let's try changing the model. (Important note: I'm skipping step 5, which would involve formal tests of the model.)

Instead of predicting a single data value, let's predict that the data values change over the x-axis (the statistics term for this is a "linear

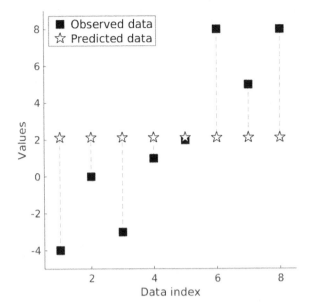

Figure 14.2: Observed and predicted data. Black squares show the data (y) and white stars show the model-predicted data ($\hat{y} = \mathbf{X}\beta$). The dashed gray lines were added to facilitate comparing data values to their predicted values.

trend"). The new model equation from step 3 will look like this:

$$
\begin{bmatrix} 1 \\ 2 \\ 3 \\ 4 \\ 5 \\ 6 \\ 7 \\ 8 \end{bmatrix} \begin{bmatrix} \beta \end{bmatrix} = \begin{bmatrix} -4 \\ 0 \\ -3 \\ 1 \\ 2 \\ 8 \\ 5 \\ 8 \end{bmatrix} \tag{14.34}
$$

Note that we are no longer predicting the *average* value; we are now predicting a *slope*. Let's see what the parameter is:

$$
\beta = (\mathbf{X}^{\mathrm{T}}\mathbf{X})^{-1}\mathbf{X}^{\mathrm{T}}\mathbf{y} \tag{14.35}
$$

$$
\beta = 204^{-1} \times 148 \tag{14.36}
$$

$$
\beta = \frac{204}{148} = .7255 \tag{14.37}
$$

Figure 14.3 shows the same data with the new model-predicted data values.

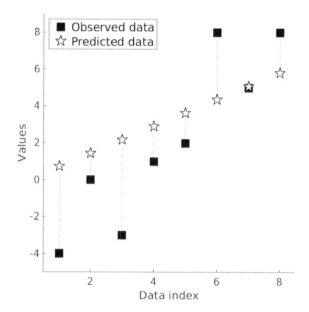

Figure 14.3: Our second modeling attempt.

It looks better compared to Figure 14.2, but still not quite right: The predicted data are too high (over-estimated) in the beginning and too low (under-estimated) in the end. The problem here is that the model lacks an *intercept term*.

The intercept is the expected value of the data when all other parameters are set to 0. That's not the same thing as the average value of the data. Instead, it is the expected value when all model parameters have a value of zero. Thinking back to the example model in the beginning of this chapter (predicting adult height as a function of sex, parents' height, and childhood nutrition), the intercept term captures the expected height of an adult female whose parents' height is zero cm and who had a score of 0 on childhood nutrition. Not exactly a plausible situation. So why do these models need an intercept term?

The reason is that without an intercept, the model is forced to include the origin of the graph (X,Y=0,0). This caused the model in Figure 14.3 to be a poor fit. The intercept term allows the best-fit line to shift off the origin (that is, to intersect the Y-axis at any value other than zero). Thus, in many statistical models, the intercept is not necessarily easily interpretable, but is necessary for proper model fitting (unless all data and regressors are mean-subtracted, in which case the best-fit line touches the origin).

Now let's expand the model to include an intercept term, which involves including an extra column of 1's in the design matrix. We'll also need two βs instead of one.

$$\begin{bmatrix} 1 & 1 \\ 1 & 2 \\ 1 & 3 \\ 1 & 4 \\ 1 & 5 \\ 1 & 6 \\ 1 & 7 \\ 1 & 8 \end{bmatrix} \begin{bmatrix} \beta_1 \\ \beta_2 \end{bmatrix} = \begin{bmatrix} -4 \\ 0 \\ -3 \\ 1 \\ 2 \\ 8 \\ 5 \\ 8 \end{bmatrix} \tag{14.38}$$

The arithmetic gets a bit more involved, but produces the following.

$$\beta = (\mathbf{X}^{\mathrm{T}}\mathbf{X})^{-1}\mathbf{X}^{\mathrm{T}}\mathbf{y} \tag{14.39}$$

$$\beta = \begin{bmatrix} 8 & 36 \\ 36 & 204 \end{bmatrix}^{-1} \begin{bmatrix} 17 \\ 148 \end{bmatrix} \tag{14.40}$$

$$\beta = \begin{bmatrix} -5.5357 \\ 1.7024 \end{bmatrix} \tag{14.41}$$

I'm sure you agree that this third model (linear trend plus intercept) fits the data reasonably well (Figure 14.4). There are still residuals that the model does not capture, but these seem like they could be random fluctuations. Notice that the best-fit line does not go through the origin of the graph. We don't see exactly where the line will cross the y-axis because the x-axis values start at 1. However, β_1, the intercept term, predicts that this crossing would be at $y = -5.5357$, which looks plausible from the graph.

The final thing I want to do here is confirm that $\epsilon \perp \mathbf{X}\beta$. The two

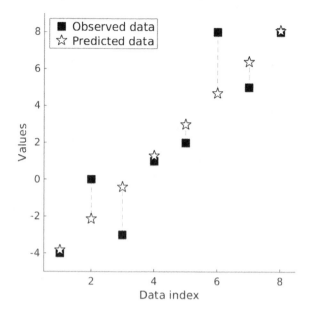

Figure 14.4: Our final model of this dataset.

columns below show the residual and predicted values, truncated at 4 digits after the decimal point.

ϵ	$\mathbf{X}\beta$
0.1667	−3.8333
−2.1310	−2.1310
2.5714	−0.4286
0.2738	1.2738
0.9762	2.9762
−3.3214	4.6786
1.3810	6.3810
0.0833	8.0833

$$\epsilon^{\mathrm{T}}(\mathbf{X}\beta) = 0.0000000000000142...$$

It may seem like the dot product is not exactly zero, but it is 14 orders of magnitude smaller than the data values, which we can consider to be zero plus computer rounding error.

14.9 Code challenges

Imagine you work as a data scientist in a company that sells widgets online. The company gives you a dataset of information from 1000 sales, which includes the time of the sale (listed in hours of the day using a 24-hour clock, e.g., 15 = 3pm), the age of the buyer (in years), and the number of widgets sold. The data are available at sincxpress.com/widget_data.txt (Note: these are data I made up for this exercise.)

1. Explain and write down a mathematical model that is appropriate for this dataset.

2. Write the matrix equation corresponding to the model, and describe the columns in the design matrix.

3. Compute the model coefficients using the least-squares algorithm in MATLAB or Python. You can also divide the β coefficients by the standard deviations of the corresponding independent variables, which puts the various model terms in the same scale and therefore more comparable.

4. Produce scatter plots that visualize the relationship between the independent and dependent variables.

5. One measure of how well the model fits the data is called R^2 ("R-squared"), and can be interpreted as the proportion of variance in the dependent variable that is explained by the design matrix. Thus, an R^2 of 1 indicates a perfect fit between the model. The definition of R^2 is

$$R^2 = 1 - \frac{\sum_i \epsilon_i^2}{\sum_i (y_i - \bar{y})^2} \tag{14.42}$$

ϵ_i is the error (residual) at each data point that was introduced earlier, and $\bar{y}$ is the average of all elements in y.

Compute R^2 for the model to see how well it fits the data. Are you surprised, based on what you see in the scatterplots?

1. *Note:* There are multiple correct answers to this problem.

A simple model would predict that time and age are both linear predictors of widget purchases. There needs to be an intercept term, because the average number of widgets purchased is greater than zero. The variables could interact (e.g., older people buy widgets in the morning while younger people buy widgets in the evening), but I've excluded interaction terms in the interest of brevity.

Thus, a basic model would look like this:

$$y = \beta_1 + \beta_2 \mathbf{t} + \beta_3 \mathbf{a}$$

y is the number of widgets sold, β_1 is the intercept, $\mathbf{t}$ is the time of day, and $\mathbf{a}$ is the age.

2. The matrix equation is $\mathbf{X}\beta = \mathbf{y}$. $\mathbf{X}$ has three columns: intercept, which is all 1's; time of day; age.

3. Python and MATLAB code are on the following page.

Code block 14.1: Python

```
1   import numpy as np
2
3   # load the data
4   data = np.loadtxt(fname='widget_data.txt',
5                       delimiter=',')
6
7   # design matrix
8   X = np.concatenate((np.ones((1000,1)),
9                         data[:,:2]),axis=1)
10
11  # outcome variable
12  y = data[:,2]
13
14  # beta coefficients
15  beta = np.linalg.lstsq(X,y)[0]
16
17  # scaled coefficients (intercept not scaled)
18  betaScaled = beta/np.std(X,axis=0,ddof=1)
```

Code block 14.2: MATLAB

```
1   % load the data
2   data = load('widget_data.txt');
3
4   % design matrix
5   X = [ones(1000,1) data(:,1:2)];
6
7   % outcome variable
8   y = data(:,3);
9
10  % beta coefficients
11  beta = X\y;
12
13  % scaled coefficients (intercept not scaled)
14  betaScaled = beta'./std(X);
```

411

4. The figure is below, code thereafter.

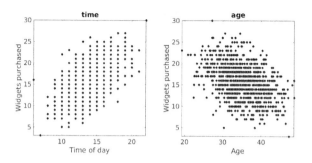

Figure 14.5: Image for question 1

Code block 14.3: Python

```
1  import matplotlib.pyplot as plt
2  fig,ax = plt.subplots(1,2,figsize=(8,4))
3  ax[0].plot(X[:,1],y,'o',markerfacecolor='k')
4  ax[0].set_title('Time variable')
5  ax[0].set_xlabel('Time of day')
6  ax[0].set_ylabel('Widgets purchased')
7
8  ax[1].plot(X[:,2],y,'o',markerfacecolor='k')
9  ax[1].set_title('Age variable')
10 ax[1].set_xlabel('Age')
11 ax[1].set_ylabel('Widgets purchased')
12 plt.show()
```

Code block 14.4: MATLAB

```
1  subplot(121)
2  plot(X(:,2),y,'o','markerfacecolor','k')
3  axis square, title('Time variable')
4  xlabel('Time of day')
5  ylabel('Widgets purchased')
6  subplot(122)
7  plot(X(:,3),y,'o','markerfacecolor','k')
8  axis square, title('Age variable')
9  xlabel('Age'), ylabel('Widgets purchased')
```

5. The model accounts for 36.6% of the variance of the data. That seems plausible given the variability in the data that can be seen in the graphs.

Code block 14.5: Python

```
1  yHat = X@beta
2  r2 = 1 - np.sum((yHat-y)**2)
3          / np.sum((y-np.mean(y))**2)
```

Code block 14.6: MATLAB

```
1  yHat = X*beta;
2  r2 = 1 - sum((yHat-y).^2) ...
3         / sum((y-mean(y)).^2);
```

. Least-squares

CHAPTER 15
EIGENDECOMPOSITION

START THIS CHAPTER HAPPY

A typical interaction between a student and a teacher about eigen-decomposition goes something like this:

Student: Honored and respected professor: What is an eigenvalue?

Teacher: Courteous and ambitious student: It's the thing that you use to find an eigenvector.

Student: Oh. OK, but then what's an eigenvector?

Teacher: It's the thing you get when you know the eigenvalue.

Student:

Teacher:

Student: "Crystal clear." I'll go spend some time on YouTube.

The terms eigenvalue decomposition, eigen-vector decomposition, and eigendecomposition are all used inter-changeably; here I will use eigendecomposition.

There are myriad explanations of eigenvectors and eigenvalues, and in my experience, most students find most explanations incoherent on first impression. In this section, I will provide three explanations that I hope will build intuition; additional explanations and insights will come in subsequent sections as well as subsequent chapters.

But there are two key properties to know about eigendecomposition before we get to interpretations. First, eigendecomposition is defined only for square matrices. They can be singular or invertible, symmetric or triangular or diagonal; but eigendecomposition can be performed only on square matrices. All matrices in this chapter are square (the singular value decomposition is defined for any sized matrix, and is the main topic of the next chapter).

Second, the purpose of eigendecomposition is to extract two sets of features from a matrix: eigenvalues and eigenvectors. Needless to say, eigenvalues are scalars and eigenvectors are vectors. Typically, eigenvalues are labeled λ and eigenvectors are labeled $\mathbf{v}$.

An $M \times M$ matrix has M eigenvalues and M eigenvectors. The eigenvalues and eigenvectors are paired, meaning that each eigen-value has an associated eigenvector. There are occasional points of additional complexity, for example with repeated eigenvalues; we'll get to that later. But in general, each eigenvalue has an associated eigenvector (Figure 15.1).

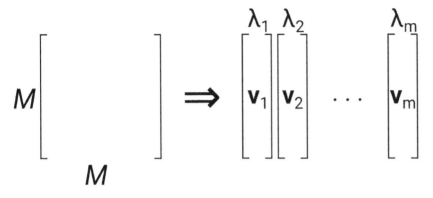

Figure 15.1: The big picture of eigendecomposition. Each $M{\times}M$ matrix "hides" M eigenvalues and M associated eigenvectors; eigendecomposition is the process of revealing the matrix's deep-est secrets.

Geometric interpretation   One way to think about matrix-vector multiplication is that matrices act as input-output transformers (section 6.5): Vector $\mathbf{w}$ goes in, and vector $\mathbf{Aw} = \mathbf{y}$ comes out. In the overwhelming vast majority of possible combinations of different matrices $\mathbf{A}$ and vectors $\mathbf{w}$, the resulting vector $\mathbf{y}$ will point in a different direction than $\mathbf{w}$. In other words, $\mathbf{A}$ rotates the vector. Figure 15.3 (left panel) shows an example.

But something is different in the right-side panel of Figure 15.3: *The output vector points in the same direction as the input vector.* The matrix did not change the direction of the vector; it merely scaled it down.

In other words, the <u>matrix-vector</u> multiplication had the same effect as <u>scalar-vector</u> multiplication. The entire matrix is acting on the vector as if that matrix were a single number. That might not sound so impressive in a 2×2 example, but the same concept applies to a $10^{10} \times 10^{10}$ (total of 10^{100} [a googel] elements!) matrix. If we could find that single number that has the same effect on the vector as

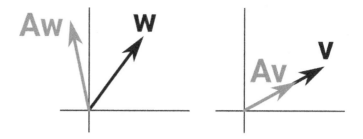

Figure 15.2: Vector w is *not* an eigenvector of matrix A, but vector v *is* an eigenvector of A. Its associated eigenvalue is $\lambda = .5$.

does the matrix, we would be able to write the following equality, which is also known as the *fundamental eigenvalue equation*:

Eigenvalue equation

$$\mathbf{Av} = \lambda\mathbf{v} \tag{15.1}$$

When the above equation is satisfied, then **v** is an eigenvector and λ is its associated eigenvalue (geometrically, λ is the amount of stretching). Let's be clear about this equation: It is not saying that the matrix *equals* the scalar; both sides of this equation produce a vector, and we cannot simply divide by **v**. Instead, this equation is saying that the *effect of the matrix on the vector* is the same as the *effect of the scalar on the vector*.

The example shown in Figure 15.3 has $\lambda = .5$. That means that $\mathbf{Av} = .5\mathbf{v}$. In other words, the matrix shrunk the vector by half, without changing its direction.

Importantly, eigenvectors/values are not special properties of the vector alone, nor are they special properties of the matrix alone. Instead, it is the combination of a particular matrix, a particular vector, and a particular scalar. Changing any of these quantities (even a single element) will likely destroy this special relationship. Thus, the vector **v** shown in Figure 15.3 is unlikely to be an eigenvector of a different matrix $\mathbf{B} \neq \mathbf{A}$.

Statistical interpretation Do you make New Year's resolutions? Many people make a New Year's resolution to eat healthier and go to the gym more often. Unfortunately, most people break their resolutions after a few days or weeks. Imagine you are a researcher, and you want to know how long it takes people to fall back to their old habits. Lucky for you, your town has one fast-food restaurant and one gym, next to each other. So you sit across the street each day and count how many people walk into the fast-food place vs. the gym. The data you collect are organized in a 40×2 table, with each row corresponding to a day and each column corresponding to the number of people that walked into the fast-food place, and the number of people who walked into the gym. You make a plot of the data with a "fast-food axis" and a "gym axis," and each dot in the graph corresponds to the data recorded on one day (Figure 15.3).

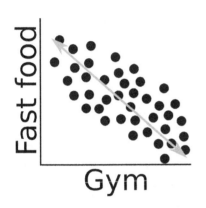

Figure 15.3: Each dot corresponds to one day's measurement of the number of people going into the fast-food place (y-axis) vs. the gym (x-axis).

Clearly there is meaningful structure in this dataset; there is some relationship between the axes, such that on days when more people walk into the gym, fewer people walk into the fast-food place.

Our concern is that neither axis seems optimal for understanding the structure in the data. Clearly, a better—more efficient and more informative—axis would reflect this structure. I'm sure you agree that the grey line drawn on top of the dots is an appropriate axis.

Why am I writing all of this? It turns out that that the gray line is an eigenvector of the data matrix times its transpose, which is also called a covariance matrix. In fact, the gray line shows the first principal component of the data. Principal components analysis (PCA) is one of the most important tools in data science (for example, it is a primary method used in unsupervised machine learning), and it is nothing fancier than an eigendecomposition of a data matrix. More on this in Chapter 19.

Rubik's cube   This explanation is the most conceptual of the three introductions to eigendecomposition, but I think it provides a nice mental image of the procedure, and of the outcome.

Think of a Rubik's cube as a matrix (I know, technically it would be a sparse tensor; as I wrote, this is a conceptual not a literal analogy). When you pick up the Rubik's cube, all of the colors are randomized; in other words, the information in the cube is randomly scattered around. Likewise, patterns of information in a data matrix are often distributed across different rows and columns.

To solve the Rubik's cube, you apply a specific sequence of rotations. You twist the rows and columns in a specific way to get each side of the cube filled with only one color.

That specific sequence of rotations is like the eigenvectors: The eigenvectors provide a set of instructions for how to rotate the information in the matrix, and once you apply all of the rotations, the information in the matrix becomes "ordered," with all of the similar information packed into one eigenvalue. Thus, the eigenvalue is analogous to a color.

The completed Rubik's cube is analogous to a procedure called "diagonalization," which means to put all of the eigenvectors into a matrix, and all of the eigenvalues into a diagonal matrix. That diagonal matrix is like the solved Rubik's cube.

If this analogy is confusing, then hopefully it will make more sense by the end of the chapter. And if it's still confusing after this chapter, then please accept my apologies and I hope the previous two explanations were sensible.

15.2 Finding eigenvalues

Eigenvectors are like secret passages that are hidden inside the matrix. In order to find those secret passages, we first need to find the secret keys. Eigenvalues are those keys. Thus, eigendecomposition requires first finding the eigenvalues, and then using those eigenvalues as "magic keys" to unlock the eigenvectors.

The way to discover the eigenvalues of a matrix is to re-write Equation 15.1 so that we have some expression equal to the zeros vector.

$$\mathbf{Av} - \lambda\mathbf{v} = \mathbf{0} \tag{15.2}$$

Notice that both terms of the left-hand side of the equation contain vector $\mathbf{v}$, which means we can factor out that vector. In order to make this a valid operation, we need to insert an identity matrix before the vector.

$$\mathbf{Av} - \lambda\mathbf{Iv} = \mathbf{0} \tag{15.3}$$

$$(\mathbf{A} - \lambda\mathbf{I})\mathbf{v} = \mathbf{0} \tag{15.4}$$

Equation 15.4 is important. It means that a matrix shifted by λ times a vector $\mathbf{v}$ gives us the zeros vector. Where have you seen something like this before? Yes, you saw it in section 8.6 (page 214): this is the definition of the null space of a matrix.

Of course, we could set $\mathbf{v} = \mathbf{0}$ to make Equation 15.4 true for any matrix and any λ. But this is a trivial solution, and we do not consider it. Thus, the eigenvalue equation tells us that $(\mathbf{A} - \lambda\mathbf{I})$—the matrix shifted by λ—has a non-trivial null space.

Thus, we've discovered that when shifting a matrix by an eigenvalue, the eigenvector is in its null space. That becomes the mechanism for finding the eigenvector, but it's all very theoretical at this point—we still don't know how to find λ!

The key here is to remember what we know about a matrix with a non-trivial null space, in particular, about its rank: We know that any square matrix with a non-trivial null space is reduced rank. And we also know that a reduced-rank matrix has a determinant of zero. And this leads to the mechanism for finding the eigenvalues of a matrix.

Finding eigenvalues

$$|\mathbf{A} - \lambda\mathbf{I}| = 0 \tag{15.5}$$

In section 11.3 you learned that the determinant of a matrix is computed by solving the characteristic polynomial. And you saw examples of how a known determinant can allow us to solve for some unknown variable inside the matrix. That's exactly the situation we have here: We have a matrix with one missing parameter (λ) and we know that its determinant is zero. And that's how you find the eigenvalues of a matrix. Let's work through some examples.

Eigenvalues of a 2×2 matrix   For a 2×2 matrix, the characteristic polynomial is a quadratic equation. Let's start with a lettered example.

$$\left| \begin{bmatrix} a & b \\ c & d \end{bmatrix} - \lambda \begin{bmatrix} 1 & 0 \\ 0 & 1 \end{bmatrix} \right| = 0$$

$$\begin{vmatrix} a - \lambda & b \\ c & d - \lambda \end{vmatrix} = 0$$

$$(a - \lambda)(d - \lambda) - bc = 0$$

$$\lambda^2 - (a + d)\lambda + (ad - bc) = 0 \tag{15.6}$$

The characteristic polynomial of a 2×2 matrix is a 2nd degree algebraic equation, meaning there are two λ's that satisfy the equation (they might be complex). The solutions can be found using the quadratic formula, which is one of those things that people try but fail to memorize in high-school math class.

$$\lambda = \frac{-b \pm \sqrt{b^2 - 4ac}}{2a} \tag{15.7}$$

EIGENDECOMPOSITION

WARNING. *a*, *b*, and *c* in Equation 15.7 are *not the same* as *a*, *b*, and *c* in Equation 15.6; the former are polynomial coefficients whereas the latter are matrix elements. Let me rewrite these two equations using distinct variables.

$$\alpha\lambda^2 - \beta\lambda + \gamma = 0 \tag{15.8}$$

$$\alpha = 1$$

$$\beta = -(a + d)$$

$$\gamma = ad - bc$$

$$\lambda = \frac{-\beta \pm \sqrt{\beta^2 - 4\gamma}}{2} \tag{15.9}$$

$$\lambda = \frac{(a + d) \pm \sqrt{(a + d)^2 - 4(ad - bc)}}{2} \tag{15.10}$$

If you're lucky, then your teacher or linear algebra textbook author designed matrices with entries that can be factored into the form $(\lambda_1 - \lambda)(\lambda_2 - \lambda) = 0$. Otherwise, you'll have to try again to memorize the quadratic formula, or at least keep it handy for quick reference.

Let's solve a few numerical examples.

$$\begin{bmatrix} 1 & 2 \\ 2 & 1 \end{bmatrix} \quad \Rightarrow \quad \begin{vmatrix} 1 - \lambda & 2 \\ 2 & 1 - \lambda \end{vmatrix} = 0 \tag{15.11}$$

$$(1 - \lambda)(1 - \lambda) - 4 = 0$$

$$\lambda^2 - 2\lambda - 3 = 0$$

$$(\lambda - 3)(\lambda + 1) = 0$$

$$\Rightarrow \lambda_1 = 3, \ \lambda_2 = -1$$

You should always check to see whether the characteristic polynomial can be factored before applying the quadratic formula. In the next example, you won't be so lucky.

$$\begin{bmatrix} 1 & 2 \\ 2 & 3 \end{bmatrix} \quad \Rightarrow \quad \begin{vmatrix} 1-\lambda & 2 \\ 2 & 3-\lambda \end{vmatrix} = 0$$

$$(1-\lambda)(3-\lambda) - 4 = 0$$

$$\lambda^2 - 4\lambda - 1 = 0$$

$$\lambda = \frac{4 \pm \sqrt{20}}{2}$$

$$\lambda = 2 \pm \sqrt{5}$$

Practice problems Find the eigenvalues of the following matrices.

a) $\begin{bmatrix} -4 & 2 \\ 0 & 4 \end{bmatrix}$ b) $\begin{bmatrix} 0 & 3 \\ 5 & 0 \end{bmatrix}$ c) $\begin{bmatrix} 3 & 0 \\ 0 & 5 \end{bmatrix}$ d) $\begin{bmatrix} 2 & 5 \\ 6 & 3 \end{bmatrix}$

Answers

a) $4, -4$ b) $\pm\sqrt{15}$ c) $3, 5$ d) $-3, 8$

There is a small short-cut you can take for finding eigenvalues of a 2×2 matrix. It comes from careful inspection of Equation 15.6. In particular the λ^1 coefficient is the trace of the matrix and the λ^0 coefficient is the determinant of the matrix. Hence, we can rewrite Equation 15.6 as follows:

$$\lambda^2 - tr(\mathbf{A})\lambda + |\mathbf{A}| = 0 \tag{15.12}$$

You still need to solve the equation for λ, so this admittedly isn't such a brilliant short-cut. But it will get to you the characteristic polynomial slightly faster.

Be mindful that this trick works only for 2×2 matrices; don't try to apply it to any larger matrices.

Eigenvalues of a 3×3 matrix The algebra gets more complicated, but the principle is the same: Shift the matrix by $-\lambda$ and solve for $\Delta = 0$. The characteristic polynomial produces a third-order equation, so you will have three eigenvalues as roots of the equation. Here is an example.

$$\begin{bmatrix} 9 & 0 & -8 \\ 15 & 3 & -15 \\ 0 & 0 & 1 \end{bmatrix} \Rightarrow \begin{vmatrix} 9-\lambda & 0 & -8 \\ 15 & 3-\lambda & -15 \\ 0 & 0 & 1-\lambda \end{vmatrix} = 0$$

$$(9-\lambda)(3-\lambda)(1-\lambda) = 0$$

$$\lambda_1 = 9, \ \lambda_2 = 3, \ \lambda_3 = 1$$

That example was easy because the characteristic polynomial was already factored due to the zeros in the matrix. It's not always so simple.

$$\begin{bmatrix} -2 & 2 & -3 \\ -4 & 1 & -6 \\ -1 & -2 & 0 \end{bmatrix} \Rightarrow \begin{vmatrix} -2-\lambda & 2 & -3 \\ -4 & 1-\lambda & -6 \\ -1 & -2 & 0-\lambda \end{vmatrix} = 0$$

$$(-2-\lambda)(1-\lambda)(-\lambda) + 12 - 24 - 3(1-\lambda) - 8\lambda + 12(2+\lambda) = 0$$

$$-\lambda^3 + \lambda^2 + 5\lambda + 9 = 0$$

$$(3-\lambda)(1-\lambda)(3-\lambda) = 0$$

The three λ's are 3, 1, and -3.

M columns, M λs It is no coincidence that the 2×2 matrices had 2 eigenvalues and the 3×3 matrices had 3 eigenvalues. Indeed, the Fundamental Theorem of Algebra states that any m-degree polynomial has m solutions. And because an $M \times M$ matrix has an Mth order characteristic polynomial, it will have M roots, or M eigenvalues. Hence, an $M \times M$ matrix has M eigenvalues (some of those eigenvalues may be repeated, complex numbers, or zeros).

Reflection

You can already see from the examples above that eigenvalues have no *intrinsic* sorting. We can come up with *sensible* sorting, for example, ordering eigenvalues according to their position on the number line or magnitude (distance from zero), or by a property of their corresponding eigenvectors. Sorted eigenvalues can facilitate data analyses, but eigenvalues are an intrinsically unsorted set.

15.3 Finding eigenvectors

The eigenvectors of a matrix reveal important "directions" in that matrix. You can think of those directions as being invariant to rotations, like in the illustration in Figure 15.3. The eigenvectors are encrypted inside the matrix, and each eigenvalue is the decryption key for each eigenvector. Once you have the key, slot it into the matrix, turn it, and the eigenvector will be revealed.

In particular, once you've identified the eigenvalues, shift the matrix by each $-\lambda_i$ and find a vector $\mathbf{v}_i$ in the null space of that shifted matrix. This is the eigenvector associated with eigenvalue λ_i. This can be written down in two alternative ways; both are presented below to make sure you get the idea.

Remember that the trivial zeros vector is not considered a solution.

Finding eigenvectors

$$\mathbf{v}_i \in N(\mathbf{A} - \lambda_i\mathbf{I}) \qquad (15.13)$$

$$(\mathbf{A} - \lambda_i\mathbf{I})\mathbf{v}_i = \mathbf{0} \qquad (15.14)$$

Let's work through a practice problem. I'll use the matrix presented on page 423. As a quick reminder, that matrix and its eigenvalues are:

$$\begin{bmatrix} 1 & 2 \\ 2 & 1 \end{bmatrix} \quad \Rightarrow \quad \lambda_1 = 3, \ \lambda_2 = -1$$

Before looking at the numbers below, I encourage you to work through this on your own: Shift the matrix by each λ and find a vector in its null space.

Here is my solution for λ_1:

$$\begin{bmatrix} 1-3 & 2 \\ 2 & 1-3 \end{bmatrix} = \begin{bmatrix} -2 & 2 \\ 2 & -2 \end{bmatrix} \quad \Rightarrow \quad \begin{bmatrix} -2 & 2 \\ 2 & -2 \end{bmatrix}\begin{bmatrix} 1 \\ 1 \end{bmatrix} = \begin{bmatrix} 0 \\ 0 \end{bmatrix}$$

Now let's repeat for the other eigenvalue.

$$\begin{bmatrix} 1--1 & 2 \\ 2 & 1--1 \end{bmatrix} = \begin{bmatrix} 2 & 2 \\ 2 & 2 \end{bmatrix} \quad \Rightarrow \quad \begin{bmatrix} 2 & 2 \\ 2 & 2 \end{bmatrix}\begin{bmatrix} -1 \\ 1 \end{bmatrix} = \begin{bmatrix} 0 \\ 0 \end{bmatrix}$$

I know, it looks weird to write $--$ instead of $+$. If you don't like it, then feel free to write on the page or screen.

That gives us our eigendecomposition for this matrix:

$$\begin{bmatrix} 1 & 2 \\ 2 & 1 \end{bmatrix} \begin{cases} \lambda_1 = 3, & \mathbf{v}_1 = \begin{bmatrix} 1 & 1 \end{bmatrix}^{\mathrm{T}} \\ \lambda_2 = -1, & \mathbf{v}_2 = \begin{bmatrix} -1 & 1 \end{bmatrix}^{\mathrm{T}} \end{cases} \qquad (15.15)$$

I wonder whether you got the same answers that I wrote above. The eigenvalues are unique—there are no other possible solutions to the characteristic polynomial. But are the eigenvectors unique?

Are the eigenvectors I printed above the *only possible* solutions? Take a moment to test the following possible eigenvectors to see whether they are also in the null space of the shifted matrix.

$$\mathbf{v}_1 \overset{?}{=} \begin{bmatrix} -1 \\ -1 \end{bmatrix}, \begin{bmatrix} 2 \\ 2 \end{bmatrix}, \begin{bmatrix} \pi \\ \pi \end{bmatrix}$$

$$\mathbf{v}_2 \overset{?}{=} \begin{bmatrix} 1 \\ -1 \end{bmatrix}, \begin{bmatrix} 13 \\ -13 \end{bmatrix}, \begin{bmatrix} -a \\ a \end{bmatrix}$$

I believe you see where this is going: There is an infinite number of equally good solutions, and they are all connected by being scaled versions of each other. Thus, **the true interpretation of an eigenvector is a basis vector for a 1D subspace.** Therefore, we could re-imagine solution 15.15 as

$$\begin{bmatrix} 1 & 2 \\ 2 & 1 \end{bmatrix} \begin{cases} \lambda_1 = 3, & \mathbf{v}_1 = \alpha \begin{bmatrix} 1 & 1 \end{bmatrix}^{\mathrm{T}}, & \alpha \in \mathbb{R} \\ \lambda_2 = -1, & \mathbf{v}_2 = \beta \begin{bmatrix} -1 & 1 \end{bmatrix}^{\mathrm{T}}, & \beta \in \mathbb{R} \end{cases} \tag{15.16}$$

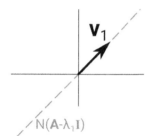

Figure 15.4: The "preferred" eigenvector is the unit-length basis vector for the null space of the matrix shifted by its eigenvalue.

Given that we have an infinite number of equally accurate eigenvectors for each eigenvalue, how can we pick just one? For a variety of practical reasons (which you will learn about later), the best eigenvector to pick is the one that has a unit norm. Thus, out of the infinity of possible eigenvectors, we generally prefer the one such that $\|\mathbf{v}\| = 1$ (Figure 15.4). That's what numerical processing software programs like MATLAB and Python will do. This leads to our final re-expression of solution 15.15:

$$\begin{bmatrix} 1 & 2 \\ 2 & 1 \end{bmatrix} \begin{cases} \lambda_1 = 3, & \mathbf{v}_1 = \frac{1}{\sqrt{2}} \begin{bmatrix} 1 \\ 1 \end{bmatrix} \\ \\ \lambda_2 = -1, & \mathbf{v}_2 = \frac{1}{\sqrt{2}} \begin{bmatrix} -1 \\ 1 \end{bmatrix} \end{cases} \tag{15.17}$$

That said, when solving problems by hand, it's usually easier to have eigenvectors with integer elements, rather than having to worry about all the fractions and square roots that arise in normalization.

Practice problems Find the eigenvectors of the following matrices.

a) $\begin{bmatrix} 3 & 1 \\ 4 & 6 \end{bmatrix}$
b) $\begin{bmatrix} 3 & -2 \\ 1 & 0 \end{bmatrix}$

Answers Vectors are not normalized for computational ease.

a) $\lambda_1 = 2, \mathbf{v}_1 = \begin{bmatrix} 1 \\ -1 \end{bmatrix}$, $\lambda_2 = 7, \mathbf{v}_2 = \begin{bmatrix} 1 \\ 4 \end{bmatrix}$
b) $\lambda_1 = 1, \mathbf{v}_1 = \begin{bmatrix} 1 \\ 1 \end{bmatrix}$, $\lambda_2 = 2, \mathbf{v}_2 = \begin{bmatrix} 2 \\ 1 \end{bmatrix}$

I'd like to show another example of eigendecomposition of a 3×3 matrix. You'll see that the concept is the same, but the arithmetic quickly gets challenging. It's important to work through enough examples that you understand the concept, and then you let computers do the hard work for you.

Again, the concept is that we find the 3 eigenvalues of the 3×3 matrix by shifting by $-\lambda$, setting the determinant to zero, and solving for λ. Then we shift the matrix by each solved λ and find a vector in the null space of that shifted matrix. Easy peasy, right? Let's see...

$$\begin{bmatrix} 1 & 2 & 3 \\ 4 & 3 & 7 \\ 3 & 3 & 6 \end{bmatrix} \quad \Rightarrow \quad \begin{vmatrix} 1-\lambda & 2 & 3 \\ 4 & 3-\lambda & 7 \\ 3 & 3 & 6-\lambda \end{vmatrix} = 0$$

$$(1 - \lambda)(3 - \lambda)(6 - \lambda) + 42 + 36 - 9(3 - \lambda) - 8(6 - \lambda) - 21(1 - \lambda) = 0$$

$$-\lambda^3 + 10\lambda^2 - 27\lambda + 18 + 42 + 33 - 27 + 9\lambda - 48 + 8\lambda - 21 + 21\lambda = 0$$

$$-\lambda^3 + 10\lambda^2 + 11\lambda = 0$$

$$-\lambda(\lambda^2 - 10\lambda - 11) = 0$$

$$-\lambda(\lambda + 1)(\lambda - 11) = 0$$

Our three eigenvalues are 0, -1, and 11. Notice that we got a $\lambda = 0$, and the matrix is reduced-rank (the third column is the sum of the first two). That's not a coincidence, but a deeper discussion of the interpretation of zero-valued eigenvalues will come later.

Now we can solve for the three eigenvectors, which are the vectors just to the left of the equals sign (non-normalized).

$$\lambda_1 : \begin{bmatrix} 1-0 & 2 & 3 \\ 4 & 3-0 & 7 \\ 3 & 3 & 6-0 \end{bmatrix} \Rightarrow \begin{bmatrix} 1 & 2 & 3 \\ 4 & 3 & 7 \\ 3 & 3 & 6 \end{bmatrix} \begin{bmatrix} 1 \\ 1 \\ -1 \end{bmatrix} = \begin{bmatrix} 0 \\ 0 \\ 0 \end{bmatrix}$$

$$\lambda_2 : \begin{bmatrix} 1-1 & 2 & 3 \\ 4 & 3-1 & 7 \\ 3 & 3 & 6-1 \end{bmatrix} \Rightarrow \begin{bmatrix} 2 & 2 & 3 \\ 4 & 4 & 7 \\ 3 & 3 & 7 \end{bmatrix} \begin{bmatrix} 1 \\ -1 \\ 0 \end{bmatrix} = \begin{bmatrix} 0 \\ 0 \\ 0 \end{bmatrix}$$

$$\lambda_3 : \begin{bmatrix} 1-11 & 2 & 3 \\ 4 & 3-11 & 7 \\ 3 & 3 & 6-11 \end{bmatrix} \Rightarrow \begin{bmatrix} -10 & 2 & 3 \\ 4 & -8 & 7 \\ 3 & 3 & -5 \end{bmatrix} \begin{bmatrix} 19 \\ 41 \\ 36 \end{bmatrix} = \begin{bmatrix} 0 \\ 0 \\ 0 \end{bmatrix}$$

15.4 Diagonalization via eigendecomposition

It is time to take a step back and look at the big picture. An $M \times M$ matrix contains M eigenvalues and M associated eigenvectors. The set of eigenvalue/vector pairs produces a set of similar-looking equations:

$$\begin{aligned} \mathbf{A}\mathbf{v}_1 &= \lambda_1 \mathbf{v}_1 \\ \mathbf{A}\mathbf{v}_2 &= \lambda_2 \mathbf{v}_2 \\ &\vdots \\ \mathbf{A}\mathbf{v}_m &= \lambda_m \mathbf{v}_m \end{aligned} \tag{15.18}$$

This is clunky and ugly, and therefore violates an important principle in linear algebra: Make equations compact, elegant, and simple. Fortunately, all of these equations can be simplified by having each eigenvector be a column in a matrix, and having each eigenvalue be an element in a diagonal matrix.

$$\mathbf{A}\mathbf{V} = \mathbf{V}\mathbf{\Lambda} \tag{15.19}$$

On first glance, it may seem inconsistent that I wrote $\lambda \mathbf{v}$ in Equation 15.18 but $\mathbf{V}\mathbf{\Lambda}$ in the matrix Equation 15.19. There are two reasons why it must be **VΛ** and cannot be **ΛV**. Both reasons can be appreciated by seeing the right-hand side of Equation 15.19 written out for a 3×3 matrix. Before reading the text below the equation, try to understand why (1) the λ's have to be the diagonal elements and (2) why we need to *post*-multiply by **Λ**. In the eigenvectors below, the first subscript number corresponds to the eigenvector, and the second subscript number corresponds to the eigenvector element. For example, v_{12} is the second element of the first eigenvector.

$$\begin{bmatrix} v_{11} & v_{21} & v_{31} \\ v_{12} & v_{22} & v_{32} \\ v_{13} & v_{23} & v_{33} \end{bmatrix} \begin{bmatrix} \lambda_1 & 0 & 0 \\ 0 & \lambda_2 & 0 \\ 0 & 0 & \lambda_3 \end{bmatrix} = \begin{bmatrix} \lambda_1 v_{11} & \lambda_2 v_{21} & \lambda_3 v_{31} \\ \lambda_1 v_{12} & \lambda_2 v_{22} & \lambda_3 v_{32} \\ \lambda_1 v_{13} & \lambda_2 v_{23} & \lambda_3 v_{33} \end{bmatrix} \quad (15.20)$$

Those two questions are closely related. The reason why the eigenvalues go in the diagonal of a matrix that post-multiplies the eigenvectors matrix is that the eigenvalues must scale each column of the **V** matrix, not each row (refer to page 151 for the rule about pre- vs. post-multiplying a diagonal matrix). If **Λ** pre-multiplied **V**, each element of each eigenvector would be scaled by a different λ.

There is another reason why it's **VΛ** and not **ΛV**. If the equation read $\mathbf{AV} = \mathbf{\Lambda V}$, then we could multiply both sides by $\mathbf{V}^{-1}$, producing the statement $\mathbf{A} = \mathbf{\Lambda}$, which is not generally true.

So then why did I write $\lambda \mathbf{v}$ for the single equation instead of the more-consistent $\mathbf{v}\lambda$? For better or worse, $\lambda \mathbf{v}$ is the common way to write it, and that's the form you will nearly always see.

Diagonalization   The elegant Equation 15.19 is not only a practical short-hand for a set of equations; it provides an important conceptual insight into one of the core ideas of eigendecomposition: Finding a set of basis vectors such that the matrix is diagonal in that basis space. This can be seen by left-multiplying both sides of the equation by $\mathbf{V}^{-1}$. This is a valid operation if we assume that all eigenvectors form an independent set. This assumption is valid when there are M distinct eigenvalues (more on this in the next

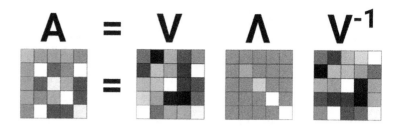

Figure 15.5: Diagonalization of a matrix in pictures.

section).

$$A = V\Lambda V^{-1} \tag{15.21}$$

Thus, matrix A is diagonal in basis V. That's why eigendecomposition is also sometimes called *diagonalization*. To diagonalize a matrix A means to find some matrix of basis vectors such that A is a diagonal matrix in that basis space.

Let's now revisit the Rubik's cube analogy from the beginning of this chapter: In Equation 15.21, A is the scrambled Rubik's cube with all sides having inter-mixed colors; V is the set of rotations that you apply to the Rubik's cube in order to solve the puzzle; Λ is the cube in its "ordered" form with each side having exactly one color; and V^{-1} is the inverse of the rotations, which is how you would get from the ordered form to the original mixed form.

Figure 15.5 shows what diagonalization looks like for a 5×5 matrix; the gray-scale intensity corresponds to the matrix element value.

Practice problems Diagonalize the following matrices.

a) $\begin{bmatrix} 2 & 6 \\ 6 & 7 \end{bmatrix}$
b) $\begin{bmatrix} 1 & 0 \\ -7 & 5 \end{bmatrix}$

Answers Matrices below are V, Λ, V^{-1}.

a) $\frac{1}{\sqrt{13}}\begin{bmatrix} -3 & 2 \\ 2 & 3 \end{bmatrix}, \begin{bmatrix} -2 & 0 \\ 0 & 11 \end{bmatrix}, \frac{1}{\sqrt{13}}\begin{bmatrix} -3 & 2 \\ 2 & 3 \end{bmatrix}$
b) $\begin{bmatrix} 0 & 4 \\ 1 & 7 \end{bmatrix}, \begin{bmatrix} 5 & 0 \\ 0 & 1 \end{bmatrix}, \frac{1}{-4}\begin{bmatrix} 7 & -4 \\ -1 & 0 \end{bmatrix}$

$\begin{array}{l} \textit{Reflection} \end{array}$ The previous reflection box mentioned sorting eigenvalues. Figure 15.5 shows that the eigenvalues are sorted ascending along the diagonal. Re-sorting eigenvalues is fine, but you need to be diligent to apply the same re-sorting to the columns of **V**, otherwise the eigenvalues and their associated eigenvectors will be mismatched.

Code Obtaining eigenvalues and eigenvectors is really easy in Python and in MATLAB. Annoyingly, the outputs are different between the programs: Python returns the eigenvalues in a vector and the eigenvectors in a matrix (note that I create the diagonal $\mathbf{\Lambda}$ in a separate line); in contrast, MATLAB outputs the eigenvectors and the eigenvalues in the diagonal of a matrix, unless you request only one output, in which case you get the vector of eigenvalues.

Code block 15.1: Python

```
1  import numpy as np
2  A = np.array([[2,3],[3,2]])
3  L,V = np.linalg.eig(A)
4  L = np.diag(L)
```

Code block 15.2: MATLAB

```
1  A = [ 2 3; 3 2 ];
2  L = eig(A);
3  [V,L] = eig(A);
```

Conditions for diagonalization

Not all square matrices are diagonalizable. It might seem circular, but the definition of a diagonalizable matrix is a matrix that can be diagonalized, that is, that Equation 15.21 ($\mathbf{A} = \mathbf{V}\mathbf{\Lambda}\mathbf{V}^{-1}$) is true.

Fortunately, if you are interested in applied linear algebra, then "most" matrices are diagonalizable. "Most" is a difficult word in math, because there is an infinite number of diagonalizable and non-diagonalizable matrices. But what I mean is that most of the square matrices that show up in statistics, machine-learning, data science, computational simulations, and other applications, are likely to be diagonalizable. **Importantly, all symmetric matrices are diagonalizable**.

But there are matrices for which no matrix $\mathbf{V}$ can make that decomposition true. Here's an example of a non-diagonalizable matrix.

$$\mathbf{A} = \begin{bmatrix} 1 & 1 \\ -1 & -1 \end{bmatrix}, \quad \lambda = \{0,0\}, \quad \mathbf{V} = \begin{bmatrix} 1 & -1 \\ -1 & 1 \end{bmatrix}$$

Notice that the matrix is rank-1 and yet has two zero-valued eigenvalues. This means that our diagonal matrix of eigenvalues would be the zeros matrix, and it is impossible to reconstruct the original matrix using $\mathbf{\Lambda} = \mathbf{0}$.

There is an entire category of matrices that is non-diagonalizable, called *nilpotent* matrices[1]. A nilpotent matrix means that for some matrix power k, $\mathbf{A}^k = \mathbf{0}$. In other words, keep multiplying the matrix by itself and eventually you'll get the zeros matrix; below is an example of a rank-1 nilpotent matrix with $k = 2$. I encourage you to take a moment to confirm that $\mathbf{A}\mathbf{A} = \mathbf{0}$.

$$\begin{bmatrix} 0 & 1 \\ 0 & 0 \end{bmatrix}$$

All triangular matrices that have zeros on the diagonal are nilpotent, have all zero-valued eigenvalues, and thus cannot be diagonalized.

All hope is not lost, however, because the singular value decomposition is valid on all matrices, even the non-diagonalizable ones. The two non-diagonalizable example matrices above have singular values, respectively, of $\{2,0\}$ and $\{1,0\}$.

---

[1] A proof for this statement is given in section 15.11.

15.6 Distinct vs. repeated eigenvalues

Distinct eigenvalues means $\lambda_i \neq \lambda_j$; distinct eigenvectors means they form a linearly independent set.

Distinct eigenvalues   Many square matrices have M distinct eigenvalues. That's nice because **distinct eigenvalues always lead to distinct eigenvectors**. You might already have the intuition that plugging different λ's into a matrix should reveal different eigenvectors. But we need to prove that this is the case.

We are going to prove the claim that distinct eigenvalues lead to distinct eigenvectors by trying to disprove it and failing (a good strategy in scientific research).

We start with the following assumptions:

1. Matrix $\mathbf{A}$ has *distinct* eigenvalues λ_1 and λ_2 ($\lambda_1 \neq \lambda_2$).
2. Their associated eigenvectors $\mathbf{v}_1$ and $\mathbf{v}_2$ are linearly *dependent*, meaning that one can be expressed as a scaled version of the other. This assumption can be written as follows.

$$\beta_1 \mathbf{v}_1 + \beta_2 \mathbf{v}_2 = \mathbf{0}, \qquad \beta_1, \beta_2 \neq 0 \qquad (15.22)$$

Equation 15.22 is the starting point for our proof. We proceed by multiplying the entire equation by matrix $\mathbf{A}$. And from there we can replace $\mathbf{Av}$ with $\lambda\mathbf{v}$.

$$\beta_1 \mathbf{A}\mathbf{v}_1 + \beta_2 \mathbf{A}\mathbf{v}_2 = \mathbf{A0}$$

$$\beta_1 \lambda_1 \mathbf{v}_1 + \beta_2 \lambda_2 \mathbf{v}_2 = \mathbf{0} \qquad (15.23)$$

Next I will multiply Equation 15.22 by λ_1, and then subtract equations 15.23 from 15.22.

$$
\begin{aligned}
& \beta_1 \lambda_1 \mathbf{v}_1 + \beta_2 \lambda_1 \mathbf{v}_2 = \mathbf{0} \\
- \quad & \beta_1 \lambda_1 \mathbf{v}_1 + \beta_2 \lambda_2 \mathbf{v}_2 = \mathbf{0} \\
\hline
& \beta_2 \lambda_1 \mathbf{v}_2 - \beta_2 \lambda_2 \mathbf{v}_2 = \mathbf{0}
\end{aligned}
$$

The two terms in the left-hand side of the difference equation both contain $\beta_2\mathbf{v}_2$, so that can be factored out, revealing the final nail in the coffin of our to-be-falsified hypothesis:

$$(\lambda_1 - \lambda_2)\beta_2\mathbf{v}_2 = \mathbf{0} \qquad (15.24)$$

Why is this the key equation? It says that we multiply three terms to obtain the zeros vector, which means at least one of these terms must be zero. $(\lambda_1 - \lambda_2)$ cannot equal zero because we began from the assumption that they are distinct. $\mathbf{v}_2 \neq \mathbf{0}$ because we do not consider zero eigenvectors.

Thus, we are forced to conclude that $\beta_2 = 0$. This violates the assumption in Equation 15.22, which proves that the assumption is invalid, which proves that distinct eigenvalues lead to linearly independent eigenvectors.

However, when we consider a set with more than two eigenvectors, it is possible to have a linearly dependent set with one $\beta = 0$. So let's allow $\beta_2 = 0$ and plug that into Equation 15.22. This forces us to conclude that $\beta_1 = 0$. Thus, the only way to combine the two vectors to produce the zeros vector is by weighting both vectors by zero; in other words, there is no nontrivial combination of the two vectors that produces the zeros vector, which means the two vectors are linearly independent. If our set contained more than two eigenvectors, then repeating the above logic (setting each $\beta = 0$) ultimately leads to the conclusion that all βs must be zero.

Either way you look at it, the conclusion is that *distinct eigenvalues lead to linearly independent eigenvectors.*

We did not need to impose any assumptions about the field from which the λs are drawn; they can be real or complex-valued, rational or irrational, integers or fractions. The only important quality is that each λ is distinct.

Repeated eigenvalues Repeated eigenvalues complicate matters because they sometimes have distinct eigenvectors and sometimes not. I'll start by showing two examples before discussing the more general principle. Consider the following matrix and its eigenvalues.

$$\begin{bmatrix} 6 & -4 \\ 1 & 2 \end{bmatrix} \Rightarrow \begin{vmatrix} 6 - \lambda & -4 \\ 1 & 2 - \lambda \end{vmatrix} \Rightarrow \lambda^2 - 8\lambda + 16 = 0 \Rightarrow (\lambda - 4)^2 = 0$$

The two solutions are $\lambda_1 = \lambda_2 = 4$. Plugging 4 into the shifted matrix yields

$$\begin{bmatrix} 2 & -4 \\ 1 & -2 \end{bmatrix} \begin{bmatrix} v_1 \\ v_2 \end{bmatrix} = \mathbf{0} \quad \Rightarrow \quad \mathbf{v}_1 = \begin{bmatrix} 2 \\ 1 \end{bmatrix}$$

It's clear how to get the first eigenvector, but then how do you get the second eigenvector? The answer is you don't—there is only one eigenvector. MATLAB will return the following.

MATLAB normalized the vectors to be unit-length vectors: the vector $[1\ 2]$ points in the same direction as $[1\ 2]/\sqrt{5}$.

```
>> [V,L] = eig([6 -4; 1 2])
V =
    0.8944    -0.8944
    0.4472    -0.4472


L =
    4.0000    0
    0         4.0000
```

The columns of output matrix V are the same subspace, although one points in the opposite direction. There isn't anything "wrong" with the matrix—it has a rank of 2 and a non-zero determinant. But it has a single eigenvalue that reveals only a single eigenvector. Let's see another example of a matrix with repeated eigenvalues.

$$\begin{bmatrix} 4 & 0 \\ 0 & 4 \end{bmatrix} \Rightarrow \begin{vmatrix} 4 - \lambda & 0 \\ 0 & 4 - \lambda \end{vmatrix} \Rightarrow \lambda^2 - 8\lambda + 16 = 0 \Rightarrow (\lambda - 4)^2 = 0$$

Again, the two solutions are $\lambda = 4$. Plugging this into the matrix yields

$$\begin{bmatrix} 0 & 0 \\ 0 & 0 \end{bmatrix} \begin{bmatrix} v_1 \\ v_2 \end{bmatrix} = \mathbf{0} \quad \Rightarrow \quad ? \tag{15.25}$$

Now we have an interesting situation: *any* vector times the zeros matrix produces the zeros vector. So *all* vectors are eigenvectors of this matrix. Which two vectors to select? The standard basis vectors are a good practical choice, because they are easy to work with, are orthogonal, and have unit length. Therefore, for the matrix above, $\mathbf{V}=\mathbf{I}$. To be clear: $\mathbf{V}$ *could be* $\mathbf{I}$, or it could be any other 2×2 full-rank matrix. This is a special case of eigendecomposition of the identity matrix. I just multiplied it by 4 so we'd get the same eigenvalues as in the previous example.

Perhaps that was too extreme an example. Consider the following matrix.

$$\begin{bmatrix} 5 & -1 & 0 \\ -1 & 5 & 0 \\ 1/3 & -1/3 & 4 \end{bmatrix} \quad \Rightarrow \quad \lambda = 6, 4, 4 \tag{15.26}$$

This matrix has one distinct eigenvalue and one repeated eigenvalue. We know with certainty that the eigenvector associated with $\lambda = 6$ will be distinct (I encourage you to confirm that a good integer-valued choice is $[3 \; \text{-}1 \; 1]^{\mathrm{T}}$); what will happen when we plug 4 into the shifted matrix?

$$\begin{bmatrix} 1 & -1 & 0 \\ -1 & 1 & 0 \\ 1/3 & -1/3 & 0 \end{bmatrix} \begin{bmatrix} v_1 \\ v_2 \\ v_3 \end{bmatrix} = \begin{bmatrix} 0 \\ 0 \\ 0 \end{bmatrix} \quad \Rightarrow \quad \mathbf{v_1} = \begin{bmatrix} 1 \\ 1 \\ 0 \end{bmatrix}, \; \mathbf{v_2} = \begin{bmatrix} 0 \\ 0 \\ 1 \end{bmatrix} \tag{15.27}$$

Again, we can ask the question whether these are the only two eigenvectors. I'm not referring to scaled versions of these vectors such as $\alpha \mathbf{v_2}$, I mean whether we could pick equally good eigenvectors with *different directions* from the two listed above.

Consider vector $\mathbf{v_2}$. Because the third column of the shifted matrix is all zeros, the third element of the eigenvector can be any number.

I could have picked [1 1 1] or [1 1 10]. As long as the first two elements are the same, the third element can be anything. The pair of eigenvectors I picked is a *convenient* choice because they are orthogonal and contains 0's and 1's; but these weren't the only possible vectors I could have selected.

Now you've seen several examples of the possible outcomes of repeated eigenvalues: there can be only one eigenvector or distinct eigenvectors, or an infinity of possible sets of distinct eigenvectors. Which of these possibilities is the case depends on the numbers in the matrix.

To understand why this can happen, let's revisit the proof in the beginning of this section. We need to modify the first assumption, though: We now assume that the two eigenvalues are the same, thus $\lambda_1 = \lambda_2$. Most of the rest of the proof continues as already written above. Below is Equation 15.24, re-written for convenience.

$$(\lambda_1 - \lambda_2)\beta_2 \mathbf{v}_2 = \mathbf{0}$$

Again, we have the product of three terms producing the zeros vector. What do we know now? We still don't accept the zeros vector as an eigenvector, so $\mathbf{v}_2 \neq \mathbf{0}$. However, we also know that the first term *is* equal to zero. Thus, the equation really is

$$0\beta_2 \mathbf{v}_2 = \mathbf{0}$$

What can we now conclude? Not much. We have the zeros vector without the trivial solution of a zeros eigenvector, so assumption 2 can be maintained (any vector set that includes the zeros vector is linearly dependent). We could now drop assumption 2 and say that the set of eigenvectors could dependent or independent, depending on the entries in the matrix.

Geometric interpretation of repeated eigenvalues   Here's the situation: Each distinct eigenvalue has its own distinct eigenvector, and that eigenvector is a basis vector for a 1D subspace (Figure 15.6).

Repeated eigenvalues can lead to one of two situations. First, both eigenvectors can lie on the same 1D subspace. In that case, the

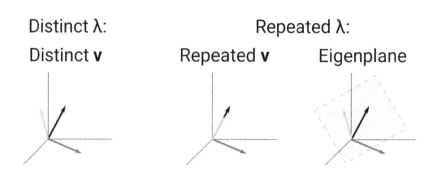

Figure 15.6: The geometric possibilities of eigenvectors with repeated eigenvalues, shown in $\mathbb{R}^3$ for convenient visualization.

eigenspace won't span the entire ambient space $\mathbb{R}^M$; it will be a smaller-dimensional subspace. The second possibility is that there are two distinct eigenvectors associated with one eigenvalue. In this case, there isn't a unique eigen*vector*; instead, there is a unique eigen*plane* and the two eigenvectors are basis vectors for that eigenplane. Any two independent vectors in the plane can be used as a basis. It is convenient to define those vectors to be orthogonal, and this is what computer programs will return.

Reflection

> Do you really need to worry about repeated eigenvalues for applications of eigendecomposition? Repeated eigenvalues may seem like some weird quirk of abstract mathematics, but real datasets can have eigenvalues that are exactly repeated or statistically indistinguishable. In my own research on multivariate neural time series analysis, I find nearly identical eigenvalues to be infrequent, but common enough that I keep an eye out for them.

15.7 Complex eigenvalues or eigenvectors

If $4ac > b^2$ in Equation 15.6, then you end up with the square root of a negative number, which means the eigenvalues will be complex numbers. And complex eigenvalues lead to complex eigenvectors.

Don't be afraid of complex numbers or complex solutions; they are perfectly natural and can arise even from matrices that contain all real values. The typical example of complex eigenvalues is the identity matrix with one row-swap and a minus sign:

$$\begin{bmatrix} 0 & -1 \\ 1 & 0 \end{bmatrix} \quad \Rightarrow \quad \Lambda = \begin{bmatrix} i & 0 \\ 0 & -i \end{bmatrix}, \ V = \begin{bmatrix} 1 & 1 \\ -i & i \end{bmatrix}$$

$$\begin{bmatrix} 1 & 0 & 0 \\ 0 & 0 & 1 \\ 0 & -1 & 0 \end{bmatrix} \quad \Rightarrow \quad \Lambda = \begin{bmatrix} i & 0 & 0 \\ 0 & -i & 0 \\ 0 & 0 & 1 \end{bmatrix}, \ V = \begin{bmatrix} 0 & 0 & 1 \\ -1 & -1 & 0 \\ -i & i & 0 \end{bmatrix}$$

Complex solutions can also arise from "normal" matrices with real-valued entries. Consider the following matrix, which I generated in MATLAB from random integers (that is, I did not carefully hand-select this matrix or look it up in a secret online website for math teachers who want to torment their students). (Numbers are rounded to nearest tenth.)

$$\begin{bmatrix} -1 & 15 \\ -6 & 4 \end{bmatrix} \quad \Rightarrow \quad \Lambda = \begin{bmatrix} 1.5 + 9.2i & 0 \\ 0 & 1.5 - 9.2i \end{bmatrix}, \ V = \begin{bmatrix} .85 & .85 \\ .1 + .5i & .1 - .5i \end{bmatrix}$$

It is no coincidence that the two solutions is a pair of complex conjugates. For a 2×2 matrix, complex conjugate pair solutions are immediately obvious from Equation 15.7 (page 422): A complex number can only come from the square-root in the numerator, which is preceded by a ± sign. Thus, the two solutions will have the same real part and flipped-sign imaginary part.

This generalizes to larger matrices: A real-valued matrix with complex eigenvalues has solutions that come in pairs: λ and $\bar{\lambda}$. Furthermore, their associated eigenvectors also come in conjugate pairs $\mathbf{v}$ and $\bar{\mathbf{v}}$. This can be shown by inspecting the complex conjugate of the fundamental eigenvalue equation.

$$\mathbf{Av} = \lambda\mathbf{v}$$

$$\overline{\mathbf{Av}} = \overline{\lambda\mathbf{v}}$$

$$\mathbf{A\bar{v}} = \bar{\lambda}\bar{\mathbf{v}} \tag{15.28}$$

Equation 15.28 follows from the previous line because the matrix is real-valued, thus $\overline{\mathbf{A}} = \mathbf{A}$.

Complex-valued solutions in eigendecomposition can be difficult to work with in applications with real datasets, but there is nothing in principle weird or strange about them.

Practice problems   Identify the eigenvalues from the following matrices (consult page 423 for the quadratic formula).

a) $\begin{bmatrix} 2 & -3 \\ 1 & 2 \end{bmatrix}$
b) $\begin{bmatrix} 3 & 7 \\ -7 & 3 \end{bmatrix}$
c) $\begin{bmatrix} a & b \\ -b & a \end{bmatrix}$

Answers

a) $\lambda = 2 \pm i\sqrt{3}$
b) $\lambda = 3 \pm i7$
c) $\lambda = a \pm ib$

15.8 Eigendecomposition of a symmetric matrix

By this point in the book, you know that I'm a HUGE fan of symmetric matrices. And I'm not the only one—everyone who works with matrices has a special place in their heart for the elation that comes with symmetry across the diagonal. In this section, you are going to learn two additional properties that make symmetric matrices really great to work with.

Eigendecomposition of a symmetric matrix has two notable features: orthogonal eigenvectors (assuming distinct eigenvalues; for repeated eigenvalues the eigenvectors can be crafted to be orthogonal, as discussed earlier), and real-valued (as opposed to complex) solutions.

Orthogonal eigenvectors   If the matrix is symmetric, then all of its eigenvectors are pairwise orthogonal. There is an example showing this property earlier in this chapter, and I encourage you to find the symmetric matrix and confirm that its eigenvectors are orthogonal.

But of course we need to prove this rigorously for all symmetric matrices. The goal is to show that the dot product between any pair of eigenvectors is zero. We start from two assumptions: (1) matrix $\mathbf{A}$ is symmetric ($\mathbf{A} = \mathbf{A}^T$) and (2) λ_1 and λ_2 are distinct eigenvalues of $\mathbf{A}$ (thus $\lambda_1 \neq \lambda_2$). $\mathbf{v}_1$ and $\mathbf{v}_2$ are their corresponding eigenvectors. I'm going to write a series of equalities; make sure you can follow each step from left to right.

$$\lambda_1 \mathbf{v}_1^T \mathbf{v}_2 = (\mathbf{A}\mathbf{v}_1)^T \mathbf{v}_2 = \mathbf{v}_1^T \mathbf{A}^T \mathbf{v}_2 = \mathbf{v}_1^T \lambda_2 \mathbf{v}_2 = \lambda_2 \mathbf{v}_1^T \mathbf{v}_2 \quad (15.29)$$

The middle steps are actually just way-points; we care about the equality between the first and last terms. I'll write them below, and then set the equation to zero.

$$\lambda_1 \mathbf{v}_1^T \mathbf{v}_2 = \lambda_2 \mathbf{v}_1^T \mathbf{v}_2 \qquad (15.30)$$

$$\lambda_1 \mathbf{v}_1^T \mathbf{v}_2 - \lambda_2 \mathbf{v}_1^T \mathbf{v}_2 = 0 \qquad (15.31)$$

Notice that both terms contain the dot product $\mathbf{v}_1^T \mathbf{v}_2$, which can be factored out, bringing us to the crux of the proof:

$$(\lambda_1 - \lambda_2)\mathbf{v}_1^T \mathbf{v}_2 = 0 \qquad (15.32)$$

Equation 15.32 says that two quantities multiply to produce 0, which means that one or both of those quantities must be zero. $(\lambda_1 - \lambda_2)$ cannot equal zero because we began from the assumption that they are distinct. Therefore, $\mathbf{v}_1^T \mathbf{v}_2$ must be zero, which means that $\mathbf{v}_1 \perp \mathbf{v}_2$, i.e., the two eigenvectors are orthogonal. Note that this proof is valid only for symmetric matrices, when $\mathbf{A}^T = \mathbf{A}$. Otherwise, you'll get stuck in the middle of line 15.29—it won't be possible to set the first and last expressions equal to each other.

Orthogonal eigenvectors are a big deal. It means that the dot product between any two non-identical columns will be zero:

$$\mathbf{v}_i^T \mathbf{v}_j = \begin{cases} \|\mathbf{v}_i\|^2 & \text{if } i = j \\ 0 & \text{if } i \neq j \end{cases} \qquad (15.33)$$

When putting all of those eigenvectors as columns into a matrix $\mathbf{V}$, then $\mathbf{V}^T\mathbf{V}$ is a diagonal matrix.

But wait, there's more! Remember that eigenvectors are important because of their direction, not their magnitude. And remember that I wrote that it's convenient to have unit-length eigenvectors. So let's rewrite 15.33 assuming unit-norm eigenvectors:

$$\mathbf{v}_i^{\mathrm{T}}\mathbf{v}_j = \begin{cases} 1 & \text{if } i = j \\ 0 & \text{if } i \neq j \end{cases} \tag{15.34}$$

I hope this looks familiar. This is also the definition of an orthogonal matrix. And that means:

$$\mathbf{V}^{\mathrm{T}}\mathbf{V} = \mathbf{I} \tag{15.35}$$

$$\mathbf{V}^{\mathrm{T}} = \mathbf{V}^{-1} \tag{15.36}$$

Thus, the eigenvectors of a symmetric matrix form an orthogonal matrix. This in an important property with implications for statistics, multivariate signal processing, data compression, and other applications. You'll see several examples of this property later in this book, for example in Chapter 19.

Real solutions Now let's examine the property that real-valued symmetric matrices always have real-valued eigenvalues (and therefore also real-valued eigenvectors). There are 6 steps to this proof. Before reading the text below, try to understand the proof only from the equations.

Recall from Chapter 8 that the superscript ^{H} indicates the Hermitian transpose, which means transpose and flip the sign of the imaginary parts.

1) $\mathbf{A}\mathbf{v} = \lambda\mathbf{v}$

2) $(\mathbf{A}\mathbf{v})^{\mathrm{H}} = (\lambda\mathbf{v})^{\mathrm{H}}$

3) $\mathbf{v}^{\mathrm{H}}\mathbf{A} = \lambda^{\mathrm{H}}\mathbf{v}^{\mathrm{H}}$

4) $\mathbf{v}^{\mathrm{H}}\mathbf{A}\mathbf{v} = \lambda^{\mathrm{H}}\mathbf{v}^{\mathrm{H}}\mathbf{v}$

5) $\lambda\mathbf{v}^{\mathrm{H}}\mathbf{v} = \lambda^{\mathrm{H}}\mathbf{v}^{\mathrm{H}}\mathbf{v}$

6) $\lambda = \lambda^{\mathrm{H}}$

Could you understand it just from the equations? Here's my explanation, just in case you want to confirm your own understanding.

Step 1 is the basic eigenvalue equation. Step 2 says to take the Hermitian of both sides of the equation, which is then implemented in Step 3. Because $\mathbf{A}$ is symmetric and comprises real numbers, $\mathbf{A}^H = \mathbf{A}^T = \mathbf{A}$. In Step 4, both sides of the equation are right-multiplied by the eigenvector $\mathbf{v}$. In Step 5, $\mathbf{Av}$ is turned into its equivalent $\lambda\mathbf{v}$. $\mathbf{v}^H\mathbf{v}$ is the magnitude squared of vector $\mathbf{v}$ and can simply be divided away (remember that $\mathbf{v} \neq \mathbf{0}$). This brings us to the conclusion that $\lambda = \lambda^H$. A number is equal to its complex conjugate $(a + ib = a - ib)$ only when $b = 0$, i.e., it is a real-valued number. This concludes the proof that λ must have an imaginary part equal to 0, which means it is real-valued. If the matrix is not symmetric, we cannot proceed to Step 3.

Final note for this section: Some people use different letters to indicate the eigendecomposition of a symmetric matrix. In other texts or lectures you might see the following options.

$$\mathbf{A} = \mathbf{PDP}^{-1}$$

$$\mathbf{A} = \mathbf{UDU}^{-1}$$

Practice problems   Each problem gives a matrix and its unscaled eigenvectors. Fill in the missing eigenvector element. Then find the eigenvalues using the trace and determinant. Finally, compute $\mathbf{V\Lambda V}^T$ to confirm that it reproduces the original matrix.

a) $\begin{bmatrix} -2 & 2 \\ 2 & 1 \end{bmatrix}, \begin{bmatrix} -2 & 1 \\ * & 2 \end{bmatrix}$ b) $\begin{bmatrix} 52 & 16 \\ 16 & 28 \end{bmatrix}, \begin{bmatrix} 2 & * \\ -4 & -2 \end{bmatrix}$ c) $\begin{bmatrix} 3 & -3 \\ -3 & 3 \end{bmatrix}, \begin{bmatrix} * & 1 \\ 1 & -1 \end{bmatrix}$

Answers

a) $* = 1$ b) $* = -4$ c) $* = 1$
     $\lambda = -3, 2$ $\lambda = 20, 60$ $\lambda = 0, 6$

15.9   Eigenvalues of singular matrices

Every singular matrix has at least one zero-valued eigenvalue. And every full-rank matrix has no zero-valued eigenvalues. Before discussing why singular matrices have zero-valued eigenvalues, I want to show a few examples to illustrate that eigenvectors associated with zero-valued eigenvalues are not unusual (for example, they are not zeros, complex-valued, necessarily irrational, or have any bizarre properties; they're just regular eigenvectors).

$$\mathbf{A} = \begin{bmatrix} 1 & 2 \\ 1 & 2 \end{bmatrix} \quad \Rightarrow \quad |\mathbf{A} - \lambda\mathbf{I}| = 0 \quad \Rightarrow \quad \begin{vmatrix} 1 - \lambda & 2 \\ 1 & 2 - \lambda \end{vmatrix} = 0$$

$$(1 - \lambda)(2 - \lambda) - 2 = 0 \quad \Rightarrow \quad \lambda^2 - 3\lambda = 0 \quad \Rightarrow$$

$$\lambda(\lambda - 3) = 0 \quad \Rightarrow \quad \lambda_1 = 0, \ \lambda_2 = 3$$

Now we can substitute in each λ to find the two eigenvectors.

$$\lambda_1 : \begin{bmatrix} 1 - 0 & 2 \\ 1 & 2 - 0 \end{bmatrix} \begin{bmatrix} v_1 \\ v_2 \end{bmatrix} = \begin{bmatrix} 0 \\ 0 \end{bmatrix} \quad \Rightarrow \quad \mathbf{v} = \begin{bmatrix} -2 \\ 1 \end{bmatrix}$$

$$\lambda_2 : \begin{bmatrix} 1 - 3 & 2 \\ 1 & 2 - 3 \end{bmatrix} \begin{bmatrix} v_1 \\ v_2 \end{bmatrix} = \begin{bmatrix} 0 \\ 0 \end{bmatrix} \quad \Rightarrow \quad \mathbf{v}_2 = \begin{bmatrix} 1 \\ 1 \end{bmatrix}$$

Lest you think I carefully selected that matrix to give a zero eigenvalue, the next example shows that even in the general case of a matrix where one column is a multiple of another column (thus, a rank-1 matrix), one of the eigenvalues will be zero.

$$\mathbf{A} = \begin{bmatrix} a & \sigma a \\ b & \sigma b \end{bmatrix} \quad \Rightarrow \quad |\mathbf{A} - \lambda\mathbf{I}| = 0 \quad \Rightarrow \quad \begin{vmatrix} a - \lambda & \sigma a \\ b & \sigma b - \lambda \end{vmatrix} = 0$$

$$(a - \lambda)(\sigma b - \lambda) - \sigma ab = 0 \quad \Rightarrow \quad \lambda^2 - (a + \sigma b)\lambda = 0 \quad \Rightarrow$$

$$\lambda(\lambda - (a + \sigma b)) = 0 \quad \Rightarrow \quad \lambda_1 = 0, \ \lambda_2 = a + \sigma b$$

You can see from this example that the off-diagonal product ($-(\sigma a \times b)$) will cancel with the "left" terms from the diagonal product ($a \times \sigma b$); it doesn't matter what values you assign to a, b, and σ. (The same effect happens if you construct one row to be a multiple of the other, which you should try on your own.) The canceling of the constant term means all terms on the left-hand side of the characteristic polynomial contain λ, which means 0 will always be a solution.

At this point, you might be jumping to the conclusion that the rank of a matrix corresponds to the number of non-zero eigenvalues. Although this is a good thought, it's incorrect (it is, however, true for singular values, which you will learn in the next chapter). Let me make that more clear: The number of non-zero eigenvalues equals the rank for some matrices, but this is not generally true for all matrices. You've already seen an example of this in the section about conditions for diagonalizability. As an additional demonstration, create matrix $\mathbf{A}$ above using a=-4, b=2, σ=2. You will find that that matrix has both eigenvalues equal to zero, and yet is a rank-1 matrix. (This is another example of a nilpotent matrix. You can confirm that the suggested matrix has $\mathbf{AA} = \mathbf{0}$.)

Let's see how this would work with a 3×3 rank-2 matrix (I encourage you to work through this problem on your own before inspecting the equations below).

$$\mathbf{A} = \begin{bmatrix} a & d & \sigma a \\ b & e & \sigma b \\ c & f & \sigma c \end{bmatrix} \quad \Rightarrow \quad \begin{vmatrix} a - \lambda & d & \sigma a \\ b & e - \lambda & \sigma b \\ c & f & \sigma c - \lambda \end{vmatrix} = 0$$

$$(a - \lambda)(e - \lambda)(\sigma c - \lambda) + d\sigma be + \sigma abf - \sigma ac(e - \lambda) - db(\sigma c - \lambda) - \sigma bf(a - \lambda) = 0$$

$$-\lambda^3 + (a + e + \sigma c)\lambda^2 - (ae + a\sigma c + e\sigma c - \sigma ac - db - \sigma bf)\lambda = 0$$

There is a bit of algebra in that final step, but you can see that λ appears in all terms, which means $\lambda = 0$ is one of the three solutions.

I hope you find those examples compelling. There are several explanations for why singular matrices have at least one zero-valued eigenvalue. One is that the determinant of a matrix equals the product of the eigenvalues, and the determinant of a singular matrix is 0, so at least one eigenvalue must be zero.

But I think it's more insightful to reconsider Equation 15.4, rewritten below for convenience.

$$(\mathbf{A} - \lambda\mathbf{I})\mathbf{v} = \mathbf{0} \qquad (15.4)$$

We can interpret this equation in two ways. First let's assume that $\lambda = 0$. Then we're not actually shifting the matrix and the equation can be rewritten as $\mathbf{Av} = \mathbf{0}$. Because we do not consider the zeros vector to be an eigenvector, matrix $\mathbf{A}$ already has a non-trivial vector in its null space, hence it is singular.

Another way to interpret Equation 15.4 is to work the other way around: start from the assumption that $\mathbf{A}$ is singular, hence there is a non-trivial solution to $\mathbf{Av} = \mathbf{0}$. The way to reconcile that statement with Equation 15.4 is to assume that at least one $\lambda = 0$.

Practice problems Compute the missing eigenvalues of these matrices (hint: remember that the sum of eigenvalues equals the trace of the matrix).

a) $\begin{bmatrix} 1 & 0 \\ 1 & 0 \end{bmatrix}, \lambda = 1, ?$
b) $\begin{bmatrix} 3 & 4 \\ 6 & 8 \end{bmatrix}, \lambda = ?, ?$
c) $\begin{bmatrix} 2 & -2 & -2 \\ 3 & -3 & -2 \\ 2 & -2 & -2 \end{bmatrix}, \lambda = -2, ?, ?$

Answers Printed below are all eigenvalues.

a) $\lambda = 1, 0$
b) $\lambda = 0, 11$
c) $\lambda = -2, -1, 0$

15.10 Eigenlayers of a matrix

This section will tie together eigendecomposition with the "layer perspective" of matrix multiplication. It will also set you up to understand the "spectral theory of matrices" and applications such as data compression and PCA. We're going to discover how to reconstruct a matrix one "layer" at a time, where each layer comes from an eigenvector.

Consider computing the outer product of one eigenvector with itself. That will produce an $M \times M$ rank-1 matrix. The norm of this matrix will also be 1, because it is formed from a unit-norm vector. An $M \times M$ matrix has M eigenvectors, and thus, M outer product matrices can be formed from the set of eigenvectors.

What would happen if we sum together all of those outer product matrices? Well, nothing terribly important. It's a valid operation, but that sum would not equal the original matrix $\mathbf{A}$. Why not?

It's because eigenvectors have no intrinsic length; they need the eigenvalues to scale them.

Therefore, we'll multiply each eigenvector outer product matrix by its corresponding eigenvalue. And now we have an interesting situation, because this sum will exactly reproduce the original matrix. In other words, we can reconstruct the matrix one "eigenlayer" at a time.

$$\mathbf{A} = \sum_{i=1}^{M} \mathbf{v}_i \lambda_i \mathbf{v}_i^{\mathrm{T}} \tag{15.37}$$

Expanding out the summation sign leads to the insight that we are re-expressing diagonalization:

$$\mathbf{A} = \mathbf{V}\mathbf{\Lambda}\mathbf{V}^{\mathrm{T}} \tag{15.38}$$

But actually, this is not exactly Equation 15.21 (page 432). Previously we right-multiplied by $\mathbf{V}^{-1}$ but here we're right-multiplying by $\mathbf{V}^{\mathrm{T}}$. Can you guess what that means? It means that reconstructing a matrix using Equation 15.37 is valid only for symmetric matrices, because $\mathbf{V}^{-1} = \mathbf{V}^{\mathrm{T}}$.

But don't worry, reconstructing a matrix via eigenlayers is still valid for non-symmetric matrices. We just need a different formulation. In fact, now the vector on the right is the ith row of $\mathbf{V}^{-1}$. This comes from the definition of the outer product, as the multiplication between a column vector and a row vector. Some additional notation should minimize confusion.

$$\mathbf{W} = \mathbf{V}^{-\mathrm{T}} \tag{15.39}$$

$$\mathbf{A} = \sum_{i=1}^{M} \mathbf{v}_i \lambda_i \mathbf{w}_i^{\mathrm{T}} \tag{15.40}$$

What happens here for $\lambda_i = 0$?

Now we have the outer product between the eigenvector and the corresponding row of the inverse of the eigenvector matrix transposed, which here is printed as the ith column of matrix $\mathbf{W}$. I hope it is clear why Equation 15.37 is a simplification of Equation 15.40: $\mathbf{V}^{-\mathrm{T}} = \mathbf{V}$ for an orthogonal matrix.

It is important to appreciate that Equation 15.37 is valid only when the eigenvectors are unit-normalized. The eigenvectors need to be

Eigenvector normalization is also relevant for the SVD.

unit-normalized so that they provide only direction with no magnitude, allowing the magnitude to be specified by the eigenvalue. That equation could be generalized to non-unit vectors by dividing by the magnitudes of the vectors.

On the other hand, Equation 15.40 does not require unit-normalized eigenvectors. Can you think about why that's the case? It's because Equation 15.40 includes the matrix inverse. Thus, $\mathbf{V}\mathbf{V}^{-1} = \mathbf{I}$ regardless of the magnitude of the individual eigenvectors, whereas $\mathbf{V}\mathbf{V}^{\mathrm{T}} = \mathbf{I}$ only when each eigenvector is unit-normalized.

Let's see an example with a 2×2 matrix.

$$\mathbf{A} = \begin{bmatrix} 2 & 3 \\ 3 & 2 \end{bmatrix} \begin{cases} \lambda_1 = -1, & \mathbf{v}_1 = \frac{1}{\sqrt{2}} \begin{bmatrix} -1 \\ 1 \end{bmatrix} \\ \\ \lambda_2 = 5, & \mathbf{v}_2 = \frac{1}{\sqrt{2}} \begin{bmatrix} 1 \\ 1 \end{bmatrix} \end{cases}$$

$$\mathbf{A_1} = \mathbf{v}_1 \lambda_1 \mathbf{v}_1^{\mathrm{T}} = \begin{bmatrix} -.5 & .5 \\ .5 & -.5 \end{bmatrix}$$

$$\mathbf{A_2} = \mathbf{v}_2 \lambda_2 \mathbf{v}_2^{\mathrm{T}} = \begin{bmatrix} 2.5 & 2.5 \\ 2.5 & 2.5 \end{bmatrix}$$

$$\mathbf{A_1} + \mathbf{A_2} = \begin{bmatrix} -.5 & .5 \\ .5 & -.5 \end{bmatrix} + \begin{bmatrix} 2.5 & 2.5 \\ 2.5 & 2.5 \end{bmatrix} = \begin{bmatrix} 2 & 3 \\ 3 & 2 \end{bmatrix} = \mathbf{A}$$

It is easy to confirm that the rank of $\mathbf{A}$ is 2 and the ranks of $\mathbf{A_1}$ and $\mathbf{A_2}$ are both 1.

Practice problems The matrices below are eigenvectors and eigenvalues. Reconstruct the matrix from which these were extracted by summing over eigenlayers. It's safer to apply Equation 15.40 if you don't know for sure that the matrix is symmetric.

a) $\begin{bmatrix} 2 & 3 \\ -4 & 2 \end{bmatrix}, \begin{bmatrix} 1 & 0 \\ 0 & 3 \end{bmatrix}$

b) $\begin{bmatrix} 1 & 2 \\ 0 & 1 \end{bmatrix}, \begin{bmatrix} 2 & 0 \\ 0 & 3 \end{bmatrix}$

c) $\begin{bmatrix} -2 & 2 & 0 \\ 1 & 1 & 0 \\ 1 & 0 & 1 \end{bmatrix}, \begin{bmatrix} 1 & 0 & 0 \\ 0 & 2 & 0 \\ 0 & 0 & 3 \end{bmatrix}$

Answers

a) $\begin{bmatrix} 2.5 & .75 \\ 1 & 1.5 \end{bmatrix}$

b) $\begin{bmatrix} 2 & 2 \\ 0 & 3 \end{bmatrix}$

c) $\begin{bmatrix} 1.5 & 1 & 0 \\ .25 & 1.5 & 0 \\ .5 & -1 & 3 \end{bmatrix}$

Reflection

Who cares about eigenlayers? It may seem circuitous to deconstruct a matrix only to reconstruct it again. But consider this: do you need to sum up *all* of the layers? What if you would sum only the layers with the largest $k < r$ eigenvalues? That will actually be a low-rank approximation of the original matrix. Or maybe this is a data matrix and you identity certain eigenvectors that reflect noise; you can then reconstruct the data without the "noise layers." More on this in the next few chapters!

15.11 Matrix powers and inverse

One of the reasons that eigendecomposition has many applications is that diagonal matrices are really easy to compute with. You've already seen examples of this with matrix multiplication and the inverse. In this section I'm going to show you two applications of eigendecomposition that follow from the special properties of diagonal matrices.

Matrix powers Compute $\mathbf{A}^2 = \mathbf{AA}$ for the following two matrices:

$$\mathbf{A} = \begin{bmatrix} 0 & 1 \\ 0 & 0 \end{bmatrix} \quad , \quad \mathbf{A} = \begin{bmatrix} 1 & 0 \\ 2 & 3 \end{bmatrix}$$

For simple matrices like this, a few minutes of pen-and-paper work will easily reveal the answer. What if the matrix were larger, and what if you had to compute $\mathbf{A}^5 = \mathbf{AAAAA}$?

Raising matrices to powers can be computationally intensive. But watch what happens when we raise the diagonalized version of a matrix to a higher power.

$$\mathbf{A}^2 = (\mathbf{VDV}^{-1})^2 = \mathbf{VDV}^{-1}\mathbf{VDV}^{-1} = \mathbf{VD}^2\mathbf{V}^{-1} \qquad (15.41)$$

The matrix of eigenvectors cancels with its inverse in the middle of that expression ($\mathbf{V}^{-1}\mathbf{V} = \mathbf{I}$). And you will remember from the chapter on matrix multiplication that multiplying two diagonal matrices simply involves multiplying their diagonal elements and ignoring all the off-diagonal zeros. Let's see how this looks for $\mathbf{A}^3$.

$$\mathbf{A}^3 = (\mathbf{VDV}^{-1})^3 = \mathbf{VDV}^{-1}\mathbf{VDV}^{-1}\mathbf{VDV}^{-1} = \mathbf{VD}^3\mathbf{V}^{-1}$$
$$(15.42)$$

You see where this is going: The general form for matrix powers is:

$$\mathbf{A}^n = (\mathbf{VDV}^{-1})^n = \mathbf{VD}^n\mathbf{V}^{-1} \qquad (15.43)$$

Therefore, once you've completed the eigendecomposition, taking matrices to higher powers requires very few FLOPs (floating point operations, the count of basic computer arithmetic operations). Of course, if you will square a matrix only once, then it might be more hassle than advantage to diagonalize it. But Equation 15.43 becomes very efficient if you need to raise the matrix to powers multiple times.

While we're on the subject of matrix powers and eigendecomposition, we can take a small tangent to show that squaring a matrix squares its eigenvalues without changing the eigenvectors. Here's the proof (assume $\mathbf{v}$ is an eigenvector of $\mathbf{A}$ and λ is the associated eigenvalue):

$$\mathbf{A}^2\mathbf{v} = \mathbf{A}\mathbf{A}\mathbf{v} = \mathbf{A}\lambda\mathbf{v} = \lambda(\mathbf{A}\mathbf{v}) = \lambda^2\mathbf{v} \qquad (15.44)$$

This generalizes to any power. Extending this proof to $\mathbf{A}^n$ involves additional replacements of $\mathbf{A}\mathbf{v}$ with $\lambda\mathbf{v}$.

In case you were curious:
$\mathbf{A}^0 = \mathbf{I}$

Matrix powers and eigenvalues

For eigenvalue/vector $\lambda\mathbf{v}$ of matrix $\mathbf{A}$,

$$\mathbf{A}^n\mathbf{v} = \lambda^n\mathbf{v} \qquad (15.45)$$

This proof also shows why nilpotent matrices have zero-valued eigenvalues: If there is some k for which $\mathbf{A}^k = \mathbf{0}$, then $\mathbf{0} = \mathbf{A}^k\mathbf{v} = \lambda^k\mathbf{v}$, which means that $\lambda = 0$ if $\mathbf{v} \neq \mathbf{0}$.

Practice problems Compute $\mathbf{A}^3$ for the following matrices. The eigenvalues are provided but you'll have to compute the eigenvectors.

a) $\begin{bmatrix} 1 & 0 \\ 6 & -1 \end{bmatrix}, \lambda = 1, -1$ 　　 b) $\begin{bmatrix} 4 & -2 \\ -1 & 5 \end{bmatrix}, \lambda = 3, 6$ 　　 c) $\begin{bmatrix} 4 & 0 & 1 \\ -2 & 1 & 0 \\ -2 & 0 & 1 \end{bmatrix}, \lambda = 1, 2, 3$

Answers

a) $\begin{bmatrix} 1 & 0 \\ 6 & -1 \end{bmatrix}$ 　　 b) $\begin{bmatrix} 90 & -126 \\ -63 & 153 \end{bmatrix}$ 　　 c) $\begin{bmatrix} 46 & 0 & 19 \\ -38 & 1 & -12 \\ -38 & 0 & -11 \end{bmatrix}$

Matrix inverse The other application in this section follows the same logic: Diagonalize a matrix, apply some operation to the diagonal elements of $\mathbf{\Lambda}$, then optionally reassemble the three matrices into one.

Remember from Chapter 12 that the inverse of a diagonal matrix is the diagonal elements individually inverted. That's the key insight to inverse-via-eigendecomposition.

$$\mathbf{A}^{-1} = (\mathbf{V}\mathbf{D}\mathbf{V}^{-1})^{-1} = (\mathbf{V}^{-1})^{-1}\mathbf{D}^{-1}\mathbf{V}^{-1} = \mathbf{V}\mathbf{D}^{-1}\mathbf{V}^{-1} \quad (15.46)$$

Of course, this procedure is valid only for matrices with all non-zero diagonal elements, which unsurprisingly excludes all singular matrices.

You might wonder whether this is really a short-cut, considering that $\mathbf{V}$ still needs to be inverted. There are two computational advantages of Equation 15.46. One advantage is obviously from inverting a symmetric matrix (with an orthogonal eigenvectors matrix), where $\mathbf{V}^{-1} = \mathbf{V}^{\mathrm{T}}$. A second advantage is that because the eigenvectors are normalized, $\mathbf{V}$ has a low condition number and is therefore more numerically stable. Thus, the $\mathbf{V}$ of a non-symmetric matrix might be easier to invert than $\mathbf{A}$. (Condition number is a measure of the "spread" of a matrix that characterizes the stability of a matrix to minor perturbations or noise; you'll learn more about this quantity in the next chapter. The point is that even if $\mathbf{A}$ is theoretically invertible, the inverse of $\mathbf{V}$ may have a more accurate inverse.)

Equation 15.46 also has a theoretical advantage, because it helps build intuition for the algorithm to compute the pseudoinverse via the singular value decomposition.

Practice problems Each exercise provides a matrix, its eigenvectors, and eigenvalues. Compute $\mathbf{A}^{-1}$ by $\mathbf{V}\mathbf{D}^{-1}\mathbf{V}^{-1}$. Then confirm that $\mathbf{A}\mathbf{A}^{-1} = \mathbf{I}$.

a) $\begin{bmatrix} 1 & 2 \\ 3 & -4 \end{bmatrix}, \begin{bmatrix} 2 & 1 \\ 1 & -3 \end{bmatrix}, \lambda = 2, -5$

b) $\begin{bmatrix} 3 & -2 \\ 1 & 0 \end{bmatrix}, \begin{bmatrix} 2 & 1 \\ 1 & 1 \end{bmatrix}, \lambda = 2, 1$

Answers Matrices are $\mathbf{A}^{-1}$

a) $\begin{bmatrix} .4 & .2 \\ .3 & -.1 \end{bmatrix}$

b) $\begin{bmatrix} 0 & 1 \\ -.5 & 1.5 \end{bmatrix}$

15.12 Generalized eigendecomposition

One quick glance will reveal that the following two equations are equivalent.

$$\mathbf{Av} = \lambda\mathbf{v}$$

$$\mathbf{Av} = \lambda\mathbf{Iv}$$

What if we replace $\mathbf{I}$ with another (suitably sized) matrix?

Generalized eigenvalue equation	
$$\mathbf{Av} = \lambda\mathbf{Bv}$$	(15.47)
$$\mathbf{AV} = \mathbf{BV\Lambda}$$	(15.48)

Generalized eigendecomposition is also called *simultaneous diagonalization of two matrices* and leads to several equations that are not immediately easy to interpret, including:

$$\mathbf{V}^{-1}\mathbf{B}^{-1}\mathbf{AV} = \mathbf{\Lambda} \tag{15.49}$$

$$\mathbf{A} = \mathbf{BV\Lambda V}^{-1} \tag{15.50}$$

$$\mathbf{B} = \mathbf{V}^{-1}\mathbf{\Lambda}^{-1}\mathbf{AV} \tag{15.51}$$

Perhaps a better way to interpret generalized eigendecomposition is to think about "regular" eigendecomposition on a matrix product involving an inverse.

Interpretation of generalized eigendecomposition	
$$(\mathbf{B}^{-1}\mathbf{A})\mathbf{v} = \lambda\mathbf{v}$$	(15.52)
$$\mathbf{Cv} = \lambda\mathbf{v}, \quad \mathbf{C} = \mathbf{B}^{-1}\mathbf{A}$$	

This interpretation is valid only when $\mathbf{B}$ is invertible. In practice, even when $\mathbf{B}$ is invertible, inverting large or high-conditioned matrices can lead to numerical inaccuracies and therefore should be avoided. Computer programs will perform the eigendecomposition without actually inverting matrices. Nonetheless, Equation 15.52 helps build intuition.

In section 6.7 I showed how the product of two symmetric matrices is generally not symmetric. That is important because even if matrices $\mathbf{A}$ and $\mathbf{B}$ are both symmetric, $\mathbf{B}^{-1}\mathbf{A}$ will generally not be symmetric. That means that the special properties of eigendecomposition for symmetric matrices (orthogonal eigenvectors, real-valued eigenvalues) do not apply to generalized eigendecomposition.

Code Generalized eigendecomposition is easy to implement. Just be mindful of the order of function inputs: Following Equation 15.52, $\mathbf{A}$ must be the first input and $\mathbf{B}$ must be the second input. Numpy cannot perform generalized eigendecomposition (at the time of this writing), but scipy's implementation can.

Code block 15.3: Python

```
1  import numpy as np
2  from scipy.linalg import eig
3  n = 3
4  A = np.random.randn(n,n)
5  B = np.random.randn(n,n)
6  evals,evecs = eig(A,B)
```

Code block 15.4: MATLAB

```
1  n = 3;
2  A = randn(n);
3  B = randn(n);
4  [evecs,evals] = eig(A,B);
```

You can also think of $\mathbf{B}^{-1}\mathbf{A}$ as the matrix version of a *ratio* of $\mathbf{A}$ to $\mathbf{B}$. This interpretation makes generalized eigendecomposition a computational workhorse for several multivariate data science and machine-learning applications, including linear discriminant analysis, source separation, and classifiers.

1. Find the eigenvalues of the following matrices.

a) $\begin{bmatrix} 4 \end{bmatrix}$

b) $\begin{bmatrix} 0 & 3 \\ 5 & 0 \end{bmatrix}$

c) $\begin{bmatrix} 3 & 0 \\ 0 & 5 \end{bmatrix}$

d) $\begin{bmatrix} 2 & 5 \\ 6 & 3 \end{bmatrix}$

e) $\begin{bmatrix} -4 & 1 \\ 1 & 3 \end{bmatrix}$

f) $\begin{bmatrix} -2 & 2 \\ -3 & 2 \end{bmatrix}$

g) $\begin{bmatrix} 2 & 5 & -1 \\ 0 & 4 & 3 \\ 0 & 0 & 1 \end{bmatrix}$

h) $\begin{bmatrix} a & 34 & \sqrt{23} \\ 0 & b & e^{i\pi^3} \\ 0 & 0 & c \end{bmatrix}$

i) $\begin{bmatrix} a & 0 & 0 \\ 34 & b & 0 \\ \sqrt{23} & e^{i\pi^3} & c \end{bmatrix}$

2. Diagonalize the following matrices.

a) $\begin{bmatrix} 1 & 1 \\ -3 & 5 \end{bmatrix}$

b) $\begin{bmatrix} -1 & 0 \\ -1 & 0 \end{bmatrix}$

c) $\begin{bmatrix} 4 & 0 & 1 \\ -2 & 1 & 0 \\ -2 & 0 & 1 \end{bmatrix}$

3. The following pairs of matrices show a matrix and its eigenvectors. Without computing eigenvalues, determine the missing eigenvector component.

a) $\begin{bmatrix} -2 & 2 \\ 2 & 1 \end{bmatrix}, \begin{bmatrix} -2 & 1 \\ * & 2 \end{bmatrix}$

b) $\begin{bmatrix} 52 & 16 \\ 16 & 28 \end{bmatrix}, \begin{bmatrix} 2 & * \\ -4 & -2 \end{bmatrix}$

c) $\begin{bmatrix} 3 & -3 \\ -3 & 3 \end{bmatrix}, \begin{bmatrix} * & 1 \\ 1 & -1 \end{bmatrix}$

4. I wrote that finding eigenvectors involves computing the null space of $\mathbf{A} - \lambda\mathbf{I}$. What would happen if you started from $\lambda\mathbf{I} - \mathbf{A}$? Try this using the matrix in Equation 15.15 (page 427) to see whether the results differ. Either way, explain why this happens.

5. Left-multiply both sides of the eigenvalue equation the eigenvalue equation $(\mathbf{Av} = \lambda\mathbf{v})$ by $\mathbf{v}^\mathrm{T}$. Assume that $\|\mathbf{v}\| = 1$ and simplify. What can you conclude?

15.14 Answers

1. Following are the missing pieces.

    a) 4   **b)** $\pm\sqrt{15}$ **c)** 3, 5

    d) -3, 8   **e)** $(-1 \pm \sqrt{53})/2$ **f)** $\pm\sqrt{2}i$

    g) 2, 4, 1   **h)** a, b, c **i)** a, b, c

2. Matrices below are eigenvalues, eigenvectors (non-normalized).

    a) $\begin{bmatrix} 2 & 0 \\ 0 & 4 \end{bmatrix}, \begin{bmatrix} 1 & 1 \\ 1 & 3 \end{bmatrix}$ **b)** $\begin{bmatrix} -1 & 0 \\ 0 & 0 \end{bmatrix}, \begin{bmatrix} \pi & 0 \\ \pi & 1 \end{bmatrix}$

    c) $\begin{bmatrix} 1 & 0 & 0 \\ 0 & 3 & 0 \\ 0 & 0 & 2 \end{bmatrix}, \begin{bmatrix} 0 & 1 & -1 \\ 1 & -1 & 2 \\ 0 & -1 & 2 \end{bmatrix}$

3. Following are the eigenvector values.

    a) $* = 1$ **b)** $* = -4$ **c)** $* = 1$

4. You get the same results: Same eigenvalues and same eigenvectors. It's a bit awkward in my opinion, because you have to flip the signs of all the matrix elements, but conceptually it's the same thing as writing $(a - b) = -(b - a)$.

5. Pre- and post-multiplying a matrix by a vector produces a scalar. In a few chapters, I will call the general expression $\mathbf{v}^T \mathbf{A} \mathbf{v}$ the *quadratic form*, which will reveal some interesting properties about the definiteness and eigenvalues of the matrix.

The second thing to notice is that the matrix reduces to its eigenvalue when transformed on both sides by its eigenvector. That is: $\mathbf{v}^T \mathbf{A} \mathbf{v} = \lambda$. Again, this leads to some interesting discoveries about the matrix, which you will learn about in Chapter 17.

1. In this code challenge, you will explore the relationship between Equations 15.47 and 15.52 in the section on generalized eigendecomposition. Create two matrices $\mathbf{A}$ and $\mathbf{B}$. Then perform (1) generalized eigendecomposition of both matrices, and (2) "regular" eigendecomposition on the matrix $\mathbf{B}^{-1}\mathbf{A}$; inspect whether the eigenvalues are the same. Try this for 2×2 matrices, and then again for larger matrices like 10×10 or 50×50. Do you also need to compare the eigenvectors or is it sufficient to compare the eigenvalues?

2. In this chapter, you learned that diagonalization means to transform a matrix into a diagonal matrix, with the eigenvectors providing the transformation matrix. What happens if the matrix $\mathbf{A}$ is already a diagonal matrix? What are its eigenvalues and eigenvectors? Use code to explore this empirically by taking the eigendecomposition of diagonal matrices. Then explain why you get those results.

3. In Chapter 5 you learned about Hankel matrices (123), and I mentioned that they have aesthetically pleasing properties in eigendecomposition. Now is your chance to explore this. Create a 50×50 Hankel matrix and take its eigendecomposition. Sort the eigenvectors according to descending eigenvalues. Then produce a figure that shows Hankel matrix and its eigenvectors matrix. Then plot the first few eigenvectors.

15.16 Code solutions

1. The answer is that for random-numbers matrices, the two approaches produce basically identical eigenvalues in MATLAB, but different results in Python. These are very difficult numerical problems to solve. The two methods are similar in MATLAB because the matrices are invertible and have a low condition number. In the next chapter, you'll see that this conclusion changes for matrices with a larger condition number (you'll learn about condition number in the next chapter). It is not necessary to compare the eigenvectors—if the eigenvalues differ, so do the eigenvectors. When comparing eigenvalues, it's important to make sure they're sorted!

Code block 15.5: Python

```python
1  import numpy as np
2  from scipy.linalg import eig
3  import matplotlib.pyplot as plt
4
5  avediffs = np.zeros(100)
6  for n in range(1,101):
7      A = np.random.randn(n,n)
8      B = np.random.randn(n,n)
9      l1 = eig(A,B)[0]
10     l2 = eig(np.linalg.inv(B)@A)[0]
11
12     # important to sort eigvals
13     l1.sort()
14     l2.sort()
15
16     avediffs[n-1] = np.mean(np.abs(l1-l2))
17
18 plt.plot(avediffs);
```

```
1   for  n=1:100
2       A = randn(n);
3       B = randn(n);
4       l1 = eig(A,B);
5       l2 = eig(inv(B)*A);
6
7            % important to sort evals
8       l1 = sort(l1);
9       l2 = sort(l2);
10      avediffs(n) = mean(abs(l1-l2));
11  end
12  plot(avediffs, 's-')
13  xlabel('Matrix size')
14  ylabel('\Delta\lambda')
```

EIGENDECOMPOSITION

2. Conveniently, the eigenvalues of a diagonal matrix are simply the diagonal elements, while the eigenvectors matrix is the identity matrix. This is because $(\mathbf{A} - \lambda\mathbf{I})$ is made singular simply by setting λ to each diagonal element.

In fact, the eigenvalues of *any* triangular matrix (including diagonal matrices) are simply the elements on the main diagonal (see exercise question 1g-i). However, $\mathbf{V} = \mathbf{I}$ only for a diagonal matrix. The eigenvectors matrix of a triangular matrix is itself triangular. That's not shown in the code below, but I encourage you to test it!

Code block 15.7: Python

```python
1  import numpy as np
2  D = np.diag(range(1,6))
3  L,V = np.linalg.eig(D)
```

Code block 15.8: MATLAB

```matlab
1  D = diag(1:5);
2  [V,L] = eig(D)
```

3. The eigenvectors matrix looks cute, like a pixelated flower from a 1970's computer. Plotting the eigenvectors reveals their remarkable property—they're sine waves! (Figure is shown below the code.) If you are familiar with signal processing, then this might look familiar from the Fourier transform. In fact, there is a deep connection between the Hankel matrix and the Fourier transform. By the way, you can run this code on a Toeplitz matrix for comparison (spoiler alert: Not nearly as cool!).

Code block 15.9: Python

```python
import numpy as np
import matplotlib.pyplot as plt
from scipy.linalg import hankel

t = np.arange(1,51)
lstrow = np.append(t[-1],np.arange(1,t[-1]))
H = hankel(t,r=lstrow)
d,V = np.linalg.eig(H)
V = V[:,np.argsort(d)[::-1]]

plt.subplot(221)
plt.imshow(H)
plt.subplot(222)
plt.imshow(V)
plt.subplot(212)
plt.plot(V[:,:4]);
```

```
1  N = 50;
2  T = toeplitz(1:N);
3  H = hankel(1:N,[N 1:N−1]);
4
5  [V,D] = eig(H);
6  [~,sidx] = sort(diag(D),'descend');
7  V = V(:,sidx);
8
9  subplot(221)
10 imagesc(H), axis square
11 subplot(222)
12 imagesc(V), axis square
13 subplot(212)
14 plot(V(:,1:4),'o−')
```

Hankel matrix

Eigenvectors matrix

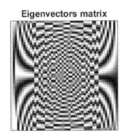

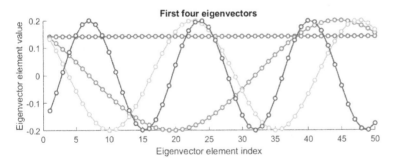

Figure 15.7: Image for code challenge 3.

. Eigendecomposition

CHAPTER 16
SINGULAR VALUE
DECOMPOSITION

START THIS CHAPTER HAPPY

16.1 Singular value decomposition

Singular value decomposition, or SVD, is closely related to eigende-composition. In fact, eigendecomposition can be seen as a special case of the SVD in which the to-be-decomposed (decomposing?) matrix is square. Alternatively, SVD can be seen as a general-ization of eigendecomposition to a matrix of any size. This latter interpretation is more consistent with how it will be introduced.

Before learning about the mechanics of the SVD, I want to present the big picture and the terminology. The core idea of SVD is to provide sets of basis vectors—called *singular vectors*—for the four matrix subspaces: the row space, the null space, the column space, and the left-null space; and to provide scalar *singular values* that encode the "importance" of each singular vector. The singular vec-tors are similar to eigenvectors, and the singular values are similar to eigenvalues (though their exact relationships are complicated and will be described later). The full SVD is expressed using the following matrix letters.

Singular value decomposition

$$\mathbf{A} = \mathbf{U}\mathbf{\Sigma}\mathbf{V}^{\mathrm{T}} \tag{16.1}$$

A	The $M{\times}N$ matrix to be decomposed. It can be square or rectangular, and any rank.
U	The *left singular vectors matrix* $(M \times M)$, which provides an orthonormal basis for $\mathbb{R}^M$. This includes the column space of **A** and its complementary left-null space.
Σ	The *singular values matrix* $(M{\times}N)$, which is diagonal and contains the singular values (the ith singular value is indicated σ_i). All singular values are non-negative (that is, positive or zero) and real-valued.
V	The *right singular vectors matrix* $(N{\times}N)$, which provides an orthonormal basis for $\mathbb{R}^N$. That includes the row space of **A** and its complementary null space. Notice that the decomposition contains $\mathbf{V}^{\text{T}}$; hence, although the right singular vectors are in the *columns* of **V**, it is usually more convenient to speak of the right singular vectors as being the *rows* of $\mathbf{V}^{\text{T}}$.

As you can see in the descriptions above, the sizes of the right-hand-side matrices depend on the size of **A**. Figure 16.1 shows graphical representations of the SVD for square, tall, and wide rectangular matrices.

Notice that the size of **U** corresponds to the number of rows in **A**, that the size of **V** corresponds to the number of columns in **A**, and that the size of **Σ** is the same as that of **A**. These sizes allow for **U** to be an orthonormal basis for $\mathbb{R}^M$ and for **V** to be an orthonormal basis for $\mathbb{R}^N$.

Let's see what the SVD looks like for a real matrix. Figure 16.2 shows a matrix (created by applying a 2D smoothing kernel to random noise; the grayscale intensity at each pixel in the image is mapped onto the numerical value at that element of the matrix) and its SVD.

So that's the purpose of the SVD: Represent a matrix using two orthogonal matrices surrounding a diagonal matrix. Now let's fig-

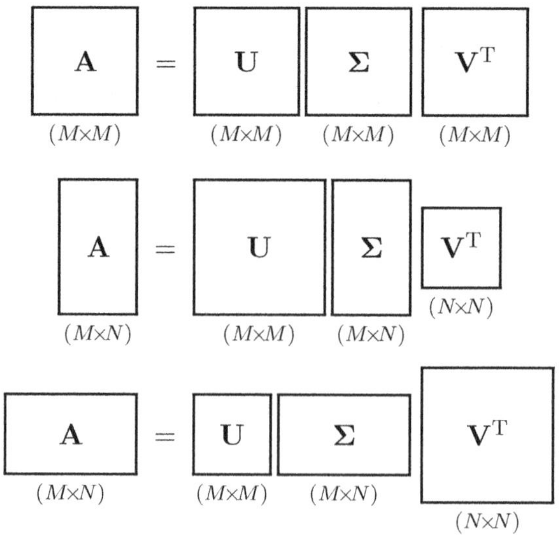

Figure 16.1: The sizes of SVD matrices for different sizes of the to-be-decomposed matrix.

ure out how to create those three matrices, and then the rest of the chapter will give you opportunities to develop intuition for why the SVD is so useful.

16.2 Computing the SVD

Given the importance of the SVD in theoretical and applied linear algebra, you might think that the SVD is really difficult to compute. Well, you're wrong (if that's what you thought). In fact, once you know eigendecomposition, the SVD is almost trivial to compute.

Let's start by considering the eigendecomposition of matrix $\mathbf{A}$ of size $M \neq N$. Actually, eigendecomposition is not defined for this non-square matrix. However, $\mathbf{A}^{\mathrm{T}}\mathbf{A}$ is eigencomposable. Replac-

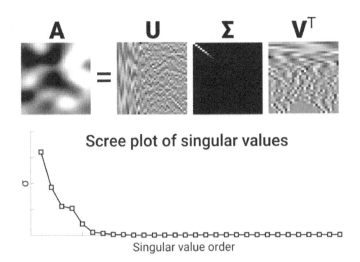

Figure 16.2: Visualization of the SVD of a smoothed random numbers matrix. The lower plot shows the singular values, which are the diagonal of the Σ matrix. This plot is called a "scree plot" in statistics nomenclature. The singular vectors are in the columns of U and the rows of V^T.

ing $\mathbf{A}^T\mathbf{A}$ with its SVD matrices gives us the following.

$$\mathbf{A}^T\mathbf{A} = (\mathbf{U}\mathbf{\Sigma}\mathbf{V}^T)^T(\mathbf{U}\mathbf{\Sigma}\mathbf{V}^T) \qquad (16.2)$$

$$= \mathbf{V}\mathbf{\Sigma}^T\mathbf{U}^T\mathbf{U}\mathbf{\Sigma}\mathbf{V}^T \qquad (16.3)$$

$$= \mathbf{V}\mathbf{\Sigma}^2\mathbf{V}^T \qquad (16.4)$$

U is orthogonal, ergo $\mathbf{U}^T\mathbf{U} = \mathbf{I}$.

We've now discovered how to find the $\mathbf{V}$ and $\mathbf{\Sigma}$ matrices from the SVD: $\mathbf{V}$ are the eigenvectors of $\mathbf{A}^T\mathbf{A}$ and $\mathbf{\Sigma}$ are the squared eigenvalues of $\mathbf{A}^T\mathbf{A}$. Remember that because $\mathbf{\Sigma}$ is a diagonal matrix, then $\mathbf{\Sigma}^2$ simplifies to the diagonal elements (the eigenvalues) squared.

You can immediately see why the singular values are non-negative—any real number squared will be non-negative. This doesn't show immediately why the singular values are real-valued, though; that comes from the proof that the eigenvalues of a symmetric matrix are real-valued (page 444).

We're missing the $\mathbf{U}$ matrix, but I'm sure you've already figured it out: Take the eigendecomposition of matrix $\mathbf{A}\mathbf{A}^{\mathrm{T}}$:

$$\mathbf{A}\mathbf{A}^{\mathrm{T}} = (\mathbf{U}\boldsymbol{\Sigma}\mathbf{V}^{\mathrm{T}})(\mathbf{U}\boldsymbol{\Sigma}\mathbf{V}^{\mathrm{T}})^{\mathrm{T}} \tag{16.5}$$

$$= \mathbf{U}\boldsymbol{\Sigma}\mathbf{V}^{\mathrm{T}}\mathbf{V}\boldsymbol{\Sigma}^{\mathrm{T}}\mathbf{U}^{\mathrm{T}} \tag{16.6}$$

$$= \mathbf{U}\boldsymbol{\Sigma}^2\mathbf{U}^{\mathrm{T}} \tag{16.7}$$

So there you have it—the way to compute the SVD of any rectangular matrix is to apply the following steps:

1. Compute the eigendecomposition of $\mathbf{A}^{\mathrm{T}}\mathbf{A}$ to get $\boldsymbol{\Sigma}$ and $\mathbf{V}$.
2. Compute the eigendecomposition of $\mathbf{A}\mathbf{A}^{\mathrm{T}}$ to obtain $\mathbf{U}$.

It is actually not necessary to compute both steps to obtain the SVD. After applying either one of these steps, you can compute the third matrix directly using one of the following two formulas.

$$\mathbf{A}\mathbf{V}\boldsymbol{\Sigma}^{-1} = \mathbf{U} \tag{16.8}$$

$$\boldsymbol{\Sigma}^{-1}\mathbf{U}^{\mathrm{T}}\mathbf{A} = \mathbf{V}^{\mathrm{T}} \tag{16.9}$$

Quick question: How do you know that $\mathbf{U}$ and $\mathbf{V}$ are orthogonal matrices? Think of your answer and then check the footnote[1].

I explained earlier in this chapter that the $\boldsymbol{\Sigma}$ matrix is the same size as $\mathbf{A}$, and yet computing $\boldsymbol{\Sigma}^{\mathrm{T}}\boldsymbol{\Sigma}$ actually produces a square matrix, even if $\mathbf{A}$ is rectangular. Thus, in practice, the "real" $\boldsymbol{\Sigma}$ matrix is the same size as $\mathbf{A}$ and its diagonal elements are drawn from the diagonal elements of $\boldsymbol{\Sigma}^{\mathrm{T}}\boldsymbol{\Sigma}$. Equivalently, you could cut out the "excess" rows or columns from square $\boldsymbol{\Sigma}^{\mathrm{T}}\boldsymbol{\Sigma}$ to trim it down to the size of $\mathbf{A}$.

When computing SVD by hand—which I recommend doing at least a few times to solidify the concept—you should first decide whether to apply step 1 and then Equation 16.8, or step 2 and Equation 16.9. The best strategy depends on the size of the matrix, because you want to compute the eigendecomposition of whichever of $\mathbf{A}^{\mathrm{T}}\mathbf{A}$ or $\mathbf{A}\mathbf{A}^{\mathrm{T}}$ is smaller. On the other hand, following steps 1 and 2 is easier than it looks, because you need to solve for the squared eigenvalues (the singular values on the diagonal of $\boldsymbol{\Sigma}^2$) only once.

[1]Because they come from the eigendecomposition of a symmetric matrix.

Normalizing singular vectors   Singular vectors, like eigenvectors, are important because of their direction. Thus, in some sense, normalizing each singular vector to be unit length is arbitrary. However, the goal of the SVD is to have an exact decomposition of the matrix. If the singular vectors are not properly normalized, then $\mathbf{A} \neq \mathbf{U\Sigma V}^T$.

Therefore, in practice, all singular vectors must be normalized to unit vectors. For the same reason, the signs of the singular vectors are not arbitrary. The singular values are all non-negative, so flipping signs of singular vectors may be necessary for reconstructing the matrix.

This is noticeably different from diagonalization via eigendecomposition, where the eigenvectors are sign- and magnitude-invariant. The key to understanding the difference is that the eigenvalues matrix is flanked on both sides by the eigenvectors matrix and its inverse ($\mathbf{V\Lambda V}^{-1}$); any non-unit-magnitudes in $\mathbf{V}$ can be absorbed into $\mathbf{V}^{-1}$. But in the SVD, $\mathbf{U}$ and $\mathbf{V}^T$ are not inverses of each other (indeed, they may even have different dimensionalities), and thus the magnitude of singular vectors is not canceled.

You can see the effects of not normalizing in the exercises below. It will take you a while to work through these two exercises by hand, but I believe it's worth the effort and will help you understand the SVD.

Practice problems Perform the following steps on each matrix below: (1) Compute the SVD by hand. Construct the singular vectors to be integer matrices for ease of visual inspection. (2) Using your non-normalized singular vectors, compute $\mathbf{U\Sigma V}^T$ to confirm that it does not equal the original matrix. (3) Normalize each singular vector (each column of $\mathbf{U}$ and row of $\mathbf{V}^T$). (4) Re-compute $\mathbf{U\Sigma V}^T$ and confirm that it exactly equals the original matrix.

a) $\begin{bmatrix} 1 & 1 & 0 \\ 0 & 1 & 1 \end{bmatrix}$

b) $\begin{bmatrix} 1 & -1 \\ 0 & 2 \\ 1 & 1 \end{bmatrix}$

Answers Matrices are ordered as $\mathbf{U}$, $\mathbf{\Sigma}$, and $\mathbf{V}^T$. Top rows show integer vectors; bottom rows show normalized versions.

a) $\begin{bmatrix} 1 & -1 \\ 1 & 1 \end{bmatrix}$, $\begin{bmatrix} \sqrt{3} & 0 & 0 \\ 0 & 1 & 0 \end{bmatrix}$, $\begin{bmatrix} 1 & 2 & 1 \\ 1 & 0 & -1 \\ 1 & -1 & 1 \end{bmatrix}$; product $= \begin{bmatrix} \sqrt{3}-1 & 2\sqrt{3} & \sqrt{3}+1 \\ \sqrt{3}+1 & 2\sqrt{3} & \sqrt{3}-1 \end{bmatrix}$

$\frac{-1}{\sqrt{2}}\begin{bmatrix} 1 & -1 \\ 1 & 1 \end{bmatrix}$, $\begin{bmatrix} \sqrt{3} & 0 & 0 \\ 0 & 1 & 0 \end{bmatrix}$, $\begin{bmatrix} -1/\sqrt{6} & -2/\sqrt{6} & -1/\sqrt{6} \\ 1/\sqrt{2} & 0 & -1/\sqrt{2} \\ 1/\sqrt{3} & -1/\sqrt{3} & 1/\sqrt{3} \end{bmatrix}$; product$=\begin{bmatrix} 1 & 1 & 0 \\ 0 & 1 & 1 \end{bmatrix}$

b) $\begin{bmatrix} 1 & 1 & -1 \\ -2 & 0 & -1 \\ -1 & 1 & 1 \end{bmatrix}$, $\begin{bmatrix} \sqrt{6} & 0 \\ 0 & \sqrt{2} \\ 0 & 0 \end{bmatrix}$, $\begin{bmatrix} 0 & 1 \\ 1 & 0 \end{bmatrix}$; product$=\begin{bmatrix} \sqrt{2} & \sqrt{6} \\ 0 & -2\sqrt{6} \\ \sqrt{2} & -\sqrt{6} \end{bmatrix}$

$\begin{bmatrix} 1/\sqrt{6} & -1/\sqrt{2} & -1/\sqrt{3} \\ -2/\sqrt{6} & 0 & -1/\sqrt{3} \\ -1/\sqrt{6} & -1/\sqrt{2} & 1/\sqrt{3} \end{bmatrix}$, $\begin{bmatrix} \sqrt{6} & 0 \\ 0 & \sqrt{2} \\ 0 & 0 \end{bmatrix}$, $\begin{bmatrix} 0 & -1 \\ -1 & 0 \end{bmatrix}$; product$=\begin{bmatrix} 1 & -1 \\ 0 & 2 \\ 1 & 1 \end{bmatrix}$

Singular values and eigenvalues

16.3

The previous section seemed to imply the trivial relationship that the eigenvalues of $\mathbf{A}^T\mathbf{A}$ equal the squared singular values of $\mathbf{A}$. That is true, but there is a more nuanced relationship between the eigenvalues and the singular values of a matrix. That relationship is organized into three cases.

Case 1: eig($\mathbf{A}^T\mathbf{A}$) vs. svd($\mathbf{A}$) The eigenvalues equal the squared singular values, for the reasons explained in the previous section.

Let's see a quick example:

$$\mathbf{A} = \begin{bmatrix} 3 & 1 & 0 \\ 1 & 1 & 0 \end{bmatrix}$$

$$\mathbf{A}^{\mathsf{T}}\mathbf{A} = \begin{bmatrix} 10 & 4 & 0 \\ 4 & 2 & 0 \\ 0 & 0 & 0 \end{bmatrix}$$

$$\lambda(\mathbf{A}^{\mathsf{T}}\mathbf{A}) = 0, \ .3431, \ 11.6569$$

$$\sigma(\mathbf{A}) = .5858, \ 3.4142$$

$$\sigma^2(\mathbf{A}) = .3431, \ 11.6569$$

Why are there three λs but only two σs? It's because $\mathbf{A}^{\mathsf{T}}\mathbf{A}$ is 3×3 but $\boldsymbol{\Sigma}$ has the same size as the matrix $\mathbf{A}$, which is 2×3; hence, the diagonal has only two elements. But the non-zero λ's equal the squared σ's.

This case concerns the eigenvalues of $\mathbf{A}^{\mathsf{T}}\mathbf{A}$, not the eigenvalues of $\mathbf{A}$. In fact, there are no eigenvalues of $\mathbf{A}$ because it is not a square matrix. This brings us to our second case.

Case 2: eig($\mathbf{A}^{\mathsf{T}}\mathbf{A}$) vs. svd($\mathbf{A}^{\mathsf{T}}\mathbf{A}$) In this case, the eigenvalues and singular values are identical—without squaring the singular values. This is because eigendecomposition and SVD are the same operation for a square symmetric matrix (more on this point later).

Case 3a: eig($\mathbf{A}$) vs. svd($\mathbf{A}$) for real-valued λ This is different from Case 2 because here we assume that $\mathbf{A}$ is not symmetric, which means that the eigenvalues can be real-valued or complex-valued, depending on the elements in the matrix. We start by considering the case of a matrix with all real-valued eigenvalues. Of course, the matrix does need to be square for it to have eigenvalues, so let's add another row to the example matrix above.

$$\mathbf{A} = \begin{bmatrix} 3 & 1 & 0 \\ 1 & 1 & 0 \\ 1 & 1 & 1 \end{bmatrix}$$

$$\lambda(\mathbf{A}) = .5858,\ 1,\ 3.4142$$

$$\sigma(\mathbf{A}) = .4938,\ 1.1994,\ 3.6804$$

There is no easy-to-spot relationship between the eigenvalues and the singular values. In fact, there isn't really a relationship at all. Of course, there is the relationship that $\mathbf{W\Lambda W}^{-1} = \mathbf{U\Sigma V}^{\mathrm{T}}$, in other words, the entire eigendecomposition equals the entire SVD (because they are both equal to $\mathbf{A}$). But that doesn't say anything about a necessary relationship between $\mathbf{\Lambda}$ and $\mathbf{\Sigma}$.

Here I'm using $\mathbf{W}$ for eigenvectors to avoid confusion with the right singular vectors $\mathbf{V}$.

Case 3b: eig($\mathbf{A}$) vs. svd($\mathbf{A}$) for complex-valued λ The lack of trivial relationship between eigenvalues and singular values is even more apparent when a matrix has complex-valued eigenvalues. You learned in the previous chapter that a real-valued matrix can have complex-valued eigenvalues. So if $\mathbf{A}$ has complex-valued eigenvalues, what can we say about its singular values?

In fact, the singular values of any matrix—real-valued or complex-valued—are always real-valued. Guaranteed. Why? Because the SVD can be obtained from the eigendecomposition of the matrix times its transpose, and that matrix is always symmetric. (The SVD of complex matrices uses the Hermitian transpose instead of the regular transpose.)

Cases 2 and 3 may initially seem contradictory. $\mathbf{A}^{\mathrm{T}}\mathbf{A}$ is simply a matrix, so if we set $\mathbf{C} = \mathbf{A}^{\mathrm{T}}\mathbf{A}$, then I've written that $\lambda(\mathbf{C})=\sigma(\mathbf{C})$ but $\lambda(\mathbf{A}) \neq \sigma(\mathbf{A})$. Would you like to guess the difference and then the reason for the difference before reading the next paragraph?

The difference is that $\mathbf{C}$ is defined as a matrix times its transpose, whereas $\mathbf{A}$ is not. And the reason why this matters is that the 2-norm of the eigenvectors matrix of a symmetric matrix is 1, whereas the 2-norm of the eigenvectors matrix for a non-symmetric matrix is not constrained to be 1. This isn't about the individual eigenvectors—computer programs will unit-norm each individual eigenvector—this is about the eigenvectors and singular vectors matrices being orthogonal matrices, and thus having a norm of 1.

The matrix induced 2-norm is the most that a matrix can stretch a vector, and is computed as the largest singular value of the matrix.

Eigendecomposition and SVD are exact decompositions, thus, all of the "energy" in the matrix $\mathbf{A}$ must be contained inside the three eigendecomposition or SVD matrices. For the SVD, matrices $\mathbf{U}$ and $\mathbf{V}$ are orthogonal and have a matrix norm of 1, which means that all of the energy in the right-hand side of the equation must come from matrix $\mathbf{\Sigma}$. That's always the case for the SVD.

all $\sigma(\mathbf{U}) = \sigma(\mathbf{V}) = 1$

Eigendecomposition, on the other hand, has an orthogonal eigenvectors matrix only when the matrix is symmetric. When the matrix is not symmetric, then the "total energy" in the matrix can be distributed over the eigenvectors and the eigenvalues. This is the reason why there seems to be a discrepancy between cases 2 and 3, which is actually due to the symmetry of the matrix. (For a related discussion, consult section 15.10 on reconstructing a matrix from eigenlayers.)

In conclusion, there is a clear relationship between the eigenvalues of $\mathbf{A}^{\mathrm{T}}\mathbf{A}$ and the singular values of $\mathbf{A}$ (or the singular values of $\mathbf{A}^{\mathrm{T}}\mathbf{A}$), but there is no relationship between the eigenvalues of non-symmetric $\mathbf{A}$ and the singular values of $\mathbf{A}$.

Code   As you might guess, the SVD is really easy to compute in Python and in MATLAB. If you use both programs, be *very* mindful that Python returns $\mathbf{V}^{\mathrm{T}}$ whereas MATLAB returns $\mathbf{V}$. Python also returns the singular values in a vector instead of in a diagonal matrix. You can use the code below to confirm the answers to the practice problems a few pages ago.

```
1  import numpy as np
2  A = [[1,1,0],[0,1,1]]
3  U,s,V = np.linalg.svd(A)
```

Code block 16.2: MATLAB

```
1  A = [1 1 0; 0 1 1];
2  [U,S,V] = svd(A);
```

16.4 SVD of a symmetric matrix

Simply stated: The left and right singular vectors of a symmetric matrix are the same. In other words,

SVD of a symmetric matrix

$$\mathbf{A} = \mathbf{U\Sigma U}^{\mathrm{T}}, \quad \text{if } \mathbf{A} = \mathbf{A}^{\mathrm{T}} \tag{16.10}$$

Proving that this is the case simply involves writing out the SVD of the matrix and its transpose:

$$\mathbf{A} = \mathbf{U\Sigma V}^{\mathrm{T}} \tag{16.11}$$

$$\mathbf{A}^{\mathrm{T}} = (\mathbf{U\Sigma V}^{\mathrm{T}})^{\mathrm{T}} = \mathbf{V\Sigma U}^{\mathrm{T}} \tag{16.12}$$

Because $\mathbf{A} = \mathbf{A}^{\mathrm{T}}$, these two these equations must be equal:

$$\mathbf{U\Sigma V}^{\mathrm{T}} = \mathbf{V\Sigma U}^{\mathrm{T}} \tag{16.13}$$

And this proves that $\mathbf{U} = \mathbf{V}$, which means that the left and right singular vectors are the same.

Notice that this is not necessarily the same thing as "Case 2" of the relationship between singular values and eigenvalues, because not all symmetric matrices can be expressed as some other matrix times its transpose.

16.5 SVD and the four subspaces

One of the remarkable features of the SVD is that it provides orthogonal basis sets for each of the four matrix subspaces. This is one of the main reasons why the SVD is such a powerful and useful decomposition.

But let me start by talking more about Σ—the matrix that contains the singular values on the diagonal and zeros everywhere else. Below is an example of a Σ matrix for a 5×3, rank-2 matrix.

$$\begin{bmatrix} \sigma_1 & 0 & 0 \\ 0 & \sigma_2 & 0 \\ 0 & 0 & 0 \\ 0 & 0 & 0 \\ 0 & 0 & 0 \end{bmatrix}$$

By construction, $\sigma_1 > \sigma_2$. Indeed, SVD algorithms always sort the singular values descending from top-left to lower-right. Thus, zero-valued singular values will be in the lower-right of the diagonal. $\sigma_3 = 0$ because this is a rank-2 matrix. You'll learn below that any zero-valued singular values correspond to the null space of the matrix. Therefore, the number of non-zero singular values corresponds to the dimensionality of the row and column spaces, which means that the number of non-zero singular values corresponds to the rank of the matrix. In fact, this is how programs like MATLAB and Python compute the rank of a matrix: Take its SVD and count the number of non-zero singular values.

Figure 16.3 shows the "big picture" of the SVD and the four subspaces. There is a lot going on in that figure, so let's go through each piece in turn. The overall picture is a visualization of Equation 16.1; as a quick review: the matrix gets decomposed into three matrices: $\mathbf{U}$ provides an orthogonal basis for $\mathbb{R}^M$ and contains the left singular vectors; Σ is the diagonal matrix of singular values (all non-negative, real-valued); and $\mathbf{V}$ provides an orthogonal basis for $\mathbb{R}^N$ (remember that the SVD uses $\mathbf{V}^T$, meaning that the *rows* are the singular vectors, not the *columns*).

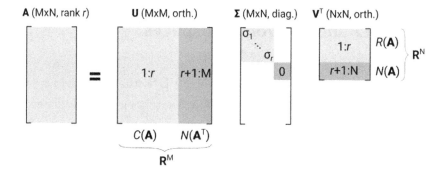

Figure 16.3: Visualization of how the SVD reveals basis sets for the four subspaces of a rank-r matrix. (orth. = orthogonal matrix; diag. = diagonal matrix; 1:r = columns (or rows) 1 through r.)

This figure additionally shows how the columns of $\mathbf{U}$ are organized into basis vectors for the column space (light gray) and left-null space (darker gray); and how the rows of $\mathbf{V}^{\mathrm{T}}$ are organized into basis vectors for the row space (light gray) and null space (darker gray). In particular, the first r columns in $\mathbf{U}$, and the first r rows in $\mathbf{V}^{\mathrm{T}}$, are the bases for the column and row spaces of $\mathbf{A}$. The columns and rows after r get multiplied by the zero-valued singular values, and thus form bases for the null spaces. The singular vectors for the column and row spaces are sorted according to their "importance" to the matrix $\mathbf{A}$, as indicated by the relative magnitude of the corresponding singular values.

You can see that the SVD reveals a lot of important information about the matrix. The points below are implicit in the visualization, and written explicitly in the interest of clarity:

- The rank of the matrix (r) is the number of non-zero singular values.
- The dimensionality of the left-null space is the number of columns in $\mathbf{U}$ from $r + 1$ to M.
- The dimensionality of the null space is the number of rows in $\mathbf{V}^{\mathrm{T}}$ from $r + 1$ to N.

It is important the realize that the organization of the SVD matrix in Figure 16.3 is not a trivial result of the decomposition. Recall from the previous chapter that eigenvalues have no intrinsic sorting; likewise, when you compute the SVD by hand, the singular values are not magically revealed in descending order. Computer algorithms will sort the singular values—and their associated singular vectors—to produce this beautiful arrangement.

Figure 16.3 also nicely captures the fact that the column space and left-null space are orthogonal: If each column in $\mathbf{U}$ is orthogonal to each other column, then any subset of columns is orthogonal to any other non-overlapping subset of columns. Together, all of these columns span all of $\mathbb{R}^M$, which means the rank of $\mathbf{U}$ is M, even if the rank of $\mathbf{A}$ is $r < M$.

The story for $\mathbf{V}^{\mathrm{T}}$ is the same, except we deal with rows instead of columns (or, if you prefer, the columns of $\mathbf{V}$) and the row space and null space of $\mathbf{A}$. So, the first r rows provide an orthonormal basis for the row space of $\mathbf{A}$, and the rest of the rows, which get multiplied by the zero-valued singular values, are a basis for the null space of $\mathbf{A}$.

Practice problems The following triplets of matrices are $\mathbf{U\Sigma V}^{\mathrm{T}}$ that were computed from a matrix $\mathbf{A}$ that is not shown. From visual inspection, determine the size and rank of $\mathbf{A}$, and identify the basis vectors for the four spaces of $\mathbf{A}$. (Note: I re-scaled $\mathbf{U}$ and $\mathbf{V}$ to integers.)

a) $\begin{bmatrix} -1 & -1 \\ -1 & 1 \end{bmatrix} \begin{bmatrix} 4.89 & 0 & 0 \\ 0 & 2 & 0 \end{bmatrix} \begin{bmatrix} -1 & -1 & -1 \\ 1 & 0 & -1 \\ 1 & -2 & 1 \end{bmatrix}$

b) $\begin{bmatrix} -1 & 0 & -3 & 0 \\ 0 & 1 & 0 & 0 \\ -3 & 0 & 1 & 0 \\ 0 & 0 & 0 & 1 \end{bmatrix} \begin{bmatrix} \pi & 0 \\ 0 & 2 \\ 0 & 0 \\ 0 & 0 \end{bmatrix} \begin{bmatrix} -1 & 0 \\ 0 & 1 \end{bmatrix}$

Answers

a) The matrix is 2×3 with rank 2. $\mathbf{U}$ is a basis for the column space; the left-null space is empty. The first 2 rows of $\mathbf{V}^{\mathrm{T}}$ are a basis for the row space, and the third row is a basis for the null space.

b) The matrix is 4×2 with rank 2. The first two columns of $\mathbf{U}$ are a basis for the column space; the latter two are a basis for the left-null space. All of $\mathbf{V}^{\mathrm{T}}$ is a basis for the row space, and the null space is empty.

Reflection $\begin{bmatrix} \\ \\ \\ \\ \\ \end{bmatrix}$ I know, Figure 16.3 is a lot to take in of first glance. Don't expect to understand everything about the SVD just by staring at that figure. You'll gain more familiarity and intuition about the SVD by working with it, which is the goal of the rest of this chapter!

16.6 SVD and matrix rank

It may seems strange that the number of non-zero eigenvalues does not necessarily equal the matrix rank (demonstrated in the previous chapter), whereas above I claimed that the number of non-zero singular values is equal to the matrix rank. In this section, I will provide two explanations for this.

One key difference between eigendecomposition and SVD is that for SVD, the two singular vectors matrices span the entire ambient spaces ($\mathbb{R}^M$ and $\mathbb{R}^N$), which is not necessarily the case with eigenvectors (e.g., for non-diagonalizable matrices).

Given that matrix rank is the dimensionality of the column space, it is sensible that the rank of the matrix corresponds to the number of columns in $\mathbf{U}$ that provide a basis for the column space (we could say the same thing about the number of rows in $\mathbf{V}^T$ that provide a basis for the row space). Thus, it is sufficient to demonstrate that each column in $\mathbf{U}$ that is in the column space of $\mathbf{A}$ has a non-zero singular value, and that each column in $\mathbf{U}$ that is in the left-null space of $\mathbf{A}$ has a singular value of zero. (Again, the same is true of $\mathbf{V}^T$, the row space, and the null space.)

Let's start by rewriting the SVD using one pair of singular vectors and their corresponding singular value. This is analogous to the single-vector eigenvalue equation.

$$\mathbf{A}\mathbf{v} = \mathbf{u}\sigma \qquad (16.14)$$

Notice that replacing the vectors with matrices and then right-multiplying by $\mathbf{V}^T$ gives the SVD matrix equation that you're now familiar with.

Now let me remind you of the definition of the column space and left-null space: The column space comprises all vectors that can be expressed by some combination of the columns of $\mathbf{A}$, whereas the left-null space comprises all non-trivial combinations of the columns of $\mathbf{A}$ that produce the zeros vector. In other words:

$$C(\mathbf{A}): \quad \mathbf{Ax} = \mathbf{b} \qquad\qquad (16.15)$$

$$N(\mathbf{A}^{\mathrm{T}}): \quad \mathbf{Ay} = \mathbf{0} \qquad\qquad (16.16)$$

Now we can think about Equation 16.14 in this context: all singular vectors are non-zeros, and thus the right-hand side of Equation 16.14 must be non-zero—and thus in the column space of $\mathbf{A}$—if σ is non-zero. Likewise, the only possible way for the right-hand side of Equation 16.14 to be the zeros vector—and thus in the left-null space of $\mathbf{A}$—is for σ to equal zero.

Thus, any $\mathbf{u}$ with a corresponding non-zero σ is in the column space of the matrix, whereas any $\mathbf{u}$ with a corresponding zero-valued σ is in the left-null space of the matrix. The elements of $\mathbf{v}$ provide those weightings across the columns of $\mathbf{A}$.

You can make the same argument for the row space, by starting from the equation $\mathbf{u}^{\mathrm{T}}\mathbf{A} = \sigma \mathbf{v}^{\mathrm{T}}$.

I hope that explanation provides intuition. There is another way to explain why the rank of $\mathbf{A}$ corresponds to the number of non-zero singular values. This second explanation comes from the rule about the rank of the product of matrix multiplications.

$\mathbf{A}$ is the product of the three SVD matrices, therefore the rank of $\mathbf{A}$ is constrained by the ranks of those matrices. $\mathbf{U}$ and $\mathbf{V}$ are by definition full-rank. $\mathbf{\Sigma}$ is of size $M{\times}N$ but could have a rank smaller than M or N. Thus, the maximum possible rank of $\mathbf{A}$ is the rank of $\mathbf{\Sigma}$. However, the rank of $\mathbf{A}$ could not be smaller than the rank of $\mathbf{\Sigma}$, because the ranks of $\mathbf{A}$ and $\mathbf{U\Sigma V}^{\mathrm{T}}$ are equal. Therefore, the rank of $\mathbf{A}$ must equal the smallest rank of the three SVD matrices, which is always $\mathbf{\Sigma}$. And as a diagonal matrix, the rank of $\mathbf{\Sigma}$ is the number of non-zero diagonal elements, which is the number of non-zero singular values.

"Effective" rank You've read many times in this book that computers have difficulties with really small and really large numbers.

These are called rounding errors, precision errors, underflow, over-flow, etc. How does a computer decide whether a singular value is small but non-zero vs. zero with rounding error?

The MATLAB source code for computing rank looks like this:

```
s = svd(A);
r = sum(s > tol);
```

In other words, retrieve the singular values, and count the number of those values that are above a tolerance (variable `tol`). So the question is, how to set that tolerance? If it's too small, then the rank will be over-estimated; if it's too large, then the rank will be under-estimated. MATLAB's solution is to set the tolerance dynamically, based on the size and elements in the matrix:

```
tol = max(size(A)) * eps(max(s));
```

The function `eps` returns the distance between a number and the next-larger number that your computer is capable of representing. For example, if your computer could only represent integers, then eps=1. (And you probably need to buy a new computer...)

Without getting any deeper into the computer science of numerical processing, I wanted to give you some sense of the way that theoretical mathematical concepts are translated into code that gives acceptable results on digital computers.

16.7 SVD spectral theory

There are several "spectral theories" in mathematics, and they all involve the concept that a complicated thing—such as a matrix, an operation, or a transformation—can be represented by the sum of simpler things. It's like how visible light can be decomposed into the colors of the rainbow.

There is a spectral theory of matrices, which is sometimes used as another term for eigendecomposition. I'm going to adapt this concept and bend the terminology slightly to the *SVD spectral theory*, which is that all matrices can be expressed as a sum of rank-1 matrices, and that the SVD provides a great decomposition to obtain these individual rank-1 matrices.

Figure 16.4: Outer product, visualized.

Let me begin by reminding you of the "layer perspective" of matrix multiplication (page 144), which involves constructing a product matrix as the sum of outer-product matrices created from the columns of a matrix on the left, and the rows of a matrix to the right. Each of those outer-product matrices has a rank of 1, because each column (or row) is a scalar multiple of one column (or one row).

With matrix multiplication via layers, the two vectors that multiply to create each "layer" of the product matrix are defined purely by their physical position in the matrix. Is that really the best way to define basis vectors to create each layer? Probably not: The position of a row or column in a matrix may not be the organizing principle of "importance"; indeed, in many matrices—particularly matrices that contain data—rows or columns can be swapped or even randomized without any change in the information content of the data matrix.

The SVD provides an interesting way to construct a matrix by summing rank-1 layers that are computed using the columns of $\mathbf{U}$ and the rows of $\mathbf{V}^{\mathrm{T}}$, scaled by their corresponding singular value. The mechanics are given by re-writing the SVD formula using a summation of vectors instead of matrices.

$$\mathbf{A} = \sum_{i=1}^{r} \mathbf{u}_i \sigma_i \mathbf{v}_i^{\mathrm{T}} \tag{16.17}$$

where r is the rank of the matrix (the singular values after σ_r are zeros, and thus can be omitted from this equation). Your delicate linear-algebraic sensibilities might be offended by going from the elegant matrix Equation 16.1 to the clumsy vector-sum Equation 16.17. But this equation will set us up for the SVD spectral theory, and will also lead into one of the important applications of SVD, which is low-rank approximations (next section).

Let's consider only the first iteration of the summation:

$$\mathbf{A}_1 = \mathbf{u}_1 \sigma_1 \mathbf{v}_1^{\mathrm{T}} \qquad (16.18)$$

We might call matrix $\mathbf{A}_1$ the "first SVD-layer of $\mathbf{A}$." It is a rank-1 matrix (same size as $\mathbf{A}$) formed as the outer product between the first left singular vector and the first right singular vector. Because the two vectors are unit length ($\|\mathbf{u}_1\| = \|\mathbf{v}_1\| = 1$), the 2-norm of their outer product is also 1. But is the norm of $\mathbf{A}_1$ also equal to 1? No, it isn't, and that's because the outer product gets scalar-multiplied by the corresponding singular value (notwithstanding when $\sigma_1 = 1$).

Because the singular values are sorted descending, $\mathbf{A}_1$ is actually the "most meaningful" SVD-layer of matrix $\mathbf{A}$ ("meaningful" can be interpreted as the amount of total variance in the matrix, or as the most important feature of the matrix; more on this in the next section). $\mathbf{A}_2$ will be the next-most-meaningful SVD-layer, and so on down to $\mathbf{A}_r$. The SVD-layers after r have zero-valued singular values and thus contribute nothing to the final matrix.

Thus, each corresponding left and right singular vector combine to produce a layer of the matrix. This layer is like a direction in the matrix space. But that direction is simply a pointer—it does not convey "importance." Instead, it is the singular *value* that indicates how "important" each direction is. It's like a sign-post that points to the nearest gas station (1 km away) and to Siberia (10,000 km away). The *signs* (the singular vectors) have the same size; you have to look at the numbers on the signs (the singular values) to know how far each destination is.

Figure 16.5 illustrates the concept of reconstructing a matrix by successively adding SVD-layers. The three singular values of this random matrix are 3.4, 1.0, and 0.5 (rounded to the nearest tenth).

In the next section, you will learn how to interpret these values and how to normalize them into a more meaningful metric.

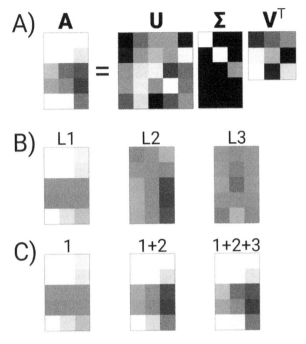

Figure 16.5: Illustration of the SVD spectral theory. Panel A shows the SVD matrices. It is visually apparent that **A** is a rank-3 matrix (3 non-zero singular values). Panel B shows the three SVD-layers formed from outer products of corresponding columns of U, rows of $\mathbf{V}^\mathrm{T}$, and singular values ("L1" = layer 1). Panel C shows the cumulative sum of layers. The first two maps are low-rank approximations of A while the final map ("1+2+3") is an exact reconstruction of A.

Notice that layer 1 ("L1" in panel B) captures the most prominent feature of the matrix **A** (the horizontal band in the middle); in the next section I will refer to this as the best rank-1 approximation of **A**.

Although it might not be obvious from the color scaling, each column of the L1 matrix is simply the left-most column of **U** scalar-multiplied by the corresponding elements of the first row of $\mathbf{V}^\mathrm{T}$, and also multiplied by $\mathbf{\Sigma}_{1,1}$. Same story for matrices L2 and L3. Columns 4 and 5 of **U** do not contribute to reconstructing **A**— that's built-in to Equation 16.17 because the rank of this matrix is $r = 3$—and it's also apparent from visualization of the multiplication: Columns 4 and 5 in $\mathbf{U}$ multiply rows 4 and 5 of Σ, which are all zeros. In terms of matrix spaces, columns 4 and 5 of $\mathbf{U}$ are in the left-null space of $\mathbf{A}$.

SVD-layer 2 captures the second-most prominent feature of the matrix $\mathbf{A}$, which is the vertical stripe in the lower-right. Layer 3 has a relatively small singular value (10% of the total variance in the matrix; I'll describe later how I compute this) and therefore accounts for relatively little information in the matrix. You can see in panel C that adding SVD-layer 3—though technically necessary for a full reconstruction of $\mathbf{A}$—changes the matrix only slightly.

16.8 SVD and low-rank approximations

Equation 16.17 in the previous section showed how to reconstruct a matrix exactly by summing up outer products from left- and right-singular values, scalar-multiplied by the corresponding singular vaule. I also wrote that SVD-layers with smaller singular values are less important for the matrix.

This leads to the idea of low-rank approximations: Create a matrix $\widetilde{\mathbf{A}}$ that is sort-of like matrix $\mathbf{A}$; it's a rank-k version of the original rank-r matrix created by adapting the full vector-sum formula slightly:

Low-rank approximation

$$\widetilde{\mathbf{A}} = \sum_{i=1}^{k} \mathbf{u}_i \sigma_i \mathbf{v}_i^{\mathrm{T}} , \quad k < r \qquad (16.19)$$

Figure 16.6 shows an example. The matrix $\mathbf{A}$ is a 30×40 random numbers matrix that was smoothed with a 2D Gaussian kernel. Panel A shows its SVD decomposition, similar to previous figures. The important addition here is that matrix $\mathbf{A}$ has rank $= 30$, whereas the right-most matrix in panel D has a rank $= 4$. And yet, visually, that matrix appears extremely similar to matrix $\mathbf{A}$.

In other words, the rank-4 approximation of the original rank-30 matrix appears to capture all the important features.

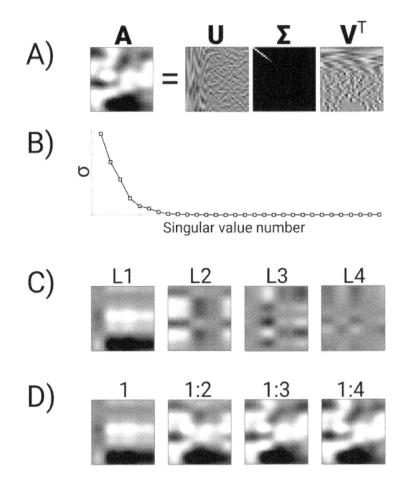

Figure 16.6: Example of using SVD for a low-rank approximation of a matrix. Panels C and D are comparable to panels B and C in Figure 16.5. 1:4 indicates the cumulative sum of SVD-layers 1 through 4.

Why did I pick $k = 4$ SVD-layers to reconstruct? That is, admittedly, an arbitrary choice that was partly driven by the visual layout of the figure. There are two ways to select an appropriate value of k. One is based on visual inspection of the "scree plot" (the plot of decreasing singular values; Figure 16.6B); you look for the set of singular values that seem to "pop out" or are relatively large compared to the distribution of singular values. From Figure 16.6B there appears to be anywhere between 4 and 6 relatively large values. You can already see in this example that this can be a non-trivial decision, and there might be disagreement about the "correct" number of SVD-layers to include. A related technique is called the "elbow method," and involves imagining that the scree plot is your arm bent at the elbow (the first singular value on the left is your shoulder; the last one is your hand). Look at the plot and decide which node is at the elbow; that's the number of components the preserve. Again, it's a bit ambiguous in this example (as it often is), but I'd say the elbow is node 4 or 5.

A second method for choosing k is less arbitrary and is based on selecting a threshold, for example, all SVD-layers that contribute at least 1% of the variance of the entire matrix. This method requires converting the singular values into a more meaningful metric, which is the topic of the next section.

Why is a low-rank approximation useful? Why not simply keep $\mathbf{A}$ in all its glorious original-rank perfection? There are several applications of low-rank approximations; below are three examples.

1. **Noise reduction**: It is possible that the data features associated with large singular values represent signal, whereas data features associated with small singular values represent noise. Thus, by reconstructing the matrix using $k < r$ layers, the matrix becomes cleaner. This technique is sometimes referred to as "projecting out noise."

2. **Machine-learning classification**: Many machine-learning analyses involve identifying features or patterns in data that predict some outcome variable. It may be the case that the most relevant data features are represented in the k largest singular vectors, and thus the analyses can be faster and more accurately done by training on the "most important" singular vectors instead of on the original data matrix.

3. **Data compression**: Let's imagine a large dataset contained in a $10,000 \times 100,000$ matrix. At floating-point precision, this matrix can take up 8 GB of hard-disk space (assuming no compression). Now let's imagine that this is a rank-100 matrix. Storing the first 100 columns of $\mathbf{U}$ and $\mathbf{V}$, and the first 100 singular values (as a vector, not as a diagonal matrix) would take up only 0.09 GB (around 90 MB). It would then

be possible to load in these vectors and scalars and recreate the full-sized $\widetilde{\mathbf{A}}$ as needed.

16.9 Normalizing singular values

Imagine you have two different matrices, and find that the largest singular value of matrix $\mathbf{A}$ is 8 and the largest singular value of matrix $\mathbf{B}$ is 678. How would you interpret that difference? Are those two numbers comparable? And what does the number "8" even mean??

The answer is that those two σ_{max} values are probably not comparable, unless you know that the matrices have numbers in exactly the same range.

Before showing you how to normalize the singular values, I want to show that singular values are scale-dependent, meaning they change with the scale of the numbers in the matrix. Below is an example; the second matrix is the same as the first but multiplied by 10. Notice that their singular values are the same except for a scaling of 10 (numbers are rounded to the nearest thousandth).

$$\mathbf{A} = \begin{bmatrix} 8 & 4 & 10 \\ 4 & 5 & 6 \end{bmatrix}, \qquad \Sigma_A = \begin{bmatrix} 15.867 & 0 \\ 0 & 2.286 \end{bmatrix}$$

The third column of Σ was trimmed.

$$\mathbf{B} = 10\mathbf{A} = \begin{bmatrix} 80 & 40 & 100 \\ 40 & 50 & 60 \end{bmatrix}, \quad \Sigma_B = \begin{bmatrix} 158.674 & 0 \\ 0 & 22.863 \end{bmatrix} = 10\Sigma_A$$

So when a matrix is multiplied by a scalar, its singular values are multiplied by that same scalar. To understand why this must be the case, remember that the singular vectors are unit-normalized to create orthogonal matrices. So it is not possible for $\mathbf{U}$ or $\mathbf{V}$ to "absorb" the scalar. Instead, the only part of the SVD that can be scalar-multiplied is Σ, the singular values.

The point here is that it is difficult or impossible to compare "raw" singular values across matrices, because those values depend both on the numerical ranges in the matrices and on the data features embedded in the matrices.

What is the solution to this limitation? As I'm sure you've guessed, the solution is to normalize the singular values. The normalization I will discuss here is converting to percent of total variance of the matrix.

See also section 6.10 about matrix norms.

Because the singular vectors are all unit-length and are scaled by the singular values when reconstructing the matrix from its SVD layers, the sum over all singular values can be interpreted as the total variance or "energy" in the matrix. This sum over all singular values is formally called the Schatten 1-norm of the matrix. For completeness, the equation below is the full formula for the **Schatten p-norm**, although here we are considering only the case of $p = 1$.

$$\|\mathbf{A}\|_p = \left(\sum_{i=1}^{r} \sigma_i^p \right)^{1/p} \tag{16.20}$$

The next step is to scale each singular value to the percent of the Schatten 1-norm:

$$\tilde{\sigma}_i = \frac{100\sigma_i}{\|\mathbf{A}\|_1} \tag{16.21}$$

This is a useful normalization, because it allows for direct interpretation of each singular value, as well as direct comparison of singular values across different matrices. In the example matrices on page 492, the two *normalized* $\mathbf{\Sigma}$ matrices would be equal to each other.

Getting back to the problem at the outset of this section, two matrices with largest singular values of 8 and 678 are not comparable, but let's say their normalized largest singular values are 35% and 82%. In this case, 35% means that the largest SVD-layer accounts for only 35% of the total variance in the matrix. One interpretation is that this is a complicated matrix that contains a lot of information along several different directions. In contrast, a largest normalized singular value of 82% means nearly all of the variance is explained by one component, so this matrix probably contains less complex information. If this were a data matrix, it might correspond to one pattern and 18% noise.

Now let's think back to the question of how many SVD-layers to use in a low-rank approximation (that is, how to select k). When the singular values are normalized, you can pick some percent variance threshold and retain all SVD-layers that contribute at least that much variance. For example, you might keep all SVD-layers with $\sigma > 1\%$, or perhaps 0.1% to retain more information. The choice of a threshold is still somewhat arbitrary, but this is at least more quantitative and reproducible than visual inspection of the scree plot.

16.10 Condition number of a matrix

The condition number of a matrix is used to evaluate the "spread" of a matrix. It is defined as the ratio of the largest to the smallest singular values, and is often indicated using the Greek letter κ.

Condition number of a matrix
$$\kappa = \frac{\sigma_{max}}{\sigma_{min}} \qquad (16.22)$$

For example, the condition number of the identity matrix is 1, because all of its singular values are 1. The condition number of any singular matrix is undefined ("not a number"; NaN), because singular matrices have at least one zero-valued singular value, thus making the condition number $\frac{\sigma}{0} = ???$

The condition number of all orthogonal matrices is the same. Can you guess what that condition number is, and why? To build suspense, I'll explain the answer at the end of this section.

A matrix is called *well-conditioned* if it has a low condition number and *high-conditioned* if it has a high condition number. However, there is no absolute threshold for when a matrix can be labeled high-conditioned. In some cases, $\kappa > 10,000$ is used as a threshold, but this can be application-specific. Furthermore, singular matrices can contain a lot of information and be useful in applications, but have a condition number of NaN. Likewise, near-singular matrices can have an astronomically high condition number while still being a meaningful matrix.

In data analysis and statistics, the condition number is used to indicate the stability of a matrix, in other words, the sensitivity of the matrix to small perturbations. A high condition number means that the matrix is very sensitive, which could lead to unreliable results in some analyses, for example those that require the matrix inverse.

But don't take the condition number of a matrix too seriously: Matrices can contain a lot of information or very little information regardless of their condition number. The condition number should not be used on its own to evaluate the usefulness of a matrix.

OK, the answer to the question about orthogonal matrices is that the condition number of any orthogonal matrix is 1, and that's because all of the singular values of an orthogonal matrix are 1. This is the case because an orthogonal matrix is defined as $\mathbf{Q}^{\mathrm{T}}\mathbf{Q} = \mathbf{I}$, and the eigenvalues of a diagonal matrix are its diagonal elements. And you know from earlier in this chapter that the singular values of $\mathbf{Q}$ are the principal square roots of the singular values of $\mathbf{Q}^{\mathrm{T}}\mathbf{Q}$.

Code You can compute the condition number on your own based on the SVD, but Python and MATLAB have built-in functions.

```
1  import numpy as np
2  A = np.random.randn(5,5)
3  s = np.linalg.svd(A)[1]
4  condnum = np.max(s)/np.min(s)
5  # compare above with cond()
6  print(condnum,np.linalg.cond(A))
```

```
1  A = randn(5,5);
2  s = svd(A);
3  condnum = max(s)/min(s);
4  disp([condnum,cond(A)])
```

16.11 SVD and the matrix inverse

Let's consider the inverse of a matrix and its SVD. Assume $\mathbf{A}$ is square full-rank.

$$\mathbf{A}^{-1} = (\mathbf{U\Sigma V}^{\mathrm{T}})^{-1} \qquad (16.23)$$

$$= \mathbf{V\Sigma}^{-1}\mathbf{U}^{-1} \qquad (16.24)$$

$$= \mathbf{V\Sigma}^{-1}\mathbf{U}^{\mathrm{T}} \qquad (16.25)$$

Because $\mathbf{U}$ and $\mathbf{V}$ are orthogonal matrices, their inverses are trivial to compute (their transposes). Furthermore, because $\mathbf{\Sigma}$ is a diagonal matrix, its inverse is also trivial to compute (simply invert each diagonal element; see section 12.2 on page 327).

Actually, $\mathbf{\Sigma}^{-1}$ might not be trivial to compute in practice, because if some singular values are close to machine precision, then tiny rounding errors or other numerical inaccuracies can make the inverse unstable (for example, $\frac{1}{10^{-15}}$ is a very large number). This shows why the explicit inverse of an ill-conditioned matrix can be numerically unstable.

Equation 16.25 also allows us to prove that the inverse of a symmetric matrix is itself symmetric. Let's write out the SVD for a symmetric matrix and its inverse (remember that symmetric matrices have identical left and right singular vectors).

$$\mathbf{A}^{\mathrm{T}} = (\mathbf{V}\mathbf{\Sigma}\mathbf{V}^{\mathrm{T}})^{\mathrm{T}} = \mathbf{V}\mathbf{\Sigma}\mathbf{V}^{\mathrm{T}} \tag{16.26}$$

$$\mathbf{A}^{-1} = (\mathbf{V}\mathbf{\Sigma}\mathbf{V}^{\mathrm{T}})^{-1} = \mathbf{V}\mathbf{\Sigma}^{-1}\mathbf{V}^{\mathrm{T}} \tag{16.27}$$

It is immediately clear that $\mathbf{A}$, $\mathbf{A}^{\mathrm{T}}$, and $\mathbf{A}^{-1}$ have the same singular vectors; the singular values may differ, but the point is that $\mathbf{\Sigma}$ is also symmetric, and thus $\mathbf{A}^{-1}$ is symmetric as long as $\mathbf{A}$ is symmetric.

Expressing the inverse via the SVD may seem like an academic exercise, but this is a crucial introduction to the pseudoinverse, as you will now learn.

16.12 The MP Pseudoinverse, part 2

In section 12.8, you read about the idea of the pseudoinverse: It is an approximation to an inverse for a singular matrix. I promised that you would find the algorithm for the Moore-Penrose pseudoinverse easily comprehensible by the time you got to this chapter. And here we are.

Here's the algorithm: Compute the SVD of a matrix, swap and transpose the $\mathbf{U}$ and $\mathbf{V}$ matrices (just like with the full inverse), invert its *non-zero* singular values, then multiply to reconstitute the matrix pseudoinverse.

$$\mathbf{A}^\dagger = (\mathbf{U}\mathbf{\Sigma}\mathbf{V}^T)^\dagger$$

$$= \mathbf{V}\mathbf{\Sigma}^\dagger\mathbf{U}^T \qquad (16.28)$$

$$\mathbf{\Sigma}^\dagger_{i,i} = \begin{cases} \frac{1}{\sigma_i} & \text{if } \sigma_i \neq 0 \\ 0 & \text{if } \sigma_j = 0 \end{cases}$$

Notice that this procedure will work for any matrix, square or rectangular, full-rank or singular. When the matrix is square and full-rank, then the Moore-Penrose pseudoinverse will equal the true inverse, which you can see yourself by considering what happens when all of the singular values are non-zero.

Computer programs that implement the MP pseudoinverse will threshold very small-but-nonzero singular values to avoid numerical instability issues. As described earlier for computing rank, that tolerance is some multiple of the machine precision, and the idea is to treat as zero any singular values that are too small to be confidently distinguished from zero.

Figure 16.7 illustrates two examples of the MP pseudoinverse for a singular matrix (top row) and a full-rank matrix (bottom row). Notice that the pseudoinverse times the original matrix is not-quite-but-trying-to-be the identity matrix.

One-sided inverse When the matrix is rectangular and either full column rank or full row rank, then the pseudoinverse will equal the left inverse or the right inverse. This makes computing the one-sided inverse computationally efficient, because it can be done without explicitly computing $(\mathbf{A}^T\mathbf{A})^{-1}$.

To understand the relationship between the one-sided inverse and the pseudoinverse, let's work through the math of the left inverse. Recall that the left inverse of a tall matrix $\mathbf{T}$ is $(\mathbf{T}^T\mathbf{T})^{-1}\mathbf{T}^T$. Let's write out its SVD, simplify, and see what happens.

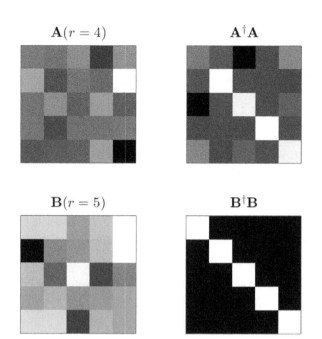

Figure 16.7: Visualization of two matrices (left column) and those matrices times their pseudoinverses (right column). A is reduced-rank whereas B is full-rank.

$$\mathbf{T} = \mathbf{U\Sigma V}^{\mathrm{T}} \tag{16.29}$$

$$(\mathbf{T}^{\mathrm{T}}\mathbf{T})^{-1}\mathbf{T}^{\mathrm{T}} = \left((\mathbf{U\Sigma V}^{\mathrm{T}})^{\mathrm{T}}\mathbf{U\Sigma V}^{\mathrm{T}}\right)^{-1}\left(\mathbf{U\Sigma V}^{\mathrm{T}}\right)^{\mathrm{T}} \tag{16.30}$$

$$= \left(\mathbf{V\Sigma}^{\mathrm{T}}\mathbf{U}^{\mathrm{T}}\mathbf{U\Sigma V}^{\mathrm{T}}\right)^{-1}\mathbf{V\Sigma U}^{\mathrm{T}} \tag{16.31}$$

$$= \left(\mathbf{V\Sigma}^{2}\mathbf{V}^{\mathrm{T}}\right)^{-1}\mathbf{V\Sigma U}^{\mathrm{T}} \tag{16.32}$$

$$= \mathbf{V\Sigma}^{-2}\mathbf{V}^{\mathrm{T}}\mathbf{V\Sigma U}^{\mathrm{T}} \tag{16.33}$$

$$= \mathbf{V\Sigma}^{-1}\mathbf{U}^{\mathrm{T}} \tag{16.34}$$

I know it's a lot to work through, but the take-home message is that when you write out the SVD of a left inverse and simplify, you end up with exactly the same expression as the SVD-based inverse of the original matrix (replace $^{-1}$ with † where appropriate).

Needless to say, the conclusion is the same for the right inverse, which you can work through on your own.

16.13 Code challenges

I decided against by-hand exercises here, because the SVD is only a few additional steps on top of eigendecomposition. Instead, I've added more code challenges to help you internalize the conceptual ideas of the SVD and implementing them on computers.

1. In Chapter 13, you learned about "economy" QR decomposition, which can be useful for large tall matrices. There is a comparable "economy" version of the SVD. Your goal here is to figure out what that means. First, generate three random matrices: square, wide, and tall. Then run the full SVD to confirm that the sizes of the SVD matrices match your expectations (e.g., Figure 16.1). Finally, run the economy SVD on all three matrices and compare the sizes to the full SVD.

2. Obtain the three SVD matrices from eigendecomposition, as described in section 16.2. Then compute the SVD of that matrix using the svd() function, to confirm that your results are correct. Keep in mind the discussions of sign-indeterminacy.

3. Write code to reproduce panels B and C in Figure 16.5. Confirm that the reconstructed matrix (third matrix in panel C) is equal to the original matrix. (Note: The matrix was populated with random numbers, so don't expect your results to look *exactly* like those in the figure.)

4. Create a random-numbers matrix with a specified condition number. For example, create a 6×16 random matrix with a condition number of $\kappa = 42$. Do this by creating random $\mathbf{U}$ and $\mathbf{V}$ matrices, an appropriate $\mathbf{\Sigma}$ matrix, and then create $\mathbf{A} = \mathbf{U\Sigma V}^{\mathrm{T}}$. Finally, compute the condition number of $\mathbf{A}$ to confirm that it matches what you specified (42).

5. This and the next two challenges involve taking the SVD of a picture. A picture is represented as a matrix, with the matrix

values corresponding to grayscale intensities of the pixels. We will use a picture of Einstein. You can download the file at https://upload.wikimedia.org/wikipedia/en/8/86/Einstein_tongue.jpg Of course, you can replace this with any other picture—a selfie of you, your dog, your kids, your grandmother on her wedding day... However, you may need to apply some image processing to reduce the image matrix from 3D to 2D (thus, grayscale instead of RGB) and the datatype must be double (MATLAB) or floats (Python).

After importing the image, construct a low-rank approximation using various numbers of singular values. Show the original and low-rank approximations side-by-side. Test various numbers of components and qualitatively evaluate the results. Tip: You don't need to include the top components!

6. Create a scree plot of the percent-normalized singular values. Then test various thresholds for reconstructing the picture (e.g., including all components that explain at least 4% of the variance). What threshold seems reasonable?

7. The final challenge for this picture-SVD is to make the assessments of the number of appropriate components more quantitative. Compute the error between the reconstruction and the original image. The error can be operationalized as the RMS (root mean square) of the difference map. That is, create a difference image as the subtraction of the original and low-rank reconstructed image, then square all matrix elements (which are pixels), average over all pixels, and take the square root of that average. Make a plot of the RMS as a function of the number of components you included. How does that function compare to the scree plot?

8. What is the pseudoinverse of a column vector of constants? That is, the pseudoinverse of $k\mathbf{1}$. It obviously doesn't have a full inverse, but it is clearly a full column-rank matrix. First, work out your answer on paper, then confirm it in MATLAB or Python.

9. The goal here is to implement the series of equations on page 498 and confirm that you get the same result as with the pinv() function. Start by creating a 4×2 matrix of random integers between 1 and 6. Then compute its SVD (Equation 16.29). Then implement each of the next four equations in code. Finally, compute the MP pseudoinverse of the tall matrix. You will now have five versions of the pseudoinverse; make sure they are all equal.

10. This challenge follows up on the first code challenge from the previous chapter (about generalized eigendecomposition implemented as two matrices vs. the product of one matrix and the other's inverse). The goal is to repeat the exploration of differences between `eig(A,B)` and `eig(inv(B)*A)`. Use only 10×10 matrices, but now vary the condition number of the random matrices between 10^1 and 10^{10}. Do you come to different conclusions from the previous chapter?

11. This isn't a specific code challenge, but instead a general suggestion: Take any claim or proof I made in this chapter (or any other chapter), and demonstrate that concept using numerical examples in code. Doing so (1) helps build intuition, (2) improves your skills at translating math into code, and (3) gives you opportunities to continue exploring other linear algebra principles (I can't cover *everything* in one book!).

16.14 Code solutions

1. "Economy" SVD involves computing only the first N columns of $\mathbf{U}$ if $\mathbf{A}$ is tall, or only the first M rows of $\mathbf{V}^{\mathrm{T}}$ if $\mathbf{A}$ is wide. For square $\mathbf{A}$, "economy" SVD is the same as the full SVD. Below is code for a tall matrix; modifying for wide and square matrices is easy.

Code block 16.5: Python

```
1  import numpy as np
2  m = 6
3  n = 3
4  A = np.random.randn(m,n)
5  Uf,sf,Vf = np.linalg.svd(A)
6  Ue,se,Ve = np.linalg.svd(A,
7                   full_matrices=False)
8  print(Uf.shape, sf.shape, Vf.shape)
9  print(Ue.shape, se.shape, Ve.shape)
```

Code block 16.6: MATLAB

```
1  m = 6;
2  n = 3;
3  A = randn(m,n);
4  [Uf,Sf,Vf] = svd(A);
5  [Ue,Se,Ve] = svd(A,'econ');
6  whos A U* S* V*
```

2. Hint: You need to sort the columns of **U** and **V** based on descending eigenvalues. You can check your results by subtracting the eigenvectors and the matching singular vectors matrices. Due to sign-indeterminacy, you will likely find a few columns of zeros and a few columns of non-zeros; comparing against $-\mathbf{U}$ will flip which columns are zeros and which are non-zeros. Don't forget that Python returns $\mathbf{V}^{\mathrm{T}}$.

Code block 16.7: Python

```python
1  A = np.random.randn(4,5)
2  L2,V = np.linalg.eig(A.T@A)
3  V = V[:,np.argsort(L2)[::-1]]
4  L2,U = np.linalg.eig(A@A.T)
5  U = U[:,np.argsort(L2)[::-1]]
6
7  S = np.zeros(A.shape)
8  for i,s in enumerate(np.sort(L2)[::-1]):
9      S[i,i] = np.sqrt(s)
10 U2,S2,V2 = np.linalg.svd(A)
```

Code block 16.8: MATLAB

```matlab
1  A = randn(4,5);
2  [V,L2] = eig(A'*A);
3  [L2,idx] = sort(diag(L2),'d');
4  V = V(:,idx);
5  [U,L2] = eig(A*A');
6  [L2,idx] = sort(diag(L2),'d');
7  U = U(:,idx);
8
9  S = zeros(size(A));
10 for i=1:length(L2)
11     S(i,i) = sqrt(L2(i));
12 end
13 [U2,S2,V2] = svd(A);
```

3. I changed the code slightly from the Figure to include the original matrix to the right of the reconstructed matrix. Anyway, the important part is creating the low-rank approximations in a for-loop. Be very careful with the slicing in Python!

Code block 16.9: Python

```python
1  import matplotlib.pyplot as plt
2  fig,ax = plt.subplots(2,4)
3
4  A = np.random.randn(5,3)
5  U,s,V = np.linalg.svd(A)
6  S = np.diag(s)
7
8  for i in range(3):
9
10     onelayer = np.outer(U[:,i],V[i,:])*s[i]
11     ax[0,i].imshow(onelayer)
12     ax[0,i].set_title('Layer %g'%i)
13     ax[0,i].axis('off')
14
15     lowrank=U[:,:i+1]@S[:i+1,:i+1]@V[:i+1,:]
16     ax[1,i].imshow(lowrank)
17     ax[1,i].set_title('Layers 0:%g'%i)
18     ax[1,i].axis('off')
19
20
21  ax[1,3].imshow(A)
22  ax[1,3].set_title('Orig. A')
23  ax[1,3].axis('off')
24  ax[0,3].axis('off');
```

```
1   A = randn(5,3);
2   [U,S,V] = svd(A);
3
4   for i=1:3
5       subplot(2,4,i)
6       onelayer = U(:,i)*S(i,i)*V(:,i)';
7       imagesc(onelayer)
8       title(sprintf('Layer %g',i))
9
10      subplot(2,4,i+4)
11      lowrank = U(:,1:i)*S(1:i,1:i)*V(:,1:i)';
12      imagesc(lowrank)
13      title(sprintf('Layers 1:%g',i))
14  end
15  subplot(248)
16  imagesc(A), title('Original A')
```

4. There are two insights to this challenge. First, **U** and **V** must be orthogonal, which you can obtain via QR decomposition on random matrices. Second, you only need to specify the target singular value; the smallest can be 1 and rest can be anything in between (for simplicity, I've made them linearly spaced from smallest to largest).

Code block 16.11: Python

```python
1  m=6; n=16
2  condnum = 42
3
4  U,r = np.linalg.qr( np.random.randn(m,m) )
5  V,r = np.linalg.qr( np.random.randn(n,n) )
6
7  s = np.linspace(condnum,1,np.min((m,n)))
8  S = np.zeros((m,n))
9  for i in range(min((m,n))):
10     S[i,i] = s[i]
11  A = U@S@V.T
12  np.linalg.cond(A)
```

Code block 16.12: MATLAB

```matlab
1  m=6; n=16;
2  condnum = 42;
3
4  [U,r] = qr( randn(m) );
5  [V,r] = qr( randn(n) );
6
7  s = linspace(condnum,1,min(m,n));
8  S = zeros(m,n);
9  for i=1:min(m,n)
10     S(i,i) = s(i);
11  end
12  A = U*S*V';
13  cond(A)
```

5. You might have struggled a bit with transforming the image, but hopefully the SVD-related code wasn't too difficult. My code below reconstructs the image using components 1-20, but you can also try, e.g., 21-40, etc.

Code block 16.13: Python

```
1   import numpy as np
2   import matplotlib.pyplot as plt
3   from imageio import imread
4   pic = imread('https://upload.wikimedia.org/
5              wikipedia/en/8/86/Einstein_tongue.jpg')
6   np.array(pic,dtype=float)
7
8   U,s,V = np.linalg.svd( pic )
9   S = np.zeros(pic.shape)
10  for i in range(len(s)):
11    S[i,i] = s[i]
12
13  comps = slice(0,21)
14  lowrank=U[:,comps]@S[comps,comps]@V[comps,:]
15
16
17  plt.subplot(1,2,1)
18  plt.imshow(pic,cmap='gray')
19  plt.title('Original')
20  plt.subplot(1,2,2)
21  plt.imshow(lowrank,cmap='gray')
22  plt.title('Comps. %g–%g'
23              %(comps.start,comps.stop−1));
```

Code block 16.14: MATLAB

```matlab
1   pic = imread('https://upload.wikimedia.org/
2      wikipedia/en/8/86/Einstein_tongue.jpg');
3   pic = double(pic); % convert to double
4
5   [U,S,V] = svd( pic );
6   comps = 1:20; % low-rank approximation
7   lowrank = U(:,comps) * ...
8            S(comps,comps)*V(:,comps)';
9
10  % show the original and low-rank
11  subplot(121)
12  imagesc(pic), axis image
13  title('Original')
14  subplot(122)
15  imagesc(lowrank), axis image
16  title(sprintf('Comps. %g-%g',...
17              comps(1),comps(end)))
18  colormap gray
```

6. The low-rank calculations and plotting are basically the same as the previous exercise. The main additions here are computing percent variance explained and thresholding. It's a good idea to check that all of the normalized singular values sum to 100.

Code block 16.15: Python

```python
1  # convert to percent explained
2  s = 100*s/np.sum(s)
3  plt.plot(s,'s-'); plt.xlim([0,100])
4  plt.xlabel('Component number')
5  plt.ylabel('Pct variance explains')
6  plt.show()
7
8  thresh = 4 # threshold in percent
9  I,J=np.ix_(s>thresh,s>thresh) # comps > X
10 lowrank = np.squeeze(U[:,J]@S[I,J]@V[J,:])
11
12 # show the original and low-rank
13 plt.subplot(1,2,1)
14 plt.imshow(pic,cmap='gray')
15 plt.title('Original')
16 plt.subplot(1,2,2)
17 plt.imshow(lowrank,cmap='gray')
18 plt.title('%g comps. at %g%%'
19                %(len(I),thresh));
```

```
1    % convert to percent explained
2    s = 100*diag(S)./sum(S(:));
3    plot(s,'s-'), xlim([0 100])
4    xlabel('Component number')
5    ylabel('Pct variance explains')
6
7    thresh = 4; % threshold in percent
8    comps = s>thresh; % comps greater than X%
9    lowrank = U(:,comps) * ...
10           S(comps,comps)*V(:,comps)';
11
12   % show the original and low-rank
13   figure, subplot(121)
14   imagesc(pic), axis image
15   title('Original')
16   subplot(122)
17   imagesc(lowrank), axis image
18   title(sprintf('%g comps with > %g%%',...
19               sum(comps),thresh))
20   colormap gray
```

7. The RMS error plot goes down when you include more components. That's sensible. The scale of the data is pixel intensity errors, with pixel values ranging from 0 to 255. However, each number in the plot is the average over the entire picture, and therefore obscures local regions of high- vs. low-errors. You can visualize the error map (variable `diffimg`).

Code block 16.17: Python

```python
1  RMS = np.zeros(len(s))
2  for si in range(len(s)):
3      i=si+1
4      lowrank = U[:,:i]@S[:i,:i]@V[:i,:]
5      diffimg = lowrank - pic
6      RMS[si] = np.sqrt(np.mean(
7                   diffimg.flatten()**2))
8
9  plt.plot(RMS,'s-')
10 plt.xlabel('Rank approximation')
11 plt.ylabel('Error (a.u.)');
```

Code block 16.18: MATLAB

```matlab
1  for si=1:length(s)
2      lowrank=U(:,1:si)*S(1:si,1:si)*V(:,1:si)';
3      diffimg = lowrank - pic;
4      RMS(si) = sqrt(mean(diffimg(:).^2));
5  end
6  plot(RMS,'s-')
7  xlabel('Rank approximation')
8  ylabel('Error (a.u.)')
```

8. This code challenge illustrates that translating formulas into code is not always straightforward. I hope you enjoyed it!

```
1  import numpy as np
2  X = np.random.randint(
3          low=1,high=7,size=(4,2))
4  U,s,V = np.linalg.svd(X)
5  S = np.zeros(X.shape)
6  for i,ss in enumerate(s):
7    S[i,i] = ss
8  longV1 = np.linalg.inv( (U@S@V).T@U@S@V )
9                        @ (U@S@V).T
10 longV2 = np.linalg.inv( V.T@S.T@U.T@U@S@V )
11                        @ (U@S@V).T
12 longV3 = np.linalg.inv(V.T@S.T@S@V)
13                        @ (U@S@V).T
14 longV4 = V@np.linalg.matrix_power(S.T@S,-1)
15                    @ V@V.T@S.T@U.T
16 MPpinv = np.linalg.pinv(X)
```

Code block 16.20: MATLAB

```
1  X = randi([1 6],[4 2]);
2  [U,S,V] = svd(X);
3  longV1 = inv((U*S*V')'*U*S*V')*(U*S*V')';
4  longV2 =inv(V*S'*U'*U*S*V')*(U*S*V')';
5  longV3 = inv(V*S'*S*V') * (U*S*V')';
6  longV4 = V*(S'*S)^(-1)*V'*V*S'*U';
7  MPpinv = pinv(X);
```

9. The pseudoinverse of a column of constants is a row vector where each element is $1/kn$ where k is the constant and n is the dimensionality. The reason is that the vector times its pseudoinverse is actually just a dot product; summing up k n times yields nk, and thus $1/nk$ is the correct inverse to yield 1. (I'm not sure if this has any practical value, but I hope it helps you think about the pseudoinverse.)

Code block 16.21: Python

```
1  import numpy as np
2  k = 5
3  n = 13
4  a = np.linalg.pinv(np.ones((n,1))*k)
5  a - 1/(k*n)
```

Code block 16.22: MATLAB

```
1  k = 5;
2  n = 13;
3  a = pinv(ones(n,1)*k);
4  a - 1/(k*n)
```

10. The differences between the two approaches is much more apparent. The issue is that high-conditioned matrices are more unstable and thus so are their inverses. In practical applications, **B** might be singular, and so an eigendecomposition on $\mathbf{B}^{-1}\mathbf{A}$ is usually not a good idea.

Code block 16.23: Python

```
1   import numpy as np
2   from scipy.linalg import eig
3   import matplotlib.pyplot as plt
4
5   M = 10
6   cns = np.linspace(10,1e10,30)
7   avediffs = np.zeros(len(cns))
8
9
10  for condi in range(len(cns)):
11
12
13      U,r = np.linalg.qr( np.random.randn(M,M) )
14      V,r = np.linalg.qr( np.random.randn(M,M) )
15      S = np.diag(np.linspace(cns[condi],1,M))
16      A = U@S@V.T
17
18
19      U,r = np.linalg.qr( np.random.randn(M,M) )
20      V,r = np.linalg.qr( np.random.randn(M,M) )
21      S = np.diag(np.linspace(cns[condi],1,M))
22      B = U@S@V.T
23
24
25      l1 = eig(A,B)[0]
26      l2 = eig(np.linalg.inv(B)@A)[0]
27      l1.sort()
28      l2.sort()
29
30      avediffs[condi] = np.mean(np.abs(l1-l2))
31
32  plt.plot(cns,avediffs);
```

```
1  M = 10;
2  cns = linspace(10,1e10,30);
3
4
5  for  condi=1:length(cns)
6
7
8      [U,~] = qr( randn(M) );
9      [V,~] = qr( randn(M) );
10     S = diag(linspace(cns(condi),1,M));
11     A = U*S*V';
12
13
14     [U,~] = qr( randn(M) );
15     [V,~] = qr( randn(M) );
16     S = diag(linspace(cns(condi),1,M));
17     B = U*S*V';
18
19
20     l1 = eig(A,B);
21     l2 = eig(inv(B)*A);
22     l1 = sort(l1);
23     l2 = sort(l2);
24
25
26     avediffs(condi) = mean(abs(l1-l2));
27  end
28
29  plot(cns,avediffs)
30  xlabel('Cond. number')
31  ylabel('\Delta\lambda')
```

. THE SVD

CHAPTER 17

QUADRATIC FORM AND DEFINITENESS

The quadratic form is one of my favorite topics in linear algebra, because it combines math, geometry, art, data visualization, multivariate signal processing, and statistics, all into one nifty little package.

One important note before we start: The quadratic form applies only to square matrices. Thus, throughout this chapter, you can assume that all matrices are square. Some will be symmetric or non-symmetric, some will be invertible and some singular. There is some debate about whether the quadratic form should be applied to non-symmetric matrices, because many special properties of the quadratic form are valid only when the matrix is symmetric. I will relax this constraint and point out when symmetry is relevant.

17.1 Algebraic perspective

Imagine an $M \times M$ matrix and an $M \times 1$ column vector. You already know that a matrix times a vector will produce another M-element vector whose orientation depends on whether the vector pre- or post-multiplies the matrix. In particular, $\mathbf{Av}$ will produce a column vector while $\mathbf{v}^{\mathrm{T}}\mathbf{A}$ will produce a row vector. But what will happen if we both pre- and post-multiply by the same vector?

$$\mathbf{v}^{\mathrm{T}}\mathbf{Av} = \zeta \tag{17.1}$$

Take a moment to check the sizes of the multiplications to confirm that this vector-matrix-vector product really does produce a scalar (that one is the Greek letter "zeta"). That's pretty neat, because in total this vector-matrix-vector expression contains $2M + M^2$ elements, which can be a huge number of computations (e.g., 10,200 elements for $M = 100$), and it all boils down to a single number.

Equation 17.1 is called the "quadratic form of matrix $\mathbf{A}$" and it represents the energy in the matrix over the coordinate space described by vector $\mathbf{v}$. That "energy" definition will make more sense in the next section when you learn about the geometric perspective of the quadratic form. First I want to show a few numerical examples, using the same matrix and different vectors.

$$\mathbf{A} = \begin{bmatrix} 2 & 4 \\ 0 & 3 \end{bmatrix} \quad \mathbf{v}_1 = \begin{bmatrix} 3 \\ -1 \end{bmatrix} \quad \mathbf{v}_2 = \begin{bmatrix} 2 \\ 1 \end{bmatrix}$$

$$\mathbf{v}_1^T \mathbf{A} \mathbf{v}_1 = \begin{bmatrix} 3 & -1 \end{bmatrix} \begin{bmatrix} 2 & 4 \\ 0 & 3 \end{bmatrix} \begin{bmatrix} 3 \\ -1 \end{bmatrix} = 9 \qquad (17.2)$$

$$\mathbf{v}_2^T \mathbf{A} \mathbf{v}_2 = \begin{bmatrix} 2 & 1 \end{bmatrix} \begin{bmatrix} 2 & 4 \\ 0 & 3 \end{bmatrix} \begin{bmatrix} 2 \\ 1 \end{bmatrix} = 19 \qquad (17.3)$$

Two things in particular to notice about this example: The matrix is always pre- and post-multiplied by the same vector; and the same matrix multiplied by different vectors will give different results (that's obvious, but it becomes important later). Again, we'll return to the interpretation of this in the next section.

Now let's generalize this by using letters instead of numbers. I will use a, b, c, d for the matrix elements and x, y for the vector elements.

$$\begin{bmatrix} x & y \end{bmatrix} \begin{bmatrix} a & b \\ c & d \end{bmatrix} \begin{bmatrix} x \\ y \end{bmatrix} = \begin{bmatrix} ax + cy & bx + dy \end{bmatrix} \begin{bmatrix} x \\ y \end{bmatrix} \qquad (17.4)$$

$$= (ax + cy)x + (bx + dy)y \qquad (17.5)$$

$$= ax^2 + (c + d)xy + dy^2 \qquad (17.6)$$

Please take a moment to work through the multiplications by hand to confirm that you arrive at the same expression. And then take a moment to admire the beauty of what we've done: We have converted a vector-matrix-vector expression into a polynomial.

Notice that we get three terms here: x^2, y^2, and their cross-product xy. The matrix elements become the coefficients on these terms, with the diagonal elements getting paired with the individual vector elements and the off-diagonal elements getting paired with the cross-term.

Now imagine that the matrix elements are fixed scalars and x and

y are continuous variables, as if this were a function of two variables:

$$f(\mathbf{A}, \mathbf{v}_i) = \begin{bmatrix} x_i & y_i \end{bmatrix} \begin{bmatrix} a & b \\ c & d \end{bmatrix} \begin{bmatrix} x_i \\ y_i \end{bmatrix} = ax_i^2 + (c+d)x_i y_i + dy_i^2 = \zeta_i$$

(17.7)

The interpretation is that for each matrix $\mathbf{A}$, we can vary the vector elements x_i and y_i and obtain a scalar value for each (x_i, y_i) pair.

It's often fruitful in math to think about what happens to functions as their variables approach 0 and $\pm\infty$. As x and y go to zero, it is trivial that ζ will also go to zero (anything times zeros vectors will be zero). As x and y grow towards infinity, the function can either go to plus infinity, minus infinity, or can balance out to zero, depending on the exact coefficients. For example, if $a > d > 0$ then ζ will grow to plus infinity as x tends to plus or minus infinity.

Whether this expression is always positive, always negative, or sometimes positive and sometimes negative, is an important question that defines the *definiteness* of the matrix. More on this later in the chapter.

Quadratic is a general term for a 2nd degree polynomial.

The squared terms are why this expression is called the *quadratic* form. Below is an example with a 3×3 matrix.

$$\mathbf{v}^{\mathrm{T}} \mathbf{A} \mathbf{v} = \begin{bmatrix} x & y & z \end{bmatrix} \begin{bmatrix} a & f & d \\ f & b & e \\ d & e & c \end{bmatrix} \begin{bmatrix} x \\ y \\ z \end{bmatrix}$$

(17.8)

$$= \begin{bmatrix} ax + fy + dz & fx + by + ez & dx + ey + cz \end{bmatrix} \begin{bmatrix} x \\ y \\ z \end{bmatrix}$$

(17.9)

$$= ax^2 + fyx + dzx + fxy + by^2 + ezy + dxz + eyz + cz^2$$

(17.10)

$$= ax^2 + by^2 + cz^2 + 2dxz + 2eyz + 2fxyz$$

(17.11)

Yeah, that's quite a lot to look at. Still, you see the squared terms and the cross-terms, with coefficients defined by the elements in the matrix, and the diagonal matrix elements paired with their corresponding squared vector elements.

I'm sure you're super-curious to see how it looks for a 4×4 matrix. It's written out below. The principle is the same: diagonal matrix elements are coefficients on the squared vector elements, and the off-diagonals are coefficients on the cross-terms. Just don't expect me to be patient enough to keep this going for larger matrices...

$$\begin{bmatrix} w & x & y & z \end{bmatrix} \begin{bmatrix} a & b & c & d \\ b & e & f & g \\ c & f & h & i \\ d & g & i & j \end{bmatrix} \begin{bmatrix} w \\ x \\ y \\ z \end{bmatrix} =$$

$$aw^2 + ex^2 + hy^2 + jz^2 + 2bwx + 2cwy + 2dwz + 2fxy + 2gxz + 2iyz$$

Symmetric matrices When the matrix is symmetric, then the quadratic form is also symmetric. This is easily proven by transposing the entire expression:

$$\left(\mathbf{v}^{\mathrm{T}} \mathbf{A} \mathbf{v} \right)^{\mathrm{T}} = \mathbf{v}^{\mathrm{T}} \mathbf{A}^{\mathrm{T}} \mathbf{v}^{\mathrm{TT}} = \mathbf{v}^{\mathrm{T}} \mathbf{A} \mathbf{v} \qquad (17.12)$$

Complex matrices The quadratic form for complex-valued matrices is nearly the same as for real-valued matrices, except that the Hermitian transpose replaces the regular transpose:

$$\mathbf{v}^{\mathrm{H}} \mathbf{A} \mathbf{v} = \zeta \qquad (17.13)$$

Recall that $\mathbf{v}^{\mathrm{T}} = \mathbf{v}^{\mathrm{H}}$ for a real-valued vector.

If the matrix $\mathbf{A}$ is Hermitian (the complex version of symmetric, thus $\mathbf{A}^{\mathrm{H}} = \mathbf{A}$), then the quadratic form is real-valued. Non-Hermitian matrices will have complex-valued quadratic forms. Equations 17.12 and 17.13 are two of the reasons why some people limit the quadratic form to symmetric (and Hermitian) matrices.

Rectangular matrices Technically, the quadratic form is mathematically valid for rectangular matrices, if the first and second vectors differ.

$$\begin{bmatrix} w & x & y \end{bmatrix} \begin{bmatrix} a & b & c & d \\ b & e & f & g \\ c & f & h & i \end{bmatrix} \begin{bmatrix} w \\ x \\ y \\ z \end{bmatrix} =$$

$$aw^2 + ex^2 + hy^2 + 2bwx + 2cwy + dzw + 2fxy + gzx + izy$$

This result is slightly harder to interpret, because the left side is in $\mathbb{R}^3$ whereas the right side is in $\mathbb{R}^4$ (in this particular example). This situation is not further considered.

Code Not much new here, but be mindful of vector orientations: The vector on the left needs to be a row vector, regardless of its original orientation. I've swapped the orientations in the code just to make it a bit more confusing (which requires you to think a bit more!).

Code block 17.1: Python

```
1  import numpy as np
2  m = 4
3  A = np.random.randn(m,m)
4  v = np.random.randn(1,m)
5  v@A@v.T
```

Code block 17.2: MATLAB

```
1  m = 4;
2  A = randn(m);
3  v = randn(1,m);
4  v*A*v'
```

> Notice that when $\mathbf{A} = \mathbf{I}$, the quadratic form reduces to the dot product of the vector with itself, which is the magnitude-squared of the vector. Thus, putting a different matrix in between the vectors is like using this matrix to modulate, or scale, the magnitude of this vector. In fact, this is the mechanism for measuring distance in several non-Euclidean geometries.

Reflection

17.2 Geometric perspective

Let's return to the idea that the quadratic form is a function that takes a matrix and a vector as inputs, and produces a scalar as an output:

$$f(\mathbf{A}, \mathbf{v}) = \mathbf{v}^{\mathrm{T}} \mathbf{A} \mathbf{v} = \zeta \qquad (17.14)$$

Now let's think about applying this function over and over again, for the same matrix and different elements in vector $\mathbf{v}$. In fact, we can think about the vector as a coordinate space where the axes are defined by the vector elements. This can be conceptualized in $\mathbb{R}^2$, which is illustrated in Figure 17.1. In fact, the graph of $f(\mathbf{A}, \mathbf{v})$ for $\mathbf{v} \in \mathbb{R}^2$ is a 3D graph, because the two elements of $\mathbf{v}$ provide a 2D coordinate space, and the function value is mapped onto the height above (or below) that plane.

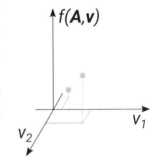

Figure 17.1: A visualization of the quadratic form result of a matrix at two specific coordinates.

Thus, the 2D plane defined by the v_1 and v_2 axes is the coordinate system; each location on that plane corresponds to a unique combination of elements in the vector, that is, when setting $\mathbf{v} = [v_1, v_2]$. The z-axis is the function result (ζ). The vertical dashed gray lines leading to the gray dots indicate the value of ζ for two particular $\mathbf{v}$'s.

Once we have this visualization, the next step is to evaluate $f(\mathbf{A}, \mathbf{v})$ for many different possible values of $\mathbf{v}$ (of course, using the same $\mathbf{A}$). If we keep using stick-and-button lines like in Figure 17.1, the plot will be impossible to interpret. So let's switch to a surface plot (17.2).

That graph is called the **quadratic form surface**, and it's like an energy landscape: The matrix has a different amount of "energy" at different points in the coordinate system (that is, plugging in different values into $\mathbf{v}$), and this surface allows us to visualize that energy landscape.

Let's make sure this is concrete. The matrix that I used to create

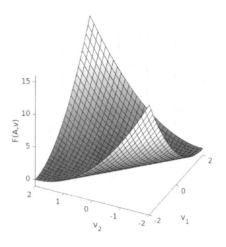

Figure 17.2: A better visualization of the quadratic form surface of a matrix.

that surface is

$$\mathbf{A} = \begin{bmatrix} 1 & 1 \\ 1 & 1 \end{bmatrix}$$

Now let's compute one specific data value, at coordinate (-2,1), which is near the lower-left corner of the plot. Let's do the math:

$$\left(\begin{bmatrix} -2 & 1 \end{bmatrix} \begin{bmatrix} 1 & 1 \\ 1 & 1 \end{bmatrix} \right) \begin{bmatrix} -2 \\ 1 \end{bmatrix} = \begin{bmatrix} -1 & -1 \end{bmatrix} \begin{bmatrix} -2 \\ 1 \end{bmatrix} = 1$$

The value (the height of the surface) of the function at coordinate (-2,1) is 1. That looks plausible from the graph.

The coordinates for this quadratic form surface are not bound by ±2; the plane goes to infinity in all directions, but it's trimmed here because I cannot afford to sell this book with one infinitely large page. Fortunately, though, the characteristics of the surface you see here don't change as the axes grow; for this particular matrix, two directions of the quadratic form surface will continue to grow to infinity (away from the origin), while two other directions will continue at 0.

This surface is the result for one specific matrix; different matrices (with the same vector $\mathbf{v}$) will have different surfaces. Figure 17.3 shows examples of quadratic form surfaces for four different matrices. Notice the three possibilities of the quadratic form surface:

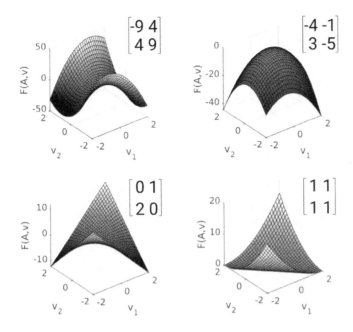

Figure 17.3: Examples of quadratic form surfaces for four different matrices. The v_1, v_2 axes are the same in all subplots, and the $f(\mathbf{A}, \mathbf{v}) = \zeta$ axis is adapted to each matrix.

The quadratic form can bend up to positive infinity, down to negative infinity, or stay along zero, in different directions away from the origin of the $[v_1, v_2]$ space.

There is more to say about the relationship between the matrix elements and the features of the quadratic form surface. In fact, the shape and sign of the quadratic form reflects the *definiteness* of the matrix, its eigenvalues, its invertibility, and other remarkable features. For now, simply notice that the shape and sign of the quadratic form surface depends on the elements in the matrix.

That said, one thing that all quadratic form surfaces have (for all matrices) is that they equal zero at the origin of the graph, corresponding to $\mathbf{v} = [0\ 0]$. That's obvious algebraically—the matrix is both pre- and post-multiplied by all zeros—but geometrically, it means that we are interested in the shape of the matrix relative to the origin.

This visualization of the quadratic form is beautiful and insightful, but is limited to 2x2 matrices. The quadratic form surface of a 3x3 matrix, for example, is some kind of 4D hyper-sheet that is floating on top of a 3D coordinate space. It could be compressed down into 3D as a solid block where each point in that block has a color value. But we still couldn't visualize that dense block. Nonetheless, the concept is the same: the quadratic form of a matrix is zero at the origin of space, and in different directions can go up to infinity, down to minus infinity, or lie flat along zero, depending on the values in the matrix. We're going to quantify those directions later, but there is more to explore about the quadratic form.

Code I bet you're hoping to see to code to generate those beautiful surfaces! That's reserved for one of the code challenges.

17.3 The normalized quadratic form

On the quadratic form surface, any direction away from the origin goes in one of three directions: down to negative infinity, up to positive infinity, or to zero. However, the surface doesn't necessarily go to infinity equally fast in all directions; some directions have steeper slopes than others. However, if a quadratic form goes up, it will eventually get to infinity.

Philosophical side-note: What does it mean to "eventually" get to ∞ and how long does that take?

That's because the value of the function at each $[v_1, v_2]$ coordinate is not only a function of the matrix; it is also a function of the vector **v**. *As the vector elements grow, so does the quadratic form.* That statement may feel intuitive, but we're going to take the time to prove it rigorously. This is important because the proof will help us discover how to normalize the quadratic form, which becomes the mathematical foundation of principal components analysis.

The Cauchy-Schwarz inequality for the dot product was on page 50 if you need a refresher.

The proof involves (1) expressing the quadratic form as a vector dot product, (2) applying the Cauchy-Schwarz inequality to that dot product, and then (3) applying the Cauchy-Schwarz inequality again to the matrix-vector product.

To start with, think about $\mathbf{v}^T\mathbf{A}\mathbf{v}$ as the dot product between two vectors: $(\mathbf{v})^T(\mathbf{A}\mathbf{v})$. Then apply the Cauchy-Schwarz inequality:

$$|\mathbf{v}^T\mathbf{A}\mathbf{v}| \leq \|\mathbf{v}\|\|\mathbf{A}\mathbf{v}\| \tag{17.15}$$

The next step is to break up $\|\mathbf{A}\mathbf{v}\|$ into the product of norms:

$$\|\mathbf{A}\mathbf{v}\| \leq \|\mathbf{A}\|_F\|\mathbf{v}\| \tag{17.16}$$

> The Cauchy-Schwarz inequality for matrix-vector multiplication was on page 168.

Then we put everything together:

$$|\mathbf{v}^T\mathbf{A}\mathbf{v}| \leq \|\mathbf{v}\|\|\mathbf{A}\|_F\|\mathbf{v}\|$$

$$|\mathbf{v}^T\mathbf{A}\mathbf{v}| \leq \|\mathbf{A}\|_F\|\mathbf{v}\|^2 \tag{17.17}$$

Equation 17.17 is the crux of our predicament: The magnitude of the quadratic form depends on the matrix *and* on our coordinate system. In other words, *of course* the quadratic form tends to plus or minus infinity (if not zero) as it moves away from the origin of the space defined by $\mathbf{v}$ (and thus as the magnitude of $\mathbf{v}$ increases).

You can call this a feature or you can call it a bug. Either way, it impedes using the quadratic form in statistics and in machine learning. We need something like the quadratic form that reveals important directions in the matrix space *independent* of the magnitude of the vector that we use for the coordinate space. That motivates including some kind of normalization factor that will allow us to explore the quadratic form in a way that is independent of the vector $\mathbf{v}$.

To discover the right normalization factor, let's think about the quadratic form of the identity matrix. What values of $\mathbf{v}$ will maximize the quadratic for $\mathbf{v}^T\mathbf{I}\mathbf{v}$? The mathy way of writing this question is:

$$\arg\max_{\mathbf{v}} \left\{\mathbf{v}^T\mathbf{I}\mathbf{v}\right\} \tag{17.18}$$

This means we are looking for the *argument* (here $\mathbf{v}$) that *maximizes* the expression.

Obviously, the quadratic form goes to infinity in all directions, because we're simply adding up all of the squared vector elements. So then, what normalization factor could we apply to remove this trivial growth?

Perhaps you've already guessed it: We normalize by the squared magnitude of $\mathbf{v}$. We can put this normalization factor in the denominator. Let's start with our simple 2×2 example (Equation 17.6):

$$f(\mathbf{A}, \mathbf{v}) = \frac{ax^2 + (c+d)xy + dy^2}{x^2 + y^2} \tag{17.19}$$

The more general expression looks like this:

The normalized quadratic form

$$f_{norm}(\mathbf{A}, \mathbf{v}) = \frac{\mathbf{v}^{\mathrm{T}}\mathbf{A}\mathbf{v}}{\mathbf{v}^{\mathrm{T}}\mathbf{v}} \tag{17.20}$$

Perhaps it isn't yet obvious why normalizing by the squared vector magnitude is the right thing to do. Let's revisit Equation 17.17 but now include the normalization factor.

$$\frac{|\mathbf{v}^{\mathrm{T}}\mathbf{A}\mathbf{v}|}{\|\mathbf{v}\|^2} \leq \frac{\|\mathbf{A}\|_F \|\mathbf{v}\|^2}{\|\mathbf{v}\|^2} \tag{17.21}$$

$$\frac{|\mathbf{v}^{\mathrm{T}}\mathbf{A}\mathbf{v}|}{\mathbf{v}^{\mathrm{T}}\mathbf{v}} \leq \|\mathbf{A}\|_F \tag{17.22}$$

Now we see that the magnitude of the normalized quadratic form is bounded by the magnitude of the matrix, and does not depend on the vector that provides the coordinate space.

Let's apply this normalization to the quadratic form of the identity matrix.

$$\frac{\mathbf{v}^{\mathrm{T}}\mathbf{I}\mathbf{v}}{\|\mathbf{v}\|^2} = \mathbf{I}$$

Geometrically, this means that the normalized quadratic form surface of the identity matrix is a flat sheet on the v_1, v_2 plane.

Have you noticed the failure scenario yet? If you don't already know the answer, I think you can figure it out from looking again at Equation 17.20. The failure happens when $\mathbf{v} = \mathbf{0}$, in other words, with the zeros vector.

The normalized quadratic form surfaces look quite different from the "raw" quadratic form surfaces. Figure 17.4 shows the surfaces from the normalized quadratic forms for each of the four matrices shown in Figure 17.3.

Reflection

$$\left[\begin{array}{l}\text{If you are reading this book carefully and taking notes} \\ \text{(which you should be doing!), then you'll remember that} \\ \text{on page 13.1 I introduced the concept of "mapping over} \\ \text{magnitude." The normalized quadratic form can be con-} \\ \text{ceptualized in the same way: It's a mapping of a matrix} \\ \text{onto a vector coordinate space, over the magnitude of that} \\ \text{coordinate space.}\end{array}\right]$$

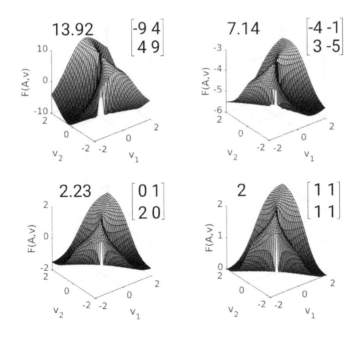

Figure 17.4: Same as Figure 17.3 but using the normalized quadratic form equation. Also notice the differences in the ζ axis; the number at the top-left of each graph is the Frobenius norm of that matrix.

Eigenvectors and quadratic form surfaces

Each normalized quadratic form surface in Figure 17.4 has two prominent features: a ridge and a valley. Going back to the interpretation that the quadratic form surface is a representation of the "energy" in the matrix along particular directions, the normalized surface tells us that there are certain directions in the matrix that are associated with maximal and minimal "energy" in the matrix.

(What does matrix "energy" mean? I put that term in apology quotes because it is an abstract concept that depends on what the matrix represents. In the next two chapters, the matrix will contain data covariances, and then "energy" will translate to pattern of covariance across the data features.)

Thus, normalizing out the magnitude of the vector $\mathbf{v}$ revealed important *directions* in the matrix. A 2×2 matrix has two important directions, and more generally, an $N \times N$ matrix has N important directions.

Higher-dimensional quadratic form surfaces are impossible to visualize and difficult to imagine, but the concept is this: The normalized quadratic form surface has an absolute ridge and an absolute valley, and $N - 2$ saddle directions. A *saddle point* is a point that goes up in some directions and down in other directions (the upper-left matrix in Figure 17.3 shows an example of a saddle-point in 3D); a *saddle line* is a hyper-line that is straight, but the surrounding space curves up in some directions and curves down in other directions. An analogy is that the absolute ridge and valley are like the global maximum and minimum, and the intermediate saddle points are like local maxima and minima.

For the 3D surfaces in these figures, you can identify the ridges and valleys simply by visual inspection. But that's obviously not very precise, nor is it scalable. It turns out that *the eigenvectors of a symmetric matrix point along the ridges and valleys of the normalized quadratic form surface.* This applies only to symmetric matrices; the eigenvectors of a non-symmetric matrix do not neces-

All analogies break down at some point, so you should never think too deeply about them.

Important information hidden inside a long paragraph. Terrible textbook writing style!

QUADRATIC FORM

sarily point along these important directions. This is another one of the special properties of symmetric matrices that make all other matrices fume with jealousy.

To be more precise: The eigenvector associated with the largest eigenvalue points from the origin along the ridge, and the eigenvector associated with the smallest eigenvalue points from the origin along the valley. You can see this in Figure 17.5, which shows the quadratic form surface from the top looking down, and the eigenvectors of the matrix plotted on top.

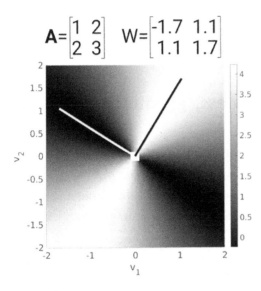

Figure 17.5: The bird's-eye-view of the quadratic form surface of a symmetric matrix, with the eigenvectors plotted on top. The matrix and its eigenvectors (W, rounded to the nearest tenth) are printed on top. Colorbar indicates the value of ζ. Notice the small missing box at the center; this was an NaN value corresponding to $v = 0$.

Why is this the case? Why do the eigenvectors point along the directions of maximal and minimal "energy" in the matrix? The short answer is that the vectors that maximize the quadratic form (Equation 17.20) turn out to be the eigenvectors of the matrix. A deeper discussion of why that happens is literally the mathematical basis of principal components analysis, and so I will go through the math in that chapter.

One of the most important applications of the normalized quadratic form is principal components analysis (PCA), which is a dimension-reduction and data-exploration method used in multivariate statistics, signal processing, and machine learning. The math of PCA is pretty simple: Compute a covariance matrix by multiplying the data matrix by its transpose, eigendecompose that covariance matrix, and then multiply the data by the eigenvectors to obtain the principal components. More on this in Chapter 19!

17.5 Definiteness, geometry, and eigenvalues

As with other properties introduced in this chapter, "definiteness" of a matrix is a property that applies only to square matrices. Some strict definitions limit definiteness to symmetric matrices, but I will relax this and say that any square matrix can have a definiteness.

Geometrically, the definiteness of a matrix refers to whether the sign of the non-normalized quadratic form surface is positive, negative, or zero in different directions away from the origin. You can see in the examples in Figure 17.3 that some matrices have positive surfaces, some negative, and some have ζ of both signs. (The zero point $\mathbf{v} = 0$ is ignored because $\zeta = 0$ is trivially the case.)

The algebraic interpretation of definiteness is whether $\mathbf{v}^{\mathrm{T}}\mathbf{A}\mathbf{v}$ is positive, negative, or zero, for all possible vectors $\mathbf{v}$ (again, excluding $\mathbf{v} = 0$).

There are five categories of definiteness. Table 17.1 provides an overview of the categories and their properties.

A few observations of Table 17.1: Definite matrices are always invertible while semidefinite matrices are never invertible (because

Category	Geometry	Eigenvalues	Invertible
Positive definite	↑	+	Yes
Positive semidefinite	↑, 0	+, 0	No
Indefinite	↑ and ↓	+, -	Possibly
Negative semidefinite	↓, 0	-, 0	No
Negative definite	↓	-	Yes

Table 17.1: Properties of matrix definiteness categories. ↑ and ↓ indicate that the quadratic form surface goes up or down relative to the origin; "0" indicates that it can also be zero outside the origin. "+" and "-" refer to the signs of the eigenvalues of the matrix.

they have at least one zero-valued eigenvalue). The invertibility of indefinite matrices is unpredictable; it depends on the numbers in the matrix. Finally, matrix definiteness is exclusive—a matrix cannot have more than one definiteness label (except for the always-bizarre zeros matrix; see *Reflection Box*).

Indefinite matrices are sometimes called *indeterminate*.

With this list in mind, refer back to Figure 17.3 and see if you can determine the definiteness of each matrix based on visual inspection and the associated descriptions.

Although I really enjoy looking at quadratic form surfaces, they are not the best way to determine the definiteness of a matrix. Instead, the way to determine the definiteness category of a matrix is to inspect the signs of the eigenvalues.

Question: Can you determine the definiteness of a matrix from its singular values? The answer is in the footnote.[1]

Complex matrices   For Hermitian matrices (remember that a Hermitian matrix is the complex version of a symmetric matrix: it equals its Hermitian transpose), the story is exactly the same. This is because $\mathbf{v}^H \mathbf{C} \mathbf{v}$ is a real-valued number, and because the eigenvalues of a Hermitian matrix are real-valued.

---

[1] The answer is No, because all singular values are non-negative.

17.6 The definiteness of $\mathbf{A}^T\mathbf{A}$

Here is yet another special property of the symmetric matrix $\mathbf{A}^T\mathbf{A}$: It is guaranteed to be positive definite or positive semidefinite [often written "positive (semi)definite"]. It cannot be indefinite or negative (semi)definite.

The proof here is fairly straightforward. Let's start by defining the quadratic form for matrix $\mathbf{S} = \mathbf{A}^T\mathbf{A}$.

$$\mathbf{w}^T\mathbf{S}\mathbf{w} = \mathbf{w}^T(\mathbf{A}^T\mathbf{A})\mathbf{w} \qquad (17.23)$$

$$= (\mathbf{w}^T\mathbf{A}^T)(\mathbf{A}\mathbf{w})$$

$$= (\mathbf{A}\mathbf{w})^T(\mathbf{A}\mathbf{w})$$

$$= \|\mathbf{A}\mathbf{w}\|^2$$

$\mathbf{w}$ instead of $\mathbf{v}$. Try to see the concepts behind the letters.

The key take-home message here is that the quadratic form of a matrix $\mathbf{A}^T\mathbf{A}$ can be re-written as the squared magnitude of a matrix times a vector. Magnitudes cannot be negative. A magnitude (and, thus, the quadratic form) can be zero when the vector is zero. In this context, it means that $\mathbf{A}\mathbf{w} = \mathbf{0}$ for at least one vector $\mathbf{w}$. And because we do not consider the zeros vector here, then it means that $\mathbf{A}$ has a non-trivial null space, which means that it is singular.

QUADRATIC FORM

(This is another nice example of how simply moving parentheses can provide important insights into linear algebra.)

The conclusion is that any matrix that can be expressed as $\mathbf{A}^T\mathbf{A}$ is positive definite if it is full-rank, and positive semidefinite if it is reduced rank.

Before going further, please take a moment to test whether the above proof works for the matrix $\mathbf{A}\mathbf{A}^T$. (Obviously it will, but it's good practice to work through it on your own.)

Important: All matrices $\mathbf{S} = \mathbf{A}^T\mathbf{A}$ are symmetric, but not all symmetric matrices can be expressed as $\mathbf{A}^T\mathbf{A}$ (or $\mathbf{A}\mathbf{A}^T$). A symmetric matrix that cannot be decomposed into another matrix times its transpose is not necessarily positive definite. **Symmetry does not guarantee positive (semi)definiteness**.

Decomposing a symmetric matrix $\mathbf{S}$ into $\mathbf{A}^T\mathbf{A}$ is the goal of the Cholesky decomposition, which is valid only for positive (semi)definite matrices.

Here is an example:

$$\begin{bmatrix} -9 & 4 \\ 4 & 9 \end{bmatrix}, \quad \lambda s = -9.8,\ 9.8$$

17.7 Eigenvalues and matrix definiteness

A few pages ago, I wrote that the best way to determine the definiteness of a matrix is to inspect the signs of its eigenvalues. You don't even need to know the magnitudes of the eigenvalues; you only need to know whether they are positive, negative, or zero.

Positive definite case Let's start by proving that all eigenvalues of a positive definite matrix are positive. We begin by writing the eigenvalue equation and left-multiplying by the eigenvector to arrive at the quadratic form. Assume that matrix $\mathbf{A}$ is positive definite.

$$\mathbf{A}\mathbf{v} = \lambda\mathbf{v} \tag{17.24}$$

$$\mathbf{v}^{\mathrm{T}}\mathbf{A}\mathbf{v} = \mathbf{v}^{\mathrm{T}}\lambda\mathbf{v} \tag{17.25}$$

$$\mathbf{v}^{\mathrm{T}}\mathbf{A}\mathbf{v} = \lambda\mathbf{v}^{\mathrm{T}}\mathbf{v} \tag{17.26}$$

$$\mathbf{v}^{\mathrm{T}}\mathbf{A}\mathbf{v} = \lambda\|\mathbf{v}\|^2 \tag{17.27}$$

Equation 17.27 says that the (non-normalized) quadratic form is equal to the squared vector magnitude times the eigenvalue. Our assumption is that $\mathbf{A}$ is positive definite, meaning that $\mathbf{v}^{\mathrm{T}}\mathbf{A}\mathbf{v}$ is positive for all vectors $\mathbf{v} \neq \mathbf{0}$. Thus, the left-hand side of the equation is *always* positive. On the right-hand side we have the product of two terms, one of which must be positive ($\|\mathbf{v}\|^2$), and the other of which (λ) in theory could be positive or negative. But if λ were negative, then the left-hand side must also be negative. Ergo, λ must be positive.

But wait a minute: the quadratic form is defined for *all* vectors, not only for eigenvectors. You might be tempted to say that our conclusion (positive definite means all positive eigenvalues) is valid only for eigenvectors.

The key to expanding this to all vectors is to appreciate that as long as the eigenvectors matrix is full-rank and therefore spans all of $\mathbb{R}^M$, *any* vector can be created by some linear combination of eigenvectors. Let's see how this works for a linear combination of two eigenvectors.

$$\mathbf{A}(\mathbf{v}_1 + \mathbf{v}_2) = (\lambda_1 + \lambda_2)(\mathbf{v}_1 + \mathbf{v}_2) \tag{17.28}$$

$$(\mathbf{v}_1 + \mathbf{v}_2)^{\mathrm{T}}\mathbf{A}(\mathbf{v}_1 + \mathbf{v}_2) = (\mathbf{v}_1 + \mathbf{v}_2)^{\mathrm{T}}(\lambda_1 + \lambda_2)(\mathbf{v}_1 + \mathbf{v}_2) \tag{17.29}$$

$$= (\lambda_1 + \lambda_2)\|\mathbf{v}_1 + \mathbf{v}_2\|^2 \tag{17.30}$$

Appreciating that $(\mathbf{v}_1 + \mathbf{v}_2)$ is simply a vector and $(\lambda_1 + \lambda_2)$ is simply a scalar, we can simplify:

$$\mathbf{w} = \mathbf{v}_1 + \mathbf{v}_2 \tag{17.31}$$

$$\beta = (\lambda_1 + \lambda_2) \tag{17.32}$$

$$\mathbf{w}^{\mathrm{T}}\mathbf{A}\mathbf{w} = \beta\|\mathbf{w}\|^2 \tag{17.33}$$

Equation 17.33 allows us to draw the same conclusion as Equation 17.27. In this case, the two eigenvectors were each weighted (implicitly) with 1. You can work through on your own how to modify this equation for any other linear combination of the eigenvectors; it will involve scalar-multiplying each vector $\mathbf{v}_i$ by some arbitrary scalar α_i. Even if you choose a negative-valued scalar, it will be squared on both sides of the equation and thus would not change the conclusion.

That conclusion is that if we assume that a matrix is positive definite, then all of its eigenvalues must be positive. You can also think about this proof the other way: If a matrix has all positive eigenvalues (meaning the right-hand side of Equation 17.33 is always positive), then it is a positive definite matrix (meaning the left-hand side of that equation is always positive).

Positive semidefinite case Let's continue our proof with positive *semi*definite matrices, which Table 17.1 claims have all non-negative eigenvalues.

We don't need to write out a new set of equations. All we need to do is change our assumption about the matrix: Now we assume that the quadratic form of $\mathbf{A}$ is non-negative, meaning that ζ can be positive and it can be zero, but it can never be negative. Below is Equation 17.27 repeated for reference.

Pro life tip: Sometimes you need to reassess your assumptions about matrices, yourself, other people, life, etc.

$$\mathbf{v}^{\mathrm{T}}\mathbf{A}\mathbf{v} = \lambda\|\mathbf{v}\|^2$$

Again, the right-hand-side of the equation has a term that is strictly positive and a term that could be positive, negative, or zero. The left-hand side of the equation can take values that are positive or zero, but not negative. This proves that at least one eigenvalue must be zero, and all non-zero eigenvalues must be positive. And the proof works the other way: If all eigenvalues are zero or positive, then the quadratic form must be non-negative, which is definition of positive semidefinite.

The other categories I trust you see the pattern here. Proving the relationship between the signs of the eigenvalues and the definiteness of a matrix does not require additional math; it simply requires changing your assumption about $\mathbf{A}$ and re-examining the above equations. As math textbook authors love to write: The proof is left as an exercise to the reader.

17.8 Code challenges

1. Write code to create and visualize the quadratic form surfaces of 2×2 matrices.

2. The goal of this code challenge is to explore the definiteness of random-integer matrices. Start by writing code that generates a 4×4 matrix of random integers between -10 and +10, and that has all real-valued eigenvalues. You *could* solve this by multiplying the matrix by its transpose, but that will limit the possibilities of definiteness categories. Thus, continue creating random matrices until all 4 eigenvalues are real-valued. Next, compute the definiteness category of that matrix.

   Once you have the code working, embed it inside a for-loop to generate 500 matrices. Store the definiteness category for each matrix. Finally, print out a list of the number of matrices in each definiteness category. What have you discovered about the quadratic forms of random matrices?

17.9 Code solutions

1. The code below computes the normalized quadratic form surfaces. You can modify the code to create the non-normalized quadratic form surface by commenting out the division (lines 14/8 for Python/MATLAB). Mind the parentheses in the normalization step.

Code block 17.3: Python

```
1   import numpy as np
2   import matplotlib.pyplot as plt
3
4   A = np.array([[-2,3],[2,8]])
5   vi = np.linspace(-2,2,30)
6   qf = np.zeros((len(vi),len(vi)))
7
8
9   X,Y = np.meshgrid(vi,vi)
10
11  for i in range(len(vi)):
12      for j in range(len(vi)):
13          v = np.array([ vi[i],vi[j] ])
14          qf[i,j] = v.T@A@v / (v.T@v)
15
16  ax = plt.axes(projection='3d')
17  ax.plot_surface(X, Y, qf.T)
18  ax.set_xlabel('v_1'), ax.set_ylabel('v_2')
19  ax.set_zlabel('$\zeta$')
20  plt.show()
```

```matlab
1  A = [1  2;  2  3];                     % matrix
2  vi = -2:.1:2;                          % vector elements
3  quadform = zeros(length(vi));
4
5  for  i=1:length(vi)
6       for  j=1:length(vi)
7            v = [vi(i)  vi(j)]';          % vector
8            quadform(i,j) = v'*A*v/(v'*v);
9       end
10 end
11
12 surf(vi,vi,quadform')
13 xlabel('v_1'),  ylabel('v_2')
14 zlabel('$\zeta$','Interpreter','latex')
```

2. Notice that I've set a tolerance for "zero"-valued eigenvalues, as discussed in previous chapters for thresholds for computing rank. You will find that all or nearly all random matrices are indefinite (positive and negative eigenvalues). If you create smaller matrices (3×3 or 2×2), you'll find more matrices in the other categories, although indefinite will still dominate. Category number corresponds to the rows of table 17.1.

Code block 17.5: Python

```python
1   import numpy as np
2   n = 4
3   nIterations = 500
4   defcat = np.zeros(nIterations)
5
6   for iteri in range(nIterations):
7
8     A = np.random.randint(-10,11,size=(n,n))
9     e = np.linalg.eig(A)[0]
10    while ~np.all(np.isreal(e)):
11      A = np.random.randint(-10,11,size=(n,n))
12      e = np.linalg.eig(A)[0]
13
14
15    t=n*np.spacing(np.max(np.linalg.svd(A)[1]))
16
17    if np.all(np.sign(e)==1):
18      defcat[iteri] = 1
19    elif np.all(np.sign(e)>-1)&sum(abs(e)<t)>0:
20      defcat[iteri] = 2
21    elif np.all(np.sign(e)<1)&sum(abs(e)<t)>0:
22      defcat[iteri] = 4
23    elif np.all(np.sign(e)==-1):
24      defcat[iteri] = 5
25    else:
26      defcat[iteri] = 3
27
28
29  for i in range(1,6):
30    print('cat %g: %g'%(i,sum(defcat==i)))
```

```
1  n = 4;
2  nIterations = 500;
3  defcat = zeros(nIterations ,1);
4
5  for iteri=1:nIterations
6
7      % create the matrix
8      A = randi([-10 10],n);
9      ev = eig(A);       % ev = EigenValues
10     while ~isreal(ev)
11         A = randi([-10 10],n);
12         ev = eig(A);
13     end
14
15     % 'zero' threshold (from rank)
16     t = n * eps(max(svd(A)));
17
18     % test definiteness
19     if all(sign(ev)==1)
20         defcat(iteri) = 1;     % pos. def
21     elseif all(sign(ev)>-1) && sum(abs(ev)<t)>0
22         defcat(iteri) = 2;     % pos. semidef
23     elseif all(sign(ev)<1) && sum(abs(ev)<t)>0
24         defcat(iteri) = 4;     % neg. semidef
25     elseif all(sign(ev)==-1)
26         defcat(iteri) = 5;     % neg. def
27     else
28         defcat(iteri) = 3;     % indefinite
29     end
30 end
31
32 % print out summary
33 for i=1:5
34     fprintf('cat %g: %g\n',i,sum(defcat==i))
35 end
```

. Quadratic form

CHAPTER 18
DATA AND COVARIANCE MATRICES

START THIS CHAPTER HAPPY

This chapter may seem like it belongs more in a statistics textbook than a linear algebra textbook, but correlation and covariance will bring linear algebra concepts—including the dot product, matrix multiplication, transposing, symmetric matrices, and inverses—to the world of statistics and data science. And covariance matrices are key to principal components analysis, which is the main focus of the next chapter.

18.1 Correlation: Motivation and interpretation

The goal of a correlation analysis is to identify commonalities between variables. Imagine, for example, the variables "height" and "weight" measured from a group of people. In general, taller people tend to weigh more than shorter people. We could visualize this relationship in a plot that shows a dot for each person, and their height on the x-axis and weight on the y-axis (Figure 18.1).

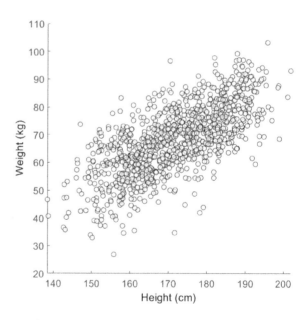

Figure 18.1: A scatter plot showing the relationship between height and weight. These are made-up data.

Clearly, these two variables are related to each other; you can imagine drawing a straight line through that relationship. The correlation coefficient is the statistical analysis method that quantifies this relationship.

Correlation is a bivariate measure, meaning it can only be computed between two variables. In the next section, you'll see correlation matrices, but a correlation matrix is just a convenient way of organizing a collection of bivariate correlations.

A correlation coefficient is a number between -1 and +1. -1 means that the two variables are perfectly negatively correlated (one goes up when the other goes down), 0 means that there is no relationship between the variables, and +1 means that the two variables are perfectly positively correlated. Figure 18.2 shows examples of various relationships and their correlation coefficients.

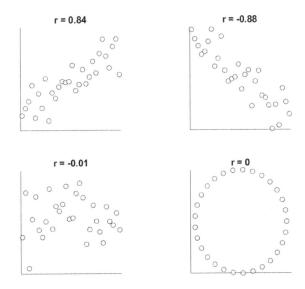

Figure 18.2: Four examples of bivariate data and their correlation coefficients ("r" value).

Limited to linearity One thing to know about the correlation is that it can detect only the linear component of an interaction between two variables. Any nonlinear interactions will not be detected by a correlation. The lower-right panel of Figure 18.2 shows an example: the value of y is clearly related to the value of x, however that relationship is *non*linear; there is no linear component of that relationship. (There are, of course, measures of nonlinear relation-

18.1 CORRELATION

ships, such as mutual information. It's also possible to transform the variables so that their relationship is linearized.)

Before learning the formula to compute the correlation, it's useful to learn the formula for a covariance. That's because the correlation coefficient is simply a normalized version of the covariance.

A covariance is the same concept as a correlation, except it is not bound by ±1. Instead, the covariance is in the same scale as the data. If you multiply the data by a factor of 1000, then the covariance will increase proportionally but the correlation will remain the same.

And before learning about covariance, we need to talk about variance.

18.2 Variance and standard deviation

Variance is a measure of dispersion, which is a general term to describe how different the data values are from each other.

Variance is defined as the average of the squared differences between each data value and the data average. It is common to use the Greek letter σ^2 to indicate variance. In the formula below, $\mathbf{x}$ is a vector of data points, $\bar{\mathbf{x}}$ is the average of all data values, and n is the total number of data points.

Subtracting the mean to enforce an average value of 0 is also called "mean-centering."

$$\sigma^2 = \frac{1}{n-1} \sum_{i=1}^{n} (\mathbf{x}_i - \bar{\mathbf{x}})^2 \tag{18.1}$$

The scalar division by $n - 1$ is a normalization that prevents the variance from increasing simply by adding more data, analogous to dividing a sum by n to compute the average. There is a longer statistical explanation for why we scale by $n - 1$ and not n; the short answer is that mean-centering reduces the degrees of freedom by 1. As soon as we know $n - 1$ data values, we necessarily know the nth data value, because we know the dataset average.

You can imagine from the formula that when all data values are close to the mean, the variance is small; and when the data values are far away from the mean, the variance is large. Figure 18.3 shows examples of two datasets with the identical means but different variances.

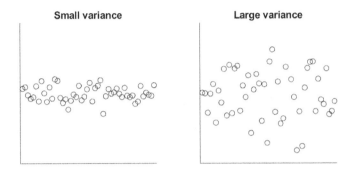

Figure 18.3: Examples of datasets with small and large variance.

It is obvious that we can expand the squared term in Equation 18.1 and rewrite as follows. This is relevant for understanding covariance.

$$\sigma^2 = \frac{1}{n-1} \sum_{i=1}^{n} (\mathbf{x}_i - \overline{\mathbf{x}})(\mathbf{x}_i - \overline{\mathbf{x}}) \tag{18.2}$$

Once you know the variance, you also know the standard deviation. Standard deviation is simply the square root of variance. It is implicit that standard deviation is the principal (positive) square root of variance, because it doesn't make sense for a measure of dispersion to be negative, just like it doesn't make sense for a length to be negative.

It is a bit confusing that σ indicates singular values in linear algebra and standard deviation in statistics. As I wrote in Chapter 14, terminological overloading is simply unavoidable in modern human civilization.

$$\sigma = \sqrt{\sigma^2} \tag{18.3}$$

Covariance

The term *covariance* means variance between two variables. The covariance between variables x and y is computed by modifying Equation 18.2.

The covariance coefficient

$$c_{x,y} = \frac{1}{n-1} \sum_{i=1}^{n} (\mathbf{x}_i - \overline{\mathbf{x}})(\mathbf{y}_i - \overline{\mathbf{y}}) \qquad (18.4)$$

where n is the number of observations, and $\overline{\mathbf{x}}$ and $\overline{\mathbf{y}}$ are the averages over all elements in $\mathbf{x}$ and $\mathbf{y}$. Needless to say, this equation is valid only when $\mathbf{x}$ and $\mathbf{y}$ have the same number of elements.

Equation 18.4, though technically correct, is ugly from a linear algebra perspective. Let's see if we can make it more compact and therefore more appealing to an airplane full of linear algebraticians traveling to Hawaii for holiday (I suppose this could happen; the universe is a strange and wondrous place):

$$c_{x,y} = \frac{\mathbf{x}^{\mathrm{T}}\mathbf{y}}{n-1}, \quad \overline{\mathbf{x}} = \overline{\mathbf{y}} = 0 \qquad (18.5)$$

This is looking better. It turns out that the normalization factor of $n-1$ is often unnecessary in applications (for example, when comparing multiple covariances that all have the same n), therefore Equation 18.5 really simplifies to $\mathbf{x}^{\mathrm{T}}\mathbf{y}$ under the assumption that both variables are mean-centered.

This is a remarkable discovery, because it means that the covariance between two variables—one of the most fundamental building-blocks of statistics, machine-learning, and signal processing—is nothing more than the dot product between two vectors that contain data.

This insight gives a huge advantage to understanding covariance and correlation for anyone who understands the algebraic and geometric properties of the dot product (that includes you!).

Do data *always* need to be mean-centered before computing the covariance? That depends on what will be done with the covariance. For example, non-mean-centered covariance matrices produce uninterpretable PCA results, which you will see in the next chapter. Furthermore, mean-centering ensures that the diagonal of the covariance matrix contains the variances of each data feature. Thus, it is convenient to mean-center all data before computing covariances, even if it not strictly necessary for a particular application.

18.4 Correlation coefficient

Take a moment to compare Equation 18.6 to Equation 18.4, and identify the similarities and differences.

The correlation coefficient

$$r_{x,y} = \frac{\sum_{i=1}^{n}(\mathbf{x}_i - \overline{\mathbf{x}})(\mathbf{y}_i - \overline{\mathbf{y}})}{\sqrt{\sum_{i=1}^{n}(\mathbf{x}_i - \overline{\mathbf{x}})^2}\sqrt{\sum_{i=1}^{n}(\mathbf{y}_i - \overline{\mathbf{y}})^2}} \qquad (18.6)$$

The numerators are the same. The denominator of Equation 18.6 has two terms, each of which is almost identical to the standard deviation, except that the $1/(n-1)$ term is missing. In fact, that normalization term is missing once in the numerator and twice in the denominator (each time inside each square root). In other words, that term cancels and thus is omitted for simplicity.

Again, the formula above is technically correct but is going to give our plane full of linear algebaticians indigestion. Let us make their flight more pleasant by rewriting Equation 18.6, again assuming that the variables are already mean-centered.

$$r_{x,y} = \frac{\mathbf{x}^{\mathsf{T}}\mathbf{y}}{\|\mathbf{x}\|\|\mathbf{y}\|} \qquad (18.7)$$

The letter r is commonly used to indicate a correlation coefficient.

Let us meditate on this equation for a moment. This is a perfect example of the principle of *mapping over magnitude*: We have a dot product between vectors, normalized by the product of their magnitudes. This formula looks similar (though not identical) to the orthogonal projection of a vector onto a subspace (page 359). And it looks even more similar to the geometric interpretation of the dot product, which I'll discuss presently.

Equation 18.7 nicely shows how a correlation of $r = 1$ would be obtained. Imagine replacing $\mathbf{y}$ with $\mathbf{x}$; the numerator and denominator would be identical. Finally, notice that if the data are already unit-normed, then the denominator is 1.

Cosine similarity I realize that Chapter 3 was a long time ago, but I hope you remember the geometric formula for the dot product, and how we derived a formula for the angle between vectors. That was Equation 3.16 (page 51), and I will reprint it below for convenience.

$$\cos(\theta_{ab}) = \frac{\mathbf{a}^{\mathrm{T}}\mathbf{b}}{\|\mathbf{a}\|\|\mathbf{b}\|}$$

Remarkably, the Pearson correlation coefficient is nothing more than the cosine of the angle between two vectors—when those vectors are mean-centered. This is another example of how we arrived at the same formula from two completely different starting points (c.f. the least-squares solution).

When the data are not mean-centered, Equation 3.16 is called *cosine similarity*. The difference in interpretation and use of correlation vs. cosine similarity is a topic for a machine-learning course, but you can already see that the two measures are somewhere between identical and similar, depending on the average of the data values.

18.5 Covariance matrices

In applications, it is common to have larger sets of variables, perhaps dozens, hundreds, or even thousands of variables, all collected from the same individuals (or animals, planets, cells, time points, whatever is the object of study). For convenience, all of those variables can be stored in a matrix, with data features (variables) in the columns, and observations in the rows. This is just like the design matrices you learned about in the discussion of least-squares fitting (Chapter 14).

To compute all pairwise covariances, we follow the same principle as for a single variable, but translate column vectors into matrices.

$$\mathbf{C} = \mathbf{X}^{\mathrm{T}}\mathbf{X} \qquad (18.8)$$

Matrix $\mathbf{X}$ is the data matrix, and we assume that the columns are mean-centered. (For simplicity, I omitted the factor $1/(n - 1)$.) Note that there is nothing magical about transposing the first matrix; if your data are stored as features-by-observations, then the correct formula is $\mathbf{C} = \mathbf{X}\mathbf{X}^{\mathrm{T}}$. The covariance matrix should be features-by-features.

Assuming the columns are mean-centered, the diagonal elements of $\mathbf{C}$ contain the variances of each variable. That is,

$$diag(\mathbf{C}) = \begin{bmatrix} \sigma_1^2 & \sigma_2^2 & \cdots & \sigma_m^2 \end{bmatrix} \qquad (18.9)$$

It is obvious from the math that the covariance matrix is symmetric. But it is also sensible from the perspective of a correlation: The correlation between x and y is the same as the correlation between y and x (e.g., the relationship between height and weight is the same as that between weight and height).

From correlation to covariance matrices

You learned that a correlation coefficient is obtained by scaling the covariance by the norms of the two variables.

Equation 18.10 below expands this translation from an individual correlation to a correlation matrix, and then uses the power of parentheses to shuffle the equation a bit. $\mathbf{R}$ is the correlation matrix and $\boldsymbol{\Sigma}$ is a diagonal matrix containing standard deviations of each corresponding data feature (again, not to be confused with the $\boldsymbol{\Sigma}$ in the SVD).

$$\mathbf{R} = \boldsymbol{\Sigma}^{-1}\mathbf{X}^{\mathrm{T}}\mathbf{X}\boldsymbol{\Sigma}^{-1} \tag{18.10}$$

$$= (\boldsymbol{\Sigma}^{-\mathrm{T}}\mathbf{X}^{\mathrm{T}})(\mathbf{X}\boldsymbol{\Sigma}^{-1}) \tag{18.11}$$

$$= (\mathbf{X}\boldsymbol{\Sigma}^{-1})^{\mathrm{T}}(\mathbf{X}\boldsymbol{\Sigma}^{-1}) \tag{18.12}$$

You might be tempted to simplify that final expression to $\|\mathbf{X}\boldsymbol{\Sigma}^{-1}\|^2$, but don't do it! $\mathbf{X}\boldsymbol{\Sigma}^{-1}$ is a matrix not a vector, so taking the norm is not the correct conclusion.

Instead, the correct conclusion is that the correlation matrix is obtained by the multiplication of the data matrix with itself (just like the covariance matrix), but first normalizing each data feature by its standard deviation. To make this more clear: set $\widetilde{\mathbf{X}} = \mathbf{X}\boldsymbol{\Sigma}^{-1}$, then the correlation matrix is obtained as $\widetilde{\mathbf{X}}^{\mathrm{T}}\widetilde{\mathbf{X}}$.

Because the data are already mean-centered, multiplying by the inverse of the standard deviations is equivalent to z-standardizing the data. Z-standardization, also called z-scoring, involves subtracting the mean and dividing by the standard deviation. It forces the data to have a mean of zero and a standard deviation of one. This means that correlation and covariance are identical metrics when the data are z-standardized.

We can also turn this equation around to compute a covariance matrix given correlation and standard deviation matrices. (Again, the normalization factor is omitted for simplicity.)

$$\mathbf{C} = \boldsymbol{\Sigma}\mathbf{R}\boldsymbol{\Sigma} \tag{18.13}$$

I've also omitted the factor of $1/(n-1)$ here.

18.7 Code challenges

1. The goal here is to implement Equations 18.10 and 18.13. Create a data matrix of random numbers with 4 features and 200 observations. Then compute the correlation and covariance matrices using the equations above. Finally, confirm that you obtain the same result as Python or MATLAB's built-in covariance and correlation functions.

18.8 Code solutions

1. I generated random numbers matrices, so the inter-variable correlations will be low—the expected correlations are 0, but with sampling variability and random numbers, the correlations will instead be small but non-zero. Anyway, the important thing is that the matrices match the outputs of Python's and MATLAB's built-in functions. Be mindful that Python's std() function computes a biased standard deviation by default, so you need to specify that the degrees of freedom is 1.

Code block 18.1: Python

```python
1  import numpy as np
2  n = 200
3  X = np.random.randn(n,4)
4  X = X-np.mean(X,axis=0)
5  covM = X.T@X / (n-1)
6  stdM = np.linalg.inv( np.diag(
7          np.std(X,axis=0,ddof=1)) )
8  corM = stdM@ X.T@X @stdM / (n-1)
9
10
11 print(np.round(covM-np.cov(X.T),3))
12 print(np.round(corM-np.corrcoef(X.T),3))
```

Code block 18.2: MATLAB

```matlab
1  n = 200;
2  X = randn(n,4);
3  X = X-mean(X,1);
4  covM = X'*X / (n-1);
5  stdM = inv( diag(std(X)) );
6  corM = stdM* X'*X *stdM / (n-1);
7
8  disp(covM-cov(X))
9  disp(corM-corrcoef(X))
```

CHAPTER 19
PRINCIPAL COMPONENTS ANALYSIS

START THIS CHAPTER HAPPY

PCA is a multivariate data analysis method widely used in statistics, machine-learning, data mining, signal processing, image processing, compression, and lots of other nerdy topics. There are entire books and courses dedicated solely to PCA. A complete discussion of this method requires venturing into statistics. That's a rabbit hole too deep to fall into here. But I do want to introduce you to PCA because it nicely ties together many linear algebra concepts you learned about in this book.

Thus, in this chapter I will present the linear algebra aspects of PCA while simplifying or ignoring some of the statistical aspects.

19.1 Interpretations and applications of PCA

A multivariate dataset with N features can be conceptualized as a set of vectors in an N-dimensional space. The data are stored in a matrix with features in the columns and observations in the rows, just like the design matrices you saw in Chapter 14. In the data space, each feature (thus, each column in the data matrix) is a basis vector, and all the columns together span some subspace of $\mathbb{R}^N$. But is this the best set of basis vectors? The goal of PCA is to identify a basis set such that each basis vector maximizes data covariance while being orthogonal to all other basis vectors.

A "feature" is a property that you measure, such as age, salary, alcohol content, pixel intensity, number of stars in a galaxy, etc.

What does it mean to "maximize covariance?" It means to identify a weighted combination of data channels, such that that weighted combination has maximal variance. Figure 19.1 provides a graphical overview of three scenarios to illustrate the concept. Let's start with panel A. Two time series (at left) are clearly correlated; the PCA scalar-multiplies each data channel by .7, adds the weighted data channels together, and the result is a "component" that has higher variance than either of the individual channels.

Now let's consider panel B. The two data channels are negatively correlated. Keeping the same weighting of .7 for each channel actually reduced the variance of the result (that is, the resulting component has less variance than either individual channel). Thus, a weighting of .7 for both channels is not a good PCA solution.

Instead, PCA will negatively weight one of the channels to flip its sign (panel C). That resulting component will maximize variance.

Why scalar-multiply by .7? If the goal is to maximize variance, then surely variance is maximized by using scalars of 7,000,000, or any arbitrarily large number. To avoid this triviality, PCA adds the constraint that the sum of squared weights must equal 1. In this example, $.7^2 + .7^2 = .98$. (I truncated the weights for visual simplicity, but you get the idea.)

This is the idea of PCA: You input the data, PCA finds the best set of weights, with "best" corresponding to the weights that maximize the variance of the weighted combination of data channels.

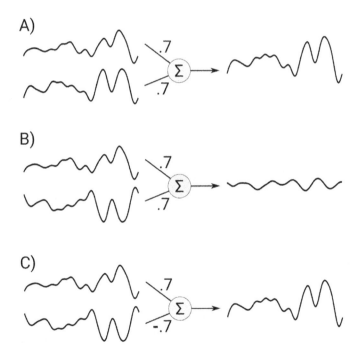

Figure 19.1: Three scenarios to illustrate PCA in 2D data.

We can visualize the data shown in panel A as a scatter plot, with each axis corresponding to a channel (Figure 19.2), and each dot corresponding to a time point. The dashed line is the first princi-

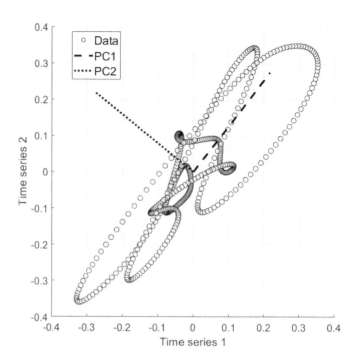

Figure 19.2: The time series data in Figure 19.1A visualized in a scatter plot, along with the principal components.

pal component—the weighting of the two channels that maximizes covariance. The second principal component is the direction in the data cloud that maximizes the residual variance (that is, all the variance not explained by the first component) subject to the constraint that that component is orthogonal to the first component.

In a 2D dataset, there is only one possible second component, because there is only one possible vector in $\mathbb{R}^2$ that is orthogonal to the first component. But for larger-dimensional datasets, there are many possible orthogonal directions.

Selecting the number of components A PCA returns M components for a M-feature dataset (because of the eigendecomposition of the $M \times M$ covariance matrix). How many of those components are meaningful and should be retained?

There are quantitative and qualitative methods for determining the number of components that have large enough eigenvalues to retain for subsequent analyses. The quantitative methods involve identifying appropriate statistical thresholds, and are beyond the scope of this book.

The qualitative method involves examining the *scree plot*, which is a plot of the sorted eigenvalues. You learned about creating and interpreting scree plots in Chapter 16 about the SVD (e.g., Figure 16.6).

Applications A common application of PCA is data compression, where only the first $k < r$ components are retained for subsequent analyses or data storage. The assumption is that directions in the data space associated with relatively little covariance are unimportant or noise, and therefore can be "squeezed out" of the data. The validity and appropriateness of this assumption depends on the type of data and the goals of the analysis, but that's the idea. Notice that this application is very similar to the low-rank approximation you learned about in the SVD chapter. In fact, you'll see by the end of this chapter that PCA can be implemented via SVD.

19.2 How to perform a PCA

In this section, I will describe how a PCA is done, and then in the next section, you'll learn about the math underlying PCA. There are five steps to performing a PCA, and you will see how linear algebra is central to those steps.

1) Compute the covariance matrix of the data, as described in the previous chapter. The data matrix may be observations-by-features or features-by-observations, but the covariance matrix must be features-by-features. Each feature in the data must be mean-centered prior to computing covariance.
2) Take the eigendecomposition of that covariance matrix.
3) Sort the eigenvalues descending by magnitude, and sort the

eigenvectors accordingly. There are several relevant facts that you learned in this book, including (1) the eigenvalues of a covariance matrix are all non-negative, (2) eigenvalues have no intrinsic sorting, (3) eigenvectors are paired with eigenvalues, so sorting one requires sorting the other. Eigenvalues are sometimes called latent factor scores.

4) Compute the "component scores" (called "component time series" if the data are time series). The component score is the weighted combination of all data features, where the eigenvector provides the weights. Hence, for data matrix $\mathbf{X}$, component 1 is calculated as $\mathbf{v}_1^T\mathbf{X}$, where $\mathbf{v}_1$ is the "first" eigenvector (the one with the largest associated eigenvalue).

5) Convert the eigenvalues to percent change to facilitate interpretation. This is the same procedure as converting singular values to percent variance explained.

Below is another example of a PCA on correlated data, using the height-weight data illustrated in the previous chapter. Figure 19.3A shows the raw data, with each person represented as a dot. The Pearson correlation is $r = .69$.

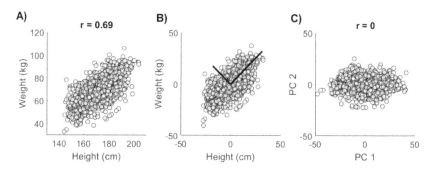

Figure 19.3: Visual overview of PCA in 2D data. Note: these are simulated data. You'll learn how to simulate these data in the code challenges.

Panel B shows the same data, mean-centered, and with the two principal components (the eigenvectors of the covariance matrix) drawn on top. Notice that the eigenvector associated with the larger eigenvalue points along the direction of the linear relationship between the two variables.

Panel C shows the same data but redrawn in PC space. Because

PCs are orthogonal, the PC space is a pure rotation of the original data space. Therefore, the data projected through the PCs are decorrelated.

Because these data are in $\mathbb{R}^2$, we can visualize the normalized quadratic form surface of the data covariance matrix. It's shown in Figure 19.4. The two panels actually show the same data. I thought the rotated view (left panel) looked really neat but was suboptimal for visualizing the eigenvectors. The right panel is the bird's-eye-view, and more clearly shows how the eigenvectors point along the directions of maximal and minimal energy in the quadratic form surface.

As expected for a positive-definite matrix, the normalized quadratic form surface energy is above zero everywhere.

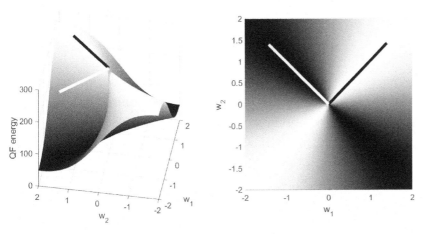

Figure 19.4: Quadratic form surface of the data covariance matrix of the data shown in Figure 19.3. The black and white lines show the two eigenvectors (scaled for visibility) corresponding to the larger (black line) and smaller (white line) eigenvalue.

19.3 The algebraic motivation for PCA

The previous section was very mechanical: I explained *how* to compute a PCA but didn't explain *why* that's the right thing to do.

Let's get back to the problem statement: Find a direction in the data space that maximizes the data covariance. This can be translated into finding a vector $\mathbf{v}$ that maximizes the quadratic form of the data covariance matrix.

$$\mathbf{v}_{max} = \arg\max_{\mathbf{v}} \left\{ \mathbf{v}^{\mathrm{T}} \mathbf{C} \mathbf{v} \right\} \tag{19.1}$$

You know from Chapter 17 that this maximization problem is difficult for the non-normalized quadratic form, because the quadratic form will grow to infinity as the elements in $\mathbf{v}$ get larger. Fortunately, avoiding this trivial solution simply requires adding the constraint that $\mathbf{v}$ be a unit vector. That can be equivalently written in one of two ways:

$$\mathbf{v}_{max} = \arg\max_{\mathbf{v}} \left\{ \mathbf{v}^{\mathrm{T}} \mathbf{C} \mathbf{v} \right\}, \quad s.t. \, \|\mathbf{v}\| = 1 \tag{19.2}$$

$$\mathbf{v}_{max} = \arg\max_{\mathbf{v}} \left\{ \frac{\mathbf{v}^{\mathrm{T}} \mathbf{C} \mathbf{v}}{\mathbf{v}^{\mathrm{T}} \mathbf{v}} \right\} \tag{19.3}$$

When we obtain $\mathbf{v}_{max}$, we can plug that value into the normalized quadratic form to obtain a scalar, which is the amount of variance in the covariance matrix along direction $\mathbf{v}_{max}$.

$$\mathbf{w} = \mathbf{v}_{max}$$

$$\lambda = \frac{\mathbf{w}^{\mathrm{T}} \mathbf{C} \mathbf{w}}{\mathbf{w}^{\mathrm{T}} \mathbf{w}} \tag{19.4}$$

But how do we find $\mathbf{v}_{max}$? This is an optimization problem, so you can use calculus: Take the derivative of Equation 19.4, set the derivative to zero, and solve for $\mathbf{w}$.

But calculus is tedious. The linear algebra solution is more elegant and allows us to solve for all M solutions simultaneously. We begin by considering not a single vector $\mathbf{v}$, but instead the total set of possible vectors, which are columns in matrix $\mathbf{V}$. That means that the denominator will be a matrix, which is not allowed. So instead we multiply by the inverse. Notice how the first equation below follows from Equation 19.4.

$$\mathbf{\Lambda} = (\mathbf{W}^\mathrm{T}\mathbf{W})^{-1}(\mathbf{W}^\mathrm{T}\mathbf{C}\mathbf{W}) \tag{19.5}$$

$$\mathbf{\Lambda} = \mathbf{W}^{-1}\mathbf{W}^{-\mathrm{T}}\mathbf{W}^\mathrm{T}\mathbf{C}\mathbf{W} \tag{19.6}$$

$$\mathbf{\Lambda} = \mathbf{W}^{-1}\mathbf{C}\mathbf{W} \tag{19.7}$$

$$\mathbf{W}\mathbf{\Lambda} = \mathbf{C}\mathbf{W} \tag{19.8}$$

Remarkably, we've discovered that the solution to our maximization problem is given by the eigendecomposition of the covariance matrix. The diagonal matrix $\mathbf{\Lambda}$ contains the eigenvalues, which are the covariance energy values from the quadratic form, and the columns of $\mathbf{W}$ are the eigenvectors, which are called the principal components.

(I put the "denominator" term on the left in Equation 19.5. What happens if you put $(\mathbf{W}^\mathrm{T}\mathbf{W})^{-1}$ on the right?)

Given that PCA is implemented as the eigendecomposition of a covariance matrix, you might be wondering whether PCA can equivalently be implemented via SVD. The answer is Yes, and you will have the opportunity to demonstrate this in the code challenges. There is no theoretical reason to prefer eigendecomposition over SVD for a PCA. However, eigendecomposition is often advantageous when working with large datasets, because covariance matrices are easy to construct and take up much less memory than the full dataset, and because it is often easier to select or filter data when creating a covariance matrix.

19.4 Regularization

Regularization is an umbrella term in machine-learning, statistics, data compression, deep learning, signal processing, image processing, etc. The overarching idea of regularization is to make numerically difficult problems easier to solve by "smoothing" the data.

There are many forms of regularization and many algorithms for regularizing. In this section, I will introduce you to *shrinkage regularization*. This method is simple and effective, and relies on linear algebra concepts you've learned throughout this book. Other regularization methods (e.g., ridge, Tikhonov, L1, L2, drop-out) are similar in concept, but have different algorithms that are optimized for particular applications.

The idea of shrinkage regularization is to replace the covariance matrix $\mathbf{C}$ with another matrix $\widetilde{\mathbf{C}}$, which is a shifted version of $\mathbf{C}$. In particular:

$$\widetilde{\mathbf{C}} = (1 - \gamma)\mathbf{C} + \gamma\alpha\mathbf{I} \tag{19.9}$$

$$\alpha = n^{-1} \sum \lambda(\mathbf{C}) \tag{19.10}$$

The scalar α is the average of all eigenvalues of $\mathbf{C}$.

The scalar γ is the key parameter, and defines the regularization amount. It is specified in proportion, so $\gamma = .01$ corresponds to 1% shrinkage regularization. Setting this parameter is non-trivial and data- and application-specific, but the general idea is to regularize as little as possible and as much as necessary.

You can see from Equation 19.9 that we reduce $\mathbf{C}$ and then inflate the diagonal by shifting. Scaling the identity by α ensures that the regularization amount reflects the numerical range of the matrix. Imagine that that scalar wasn't in the equation: The effect of 1% shrinkage could be huge or insignificant, depending on the values in $\mathbf{C}$.

You can often gain insight into mathematical or statistical operations by imagining what happens at extreme parameter settings. When $\gamma = 0$, we're not changing the matrix at all. On the other side, when $\gamma = 1$, we've completely replaced $\mathbf{C}$ by $\alpha\mathbf{I}$.

Figure 19.5 shows the effects of shrinkage regularization on a covariance matrix and its eigenvalues. To generate this figure, I created a 20×1000 data matrix, computed its covariance matrix, and re-ran eigendecomposition after various levels of shrinkage.

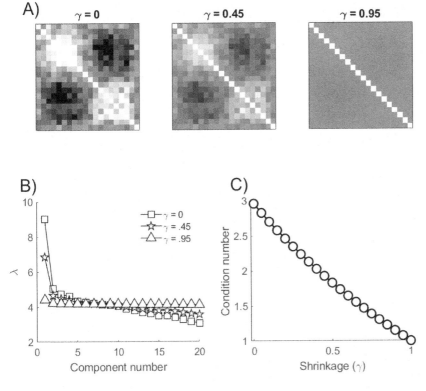

Figure 19.5: Illustration of the effects of regularization. Panel A shows the covariance matrix after three levels of shrinkage regularization ($\gamma = 0$ is the original matrix); notice that the matrix looks more like the identity matrix with increased regularization. Panel B shows eigenspectra for these three matrices. Panel C shows the condition number of the covariance matrix as a function of γ.

Figure 19.5B shows why this method is called shrinkage: The larger eigenvalues get smaller while the smaller eigenvalues get larger. This makes the matrix more numerically stable by decreasing the condition number. And of course, any shrinkage above 0% will transform a rank-deficient covariance matrix into a full-rank matrix.

19.5 Is PCA always the best?

PCA is a commonly used procedure, but it is not always the best thing to do. One important caveat is that PCA relies on the assumption that the directions of maximal variability are the most important. Whether this is a valid assumption depends on the data. For example, if a dataset contains a lot of measurement noise, then the first few components may reflect the noise instead of signal. Furthermore, if an important pattern in the data is restricted to a relatively small number of data channels, then PCA might ignore that data pattern because it does not have large covariance in the entire dataset.

A common example of a "failure scenario" with PCA is shown in Figure 19.6 (similar to Figure 4.11). The graph shows an "X" pattern in the data. The top PC points exactly in between the two branches of the "X" pattern, and the second PC is orthogonal to that, pointing in between the two branching arms (dashed lines). That seems counter-intuitive, but it is correct, according to the goals of PCA: The average of the two prongs truly is the direction in the data that maximizes covariance.

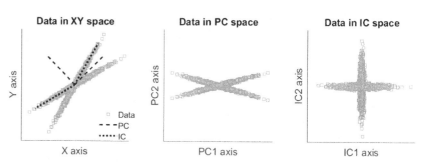

Figure 19.6: PCA and ICA (via the jade algorithm) on the same dataset.

The vectors drawn in the dotted lines correspond to basis vectors derived from an independent components analysis (ICA), which is conceptually similar to PCA in that it creates a set of weights for each data channel such that the weighted sum of data channels maximizes a statistical criteria. However, ICA maximizes independence, not variance.

The distinction between PCA and ICA is clear from the middle and right panels, which show the data transformed into those two spaces. The data in PCA space are *decorrelated*, but the data in IC space are *demixed*.

Keep in mind that this example is constructed specifically to highlight the difference between PCA and ICA; it does not mean that ICA is always better than PCA. They are simply different multivariate decomposition methods with different opimization criteria, assumptions, and outcomes. When analyzing data, it is important to understand the methods you are applying in order to obtain sensible results.

19.6 Code challenges

1. The goal of this challenge is to simulate a dataset and then perform PCA. We'll create a dataset of heights and weights from N=1000 people, similar to the datasets illustrated in this and the previous chapters. Below are descriptions of how to create the two variables. After creating those variables, perform a PCA and then make a scatter plot of the mean-centered data with the two principal components vectors drawn on top.

   Height Start by creating 1000 linearly spaced numbers between 150 and 190, then add random Gaussian noise with a standard deviation of 5. This simulates height in cm. (The imperialist reader may convert this to inches as a bonus challenge.)

   Weight The formula to create correlated weight values in kg is $w = .7h - 50$. Then add Gaussian random noise with a standard deviation of 10. (Again, you may convert this to pounds if kg isn't your thing.)

2. Now implement PCA on the same dataset via SVD of the data matrix (not the covariance matrix). Before implementing them code, think about whether the principal components are in the **U** or the **V** singular vectors matrices. Check that the singular values and singular vectors match the eigenvalues and eigenvectors from the previous exercise.

3. Is mean-centering really so important? To find out, repeat the first code challenge, but implement the PCA on the *non-mean-centered* data. But generate the plot using the mean-center the data. How do the PCs look, and what does this tell you about mean-centering and PCA?

19.7 Code solutions

1. Note the arbitrary scaling factors on the PC vectors. Those are just to make the lines look good given the range of the data.

Code block 19.1: Python

```
1   import numpy as np
2   import matplotlib.pyplot as plt
3
4
5   N = 1000
6   h = np.linspace(150,190,N) +
7       np.random.randn(N)*5
8   w = h*.7 - 50 + np.random.randn(N)*10
9
10
11  X = np.vstack((h,w)).T
12  X = X-np.mean(X,axis=0)
13  C = X.T@X / (len(h)-1)
14
15
16  eigvals,V = np.linalg.eig(C)
17  i = np.argsort(D)[::-1]
18  V = V[:,i]
19  eigvals = eigvals[i]
20  eigvals = 100*eigvals/np.sum(eigvals)
21  scores = X@V
22
23
24  fig = plt.figure(figsize=(5,5))
25  plt.plot(X[:,0],X[:,1],'ko')
26  plt.plot([0,V[0,0]*45],[0,V[1,0]*45],'r')
27  plt.plot([0,V[0,1]*25],[0,V[1,1]*25],'r')
28  plt.xlabel('Height'), plt.ylabel('Weight')
29  plt.axis([-50,50,-50,50])
30  plt.show()
```

```
1  % create data
2  N = 1000;
3  h = linspace(150,190,N) + randn(1,N)*5;
4  w = h*.7 - 50 + randn(1,N)*10;
5
6  % covariance
7  X = [h' w'];
8  X = X-mean(X,1);
9  C = X'*X / (length(h)-1);
10
11  % PCA and sort results
12  [V,D] = eig(C);
13  [eigvals,i] = sort(diag(D),'descend');
14  V = V(:,i);
15  eigvals = 100*eigvals/sum(eigvals);
16  scores = X*V;  % not used but useful code
17
18  % plot data with PCs
19  figure, hold on
20  plot(X(:,1),X(:,2),'ko')
21  plot([0 V(1,1)]*45,[0 V(2,1)]*45,'k')
22  plot([0 V(1,2)]*25,[0 V(2,2)]*25,'k')
23  xlabel('Height (cm)'), ylabel('Weight (kg)')
24  axis([-1 1 -1 1]*50), axis square
```

2. The tricky part of this exercise is normalizing the singular values to match the eigenvalues. Refer back to section 16.3 if you need a refresher on their relationship. There's also the normalization factor of $n - 1$ to incorporate. Finally, you still need to mean-center the data. That should already have been done from the previous exercise, but I included that line here as a reminder of the importance of mean-centering.

Code block 19.3: Python

```python
1  X = X-np.mean(X, axis=0)
2  U,s,Vv = np.linalg.svd(X)
3  scores = X@Vv.T
4  s = (s**2 )/(len(X)-1)
5  s = 100*s/sum(s)
```

Code block 19.4: MATLAB

```matlab
1  X = X-mean(X,1);
2  [U,S,Vv] = svd(X);
3  scores = X*Vv;
4  s = (diag(S).^2 )/(length(X)-1);
5  s = 100*s/sum(s);
```

3. All you need to do in the code is move line 11 to 24 in the Python code, or line 8 to 20 in the MATLAB code. See figure below.

The PCs look wrong—they no longer point along the direction of maximal covariance. However, they are still mathematically the correct solutions, even if that seems counter-intuitive. Because PCA vectors start at the origin, offsets in the data mean that the largest covariance is obtained from the origin to the center of the data cloud. And then PC2 must be orthogonal to that first PC. This is why mean-centering the data is important.

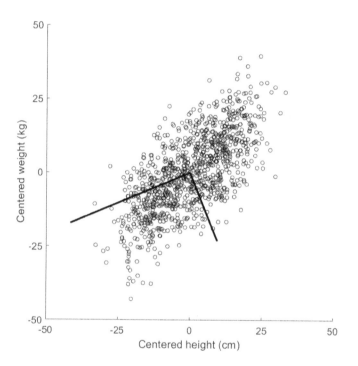

Figure 19.7: Image for code challenge 3.

CHAPTER 20
WHERE TO GO FROM HERE?

20.1 The end... of the beginning!

You are reading this either because

1. You read the chapters in order, and you've now finished the book. Congrats! Amazing! Go treat yourself to an ice cream, chocolate bar, glass of wine, pat on the back, 2-week trip to Tahiti, or whatever you like to do to reward yourself.
2. You skipped forwards because you are curious, even though you haven't finished the book. In that case, feel free to keep reading, but then get back to the important chapters!

I designed this book to contain what would be covered in 1-2 semesters of a university linear algebra course (1 or 2 depending on the particular curriculum and expectations). If you are really excited about continuing your linear algebra learning and are wondering where to go from here, then it can be challenging to know where next to turn.

I have no specific recommendations because linear algebra has such wide-ranging applications and it's not possible for me to custom-tailor such recommendations here. However, I can make two general recommendations that I hope will help you decide the right path forward for yourself.

Abstract linear algebra   As you know by now, I have tried to keep this book focused on linear algebra concepts that are most relevant for applications. I like to call it "down-to-Earth" linear algebra. However, linear algebra is a huge topic in mathematics, and there are many avenues of linear algebra that are more focused on proofs, abstractions, and topics that are mathematically intriguing but less directly relevant to applications on computers.

If you are interested in following this line of study, then a quick Internet search for something like "theoretical linear algebra" or "abstract linear algebra" will give you some places to start.

Application-specific linear algebra   I intentionally avoided focusing on any particular application or any particular field, to make the book relevant for a broad audience.

But because linear algebra is so important for so many scientific and engineering disciplines, advanced studies in most STEM fields will involve linear algebra. Control engineering, computational biology, mathematical physics, multivariate signal processing, finance and mathematical economics, machine learning, deep learning... these are all disciplines that rely on linear algebra. Again, some Internet sleuthing for the keywords you are interested in should help you find a suitable book or course.

 **Thanks!**

Thank you for choosing to learn from this book, and for trusting me with your linear algebra education. I hope you found the book useful, informative, and perhaps even a bit entertaining. Your brain is your most valuable asset, and investments in your brain always pay large dividends.

I'd be remiss if I didn't take this opportunity to invite you to check out my other educational material, which you can find linked from my website sincxpress.com.

. THE END.

Index

INDEX

Made in the USA
Las Vegas, NV
19 August 2021